BioComm™
BIOLOGY IN A COMMUNITY CONTEXT

William H. Leonard, Ph.D.
Clemson University

John E. Penick, Ph.D.
North Carolina State University

Barbara J. Speziale, Ph.D.
Clemson University

IT's ABOUT TIME®

HERFF JONES EDUCATION DIVISION

IT's ABOUT TIME ®
HERFF JONES EDUCATION DIVISION

84 Business Park Drive, Armonk, NY 10504
Phone (914) 273-2233 Fax (914) 273-2227
www.its-about-time.com

President
Tom Laster

Director of Product Development
Barbara Zahm, Ph.D

Creative Director
John R. Nordland

Editor
Todd Fishlin

Production Studio Manager
Robert J. Schwalb

Photo Research
Nicoletta E. Barolini
Carlo F. Cantavero
MaryBeth Schulze

Layout and Production
Howard Johnson
Tom Lawrence

Illustrator
Marie Killoran
John Norton
Thompson Digital

BioComm™: Biology in a Community Context

All student activities in this textbook have been designed to be as safe as possible, and have been reviewed by professionals specifically for that purpose. As well, appropriate warnings concerning potential safety hazards are included where applicable to particular activities. However, responsibility for safety remains with the student, the classroom teacher, the school principal, and the school board.

Care has been taken to trace the ownership of copyrighted material contained in this publication.
The publisher will gladly receive any information that will rectify any reference or credit line in subsequent editions.

Printed and bound in the United States.

ISBN 978-1-58591-656-6

1 2 3 4 5 RRD 11 10 09 08 07

This project was supported, in part, by the
National Science Foundation
under Grant No. MDR-9252892.
Opinions expressed are those of the authors and not necessarily
those of the National Science Foundation.

Project Team

Project Directors

William H. Leonard is Professor of Education and Biology at Clemson University, Clemson, South Carolina. He began his career in science education as a biology teacher at Piedmont Hills High School in San Jose, California. Dr. Leonard is the recipient of many awards for his teaching and work with students, including the AMOCO Distinguished Teaching Award from the University of Nebraska and the Provost Research Award from Clemson University. He has over 100 research and teaching publications.

John E. Penick is Professor and Head of the Department of Mathematics, Science, and Technology Education at North Carolina State University in Raleigh. A former high school biology and chemistry teacher in Miami, Florida, he is the author or co-author of more than 300 articles and chapters. He has been awarded two OHAUS awards for teaching excellence in physics and biology, and in 1987, he was named the AETS Outstanding Science Educator in the United States. Dr. Penick was the 1989 president of the National Association of Biology Teachers.

Barbara J. Speziale holds a Ph.D. in Zoology (Limnology). She is Associate Professor of Curriculum and Instruction, a researcher in the Department of Biological Sciences, and a Cooperative Extension Water Quality Specialist at Clemson University.

Writers

Sandra Alters, University of Missouri - St. Louis, St. Louis, MO

Ellen Averill, Kendrick High School, Columbus, GA

Royce Ballinger, University of Nebraska, Lincoln, NE

James Barufaldi, University of Texas, Austin, TX

Rick Berken, Preble High School, Green Bay, WI

Steve Case, Olathe East High School, Olathe, KS

Patricia Chandler, Clemson University, Clemson, SC

Michael Clough, University of Iowa, Iowa City, IA

Sara Clough, Memorial High School, Eau Claire, WI

Kimberly Crews, Population Reference Bureau, Inc., Washington, DC

David Dilcher, University of Florida, Gainesville, FL

Elizabeth Edmondson, Anderson, Oconee, Pickens Hub, Clemson University, Clemson, SC

Jane Ellis, Presbyterian College, Clinton, SC

Melvin Goodwin, The Harmony Project, Charleston, SC

Leslie Hays, Helix High School, La Mesa, CA

David Heckel, Clemson University, Clemson, SC

Marvin Hedgepeth, Menchville High School, Newport News, VA

Doris Helms, Clemson University, Clemson, SC

Jim Hutchins, University of Mississippi Medical Center, Jackson, MS

Brian Kick, Helix High School, La Mesa, CA

Elaine Kilmer, John Burroughs School, St. Louis, MO

Steve Krings, Southwest High School, Green Bay, WI

Janis Lariviere, Westlake High School Alternative Learning Center, Austin, TX

Arthur Lebofsky, Nyack Senior High School, Upper Nyack, NY

James Mariner, Fountain Valley School of Colorado, Colorado Springs, CO

Cheryl Mason, San Diego State University, San Diego, CA

Victoria May, Mathematics and Science Education Center, St. Louis, MO

Ellen Mayo, Mills Godwin High School, Richmond, VA

Becky Monhardt, Utah State University, Logan, UT

Patsye Peebles, LSU Laboratory School, Baton Rouge, LA

Rosalind Philips, New Century High School, Lacey, WA

Kathryn Powell, University of New Mexico, Albuquerque, NM

Steve Randak, Jefferson High School, Lafayette, IN

Judy Rhymer, University of Maine, Orono, ME

Basil Savitsky, Clark University, Worchester, MA

James Schindler, Clemson University, Clemson, SC

Charles Schwartz, Greenwood Genetic Center, Greenwood, SC

Roy Schodtler, Palatine High School, Palatine, IL

Don Shepherd, Mount Baker High School, Deming, WA

Patricia Simmons, University of Georgia, Athens, GA

JoAnne Simson, Medical University of South Carolina, Charleston, SC

Brijinder Singh, Flushing High School, Flushing, NY

Fred Stutzenberger, Clemson University, Clemson, SC

Frank Taylor, Radford High School, Radford, VA

George Tempel, Medical University of South Carolina, Charleston, SC

Teresa Thiel, University of Missouri - St. Louis, St. Louis, MO

Martha Thompson, Francis Howell North High School, St. Charles, MO

Elizabeth Thornton, Wayzata High School, Plymouth, MN

David Tonkyn, Clemson University, Clemson, SC

David Tucker, Mount Baker High School, Deming, WA

Paul Tweed, School District of Augusta, Augusta, WI

Peter Veronesi, State University of New York at Brockport, Brockport, NY

Steven Wagner, Lander University, Greenwood, SC

Jennifer Williams, Meredith Middle School, Des Moines, IA

Francis Wolak, Clemson University, Clemson, SC

Robert Yager, University of Iowa, Iowa City, IA

Student Resource Writers

Gail Anderson, M.S., Greenwood Genetic Center, Greenwood, SC

Ray C. Anderson, Interface, Inc., Atlanta, GA

John James Audubon, Ornithologist (1785-1851)

E. David Dickens, Ph.D., University of Georgia, Athens, GA

Richard B. Brugam, Ph.D., Southern Illinois University, Edwardsville, IL

Paul E. Brunkow, Ph.D., Southern Illinois University, Edwardsville, IL

Kimberly Crews, M.A., Population Reference Bureau, Washington, DC

Jane H. Dean, R.N., Greenwood Genetic Center, Greenwood, SC

Barbara Doll, M.C.E., North Carolina State University, Raleigh, NC

Robert D. Doyle, Ph.D., U.S. Army Corps of Engineers, Lewisville, TX

Ed Edmonson, M.S., Coneross Creek Wastewater Treatment Facility, Seneca, SC

Catherine Ann English, M.L.S., Pickens Co. School System, Clemson, SC

William "Rocky" English, Ph.D., Clemson University, Clemson, SC

Nancy H. Ferguson, Ph.D., Clemson University, Clemson, SC

Joann Foulk, Ph.D., Clemson University, Clemson, SC

Louis A. Frank, Ph.D., University of Iowa, Iowa City, IA

Wayne Fraser, Hudson Bay Mining and Smelting Co., Flin Flon, Manitoba, Canada

John J. Hains, Ph.D., U.S. Army Corps of Engineers, Vicksburg, MS

Jim Hutchins, Ph.D., University of Mississippi Medical Center, Jackson, MS

Virginia Landau, Ph.D., University of Arizona, Tucson, AZ

William H. Leonard, Ph.D., Clemson University, Clemson, SC

Thomas Robert Malthus Political Economist (1766-1834)

Kailash Mathur, Ph.D., South Carolina State University, Orangeburg, SC

Robert W. Matthews, Ph.D., University of Georgia, Athens, GA

Ron C. Michaelis, Ph.D., Greenwood Genetics Center, Greenwood, SC

Bartshe Miller, Mono Lake Committee, Lee Vining, CA

Stephen J. O'Brien, Ph.D., Frederick Cancer Research and Development Center, Frederick, MD

William C. Olien, Ph.D., Shenandoah University, Winchester, VA

Mary C. "Katy" Phelan, Ph.D., Greenwood Genetics Center, Greenwood, SC

J. Winston Porter, Ph.D., Waste Policy Center, Leesburg, VA

Kenneth H Reckhow, Ph.D., Duke University, Durham, NC

Sarah E. Reckhow, Riverside High Scholl, Durham, NC

Bradley B. Shepard, M.S., Montana State University, Bozeman, MT

Mary Ann Spivey, M.H.S., Medical University of South Carolina, Charleston, SC

Roger E. Stevenson, M.D., Greenwood Genetic Center, Greenwood, SC

Ann Stone, Ph.D., University of Arizona, Tucson, AZ

Patricia Swain, Ph.D., Massachusetts Division of Fisheries and Wildlife, Westborough, MA

Debbie M. Swift, Ph.D., Cary, North Carolina

Marilyn Swisher, Ph.D., University of Florida, Gainesville, FL

George E. Tempel, Ph.D., Medical University of South Carolina, Charleston, SC

David Tonkyn, Ph.D., Clemson University, Clemson, SC

Renee Wagenseil, Clemson University, Clemson, SC

Larry A. Weber, M.S., The Marshall School, Duluth, MN

Sandra Winicur, Ph.D., Indiana University, South Bend, IN

Laura R. White, Ph.D., West Stockholm, NY

Francis J. Wolak, Ph.D., Clemson University, Clemson, SC

National Advisory Panel

Royce Ballinger, University of Nebraska, Lincoln, NE

Mary Louise Bellamy, National Association of Biology Teachers, Reston, VA

George Dawson, Florida State University, Tallahassee, FL

David Dilcher, University of Florida, Gainesville, FL

David Ely, Champlain Valley High School, Hinesburg, VT

Steve Krings, Southwest High School, Green Bay, WI

Anton Lawson, Arizona State University, Tempe, AZ

Randy Moore, University of Akron, Akron, OH

Patsye Peebles, LSU Laboratory School, Baton Rouge, LA

Tom Sachse, California State Department of Education, Sacramento, CA

Rebecca Mason Simmons, American Chemical Society, Washington, DC

Charles Speilberger, University of South Florida, Tampa, FL

Robert Yager, University of Iowa, Iowa City, IA

Reviewers

Brian Alters, University of Southern California, Los Angeles, CA

Larry Bond, Wythe County Schools, Wytheville, VA

Peggy Billings Carnahan, San Antonio, TX

Jack Carter, Colorado College, Colorado Springs, CO

Michael Clough, University of Iowa, Iowa City, IA

Kimberly Crews, Population Reference Bureau, Inc., Washington, DC

James Colacino, Clemson University, Clemson, SC

Kathy Dickel, Daniel High School, Central, SC

Charlie Doyle-Warren, Forest Hills Local Schools, Cincinnati, OH

Jane Ellis, Presbyterian College, Clinton, SC

Greg Freyer, Columbia University, New York, NY

Elizabeth Gallagher, Department of Environmental Control, Town of Islip, NY

Valerie Gatchell, Presbyterian College, Clinton, SC

Sidney Gautreaux, Clemson University, Clemson, SC

John Hains, U.S. Army Corps of Engineers, Calhoun Falls, SC

Robin Kelly, San Carlos, CA

Jeff Klahn, University of Iowa, Iowa City, IA

Toby Klang, Lexington, MA

Gary Melching, Santa Theresa High School, San Jose, CA

Jack Muncy, Tennessee Valley Authority, Norris, TN

Terry McCollum, Aiken High School Annex, Cincinnati, OH

Dana Nayduch, Clemson University, Clemson, SC

Alexa Noble, Oak Ridge High School, Conroe, TX

Judy Rhymer, University of Maine, Orono, ME

Ken Rush, Ducktown Basin Museum, Ducktown, TN

Mary Ann Schneiders, Hughes Alternative Center, Cincinnati, OH

Roy Schodtler, Palatine High School, Palatine, IL

Charlotte St. Romain, Carenco High School, Lafayette, LA

Kevin Sweet, Greenwood Genetic Center, Greenwood, SC

David Tonkyn, Clemson University, Clemson, SC

Ray Turner, Clemson University, Clemson, SC

George Veomett, University of Nebraska, Lincoln, NE

Jeff Weld, University of Iowa, Iowa City, IA

Laura White, Baldwin-Wallace College, Berea, OH

Sarah Williams, Chicago, IL

Field Test Teachers

Judith Aldridge, Menchville High School, Newport News, VA

Carolyn Abbott, Piedmont Hills High School, San Jose, CA

David Astin, Wayzata Senior High School, Plymouth, MN

Janet Barks, Nathan Hale High School, Seattle, WA

Mike Barrett, School District of Augusta, Augusta, WI

Janet Bowersox, Nathan Hale High School, Seattle, WA

Steve Case, Olathe East High School, Olathe, KS

Michael Clough, University of Iowa, Iowa City, IA

Sara Clough, Memorial High School, Eau Claire, WI

Cris Cook, Winder-Barrow High School, Winder, GA

Paulette Cryer, R.B. Stall High School, North Charleston, SC

Joan Duncan, Alief Hastings South High School, Houston, TX

Alisa England, Winder-Barrow High School, Winder, GA

Geoffrey Folker, Olathe East High School, Olathe, KS

Lisa Gaines, Hillcrest High School, Simpsonville, SC

Sandy Garwood, Evergreen High School, Evergreen, CO

Shirlene Gray, B.T. Washington High School, Atlanta, GA

Leslie Hays, Helix High School, La Mesa, CA

Marvin Hedgepeth, Menchville High School, Newport News, VA

Ken Johnson, Hoffman Estates High School, Hoffman Estates, IL

Mary Jones, Gateway High School, Aurora, CO

Brian Kick, Helix High School, La Mesa, CA

Steve Krings, Southwest High School, Green Bay, WI

Janis Lariviere, Westlake High School Alternative Learning Center, Austin, TX

Bob Legge, Gateway High School, Aurora, CO

Andrea Malin, Hastings High School, Houston, TX

Lester McCall, Hillcrest High School, Simpsonville, SC

Kathleen Morris-Kortz, Thousand Islands Community School, Cape Vincent, NY

Carol Nunez, Westlake High School, Austin, TX

Patsye Peebles, LSU Laboratory School, Baton Rouge, LA

Rosalind Philips, New Century High School, Lacey, WA

Judy Porter, Columbus High School, Columbus, NE

Sylvia Sather, Abraham Lincoln High School, Denver, CO

Glenn Schlender, Southwest High School, Green Bay, WI

Marge Schneider, Cedar Shoals High School, Athens, GA

Roy Schodtler, Palatine High School, Palatine, IL

Don Shepherd, Mount Baker High School, Deming, WA

Brijinder Singh, Flushing High School, Flushing, NY

Andrea Smejkal, Columbus High School, Columbus, NE

Elizabeth Thornton, Wayzata High School, Plymouth, MN

Bob Towle, Piedmont Hills High School, San Jose, CA

Ruth Truluck, Wando High School, Mt. Pleasant, SC

David Tucker, Mount Baker High School, Deming, WA

Paul Tweed, School District of Augusta, Augusta, WI

Terri Van Wert-Perez, Land O'Lakes High School, Land O'Lakes, FL

Deborah Vasconi, Tarpon Springs High School, Tarpon Springs, FL

Sandy Wardell, Helena High School, Helena, MT

Sandra Watson, Andrew Hill High School, San Jose, CA

Robert Willis, Ballou Senior High School, Washington, DC

Project Staff

Ellie Broom
Patricia Chandler
Michael Clough
Sara Clough
Cayce Crenshaw
Kathy Dickel
Virginia Foulk
Lisa Gaines
Sharon Metzler
Becky Monhardt
Shirley Neimyer
Jean Pedersen
Peter Veronesi
Jeffrey Weld
Jennifer Williams
Erin Winstead

Other Credits

Jack Muncy
John Norton
Lucas Penick
Ken Rush
Carter & Holmes
   Orchids
Ducktown Basin
   Museum
Greenwood Genetic
   Center
Tennessee Valley
   Authority
Town of Islip,
   Department of
   Environmental
   Control

This project was partially funded by National Science Foundation grant #MDR-9252892. We wish to express our appreciation to Patricia Morse and Gerhard Salinger at the NSF for their guidance.

Brief Contents

Contents

UNIT 4   Homeostasis: The Body in Balance

UNIT 5   Inheritance

UNIT 6   Behavior and The Nervous System

xi

Contents

Welcome to BioComm: Biology in a Community Context!

BioComm: Biology in a Community Context focuses on biology, you, and your environment. Each unit begins with an authentic and troublesome issue facing you and your world. Solutions to these societal problems require that you understand biology, technology, and society. In studying these real-world issues, you will make many decisions about what you wish to know and how you can find this knowledge.

Active Learning

In this Biology class, you will be far more active than in most science classes. You will conduct science investigations, interpret the meaning of information, and apply your knowledge to issues. You will be working in the same way scientists and policy-makers work.

Sharing and discussing are part of the BioComm: Biology in a Community Context instructional method. Both you and your teacher will know why you are doing a particular activity and what you will do next. The instructional strategy in each unit takes you through a sequence of activities. In each unit you will:

◆ brainstorm ideas and questions
◆ investigate these ideas and questions
◆ share your findings and raise additional questions
◆ pursue and design your own investigations
◆ discuss your findings in a conference
◆ present the results of your research
◆ make decisions in an open forum

Investigating

To help you with your study of biology, the textbook includes two types of investigations, Guided Inquiries and Extended Inquiries. Guided Inquiries help you develop necessary skills and knowledge about biology. Extended Inquiries provide options for more advanced study. You should try to complete all of the Guided Inquiries. You may complete only a few of the Extended Inquiries.

Safety

You will be working with many different materials during your investigations. Some of these materials could be dangerous if not handled properly. To protect you and your classmates, it is important that you follow the safety guidelines that appear in this book. Inquiries will alert you to the specific safety guidelines. Be sure to follow them carefully.

Communicating

Effective communication of ideas is an important part of science and a major feature of BioComm: Biology in a Community Context. To help you present your research and ideas, each unit contains three meetings: a Conference, a Congress, and a Forum. During each of these events, you will meet with others in your class to share data, ideas, and progress, as well as make plans for necessary action.

Your *BioLog*

As you work, you will record a variety of information in your *BioLog*. The *Log* will give you a permanent record of your work, data, interpretations, and thoughts. Because you will record everything in chronological order, the *Log* will help you remember where you started, what you have accomplished, and what remains to be done. Your *Log* will make sharing ideas with others in your group and class easier. Your teacher may even let you use your *Log* while taking tests!

Preparing for Life

We have designed BioComm so that you will learn useful information and ideas as well as methods for further learning. It will prepare you to participate in the solutions of societal issues that you will face in your life.

Welcome to BioComm: Biology in a Community Context!

The Authors

Safety Guidelines

Special safety precautions required for Guided and Extended Inquiries are listed as needed throughout the units. Look for these precautions whenever you see the safety icon. Also, consult with your teacher on safety issues, and be certain to follow all guidelines that are provided to you.

The following information provides general safety recommendations that should become part of your routine in setting up and executing Inquiries. Your adherence to these safety guidelines will be especially important when you are setting up your own Extended Inquiries. Since you will be the person who designs the procedures for some of these Inquiries, you must understand the safety issues for anything that you propose to do. Even if you think that you understand the appropriate safety precautions for a situation, always consult with your teacher before attempting to handle a safety problem.

Chemicals

Handle all chemicals as if they are hazardous. Wear safety gloves and eye protection when warranted for using chemicals that are labeled as hazardous.

Avoid contamination of primary chemical stocks. Never replace a chemical in a primary stock container once it has been removed from that container (unless instructed to do so by your teacher).

Wash all glassware between uses, but do not dispose of waste chemicals down the drains of classroom sinks. Many chemicals require special disposal methods to protect you and the environment.

All chemicals in your classroom will have a Materials Safety Data Sheet (MSDS) that explains any hazards associated with them and proper disposal methods.

Biological Materials

Some of the living and preserved materials that you encounter in a biology classroom may be irritating. For example, many people are allergic to molds and fungi or to the debris that accumulates in cricket colonies. Obviously, these individuals should use caution when handling such materials. The compost columns and piles that you make in Unit 1 may harbor these and other potentially irritating biological organisms. Avoid potential problems by wearing safety gloves and a face mask whenever you handle your compost.

You must also take care when you grow populations of organisms in the classroom. Do not grow any organisms that might be hazardous or present other problems to you, your classmates, or the environment.

Before you begin growing a population, consider what you will do with it afterwards. Releasing organisms into the environment is rarely practical. Check with your state's natural resource agency to determine which organisms are prohibited. Many nuisance aquatic plants were introduced into U.S. waters by people who imported them from another country or state, grew them for a while in a fish tank or water garden, and then released them into a natural body of water.

Consult Appendix K for more information about growing organisms in the classroom.

Glassware Safety

Laboratory glassware should be segregated for laboratory use. Never use laboratory glassware for eating or drinking.

Wash glassware thoroughly in detergent after each use. Glassware that is used for some chemical analyses may require more stringent cleaning procedures, such as rinsing in a mild (10 percent) acid solution.

Only heat-resistant glassware should be heated. Handle heated glassware carefully, using laboratory tongs or heat-resistant gloves. Never touch heated glassware with your bare hands.

If glassware is broken, immediately inform your teacher. Do not attempt to pick up the pieces unless your teacher is present, and never pick up the pieces by hand. Use a whisk broom to collect the larger pieces. A wad of wet cotton should be used to pick up the tiniest pieces.

Handle microscope slides and coverslips carefully to avoid cutting your hands. Glass coverslips can be difficult to see when they are placed on tables or paper towels. Respect your classmates' safety by keeping track of slides and coverslips.

Glass Pipettes and Tubing

Inserting glass pipettes or tubing into rubber stoppers or pipette bulbs requires some special precautions. It is surprisingly easy to crush the glass in your hand or, worse yet, to drive a broken glass tube or pipette deep into your hand. The key to avoiding these problems is gentle handling. Never try to force a pipette or glass tubing into a pipette bulb or rubber stopper. If you encounter resistance, lubricate the end of the tubing or pipette that you are attempting to insert. Water can usually be used as a lubricant. If this does not work, a little soap solution or glycerin can be used if it will not interfere with the inquiry to be performed.

Both **MATTER** and *energy* are needed for LIFE

ONE

MATTER AND ENERGY FOR LIFE

Where does matter **GO** when society *discards* it?

Initial Inquiry

What does "go away" mean? Where is "away"?

THE BIOLOGY OF TRASH

Setting

For over five months, the trash barge *Mobro* (Figure 1.1) cruised from New York to Central America and back and waited for a place to dump its load of garbage. Everywhere it stopped (or tried to), it caused controversy. Most local residents just didn't want someone else's garbage. A few saw the potential for making a profit by accepting it.

Figure 1.1

Almost all of the trash on this barge was once alive!

The *Mobro* Video

You'll begin this unit by watching a short documentary about the *Mobro*, its load, and its journey. You should jot down as many observations as you can about the video in your *BioLog*, beginning on page 9. (Since you will be writing in this log frequently, it is a good idea to save the first eight pages for a table of contents.) Be sure to include today's date so that you can keep track of your ideas.

After you watch the video, read "The Voyage of the *Mobro*" for additional information. Now imagine that the owners of the *Mobro* wanted to dump their load of garbage near your house. If you knew a garbage expert, what questions would you ask? Write as many as you can in your *BioLog*. Appendix A, "Writing in Your *BioLog*," can guide you in making your *Log* entries.

The Voyage of the *Mobro*

Dimensions of Mobro: Length: 240 ft. Beam: 30 ft. Depth: 14.6 ft.
Contents of garbage: Mostly paper, plastic, and wood trash: 52 percent from New York City, 39 percent from the Town of Islip, 9 percent from Nassau County.
Mass and volume of barge contents: 3,186 tons of refuse compacted into bales. One bale has a mass of about 1.5 tons (1400 kilograms).
Total miles traveled: Approximately 6,000.
Number of days at sea (from the time the garbage left Islip until the final 400 tons of ash were returned and buried): 163 days (55 days at sea searching for a disposal site and 108 days moored in New York Bay).

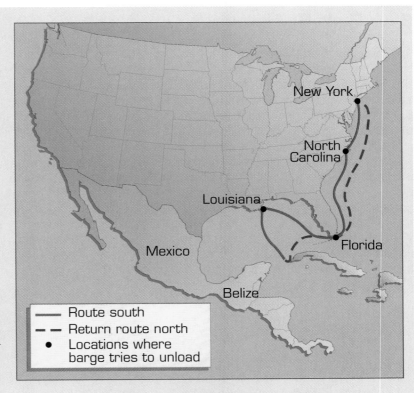

— Route south
-- Return route north
• Locations where barge tries to unload

Dates	Events in the Voyage
March 22	The barge filled with garbage leaves Islip, New York.
March 25	The barge arrives in Morehead City, NC, followed by a large flock of seagulls.
April 6	NC officials declare the *Mobro* unwelcome; the barge departs Morehead City.
April 15	Louisiana refuses to let the barge dock in New Orleans for fear of infection.
April 24	Mexico plans to send its navy to prevent the barge from entering Mexico.
April 27	Belize rejects the garbage when the barge is 100 miles northeast of Yucatan.
May 3	The barge anchors 7 miles southeast of Key West, FL. The EPA tests the

After more than five months and 6,000 miles at sea, the contents of the trash barge Mobro were incinerated and buried at a Long Island landfill.

	contents and declares that the barge is carrying "standard trash."
May 7	The government of the Bahamas refuses to let the barge dock.
May 8	The barge leaves Key West and returns to New York.
May 12	Islip and New York State agree to expand the Islip landfill.
May 16	The *Mobro* anchors at Gravesend Bay anchorage waiting for permission to unload.
Sept. 1	The trash is incinerated and the ash buried at Islip's Blydenburgh landfill.

What Is The Largest Structure Ever Built By Humans?

When you read this question, what comes to mind? We often think that *largest* means *tallest*, so you might have thought of the Sears Tower or the Empire State Building. But how about structures with enormous volume (length × width × height)? Certainly, tourists travel thousands of miles to visit the Pyramid of the Sun in Mexico or the Great Pyramids of Egypt. Yet these incredible human creations are greatly surpassed in volume by a structure that tourists seldom visit: a huge landfill on Staten Island in New York City called Fresh Kills landfill. This is the site where debris from the World Trade Center was discarded and sorted. Think about this fact from the perspectives of your future children and grandchildren and consider the implications. Will your grandchildren remember you as the builders of great mountains of trash? Will the Fresh Kills landfill become a tourist attraction in years to come? Is trash becoming our most enduring contribution to the world?

Volumes of trash in Fresh Kills, New York, landfill

Football field

Great Pyramid at Giza, Egypt

The Fresh Kills landfill is one of the largest structures ever created by humans.

Answer the following questions in your *Log*:

1. How do you think future generations will judge our habits concerning waste?

2. Who is responsible for the current trash situation?

3. How do you feel about the fact that the largest structure ever created by humans happens to be a landfill?

Brainstorming

Share your list of questions about the *Mobro* with others in a small group brainstorming session. Add new questions to the list. Once you have a list of your own questions and the ideas of others, make a mark next to each question that you might be able to answer just by watching the video again or reading "The Voyage of the *Mobro*." See what answers you and your group can find by referring only to these data and not the video. As you try to answer these questions, you will become more familiar with the situation and will probably come up with new questions.

Finally, look at the questions that are left, the ones that can't be answered just by looking at the data. Working with your group, figure out which questions might require special skills or equipment to answer. Your teacher will be asking you to complete some Guided Inquiries, which may use or teach you some of these skills. Later on, you might try to answer other of these questions during your own investigations in the Extended Inquiries.

To get you started, here are some of the questions you should explore as you brainstorm with your group.

As your group agrees on answers to these questions, jot these answers in your *Log*.

1. How many garbage bales were on the *Mobro*? Estimate using Figure 1.1 and the data on page 3. Confirm your answer.

2. What might have attracted the flock of seagulls to the barge?

3. What changes may have taken place on the barge during its journey?

The Fresh Kills landfill covers 3,000 acres (or more than 1,200 hectares), with trash mounds higher than 61 meters.

4. Why might the contents of the barge have been smaller when it returned than when it first left New York?

5. Why did other states and countries refuse to accept the barge and its contents? What reasons might they have had? How would you resolve the *Mobro's* problem?

6. Why not just dump the garbage far out in the ocean?

7. What are some long-term solutions to the *Mobro's* problem?

Revisit the *Mobro*

Now watch the video again. This time, pay attention to the measurements that are given and think of the questions you have raised. Look particularly for new details and new issues. Record your notes in your *Log*.

Why Study Garbage in a Biology Course?

Right now, you might be asking yourself, "Why should I study garbage at the beginning of a biology course?" The answer is simple: because garbage is part of biology, which is the study of life processes. All living things produce waste. In the natural world, that waste is used by other living things in the process called biodegradation. Biodegradation means, literally, breaking something down by biological processes. If the waste is not broken down, it can build up to dangerous levels and damage the ability of individual living organisms to function. Waste that is not easily broken down by biological processes is called nonbiodegradable. Only humans produce waste that can't be broken down by natural processes.

Humans can damage their own environment by producing huge amounts of waste or waste that is dangerous. Waste in unmanageable quantities is a threat to life on this planet. Landfills are filling up across the United States. For many reasons, finding new landfill sites is more difficult than you might imagine. Designing landfills or other garbage disposal sites is at least as complicated as finding new sites. How do we dispose of the many products we use every day that are toxic or dangerous in some other way? How do we make sure that these products do not contaminate our air, water, land, and food?

Human civilization is facing a critical environmental problem: how to handle our ever-increasing wastes. As you study the problem, you will come to understand important biological concepts that can help to resolve this distinctly human problem. Isn't this an excellent reason for studying garbage in a biology course? 🌎

What Can We Learn about Society from Studying Trash?

Trash, garbage, waste—these are all names that we use for things we no longer want or need. Though most of us never think about the things we throw away, some people actually make a science of studying trash. Archeologists, who study ancient civilizations, have always found garbage dumps wonderful places to find out about the people they are studying. From such trash piles, they can learn what people ate, valued, read, and used as tools. Often, archeologists find that the garbage dump of an historical site is the best record they have of its ancient inhabitants.

Some archeologists have been studying more recent trash with amazing results. Modern landfills are designed to be airtight and watertight; this prevents decay and decomposition and makes it possible to study their contents. Garbologists, the archeologists who study trash, have even found 40-year-old hot dogs and newspapers that they could still easily read in landfills (Figure 1.2).

By analyzing trash, garbologists learn about the habits of past communities. They can see how the people in the community recycled trash, what specific products they bought, and exactly how much waste they produced. For instance, soft drink and beer cans used to have flip-tops that came off the can when it was opened. If the researchers find a lot of flip-tops but no cans in the garbage, they might hypothesize that the cans were being recycled. By studying meat wrapper labels, they can determine how much meat and what cuts of meat were being eaten. By weighing discarded fat and bone, they can learn about dietary and cooking habits. They might measure disposable diaper use by counting the empty boxes, since some of the dirty diapers might have been flushed or disposed of in traveling and so would not be found in a community landfill. 🌎

Figure 1.2

After 10 years in a landfill, these hot dogs—and their packaging—are still recognizable. Materials decompose very slowly in landfills.

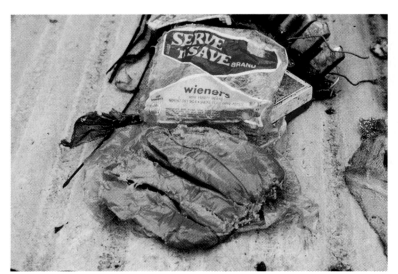

Guided Inquiry 1.1

Matter and Energy for Life

A Trash Audit

Just how much trash do you generate? What makes up your trash? Who else is involved in making the trash that is thrown in with yours? How much trash does your biology class create? You can find the answers to some of these questions by doing a trash audit.

A trash audit is a study of the amount and types of trash produced from a particular source. In this Guided Inquiry, you will examine one specific source of trash, choosing a source with which you are directly involved. There are several possible sources that you might study, such as trash in your classroom, your school, or your home. Your teacher will explain your options and also the length of time that you will be involved in the audit.

Procedure

MATERIALS

- Disposable plastic gloves
- Large plastic garbage bags
- Trash
- Containers into which to sort trash
- Bathroom scale or balance
- Meter stick
- String

Before you begin, read the safety note on page 8.

1. Collect trash for this audit. If you collect for more than two days, be sure to remove or rinse out any trash, such as food, that might rot or smell.

   A few days' worth of trash should give you a manageable amount.

2. Place the trash in a large plastic bag as you collect it.

3. Estimate the volume of the trash in your bag. Record this value in your *Log.* Use metric units.

   HINT: Shake the contents around in the bag until the bag has a roughly spherical shape. Calculate trash volume using the formula for the volume of a sphere:

   $V = 4/3\ \pi\ r^3$
   where: V = Volume π = 3.14 r = radius

   To estimate r, measure the distance through the largest part of the bag in meters (or parts of a meter) and divide by 2.

4. Determine the mass of the trash. Record this value in your *Log.*

5. Discuss as a class how you might sort the trash. Begin by listing some possible categories of trash. For example, the *Mobro* carried mostly paper, plastic, and wood trash. Record your individual and class lists in your *Log*.

6. Decide which trash can be recycled, reused, or composted. Designate a special place or container for this trash.

7. Wearing safety gloves, surgical mask, and goggles, sort out the trash that can be recycled, reused, or composted. Keep hands away from face.

8. Determine the mass and volume of the remaining trash. Record this information in your *Log*. How would you dispose of this trash?

9. Draw a flowchart showing how these materials flow from their source to you and on to the trash pile. (Directions for how to make a flowchart can be found in Appendix B.)

Interpretations: Answer these questions in your *Log*:

1. What materials are in the trash you collected?

2. How much of this trash is packaging material?

3. If you collected trash from your school or home, calculate how much garbage might be produced from that source each day. How much might be produced each year? Use metric units.

4. What percentage can be recycled, reused, or composted?

5. When you sort out all of the trash that can be recycled, reused, or composted, what percentage of the original trash is left?

6. Where does your garbage go when you throw it away?

7. What do most people think that "away" means?

8. Who is responsible for the trash that you've collected for this audit when you throw it away?

9. What types of raw materials were required to make the items you found in the trash?

Applications: Answer these questions in your *Log*:

1. If your school has a recycling program, what is recycled and how?

2. What kind of recycling program is in place in your community?

3. What does your family do with old newspapers?

4. What happens to old automobile tires in your area?

5. Some communities have what they call a disposal or reuse fee that is added to the price of items such as tires, motor oil, drinks in aluminum cans, and drinks in plastic bottles. If your community has these fees, what are they for each of these items?

6. Does your community charge other disposal fees?

7. Describe any programs in your community that attempt to reduce, reuse, or recycle commonly used materials in new or innovative ways.

8. How could you reduce the amount of packaging materials in trash?

Garbage Is Us

Dr. William Rathje, an archeologist and professor of anthropology at the University of Arizona, directs the Garbage Project (Figure 1.3). This project developed in 1971 as part of an anthropology class. Students in the class observed that garbage provides information about human behaviors. They sorted garbage collected from areas throughout Tucson and eventually ventured out to excavate landfills. These landfills provided the students with many insights into society's wasteful habits as well as its methods of garbage management.

The following is adapted from *Rubbish* by William Rathje and Cullen Murphy, HarperCollins Publishers, 1992.

Dr. William Rathje, director of the Garbage Project.

There are several important points about garbage. First, the creation of garbage is a sure sign of human presence. From Styrofoam® cups along a roadway to urine bags on the moon, there is an uninterrupted chain of garbage that reaches back more than two million years to the first "waste flake" knocked off in the making of the first stone tool (see Figure 1.4 on page 11). That the distant past often seems misty and dim is precisely because our earliest ancestors left so little garbage behind. An appreciation of the accomplishments of the first prehumans became possible only after they began making stone tools and leaving their trash behind. This trash became artifacts, evidence of human existence. Artifacts serve as markers of how our forebears coped with the evolving physical and social world.

Human beings come and go, but their garbage seems to have more staying power and informs us years later about their activities and even attitudes. The wildly extravagant habits of our own country and our own time—the sheer volume of the garbage that we create and must dispose of—will make our society an open book. The question is: Would we ourselves recognize our story when it is told, or will our garbage tell tales about us that we do not yet suspect? 🌍

Figure 1.3

Students in the Garbage Project screen landfill samples.

John Tropiano:
Waste Management

John Tropiano manages the family business. When his grandfather, Rocco Velocci, arrived in the United States from Italy in 1912, the Long Island, New York, area was mostly farmland. Waves of immigrants in the early 1900s greatly increased the population of Long Island. Rocco Velocci saw a business opportunity in hauling away the trash generated by all these people. In 1945, he and a partner created their own company, Star Carting. After many years of mergers and acquisitions, the company, today known as American Transfer Co., Inc., is managed by Rocco Velocci's grandson, John Tropiano.

The Tropiano business is a very successful and growing business. The family-owned company collects over 5×10^6 kilograms of mixed trash and over 1×10^6 kilograms of recyclable materials each month from businesses throughout Long Island.

In the early days, everything was relatively simple. The waste that was picked up was taken to a landfill or an incinerator for disposal. Now, because of the closing of many landfills in the New York area, it has become increasingly necessary to reduce the amount of material that is dumped because disposal fees are so high. The company has also needed to educate the public about recycling in order to limit disposal fees. Paper, cardboard, metal, glass, and plastic can now be recycled. The most cost-effective way is if it is source-separated by the customer. For customers who don't want to separate the material, Mr. Tropiano has a solution: a trash sorting station. This system, which is under development, will enable his employees to recover the recyclables from the trash as it flows by them on a conveyer belt.

"Is there money in recyclables?" is a question Mr. Tropiano is often asked. "You can make a bundle of money from recyclables," is something else that he often hears. His reply is "Sometimes." The prices for recyclable materials are so unstable that the company would consider storing the materials until it could get better prices, if storage space were available.

Asked about the most exciting part of the waste management business, Mr. Tropiano had an answer that might surprise you. Right now Tropiano is using a computer network. This computer system is a LAN network that also allows direct communication between the company's office and onboard truck scales. This system allows the driver to see the garbage that he or she is to pick up via an onboard video display. When each customer's container is picked up, the system actually calculates the weight of the garbage. This way, Mr. Tropiano can keep track of the flow of waste and can adjust the rates that his customers are charged for their service.

How do you train for work in waste management? Because he entered a family business, much of Mr. Tropiano's training was on the job. But he also has a high school diploma and two years of training in electronics and accounting.

What does he look for in an employee? A person who "presents a positive company image, has good communication skills, and has a clean driver's license." For high school biology students who are interested in careers in waste management, Mr. Tropiano recommends studying biochemistry, materials science, mathematics, and computers.

Figure 1.4

Humans' ways of disposing of garbage have changed throughout history. What types of artifacts would each of these methods leave for future generations to find?

Ode to a Landfill

Old rot, yet not
Useless, valuable forgot
Danger? Volume immense
Plastic stuck to the fence
A call from 1953
Read, yet still easily
Juice from our multiple weeks
Collected, yet sometimes it leaks
Growing quickly in pace
Running out of Space?

What do you think the poem means? What do the poem and Figure 1.5 tell you about landfills and garbage? In your *Log,* write your own poem, story, or riddle that describes your observations and thoughts about garbage. 🌎

A Stream of Waste

Problems with garbage involve the flow of materials from their source to their eventual disposal site. Discarded materials were present on the *Mobro,* in the Fresh Kills landfill, and in the trash that you audited in Guided Inquiry 1.1. As you talked about the garbage on the *Mobro* and in the Fresh Kills landfill and later, while you were sorting your own trash in the audit, you probably wondered, "Where did all that stuff come from?" You might have some ideas about the origin of all that trash, but a more in-depth exploration of the subject might surprise you.

Figure 1.5

Many of the items in this cross-section of a landfill are recognizable.

Soil
Gravel
Pipe collects water from surface
Plastic

Garbage

Liner
Pipe collects leachate
Soil base

Let's look at a typical piece of trash that is thrown away every day: a plastic food container used to package sandwich meat. Where did the materials to make this container come from? How much energy was used in the manufacturing process? How much energy was used to transport the container? When it is discarded, how will it affect our natural environment? When it is thrown in the garbage, will it go to the landfill? The incinerator? What will happen to the container then? Everything we use in our daily lives is made of some type of material that in science is called matter, and matter does not go away. Materials can be rearranged, reformulated, and recombined, but the stuff they are made of, the matter, always remains.

If we recycle goods—plastics, glass, paper, and other disposables—the materials are used again and again and never become waste. Materials that are not recycled become part of the waste stream. Like a natural stream, the waste stream can have one or many sources, called points of origin. Items in a waste stream flow from raw materials to a useable item to waste. Well-designed waste streams usually empty into a landfill or an incinerator, rather than a lake or an ocean. By following the flow of materials that make up a plastic food container, you can develop a picture of one item in the waste stream (Figure 1.6). Then you can apply this model to any item you throw away. 🌎

BIOprediction

What Would Happen If Households Could No Longer Count On Garbage Being Taken Away?

BioPredictions ask you to speculate on causes and effects. Speculation is an essential part of science and life. Whenever an outcome is unclear or uncertain, you can speculate on what will happen. With each Bio-Prediction, you explore issues and look for connections between events and their impacts.

Benjamin Franklin is credited with starting the first street-cleaning service in the American colonies. At about that same time, colonists began to dig refuse pits for their garbage instead of tossing it into the streets or behind houses.

Ben Franklin

Soon after the Civil War, Colonel George E. Waring, Jr., often called "the Apostle of Cleanliness," created the first municipal garbage pickup service in New York City, and the modern age of sanitation began. Since that time, garbage service has become the accepted and expected way to dispose of personal and household waste.

Respond to the following questions in your *Log*:

1. What might cause garbage pickup to be suspended?

2. What might cause recycling to be suspended?

3. What would happen if either garbage pickup or recycling services stopped? Predict the consequences. In your *Log*, list at least three possible effects of each.

WASTE STREAM ALTERNATIVES

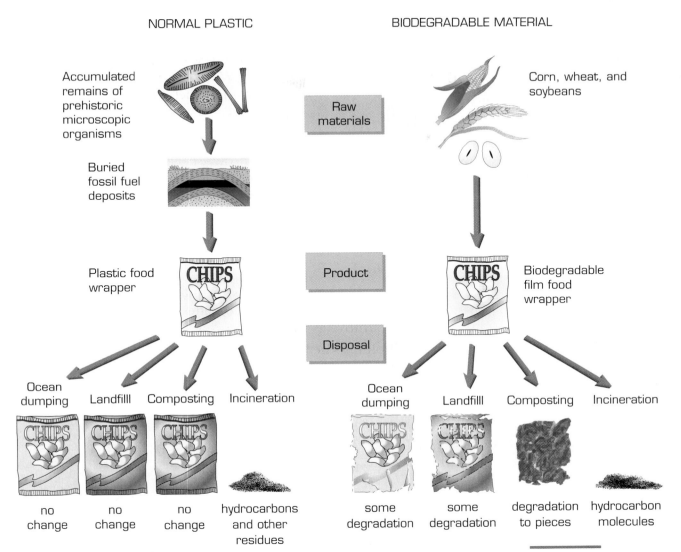

NORMAL PLASTIC

BIODEGRADABLE MATERIAL

Accumulated remains of prehistoric microscopic organisms

Raw materials

Corn, wheat, and soybeans

Buried fossil fuel deposits

Plastic food wrapper

Product

CHIPS

CHIPS

Biodegradable film food wrapper

Disposal

Ocean dumping   Landfilll   Composting   Incineration

no change   no change   no change   hydrocarbons and other residues

Ocean dumping   Landfilll   Composting   Incineration

some degradation   some degradation   degradation to pieces   hydrocarbon molecules

Figure 1.6

Contrast the waste streams of a plastic food wrapper and biodegradable packaging. Which decomposes more readily?

Guided Inquiry 1.2

Composting

What is compost? How do you make a compost column or a compost pile? What happens to compost over time? Why do these changes occur? In this activity, you will create your own individual compost column and/or pile. You will use it later for experiments and observation.

Part A: Your Own Compost Column

MATERIALS

- Three 2-liter plastic soda bottles per student or group
- Mix of leaves, grass, vegetable food scraps, water
- Very sticky, clear packing tape approximately 5 cm in width
- Dissecting needles or safety pins
- Scissors with sharp ends
- Several old shoe boxes for the class to share
- One or more moisture meters for the class (available in garden stores)

Procedure

1. Put on your goggles.
2. Cut three 2-liter plastic soda bottles, as indicated in Figure 1.7. If you place the bottles in a shoe box on a level laboratory table, the bottles will not move as you cut them.
3. Make small holes in the bottles, as indicated in Figure 1.7. These holes allow air into the compost. Your teacher will tell you how to make the holes.

Figure 1.7

Construct your compost column from three plastic bottles, as the students shown below have done.

"Top" slides down over second section; tape the seam.

Air holes

Second section slides down inside third section; tape the seam.

Netting with rubber band

Third section slides down into base; tape the seam.

* Note that these cuts are made "on the curve" of the bottle so that these ends will slide *into* other sections.

4. Join the bottles as indicated in Figure 1.7, to complete your column.

5. Fill the column with leaves, grass, vegetable food scraps, and enough water to moisten the contents. In your *Log,* record the types and estimated amounts of materials that you put in your column.

6. Seal the seams of the column with clear tape.

7. After you build your compost column, describe it in your *Log.* Decide which types of observations you will make to detect changes in your compost column over many months. Be consistent in making the same types of observations throughout the life of your compost column. For example, you can describe:

   ◆ the height and composition of materials in the column,
   ◆ moisture content (using a moisture meter),
   ◆ temperature (taken at several different places in the column),
   ◆ appearance of materials in the column (unchanged, partially degraded, much degraded), and
   ◆ living organisms in the column.

Part B: An Outdoor Compost Pile (Optional)

If an outdoor area is available at your school, your class can construct its own compost pile. Or perhaps you'd like to make one of your own at home. Check with your teacher for options.

MATERIALS

- An outdoor area about 1 meter square
- Compostable material such as grass, vegetable food scraps, or leaves
- Sturdy containment material such as chicken wire or picket fencing
- A shovel, rake, or pitchfork for turning the material
- Topsoil

Procedure

1. Building a compost pile outside, in an area over soil, works even better than the indoor compost column. Make the pile as large as you can, but 1 square meter is sufficient. Surround the area with sturdy fencing material to hold in the decomposing matter. Picket fencing or chicken wire is best because it contains the decomposing material but still allows extensive ventilation.

2. Mix a few handfuls of topsoil with each cubic foot of material to be decomposed. You can experiment with the amount of soil that will encourage the material to decompose, or biodegrade, most rapidly. Do not pack the material. Keep the material in the compost column moist by sprinkling it with water every few days, but do not soak the pile. You want high humidity but no standing water.

BIOoccupation

Jonn Foulk: Biodegradable Films Research

The next time you are cleaning up after having friends visit, take note of the empty food wrappings that your party left behind. What is going to happen to the wrappings from the fast food, chips, and candy? If Jonn Foulk has anything to do with it, you might someday eat the packaging as well as the food it contains!

Dr. Foulk is a USDA research scientist whose research interest is biopolymers, molecules that are long chains of smaller molecules derived from natural sources. The biopolymers that Dr. Foulk studies are made from soybean, corn, and wheat proteins.

Dr. Foulk is investigating the use of these biopolymers to make food packaging. These degradable packages are designed to break down when they are exposed to natural biological and environmental processes. Oxygen in the air, light, water, and digestion by animals all will speed the degradation of these packages. Widespread use of these biodegradable films would mean that food packaging would take up less space in landfills. These packages could be composted or perhaps used for livestock feed, thus reducing the amount of solid waste that we produce.

How might you become a researcher in biodegradable packaging? As he was earning undergraduate, master and Ph.D. degrees in agricultural engineering, Dr. Foulk took many courses in microbiology, chemistry, food science, math, agriculture, and environmental engineering. His research for his master's degree included designing a two-layer biopolymer film from soybeans, corn, and wheat. He then analyzed the amount of oxygen and water vapor that was able to penetrate the layers. This is a significant issue if you want your potato chips, candy, or hamburgers to stay fresh.

Dr. Foulk's advice for high school students who are interested in research on reducing solid waste is "Start with yourself and watch how much you waste. Set an example for your school, family, and friends."

3. Work your compost. Once you have built your compost structure, either indoors or outdoors, begin adding organic materials. Start with plant material such as lawn clippings with some leaves added. You might want to include some food scraps such as banana peels, apple cores, and vegetable scraps. Do not use meat products or manure; they might attract disease-causing microorganisms, called pathogens.

4. Mix air into your compost. As the material in your pile settles, be sure to turn it. Use a shovel, a sturdy rake, or a pitchfork to mix the materials (Figure 1.8). You can avoid unpleasant smells from the pile if you turn it frequently so that the interior gets air. As the material decomposes, continue to add new material. You can also add red earthworms to your individual compost column or the outdoor pile. They will aid in breaking down biological materials.

5. Observe your compost over time. You will probably notice some interesting changes. You will make specific observations about your compost in some of the inquiries that follow. If you keep your compost going all year, your observations will get really interesting.

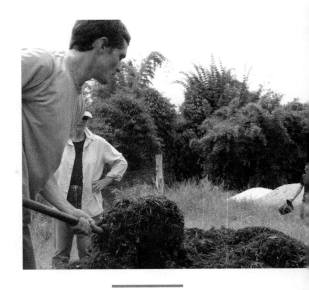

Figure 1.8

Turning a compost pile exposes all its components to air, water, and light, which speed decomposition.

So What Can We Do with Garbage?

Almost everyone grows tired of hearing about problems. But only by acknowledging problems can we hope to find solutions and, ultimately, have a positive impact on the environment. One person can make a difference! So let's explore some possible solutions to garbage problems. As you read the following discussions about what we can do with our garbage, think about what the effects would be if everyone followed these suggestions. Would the results be uniformly good for everyone? Identify potential benefits and problems for each garbage disposal method. You may find that potential solutions to society's complex problems can produce new problems.

Why Not Just Burn Our Garbage?

Citizens often suggest that if landfill space is such a big problem, we should simply burn garbage and put the resulting ash in the landfill. When most people lived in small towns and rural settings, they did just that. As more people came to live closer together, however, incineration became a problem. Incineration can release volumes of smoke and potentially damaging chemicals into the air. Newer incinerators burn trash at a very high temperature and almost completely break down the material, reducing the amount of waste expelled into the air. But many people still fear that materials released with the smoke from these incinerators can damage their health. In addition, incineration destroys many valuable materials that could be recycled. So while burning garbage seems like a natural solution to our landfill dilemma, it raises further problems.

Reduce / Reuse / Recycle

One way to reduce the volume of trash that we produce is to reduce, reuse, and recycle, (the "three Rs"). The number one way to reduce waste is to use less. When we use less, we produce less waste. Using both sides of a sheet of paper, ordering goods by phone, or sending mail and paying bills electronically reduce the amount of paper. This saves trees, natural habitats for wildlife, energy, and money. It also saves valuable landfill space.

Ordering by phone saves paper.

Reusing materials again and again is our second best option. Reusing materials requires little energy and few resources. We can, for example, use the same envelope twice or we can buy reusable items instead of paper plates and plastic utensils that have to be thrown away after one use. Stores can require a deposit on glass beverage containers, which can be washed and reused. The choice to reuse materials is not always clear. Though reuse saves materials, the cleaning or other preparations for reuse can be expensive. What potential problems with reuse can you identify?

In recycling, used materials are not reused; they are processed so that they can be used to create new materials. This process requires more energy than reusing and creates more waste, but it saves natural resources and landfill space. In Guided Inquiry 1.1, when you measured the amount of trash before and after separating out the recyclables, you saw how critical recycling is to solving our landfill problems and saving precious natural resources. Mr. Tropiano (page 10) mentioned some problems with recycling from a waste manager's viewpoint. What other problems can you think of?

The Recycling Dilemma

How good a job are we doing with the three Rs? Almost everyone knows about recycling and the benefits associated with it. In fact, most people claim that they do recycle, either by choice or by law. What do people recycle (Figure 1.9)? Aluminum cans have an extremely successful recycling story; today more than half of all aluminum beverage cans are recycled. Why? Turning aluminum ore from the earth into new aluminum is much harder on the environment and far more expensive than reprocessing used cans into new ones. This creates a strong market for used aluminum. In many instances, glass is also cheaper to recycle than to produce from raw materials, and the market for recycled glass is growing as well.

Recycling is practical only if there is a use—and a market—for the recycled goods. New uses for recycled materials are being developed every day. You can now buy book bags, clothing, and even carpets made from recycled soda bottles. This process has some limitations, however. Recycled plastic cannot be used to store or serve food because even after the plastic has been carefully cleaned, there is still a risk of contamination. Also, various types of plastics are not compatible with each other and have to be sorted before they can be recycled. Don't forget, however, that plastics are petroleum products. We do not have an infinite supply of this vital natural resource. In fact, current evidence suggests that the supply of petroleum might run out in your lifetime. Remember, petroleum is made from plants that have decayed over long periods of time. This will make it vital to recycle petroleum-based products such as plastic in spite of the inconvenience and costs.

Scientists are finding new ways to recycle as well. For example, plastic can now be recycled into fuel oil. This process may produce a source of fuel that is more economical than imported crude oil. As another example, a Canadian-based company has developed a way to use the billions of old tires that now sit in landfills. The company extracts carbon black and organic gases from the tires and steel from the steel belts. The carbon black can be used to produce other petroleum-based products, the steel can be recycled, and the organic gases provide the energy to run the recycling process.

Composting

A large portion of the trash that we discard consists of biological materials that, under the right conditions, will decompose, leaving soil, necessary nutrients, and no garbage. Food scraps, grass clippings and leaves, and paper are examples of such materials; and they have something in common: they all are materials from living things. Many of the materials in an ordinary landfill don't decompose because of the way that landfills are constructed and maintained. But you can easily create the conditions necessary for decomposition at home and recycle almost all your organic waste. By using these methods, you can help to reduce the solid waste problem and, at the same time, provide rich soil for your house plants or garden. This process is called composting.

Composting, in its simplest sense, is nothing more than putting organic materials in a place where they can rot and decay. To function properly, a compost pile must have organic materials, moisture, and air. If any of these are lacking, the pile might not decompose, or it might smell quite bad. A correctly constructed and maintained compost pile, however, is

Figure 1.9

Many communities have recycling stations where used motor oil, newspapers, plastics, glass, and aluminum are collected, removing them from the waste stream.

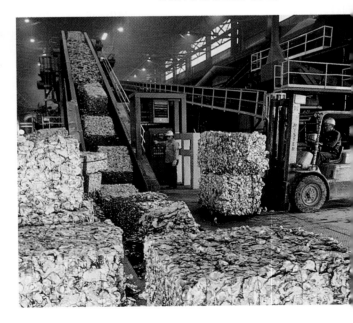

neat, clean, and efficient (Figure 1.10). A good compost pile contains organic materials, such as plant food waste; a good nitrogen source, such as grass clippings; and a source of decomposer organisms, such as are found on leaves and twigs or in the soil.

Landfills

In recent years, many companies have begun advertising their products as biodegradable and, therefore, good environmental choices. Consumers are urged to buy these products instead of using plastics, glass, and metal, which do not decompose rapidly. Unfortunately, even food, paper, and other items that we think will be broken down in the environment might not decompose in a landfill. Why not? Remember what you learned from reading about Dr. William Rathje's work in the excerpt from *Rubbish*. Food and paper will decompose if they are ground up and exposed to oxygen, light, water, and microorganisms (Figure 1.11); but the conditions in a landfill often lead instead to drying out, or mummification. In fact, after 10 years in a landfill, food and yard debris will probably be reduced by only 25 to 50 percent.

What do garbologists find in a landfill? They don't find much plastic; plastic makes up only 5 percent of an average landfill by weight and 12 percent by volume. And plastic's share of the landfill hasn't changed since 1970. Fast-food packaging makes up only about one-tenth of 1 percent of the contents of a modern landfill, and disposable diapers make up less than 1 percent. So what is the biggest category of waste in a landfill? If you performed the trash audit in Guided Inquiry 1.1, you can probably guess the answer easily. Paper makes up 40 to 50 percent of our landfills by weight and by volume! Newspapers alone make up 10 to 20 percent, and the telephone books we discard after only one year of use make up another very large category.

Where should we put all this garbage? Where is a good place for a landfill? This is another area of concern. In the past, many landfills were located in swamps or marshes, areas that were considered unsuitable for building

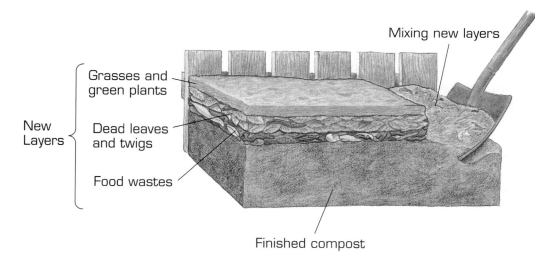

Figure 1.10

A properly constructed compost pile includes organic materials, a good nitrogen source, and a source of decomposer organisms.

Mixing new layers

Grasses and green plants

New Layers

Dead leaves and twigs

Food wastes

Finished compost

Conditions in a well-turned compost pile

Conditions in a a sealed landfill

Water

Light

Oxygen

Microorganisms

Microorganisms

Substantial degradation

Little degradation

homes and businesses. But these areas are prone to flooding, and the waste materials can leach, or seep, into the groundwater. Often, too, these areas are protected or endangered natural systems. Some landfills have been located near lakes and rivers. These older landfills are unlined and will be a source of concern for years to come. In these landfills, chemicals, pesticides, motor oil, and other harmful substances gradually seep through the ground and into our water supply. All these problems will eventually affect most living things.

Today landfills must be carefully placed, lined, drained, and monitored to avoid leaking and should not be located close to waterways. Pipes carry liquids that leach from the garbage to storage tanks for safe disposal (see Figure 1.12 on page 22). Garbage deposited in a landfill is covered with a thin layer of soil each day. Densely populated areas of the country, such as the Northeast, already have major problems finding suitable areas for landfills. In other areas, such as the western United States, plenty of space is still available. However, as you saw in the case of the *Mobro,* no one wants to put up with someone else's trash. The cry of "not in my back yard" (NIMBY) can be heard everywhere as each region searches for a place to dispose of its own garbage. 🌍

BIOthoughts

In what ways does a compost pile differ from a landfill?

How does soil help build a successful compost pile?

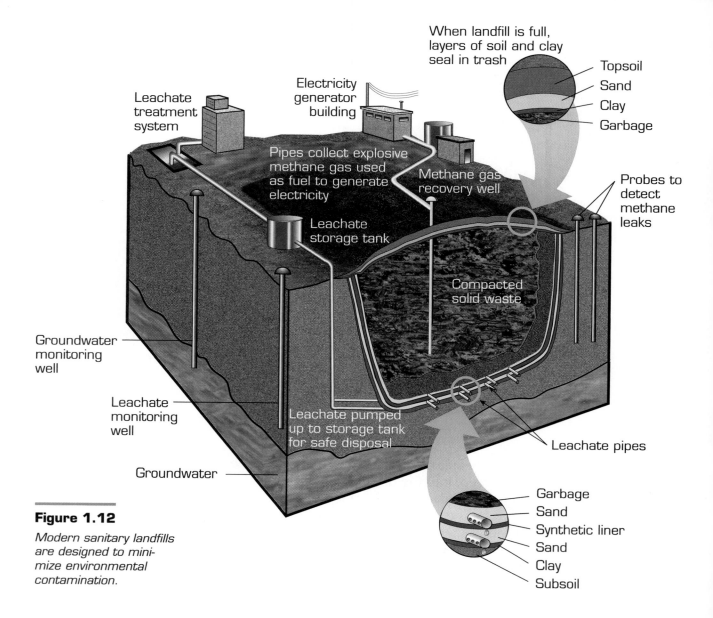

Figure 1.12

Modern sanitary landfills are designed to minimize environmental contamination.

Composting as a Model

A model is a simplified replica of a real object or process. Many children's toys, such as a doll or plastic airplane, are actually models. Scientists use models to help them understand complex phenomena.

When you made a compost pile or column, you modeled what occurs on a large scale in nature. Models are useful for interpreting and representing something in nature. Models typically show the relationship between two or more objects. For instance, wind-tunnel experiments using small model planes allow engineers to infer what would happen with full-sized aircraft.

We need to use models to gain knowledge, and these models sometimes come to be accepted as adequate descriptions or representations of reality. However, scientists do not typically see models as *exact* copies of reality. So when you are learning about and using various scientific models, or creating your own, remember that they are not exact copies of reality. Rather, think of them as helping you to understand and produce more knowledge about nature.

What type of model does the compost column in the classroom represent? Record your answers in your *Log*.

BIOprediction

What Can We Do?

When humans use resources, they always have leftover material that must be discarded in some way. According to William Rathje, "There are no ways of dealing with garbage that have not been familiar for thousands of years. The four basic methods are: dumping, burning, turning it into something useful (recycling), and minimizing the volume of material goods to start with (known in the garbage business as source reduction)."

By 1910, eight out of every ten cities in the United States had some sort of garbage pickup. In most cases, this garbage was simply dumped outside the populated area. Then came the official dump site, which was followed by the evolution of the landfill. Most recently, the high-technology sanitary landfill has become the required means to bury our garbage. But landfills are filling up all over the nation much more quickly than expected. Even with recycling, we are still throwing away much of our garbage.

Respond to the following in your *Log*:

1. What if your town or area could no longer count on using a landfill for the disposal of garbage? How would you get rid of your waste?

2. Consult Appendix C to find out how to construct a concept map. Then create a concept map to generate ideas that might solve a trash problem.

As landfills are closed, communities are finding ways to use the land. One such use is creating a ski slope. What are the benefits or disadvantages of using a closed landfill?

Decomposition Through Contamination

What would happen if you left bread out on the kitchen counter for a long time? It might eventually look like the bread in Figure 1.13. You know that it won't remain intact forever. Eventually, the bread will be decomposed, or broken down. How does this happen? What physical or biological agents cause this to happen? In this Guided Inquiry, you will explore these questions.

MATERIALS

- A hand lens or dissecting microscope
- Two sealable plastic bags or petri dishes
- Masking tape or markers (for labelling)
- Two slices of bread
- Water

Procedure

SAFETY NOTE

- Bread slices with fungal and bacterial growth must remain sealed in plastic bags. Many people have allergic reactions to spores produced by these microorganisms.
- Wear **surgical masks** to avoid inhaling spores.

1. Take one piece of bread and examine it carefully. Do you see anything unusual? Record your observations in your *Log*.

2. Moisten the bread slightly, and touch it to some surface such as the floor, your hand, or a wall. If you choose, you can just let it sit out in the open for a few hours. We now say that this bread is contaminated.

3. Put the contaminated bread into a plastic bag or petri dish. Do not open the bag. Label this contaminated.

4. The second piece of bread is your control. Taking care not to contaminate it, place it in a separate plastic bag or other petri dish. Label this uncontaminated.

5. Place both bags in a dark place.

6. After a few days, examine both pieces of bread carefully without removing them from their sealed bags or petri dishes. If you have a dissecting microscope in your classroom, examine both slices of bread, in their sealed bags or plates, at different levels of magnification. See Appendix D for instruction on using a microscope. Then draw a picture of what you see in your *Log*.

7. Observe the bread slices again every few days. Continue to record your observations in your *Log*.

Interpretations: Respond to the following in your *Log*:

1. What did you observe? Record these descriptions next to your *Log* drawings.
2. What process is taking place on your bread?
3. What types of organisms are present?
4. How many days did it take before there was noticeable growth on the bread?
5. When and where have you seen this happen before?
6. What is decomposition?
7. Design an experiment to determine the best conditions for decomposition. You may choose to pursue this topic as an Extended Inquiry later in this unit.

Applications: Answer these questions in your *Log*:

1. What products in your local grocery store depend on biological decomposition?
2. How does your local sewage disposal plant depend on decomposition?

Figure 1.13

The black bread mold Rhizopus stolonifer. *The black structures at the tops of the stalks are masses of reproductive spores.*

Biological Recycling

All living things eventually die and decompose. The process of decomposition releases energy and matter into the environment, where other organisms can use it for new growth. Without biological recycling, soil would run out of nutrients, and new growth would stop. Every environment has decomposers, organisms that break down dead organic material. Your compost pile is no exception. Many types of organisms can act as decomposers. But the most significant decomposers are microorganisms, living things that are too small to be seen by the naked eye. They are also the most abundant decomposers. Life on this planet would be difficult, if not impossible, without them.

Materials decompose at different rates. For example, dead leaves break down faster than dead pine needles, and grass decomposes faster than plants that die and fall to the bottom of a marsh. In natural environments, the process of dying, decomposing, and rebuilding goes on continuously. Consider what the American poet Walt Whitman wrote about the process in *Song of Myself*:

What do you think has become of the young and old men?
And what do you think has become of the women and children?

They are alive and well somewhere;
The smallest sprout shows there is really no death,
And if ever there was it led forward life, and does not
wait at the end to arrest it,
And ceased the moment life appeared.

All goes onward and outward. . . . and nothing
collapses,
And to die is different from what any one
supposed, and luckier. . . .

. . . And as to you Corpse I think you are good
manure, but that does not offend me, . . .

. . . I bequeath myself to the dirt to grow from
the grass I love,
If you want me again look for me under your
bootsoles.

You will hardly know who I am or what I mean,
But I shall be good health to you nevertheless,
And filter and fibre your blood.

Failing to fetch me at first keep encouraged,
Missing me one place search another,
I stop somewhere waiting for you.

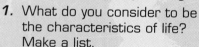

BIOprediction

What Does "Living" Mean?

In the next Guided Inquiry, you will consider what it means to be "living." Before you do, though, take the time to respond to the following in your *Log*:

1. What do you consider to be the characteristics of life? Make a list.

2. Briefly explain why you included each item on your list. What makes this a characteristic of living things?

In your *Log,* write what you think Whitman was saying in these excerpts from *Song of Myself.* How might your understanding of this poem change your view of decomposition?

Living or Nonliving?

Life can be described in many ways. Here are some commonly noted characteristics of living things:

◆ Organization: Living things are highly structured. Even single cells exhibit a tremendous amount of organization. Cells are the basic unit of life.

◆ Reproduction: Living things have the ability to produce offspring.

◆ Response to stimuli: Living things react to events that occur around them.

◆ Heredity: All living things contain genetic material that carries the information for life processes. Changes in this genetic material are the driving force of biological evolution.

◆ Homeostasis: Living things use energy to maintain certain states, such as internal temperature. When some animals get cold, for example, they involuntarily shiver, releasing energy that warms the body.

◆ Metabolism: Living things transform energy and matter to other forms. Wastes are by-products of metabolism.

◆ Growth and development: Living things use energy and matter to become larger.

◆ Evolution: Living things change over successive generations. 🌎

Reproduction enables life to continue through successive generations.

What Is a Variable?

Science often involves the study of cause-and-effect relationships. Scientists observe events or phenomena and then speculate about potential causes for the phenomena. Next, they conduct experiments by changing or controlling the probable causes and observing the effects on the phenomena. Since the probable causes and effects can change, or vary, scientists call them variables. Much of science involves looking at cause-and-effect relationships between variables.

Variables that cause events to occur are called independent variables. Variables that are the outcomes or results of events are called dependent variables.

For example, cigarette smokers have relatively high rates of some types of cancer. You might ask, "To what extent can cigarette smoke cause lung cancer?" In this case, cancer is the effect, or the dependent variable. The contents of the cigarette smoke become the cause, or the independent variable. Even in this seemingly simple question, there are many dependent variables because there are many kinds of cancers that may be produced. There are also many independent variables because there are many different components, or factors, in the smoke that may contribute to cancer.

Scientists can measure the quantity and quality of variables. For instance, we can quantify, or measure, the mass of each chemical in cigarette smoke. We can describe the flavor of a cigarette as "minty" or "harsh." Both of these factors—taste and chemical composition—are independent variables. To measure the quantity of dependent variables, scientists must first look at all the possible effects of smoking: lung cancer, emphysema, throat cancer, and lung cell deterioration (Figure 1.14). Then they must determine the degree to which each effect occurs. 🌎

Figure 1.14

What differences do you see in these two human lungs? Which of these came from a person who was a regular cigarette smoker?

Mystery Bags

The compost that you are creating in Guided Inquiry 1.2 models decomposition in nature. You can also model the process of decomposition by looking more closely at some of the specific ways in which matter is transformed during decomposition. Your compost pile was created by combining organic matter (materials from living organisms) with microorganisms and water. In this inquiry, you will investigate combinations of a living organism (yeast, shown in Figures 1.15 and 1.16), organic molecules (sugar and/or flour), and water.

When you buy yeast in a grocery store, it is in a dormant state. To increase its metabolism and allow it to grow, you have to hydrate the yeast organisms. This simply means that you have to make the yeast wet. What are the other requirements for yeast growth and reproduction? You will investigate these other requirements as you design and carry out this Guided Inquiry.

Figure 1.16

Cells of the yeast Saccharomyces.

Figure 1.15

Yeast cells reproducing by budding

MATERIALS

- Yeast
- Sugar
- Flour
- Tap water in small beaker

- Zippered plastic bags
- Masking tape
- A warm water bath (35–45°C) large enough to hold the bags

Day One Procedure

Experimental Design

1. As a class, discuss the possible requirements for yeast growth and reproduction. Record this information in your *Log*.

2. In groups of four students, discuss what might occur when you make various combinations of yeast, water, sugar, and/or flour. Also consider what might happen when you change environmental conditions such as light or temperature.

3. Decide as a group which independent variables you will test. The effect of the amount of yeast? The sugar? The flour? The bags? Something else? Identify these variables in your *Log*.

4. As a group, design an experiment, using the materials provided by your teacher, to test the effects of one variable on the growth and reproduction of yeast. Record your experimental design in your *Log*. Have your teacher check this design before you proceed with the experiment.

5. Construct a hypothesis that predicts the outcome of testing your variable. Use an "If . . . , then . . ." statement such as "If sugar is added to the bag with the yeast, then the yeast will grow." In developing your hypothesis, be sure to consider:

   ◆ the basic characteristics of life discussed in the reading "Living or Nonliving?" on page 27,

   ◆ the potential functions of each item: water, yeast, sugar, flour, and

   ◆ the difference between sugar and flour.

6. Consult Appendix E for guidance in setting up data tables. Then in your *Log,* create a data table, similar to the one in Figure 1.17, to record your observations. In this Guided Inquiry, give each experimental treatment a different number or name. Record the identifying number or name in the first column of your data table. The next few columns of your table should identify the combinations of ingredients you are testing. Use the final column to record your observations. Be sure to indicate how much time passed between the beginning of this Guided Inquiry and each of your observations.

Treatment No.	Yeast (grams)	Sugar (grams)	Flour (grams)	Water (milliliters)	Observations
1					
2					
3					
4					
5					

Figure 1.17

Sample data table for Guided Inquiry 1.4.

Day Two Procedure

Set Up and Complete the Experiment

7. At the very beginning of the period, mix the combinations of the ingredients you wish to test. Seal the bags and let them sit for 30 minutes in a beaker of warm water.

8. Observe each bag after intervals of 15, 20, 25, and 30 minutes. Each time describe the appearance of each bag in your data table.

9. Dispose of the contents of the bags as directed by your teacher, rinse out the bags, and clean up as indicated by your teacher.

Interpretations: Respond to the following questions in your *Log*:

1. What patterns do you see in your results?
2. What treatment served as a control?
3. What do you suppose are the inputs and outputs of this system?
4. What is a gas? How might you find out what gas was produced?
5. If you did this experiment again, how could you gather evidence to determine what was happening in the mystery bags? For example, what was produced, how much of it was produced, and what were its characteristics?
6. How does this experiment relate to your compost pile? What are the inputs and possible outputs of the compost pile?
7. What additional tests would you like to make?

Applications: Respond to the following in your *Log*:

1. A scientific model is a simple representation of a real process or object. Describe the results of this Guided Inquiry as a model for decomposition in your compost pile.
2. Describe a scientific model that is being used in your community.

Where Did the Gas Come From?

In your mystery bags experiment, a gas called carbon dioxide was formed. This gas is also produced by the microorganisms in your compost pile. Humans give off carbon dioxide gas each time they exhale. In all of these examples, carbon dioxide is a waste product of a metabolic process. Wastes are some of the outputs of metabolism. The materials that organisms use are the inputs to metabolism. Consider the input/output table in Figure 1.18. In each of the processes in Figure 1.18, the inputs differ, but carbon dioxide (CO_2) gas (indicated by an up arrow) is produced.

Figure 1.18

Each of the listed actions produces carbon dioxide gas (indicated by an up arrow).

ACTION	AGENT	INPUT	OUTPUT
Burning	*Example:* a campfire	Wood	Energy, $CO_2 \uparrow$, H_2O
Anaerobic respiration	*Example:* yeast	Sugar	Energy, $CO_2 \uparrow$, alcohol
Aerobic respiration	*Example:* human beings	Food	Energy, $CO_2 \uparrow$, H_2O
Decomposition	*Example:* bacteria	Compost	Energy, $CO_2 \uparrow$, H_2O

SUBSTANCE	Carbon dioxide
FORMULA	CO_2
PHYSICAL PROPERTIES	Colorless, odorless, nontoxic gas above −78.5°C. Solid CO_2 does not melt on warming but goes directly into the gaseous state (sublimates). CO_2 will not support combustion.
CHEMICAL PROPERTIES	Reacts with water to form carbonic acid (H_2CO_3). We know that the substance formed is new because it does not have the physical properties of either carbon dioxide or water.

Figure 1.19

The properties of carbon dioxide

The Value of Chemistry: Physical and Chemical Properties of Matter

Individual substances are identified by their specific physical and chemical properties, as you can see in the description of carbon dioxide in Figure 1.19 (above). Physical properties describe how a substance looks as well as how it behaves as long as its identity does not change. Physical properties also describe other characteristics that do not depend on the amount of the substance that is present. Physical properties include hardness, color, melting point, and odor. Chemical properties describe how matter behaves when it changes into another kind of matter. For example, one chemical property of iron is its ability to rust, changing from one form of matter to another, as shown in Figure 1.20. Unrusted iron is composed of only the element iron. The rust that forms on the surface of iron when it is exposed to moist air is a substance made up of iron and oxygen, an iron oxide.

Figure 1.20

A comparison of rusted and unrusted iron.

Individual substances can exist in different states, as shown in Figure 1.21. The arrangement of its molecules, their speed, and the distance between them determines whether water is in solid, liquid, or gas form. Molecules are most separated when water is in gas form and are most densely packed in liquid water. The crystal lattice form of water molecules in ice holds them farther apart than in liquid water. Since water molecules are less crowded together—less dense—in ice than in water, ice floats.

Composition of Chemical Substances

Carbon dioxide is composed of two other substances: oxygen and carbon. We can prove that this is true by burning carbon in the presence of excess oxygen gas. When the carbon is burned, a substance is formed that has the same physical and chemical properties as the substance called carbon dioxide. Substances like carbon dioxide that are made up of two or more other substances are called compounds. The smallest amount of carbon dioxide that we can identify is a molecule.

Solid   Liquid   Gas

Figure 1.21

The liquid, solid, and gas states of water.

Substances that cannot be broken down into simpler substances by chemical means are called elements. Carbon and oxygen are elements. The smallest amount of carbon that has the chemical and physical properties of carbon is an atom of carbon. An atom is the smallest portion of an element that still has the physical and chemical properties of that element. A molecule is composed of two or more atoms. For example, oxygen is an element that occurs in molecular form, as two bonded oxygen atoms in oxygen gas. Figure 1.22 illustrates some differences between compounds, elements, molecules, and atoms.

Figure 1.22

Atoms, compounds, molecules, and elements.

CHEMICAL FORMULA OF COMPOUNDS	SMALLEST UNIT (MOLECULE)	ATOMS THAT MAKE UP THE MOLECULE
Water	H_2O	Hydrogen, oxygen
Aluminum oxide	Al_2O_3	Aluminum, oxygen
Carbon dioxide	CO_2	Carbon, oxygen

ELEMENTS	CHEMICAL SYMBOL FOR SMALLEST UNIT (ATOM)
Oxygen	O
Hydrogen	H
Aluminum	Al
Carbon	C

The names of chemical substances can be written in shorthand form, using chemical symbols. There is a letter symbol for each of the 111 known elements. A number subscript after a chemical symbol, such as the 2 after the O in CO_2, indicates the number of those atoms in a substance. Thus one molecule of carbon dioxide, CO_2, is composed of one atom of carbon (C) and two atoms of oxygen (O_2). One molecule of water, H_2O, has two atoms of hydrogen (H_2) and one atom of oxygen (O).

Chemical Reactions

A chemical reaction occurs when the atoms in an existing substance are rearranged to form a new substance. The original atoms are called the reactants; the new substance is the product. A chemical reaction is described by a chemical equation, which can be read like a sentence:

Sentence: Aluminum metal plus oxygen gas yields aluminum oxide.

Chemical equation:

Reactants			Product
4 aluminum atoms	+	3 oxygen molecules ⟶	2 molecules of aluminum oxide
4 Al	+	3 O_2 ⟶	2 Al_2O_3

The number in front of the symbol for each atom or molecule is called the coefficient. These numbers tell you how many of those atoms or molecules are involved in this process. Notice that the total number of each type of atom remains the same on either side of the arrow. This is a balanced chemical equation. The numbers of specific atoms are always equal on both sides of a balanced chemical equation. The balance of atoms in reactants and products should remind you that matter cannot be destroyed, only converted to a different form. As in your compost, matter never really goes "away."

Refer to the input/output table in Figure 1.18 on page 31. The materials under "Input"—paper, sugar, food, and compost materials—are all organic substances containing abundant carbon. All living organisms contain carbon. Because you performed the experiments in the classroom, oxygen in the air was available to each of your treatments. Carbon dioxide was produced when the carbon and oxygen atoms that were available as reactants were rearranged to form a new substance, carbon dioxide, as a product. The physical and chemical properties of the carbon dioxide are different from the properties of both carbon and oxygen. Consult Figure 1.23 to determine the source(s) of carbon in your experiments. Notice in Figure 1.23 that each of these molecules contains chains of carbon atoms. These are classified as organic, or biological, molecules. 🌍

A single glucose unit

H₂COH

Amylose (starch) molecule

Single chain of subunits

Many cellulose molecules linked together form fibrils

Parallel chains of glucose subunits bound together by cross-links

Figure 1.23

All organic materials, such as these starch and cellulose molecules, contain the element carbon and other elements.

Guided Inquiry 1.5

Modeling Biological Molecules

Can you develop a model for something as small and complex as an organic molecule? In this Guided Inquiry, you will make models to see how atoms are arranged and rearranged in biological systems. Because we are investigating a part of the world that we can't directly see, using models helps us to actually see and make sense of what happens in a chemical reaction. (See page 22 for a review of scientific models.)

The atoms in molecules are held together by chemical bonds. Each atom has the ability to form a specific number of bonds with other atoms. The bonding abilities of the atoms that are most common in organic molecules are listed in Figure 1.24.

A model of glucose made from gumdrops.

Figure 1.24

Bonds formed by common atoms.

ATOM	NUMBER OF POSSIBLE BONDS
Carbon (C)	4
Oxygen (O)	2
Hydrogen (H)	1

In this Guided Inquiry, you will make models of some common organic molecules and use these models to understand how atoms are rearranged in the course of a chemical reaction. You will use toothpicks and gumdrops of different colors to construct the models. The gumdrops represent atoms, and the toothpicks represent chemical bonds. Drawings of molecules, like the ones in Figure 1.25, are called structural formulas because they represent how atoms are joined together to make molecules.

Figure 1.25

Atoms can bond with other atoms.

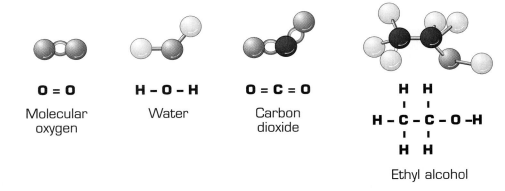

O = O

Molecular
oxygen

H – O – H

Water

O = C = O

Carbon
dioxide

$$\begin{array}{ccc} & H & H \\ & | & | \\ H - & C - C & - O - H \\ & | & | \\ & H & H \end{array}$$

Ethyl alcohol

MATERIALS

- Paper towels
- Gumdrops or marshmallows of three different colors, one color for each type of atom in your models
- Toothpicks

Procedure

1. Work in pairs. Before beginning this activity, clean your work space as directed by your teacher. Work on paper towels.

2. Decide as a class which colors of gumdrop or marshmallow will represent each atom. One color will represent a carbon atom, another color will represent hydrogen, and a third color will represent oxygen.

3. Working with your partner, break the toothpicks in half and use them to join the gumdrops or marshmallows to form the molecules listed in Figure 1.26. Consult Figure 1.24 on page 35 for the number of bonds that each atom can form. Have your teacher check your structural formulas before you actually begin to construct the models. Keep the toothpicks away from the face and eyes.

4. Draw in your *Log* the structural formula for each of the molecules that you have constructed.

Model No.	Chemical Formula	Chemical Name
1	CO_2	Carbon dioxide
2	H_2O	Water
3	O_2	Oxygen gas (molecular oxygen)
4	C_2H_5OH	Ethyl alcohol
5	$C_6H_{12}O_6$	Glucose

5. Optional student work or teacher demonstration:

   a. Make six molecules of molecular oxygen and one molecule of glucose. Then, use those to form models of the products of aerobic respiration.

   b. Draw the molecular rearrangements in your *Log*.

   c. Use the molecules that you have created to model the process of photosynthesis.

   d. Use the model of glucose that you formed to illustrate the process of anaerobic respiration. The chemical equation for this process is:

Figure 1.26

Molecules to be modeled in Guided Inquiry 1.5.

anaerobic respiration: $C_6H_{12}O_6 \rightarrow 2\ C_2H_5OH + 2\ CO_2$

Interpretations: Answer the following questions in your *Log*:

   1. How does Figure 1.28 support the idea that the two processes of photosynthesis and respiration are related?

   2. What molecules that are put together in photosynthesis are taken apart in respiration?

   3. What molecules are the products of cellular respiration?

   4. Where do the atoms that are used to produce glucose molecules come from?

   5. Why is the carbon cycle in nature called a cycle?

Applications: Respond to the following in your *Log*:

   1. Describe an example of the carbon cycle in your community.

   2. Describe an example of how a knowledge of atoms and molecules is used in your community.

   3. Describe an example of a chemical reaction in your community.

4. List examples of items at your grocery store that contain CO_2, H_2O, C_2H_5OH, and $C_6H_{12}O_6$.

How Do Living Things Obtain and Use Energy?

Did you notice that, in the input/output table in Figure 1.18 on page 31, energy was an output in each case? Energy is always involved in the making and breaking of chemical bonds. Chemistry is helpful in explaining how living things acquire their energy to carry out life processes.

For example, through the process of photosynthesis, plants and some other organisms capture energy from sunlight and use it to make organic molecules, which they can then use in their cells. This is how plants get their energy. In the process of photosynthesis, plants absorb energy from the sun. They use this energy to break apart molecules of water, releasing oxygen into the atmosphere. Oxygen, then, is a waste product of photosynthesis. A simplified equation for photosynthesis is the following:

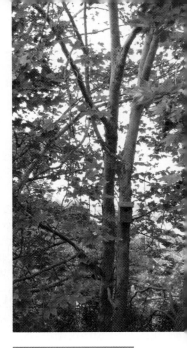

Trees' leaves capture sunlight and make organic molecules.

Photosynthesis: Sunlight + 6 H_2O + 6 $CO_2 \longrightarrow C_6H_{12}O_6$ + 6 $O_2 \uparrow$

Here six molecules of water and six molecules of carbon dioxide are used to form a six-carbon sugar molecule (glucose) and six molecules of oxygen gas. But this simplified equation does not take into account the many intermediate reactions that are required to produce the indicated products.

The process of photosynthesis has two major stages (Figure 1.27). In Stage 1, the light reactions, light energy is converted to energy stored in

Figure 1.27

The light and dark reactions of photosynthesis.

chemical bonds. A specialized molecule, called ATP (adenosine triphosphate), stores this energy. Oxygen gas (O_2) is a by-product of the light reactions. It is formed by the splitting of water (H_2O) molecules.

In Stage 2, called the Calvin-Benson cycle, energy stored as ATP, the hydrogen atoms from water, and carbon dioxide (CO_2) from the air are used to make organic molecules. This series of reactions is sometimes called the dark reactions because light is not used directly. Water molecules are split, and ATP is produced when light is available during the light reactions.

Looking at the photosynthesis equation, you see that the simple sugar, glucose ($C_6H_{12}O_6$), is one product of photosynthesis. Other organisms, such as animals, consume glucose or other molecules manufactured by photosynthetic organisms to acquire their energy. The chemical energy stored in glucose is released to cells through the process of cellular respiration (Figure 1.28). This multistep process involves: first, breakdown of glucose molecules to smaller (3 carbon) molecules; second, production of energy transport molecules and CO_2 in the Krebs cycle; and third, use of the energy transport molecules—in the electron transport system—to make ATP. If this process takes place in the presence of oxygen (aerobic respiration), then carbon dioxide and water are the main products. This process takes place as organisms use sugars for energy during everyday activities. Respiration is the primary energy-using process in *all* organisms. The equation for aerobic respiration is:

Figure 1.28

In respiration, glucose is broken down to produce energy, in the form of ATP, for the cell. In the process, carbon dioxide is produced.

Aerobic Respiration: $C_6H_{12}O_6 + 6\ O_2 \longrightarrow 6\ H_2O + 6\ CO_2 \uparrow$

Compare this with the equation for photosynthesis. What do you find? In yeasts, many other microorganisms, and even animal cells, respiration can take place without oxygen (anaerobic respiration). In this case, other products, such as alcohol or acids, are produced. When alcohol and CO_2 are the products of anaerobic respiration, the process is called fermentation.

Anaerobic Respiration
   (Fermentation): $C_6H_{12}O_6 \longrightarrow 2\ CO_2 \uparrow + 2\ C_2H_5OH$

Together the processes of photosynthesis and respiration form the basis of the biological carbon cycle (see Figure 1.29 on page 40). Photosynthesis removes carbon dioxide from the atmosphere and makes organic compounds. Through respiration, these organic compounds are broken down, and carbon dioxide is expelled as a waste product. Globally, CO_2 production by respiration and use by photosynthesis would be relatively balanced, were it not for human activities. Burning of wood and fossil fuels and harvesting of forests raises atmospheric CO_2 levels. 🐾

Figure 1.29

The carbon cycle.

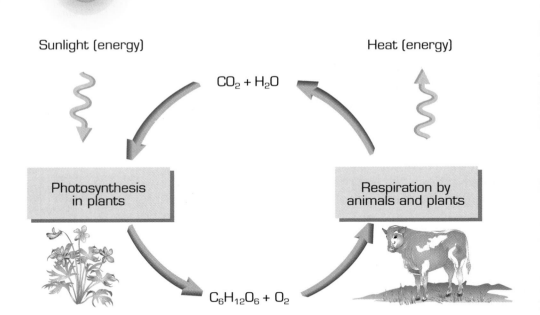

Sunlight (energy)

Heat (energy)

$CO_2 + H_2O$

Photosynthesis
in plants

Respiration by
animals and plants

$C_6H_{12}O_6 + O_2$

Guided Inquiry 1.6

What Lives in Compost?

What organisms, if any, live in a compost pile? Why are they there? Where did they come from? How do they interact with the composted materials and with each other?

Your compost has been developing for only a short time, but it should already contain many microorganisms. The best way to col-

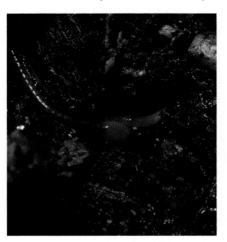

lect and observe these microorganisms is to soak some composted material overnight in distilled water (tap water with most of the dissolved materials removed). Organisms on the composting materials will soak off into the water. Soon, organisms on the composted material will be in the water, forming a suspension called compost tea.

Microorganisms such as those shown here help create compost.

- Compost tea (10 milliliters of compacted compost soaked overnight in 50–100 milliliters of distilled water)
- A compound microscope
- Clean slides, both flat and concave
- Cover slips
- A graduated cylinder
- Pipettes or droppers
- One or more petri dishes or other small, shallow containers
- Taxonomic keys or drawings of microorganisms that live in compost (see Figure 1.30 on page 43 and Appendix F)

Procedure

1. Before beginning this Guided Inquiry, read Appendices D and G to review how to use the microscope, prepare slides, make drawings and diagrams, and measure objects under the microscope.

2. Obtain a sample of compost tea and place it in your petri dish.

3. Prepare a microscope slide of the compost tea. Appendix D will tell you how.

4. Examine the slide under the microscope. Look for microorganisms. In your *Log,* make a drawing of each organism you find. (Appendix F will show you how to make useful scientific drawings.)

5. Try to identify some of the organisms that you have found. Use Figure 1.30 on page 43 to identify the broad categories of organisms that you may find.

6. Repeat this investigation at intervals (perhaps monthly) throughout this year to see how the microorganisms in the compost tea multiply and change.

7. In your *Log,* create a chart to help you keep track of your findings. Decide what you should observe and what you should record.

8. Wash your hands when you are finished, and dispose of the compost tea according to your teacher's directions.

Interpretations: Respond to the following in your *Log:*

1. Why is it important to know how much compost was used to make the compost tea? How can you use this information?

2. Review your data and categorize the organisms you found into groups. The organisms in each group should have similar characteristics.

3. How many groups of organisms did you find?

4. What characteristics did you use to separate the organisms into groups? How did these help you to separate them? What other characteristics could you have used?

5. Why is distilled water a better choice than tap water for making compost tea?

6. If you were to sample more compost tea, what could you do to improve your method?

7. How would you find out which organisms occur most frequently in the compost tea?

8. How would you collect enough evidence to convince others that your conclusions are valid?

9. Look back at the list of the characteristics of life that you made for the BioPrediction on page 26. Did the list help you separate living things from nonliving things? Would you change your list now that you have had experience in looking for living organisms?

Applications: Respond to the following in your *Log:*

1. Some septic tank cleaners contain essentially a large culture of bacteria. How would bacteria help to clean a septic tank?

2. Describe several reasons why the mass of the solid material flowing into a sewage disposal plant would be significantly greater than the mass of solid material that flows out at the end of the disposal process.

3. Where could you find a compost pile in your community?

If you want to reduce the need for landfill space and still retain as many natural resources as possible, in which order would you perform the following steps?

- Reuse materials.
- Incinerate materials.
- Recycle materials.

- Compost materials.
- Place materials in landfills.
- Reduce what we use.

Justify your answer. Discuss this BioPrediction in your *Log.*

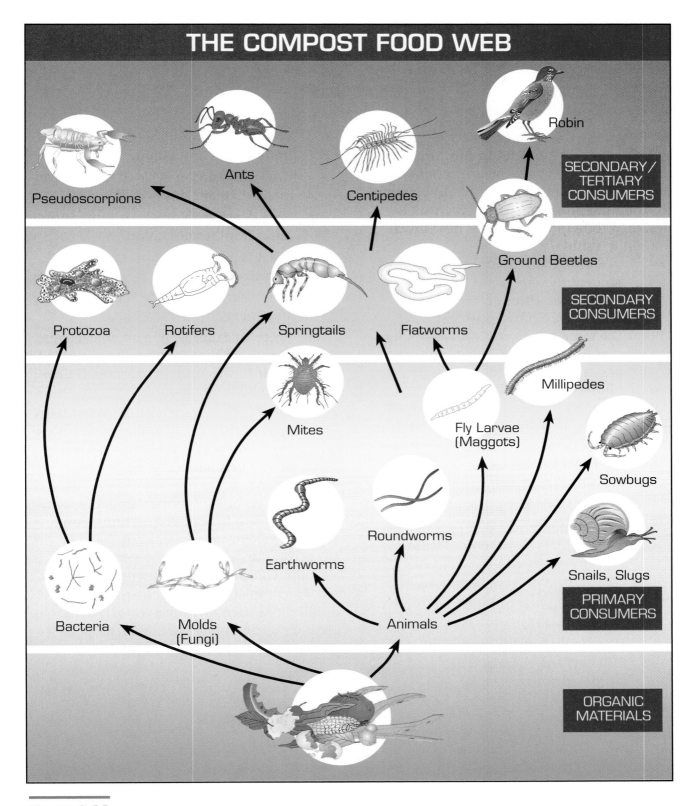

Figure 1.30

The compost food web. The energy flow follows the path of the arrows from composting organic materials to organisms at successively higher feeding levels.

Self-Check 1

By the time you complete most of the Guided Inquiries in this unit, you should have some understanding of how living things use matter and energy for their life processes. This self-check is designed to help you find out how much you understand.

Form groups of four students. Each student in your group should select and answer three of the following questions. No two people should choose the same question. As resources, use the work you did on the Guided Inquiries, your notes in your *Log,* and books in the classroom or library. Your teacher will guide you if you need help. You might want to work in advance on some answers as homework.

1. What are the benefits of the following practices: reduce, reuse, and recycle?

2. What is a trash audit and how is it carried out? Of what use is it?

3. What happens in a compost pile over time? Why is this useful to learn about?

4. Explain the differences between degradability by physical forces and biodegradability. Why is degradability important in dealing with trash?

5. What are the characteristics that are unique to living things?

6. What is mass and how does it differ from weight and volume?

7. How does carbon cycle in the environment? Explain this cycle.

8. How does aerobic cellular respiration differ from fermentation?

9. What is matter and how is it organized?

10. What is the difference between matter and energy?

11. Write an example of a chemical equation other than one you have studied so far in this unit. What process does this equation describe?

12. What are chemical bonds? What happens to the energy in chemical bonds when molecules are built? What happens when molecules are broken down?

When everyone in your group has reasonable answers to his or her questions, come together as a group and let each member share these answers with the entire group. As a group, you should then discuss and evaluate the completeness of each answer and modify it as necessary. Everyone in the group should eventually have a complete set of answers to all questions.

Conference

The Conference is a regular feature in each unit of this curriculum. Your goal in the Conference is to exhibit your best work from the Guided Inquiries, share what you have learned with the rest of the class, and address the following questions:

◆ What do we know?

◆ How do we know it?

◆ What else do we need to know?

◆ How can we find out what we need to know?

To prepare for the Conference, you will concentrate on creating an effective presentation of your best work from the Guided Inquiries. The Conference in this unit will focus on the construction and presentation of an abstract. An abstract is a written document that *briefly* summarizes the results of an experiment and suggests what new research needs to be done on the topic.

Procedure

1. Ask your teacher to explain the evaluation criteria for the abstract.

2. Work in pairs. Select the Guided Inquiry in this unit from which you feel you learned the most. Identify what is important about what you learned.

3. With your partner, prepare a written abstract that contains:

◆ The title of this Guided Inquiry,

◆ The particular question or hypothesis you were investigating,

◆ The procedure you followed,

◆ What you learned from the inquiry,

◆ What more you need to know,

◆ Which of the Extended Inquiries that follow would help you find out what you need to know, and

◆ A research plan for your new inquiry.

4. Organize your abstract carefully so that it is very concise. One page is best.

5. When the draft of your abstract is complete, form groups of six or eight that represent three or four abstracts. Each pair will then present their abstract to this group. The group should provide feedback to the presenting pair on the value of the abstract. Record your comments and the group's comments in your *Log*.

6. Discuss with your partner how you can improve your own abstract. For homework, revise your abstract with your partner for submission to the teacher the next day.

A lthough almost everyone enjoys doing experiments, sometimes lab activities can rob you of authentic science experiences because they present the question to be investigated, provide the step-by-step procedure, and outline exactly how you are to communicate results. But since asking questions, proposing experiments, and interpreting and communicating results are what science is all about, you must learn how to work without being told what to do. After all, no one makes these decisions for scientists.

At first, you might find the experience confusing and uncomfortable. Scientists often feel the same way. The following questions will help you to get started and gain the experience you need to complete Extended Inquiries successfully.

What is the question that needs answering? The question should be narrow enough that you can address it with the time and resources you have available. The question must also state a clear and specific idea.

What kind of research does your question require? To answer your question, you might need to use evidence gathered by others. Library research is an example of the type of research you would need. Once you have decided what information to retrieve, you must determine its significance and accuracy and then put it together conclusively to answer your question or questions. On the other hand, your question might require gathering your own evidence, testing ideas against the natural world. This type of evidence, called empirical evidence, is at the heart of science! To acquire empirical evidence, you have to devise an experiment that addresses the question you have posed. Experiments have been described as an active interrogation of nature—acquiring information that nature doesn't readily give up.

How will you interpret the results of your research? In textbooks, this process often seems straightforward. In reality, you will find it very challenging. Most experiments do not provide crystal clear results. Watching scientists in action shows that making sense of experimental work is a social and experimental process. This process requires extended discussions, explanations, and further experiments. You will often find that different individuals bring new interpretations to the results of an experiment. You might even find yourself changing or extending the questions you began with. Don't see this as failure. Rather, it is an opportunity to revise your thinking and redirect your efforts.

How will you communicate your results? Your audience has not been with you through your research, and it does not know what you know. So you must decide how to get your readers from where they are to where your understanding is.

Extended Inquiries

Much will depend on whether your communication is verbal or written, but here are some steps you might want to follow:

1. State your question clearly.

2. Describe your experimental setup and explain why your approach was appropriate.

3. Communicate your data in a way that is easily understood. This might mean creating a table, a graph, or some other visual display.

4. Interpret your results. What do your data mean? What conclusions can you make?

5. Give your final judgment. This might be a tentative resolution of your original question, or it might be a description of what needs to be done next to address the original question and/or questions that came up during the process. You should also address any problems you ran into, analyze mistakes you made, and explain discrepancies that arose during your research.

Organizing Your Research

Setting up your own research can be difficult. This rough outline might help you in choosing a course of action.

Planning Your Extended Inquiry

1. Select, with the guidance of your teacher, one or more Extended Inquiries that interest you.

2. Formulate your question carefully.

3. Choose a research strategy that will help you answer your research question. Which would be most appropriate: a survey, a case study, long-term monitoring, experimentation, or modeling?

4. Make a list of all necessary equipment.

5. Describe how you will collect the necessary observations and measurements.

6. If you perform experiments, choose your variables and controls. Make predictions about outcomes.

7. Consider the safety of your planned inquiry. You should think not only about the materials you will need and the processes you will complete, but also about any traveling you might have to do if your inquiry is outside of the classroom.

8. Design a conceptual model that graphically represents the interaction between variables.

Feel free to propose experiments that you might be unable to carry out right now. Setting up well-designed experiments that have to be carried out later is part of doing science. The history of science is full of thought experiments that had to wait for technology to catch up before they could actually be performed. Some thought experiments can never be carried out because they assume idealized conditions that do not exist; however, they can still help us to understand nature.

See pages 61 and 62 for information on how to develop a research report based on your Extended Inquiry learning.

An outside compost bin.

Extended Inquiry 1.1

Collecting Composting Data

What are the actual contents of the compost column or pile you created in Guided Inquiry 1.2? What are its temperature and its moisture content? What organisms are present? How do the organisms in the compost pile interact? How does the material change in size and texture? How acidic or basic is the pile? This activity provides some techniques for analyzing data from your compost. You can also make other, more detailed analyses. This Extended Inquiry contains four parts, asking you to measure temperature, moisture, pH, and living organisms. Depending on how much time you have for this Extended Inquiry, you might want to select only some of these parts.

Part A. Measuring Temperature

Have you ever felt the warmth of a rotting pile of lawn cuttings? You can investigate the heat generated by decomposition in your pile by taking its temperature periodically. Ask your teacher for a thermometer. Measure the temperature at different places in your compost pile and at different times. Set a schedule for where and when to take the temperature and enter this into your *Log*. Collect enough data in your *Log* to confidently answer the following questions:

1. What is the pattern of temperature distribution in the compost?
2. What is the range of temperature variation?
3. What is the range of temperature change over time? Create a graph of temperature versus time.
4. What is the source of the heat? (Be specific and refer back to ideas introduced in the Guided Inquiries.)

Procedure

To answer these questions, you will need to design a research method to collect the proper data on temperature in the compost pile. In your *Log*:

1. List possible ways to measure the temperature of the compost.
2. List several ways to collect and document the temperature data.
   ◆ How will you locate and measure temperature sites?
   ◆ How will you document these locations and the data you collect from them?
3. Predict what the temperature distributions will look like.
4. Graph the data. When graphing, place the independent variable on the horizontal axis, or X axis, and the dependent variable on the Y axis so that you can easily see the changes (up or down) in the dependent variable (Figure 1.31). In measuring the temperature of your compost pile, graph time (probably in days, since the changes are fairly slow) on the X axis. Graph temperature on the Y axis. To determine the variables in other cases, simply ask yourself, "What is causing something to happen?" (independent variable) and "What are the results?" (dependent variable).

Figure 1.31

In creating a graph, the independent variable (here, time) is placed on the X axis and the dependent variable (here, temperature) is placed on the Y axis.

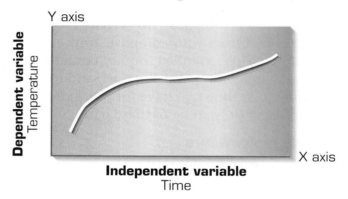

Part B. Determining Moisture Content

To determine the moisture content of your compost pile, place samples in an oven at 110°C for one day to evaporate all water.

MATERIALS

- A drying oven or kitchen oven
- A 1/4-inch sieve
- Heatproof baking dishes
- Several 8-ounce and 4-ounce jars
- Balances accurate to a minimum of 0.01 gram
- Goggles, plastic gloves, mask

Procedure

1. In your *Log,* set up a table similar to the one in Figure 1.32 to record your data.

Sample Number	Mass of Container	Mass of Container + Specimen BEFORE Drying	Mass of Container + Specimen AFTER Drying	Mass of Dried Specimen
1				
2				
3				

Figure 1.32

Data table for Extended Inquiry 1.1.

2. Collect compost samples and store them in clean 8-ounce jars in the refrigerator.

3. When you are ready to check for moisture, pass the materials through the sieve. Keep the material that goes through the sieve.

4. Record the masses of the clean, dry 4-ounce glass containers (enter into the table as "Mass of Container"). Number or otherwise label the jars.

5. Place a moist specimen from the 8-ounce containers stored in the refrigerator in a clean, dry 4-ounce glass container of known mass, and record the data in your *Log* (enter into the table as "Mass of Container + Specimen before Drying"). Find the mass of at least three subsamples from each compost sample.

6. Place the containers containing moist material in a drying oven maintained at 110°C, and dry them overnight or longer to a constant mass. Mass the samples periodically to monitor the change in mass. Your specimens will be at their constant mass when the mass remains the same for two sequential measurements.

7. After the material has dried to a constant mass, remove the container from the oven and allow the material to cool to room temperature. Figure 1.33 shows a compost sample before and after drying.

8. Determine the mass of the 4-ounce glass containers and the oven-dried materials, and write the masses in your *Log* (enter into the table as "Mass of Container + Specimen after Drying"). Keep these samples for use in "Determination of Organic Content."

Calculate the dry mass of the compost as

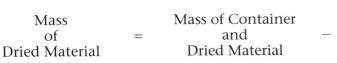

$$\begin{matrix} \text{Mass} \\ \text{of} \\ \text{Dried Material} \end{matrix} = \begin{matrix} \text{Mass of Container} \\ \text{and} \\ \text{Dried Material} \end{matrix} - \begin{matrix} \text{Mass} \\ \text{of} \\ \text{Container} \end{matrix}$$

SAFETY NOTE

- Wear **goggles**, a **surgical mask**, and **surgical gloves** when handling compost.

Figure 1.33

What differences can you see in these samples of moist and dried compost?

The total mass of a specimen taken from the compost pile is the sum of the moisture and the dry component masses. To find the moisture content as a percent of total mass, you first need to determine the mass of the moisture. Since moisture can easily be removed by drying, what remains after drying is the dry component mass.

$$\text{Percent Moisture Content} = \frac{\text{Total Mass} - \text{Dry Mass}}{\text{Total Mass}} \times 100$$

9. Wash your hands when you finish.

Part C. Determining pH

MATERIALS

- A pH meter or pH paper
- Beakers
- Distilled water

The pH scale is used to describe the acidity of a sample. The simplest way to think about pH is to dissect the term itself. The *H* refers to the hydrogen atom, because pH refers to the concentration of these atoms. The *p* is a symbol for the mathematical term that means "negative log." Thus pH is the negative log of the hydrogen ion concentration of a given sample. Each change of one unit represents a 10-fold difference in the concentration of hydrogen ions. See Appendix H for an expanded discussion of math terms.

The pH scale ranges from 0 to 14. A pH of 7 is considered neutral, neither acidic nor basic. Values above 7 indicate lower acidity; values below 7 indicate higher acidity. Samples that have very large concentrations of hydrogen ions have a low pH and so are acidic. Samples with low concentrations of hydrogen ions have a high pH and so are basic.

Procedure

Take a small sample from three different levels of your pile and place each sample in a clean container. Use a spoon to avoid handling the compost. Add enough distilled water to nearly fill each container. Stir the contents with a clean glass rod. Let the containers sit for at least 10 minutes. Using pH paper or a pH meter, determine the pH of each sample and enter these data into your *Log.* Test the samples periodically to monitor any changes in pH of the pile.

In your *Log:*

1. Describe qualitatively the relative acidity of the pile.
2. Describe pH differences in different locations of the pile.
3. Describe how pH might influence decomposition.
4. Describe changes in pH that you notice over time. Graph these data if appropriate.

Part D. A Further Study of Life in the Compost Pile

MATERIALS

- Small sticks or probes
- Gloves, surgical mask, goggles
- Taxonomic guides
- Microscopes
- White paper

Procedure

Put on your plastic gloves, surgical mask, and goggles. Working in teams of three, have each person take a small sample from a different layer of the pile. Spread the contents of each sample on a separate sheet of white paper. Sort through the contents with a small probe or stick. Record in your *Log* either the general name or a description of any organisms you find. Figure 1.30 on page 43 and available library resources can help you to identify organisms. Your teacher may also know of some valuable resources. If you have both compound and dissecting microscopes, examine the contents under these instruments. Dispose of the contents and clean up as indicated by your teacher.

Respond to the following in your *Log:*

1. What organisms are most common in your sample? How do you explain this?
2. Did you find different organisms at different levels? How do you account for these differences?
3. What organisms do you believe are not only present but very abundant even though you can't observe them with the instruments available?
4. Make a diagram that includes all the organisms you observed in your pile. Try to add arrows indicating the direction of food energy flow. Look up information about the feeding habits of some of the organisms that you found in a reference such as *Compost Critters* by Bianca Lavies (1993).

This procedure can be repeated periodically during the school year to monitor changes in the kinds and abundance of organisms in your compost pile.

Extended Inquiry 1.2

The Disappearing Sugar Act

You know from Guided Inquiry 1.4 (Mystery Bags) that yeast uses an energy source such as sugar to produce alcohol and carbon dioxide. (This is essentially the principle underlying the manufacture of beer and wine.) But what happens to the mass? Do you end up with the same mass, or is there actually a loss?

MATERIALS

- 10 plastic cups
- Plastic wrap
- A few milliliters of isopropyl alcohol
- 14 grams of yeast
- Water
- Sugar
- A balance
- Markers and masking tape

Procedure

1. Count out 10 plastic cups. Label two cups with each of the following labels: Trial 1, Trial 2, Trial 3, Trial 4, Trial 5. See Figure 1.34.
2. Cut out 10 equal-sized sheets of plastic wrap just large enough to cover a cup with some overlap, so that it seals the sides of the cup.
3. Add water and/or alcohol to each cup, as indicated in Figure 1.35. Drape a square of plastic wrap over each cup. Determine the mass of each cup + liquid + plastic wrap.
4. In your *Log,* make a table like that in Figure 1.35, allowing room to record mass. Record your masses.
5. Label each cup of each trial as *a* or *b*. Add yeast and sugar to each cup, using the treatment plan described in Figure 1.35.
6. Swirl the contents of each cup to dissolve the yeast. Cover each cup loosely with the plastic wrap. Mass each cup + contents.
7. Record masses immediately (setup masses) and then daily after one and two days (final masses) in a table similar to that in Figure 1.36.

Figure 1.34

Materials for Extended Inquiry 1.2.

Treatment	Water (milliliters)	Alcohol (milliliters)	Grams of Yeast	Mass of Sugar
Trial 1	50	0	3.5 grams	(0 sugar)
Trial 2	50	0	7 grams	(2 times mass of yeast)
Trial 3	50	0	0 grams	(2 times mass of yeast)
Trial 4	50	20	3.5 grams	(2 times mass of yeast)
Trial 5	50	20	0 grams	(2 times mass of yeast)

Figure 1.35

Disappearing Sugar Act Procedure Table.

Interpretations: Respond to the following in your *Log*.

1. Sucrose has the formula $C_{12}H_{22}O_{11}$, and ethyl alcohol has the formula C_2H_5OH. Write a balanced equation for fermentation.

2. Explain your results.

3. Describe at least three hypotheses for the change in mass in this fermentation system.

4. Relate the change in mass in this system to your compost pile.

5. Why did the cups need to be covered?

6. What other variables needed to be controlled?

Setup Masses					Final Masses	
Number	Yeast mass (grams)	Sugar mass (grams)	Mass of cup + liquid + plastic wrap (grams)	Total mass (grams)	Mass after 1 day	Mass after 2 days
1a						
1b						
2a						
etc.						

Figure 1.36

Disappearing Sugar Act Mass Table.

Landfills and Landfill Use

A well-built landfill is sealed so that it can't leak, and everything in it is covered by layers of topsoil. The final layer, on top, will be topsoil and then grass and trees.

What can be done with a landfill when it is full? What is safe? What is smart? Where are the old landfills in your community? What are former landfills eventually used for in different areas of the country? Are there restrictions on their use in some areas? Does it matter how the landfill was constructed? Are all old landfill sites suitable for other use (see Figure 1.37)? What are some biological problems with landfills? What about landfills with hazardous or toxic wastes in them? Have there been problems with reuses of landfill sites? (Don't confuse this issue with the problem of building on areas where unconfined toxic wastes have been dumped.) Record your answers in your *Log*.

Generate additional questions about landfill use and try to find answers. Survey community members to learn their reactions to local landfill issues.

Figure 1.37

Old sanitary landfills, which were not designed to isolate garbage from the environment, may leak contaminants into the surrounding soil and water.

Portable fence

Final earth cover

Daily earth cover (15cm, or 6 in.)

Original ground

Incineration

Are any incinerators located in your area? How old are they? What kind of wastes are burned in them? Does your community have plans to build more? How do incinerators work? What materials come out of the smokestack? What is done with the ash? Investigate these and other questions. Conduct a survey in your community to learn individual reactions to local incineration issues.

Recycling

How successful is recycling in your community? What kind of things are recycled? Is there a market for them? If so, is it profitable? If you don't have a recycling program, does your community plan to start one? What factors influence the success of recycling? Brainstorm additional questions about recycling, and research this issue. Survey community members to learn their reactions to recycling issues.

Local Issues

Does your community have a trash problem? What happens to your garbage? What does it cost to remove your garbage? How much does the landfill charge for dumping? Who owns the landfill? Has there been any controversy dealing with environmental issues or disposal of trash? What are the biological issues?

You may choose to investigate these local issues or others relating to your state or region. The first step would involve research at the library using newspapers to help you identify pertinent local issues. You can generate a list of news-making issues and then seek further information to determine how these controversies were resolved.

After researching for background information, make a list of government agencies, industries, businesses, individuals, and environmental groups that can give you further information. Any sources that are quoted or listed in the newspaper articles might be a starting point. You can then use the phone book to search for additional resources among government agencies, businesses,

Bio thoughts

Should we we take the beautifully landscaped ground that was once a landfill and build houses, schools, or other buildings on it? Or should it become a ski slope or park? It looks good, it won't flood, and it may be available at low cost. What are some other potential advantages for using this land? What are some disadvantages? Would you be willing to live on a former landfill? Why or why not?

and groups. Telephone or personal interviews will give you information, and many agencies and industries have printed material that will be useful. Always ask about any pamphlets or handouts to explain the issue. When you find an article in a magazine or journal, always check the references or works cited for other sources.

Toxic Waste

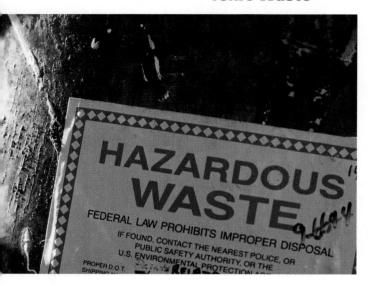

Toxic waste includes household hazardous waste as well as commercial hazardous waste. What determines toxicity? How is toxicity measured? What are the effects of various toxins on living organisms? How are these wastes handled? What laws govern this type of waste disposal? This is a very controversial area, so you should be able to come up with plenty of questions of your own to research.

Once you have defined a question about toxic waste, research it in the library and in your community. Prepare a report for the class describing the particular waste problem and how it can be remedied. Investigate in your own community for this toxic waste problem.

Sewage

Sewage is waste matter that is carried off in a drain or sewer. The disposal route depends on whether you have a septic tank or are connected to a sewer system. The ultimate disposal site in either case is in soil and bodies of water (see Figure 1.38).
Sewage includes water and organic materials washed down your sinks and your bathtub or shower drain, dirty water from your washing machine, and human waste that is flushed down the toilet. Until about 1900, humans depended on nature to clean sewage. For the most part, nature did a fine job, but human population density increased the amount of sewage in certain areas until the natural system became overloaded.

Surprisingly, average domestic sewage is 99.94 percent water and only 0.06 percent dissolved and suspended solids. As the human population grows, it becomes increasingly important to take out as much of that 0.06 percent dissolved and suspended matter as possible before

Wastewater from home

Sewage treatment plant

Treated (purified) wastewater enters river, lake or ocean via pipe

Septic tank

Drain field

Wastewater from home

Septic tank effluent leaches through drain field and soil, enters groundwater, then flows to river, lake or ocean

Figure 1.38

Where do household wastes go when they leave your home?

returning the water to our lakes or rivers. Usually, sewage ends up at the sewage treatment plant. However, some people live so far from sewage treatment plants that they use septic tanks. No matter how your sewage is treated, you should know that the invention of sewage treatment not only made life more pleasant, but also cut down tremendously on disease transmission. Sewage is something few people think about until there is a problem. Imagine what life was like in highly populated areas before the invention of sewage treatment—and still is in many parts of the world. Even now, many municipal sewage treatment facilities are antiquated or have inadequate capacity to handle the ever increasing loads of waste. Such problems may lead to discharge of untreated waste into waterways, especially after heavy rains. What could you do to assure this does not happen in your community?

In this inquiry, you will investigate sewage treatment plants and/or septic tanks. As you investigate these two types of sewage treatment, consider how much each process has in common with your compost piles.

Part A: The Sewage Treatment Plant

This portion of the inquiry requires a visit to your nearby sewage treatment plant and/or library. Determine how sewage is treated in your community. Find out where your sewage plant is located and why it was built there. Research how a sewage treatment plant operates, including

Wastewater processing at a sewage treatment plant.

the various methods of separating and treating the sewage. What is done with the separated material? To what extent has the sewage been purified? Where does the treated liquid now go? Where does biology come into play in sewage treatment? Working individually or in small groups, prepare a presentation of what you have learned.

Part B: The Septic Tank

Conventional septic systems usually consist of a septic tank and a drain field. The tank is buried in the ground along with a number of gravel-filled trenches, which provide a drain field (Figure 1.39). Household waste from the kitchen, bathroom, and laundry flow into the septic tank. Solids and grease remain in the tank, and bacteria in the tank start the decomposition process. Liquid and small particles, the septic tank effluent, flow out of the tank to the drain field, where they leach through the soil. In a properly functioning septic system, bacteria and viruses in the effluent are removed in the soil treatment zone by filtering and soil microorganisms before they reach the groundwater.

However, septic systems do not consistently remove all impurities from household waste. Some chemicals, such as nitrates, may not be removed in the soil treatment zone. Furthermore, not all soils are capable of absorbing and purifying septic tank effluent. An odor of sewage and a wet area around the drain field are signs that a septic system is not functioning properly.

Septic tank
(biodegradation)

Drainage field
(crushed stone)

Vent pipe

Household
wastes

Perforated pipe
distributes leachate
into drainage field

Use this information and any additional facts acquired from other sources to make a diagram illustrating a septic tank and how it works. What does *septic* mean? Where should a septic system be located and why is location important? What is done with the separated material? To what extent has the sewage been purified? Where does the treated liquid now go? Where does biology come into play in septic systems? Compare a septic system to a sewage treatment plant and to nature's way of dealing with sewage. Working individually or in small groups, prepare a presentation of what you have learned.

Presenting Your Research

After you have chosen your independent research and begun work, you need to keep in mind the final product you will develop for reporting purposes. This section will help you stay organized and make sure you include the information needed to describe your project to your classmates. Use this list as a guide for your development of a research report.

Key Elements

1. What is your research question? (INTRODUCTION)
   a. Outline the origin of your question.
   b. List reasons for conducting the test or experiment, including background information from literature searches.
   c. Highlight key findings.

2. How did you study the question? (MATERIALS AND METHODS)
   a. Include enough details, in proper order, that your work can be repeated. Make sure you include references to common procedures or include them in an appendix.
   b. Remember that repeatability is important.

3. What did you find? (RESULTS)
   a. Describe your data.
   b. Number each graph or table, and explain what each means.
   c. Use averages, ranges, or percent calculations to express results.

4. What do your findings mean? (DISCUSSION)
   a. Explain results clearly and briefly.
   b. Start with the most significant finding.
   c. Interpret results; do not merely repeat them.
   d. Interpret within the context of what is already known about the subject.

5. Statement of final conclusion (CONCLUSION)
   a. State all conclusions, and give evidence for each.
   b. Be brief but thorough.

Self-Check 2

Now that you have completed some Extended Inquiries, you should have some additional understanding about how matter and energy are used for life processes, about scientific skills, and about some of the issues presented by the accumulation of societal wastes. This self-check is designed to help you find out how much of the material you understand.

Form groups of four students. Each student in your group should select and answer three of the following questions. No two students should choose the same question. As resources, use the work you did on the Guided Inquiries and Extended Inquiries, your notes in your *Log,* and books in the classroom or library. You might want to work in advance on some answers as homework.

When everyone in your group has reasonable answers to the selected questions, assemble as a group to have each member share her or his answers with the entire group. As a group, you should then discuss and evaluate the completeness of each answer and modify it as necessary. Everyone in the group should eventually have a complete set of answers to all questions. Then everyone in the group will be ready for the Forum and the Unit Exam.

1. What are some of the specific challenges that result from the production of personal and industrial wastes by a relatively affluent society?

2. What are some specific ecological problems caused by the release of toxic chemicals into the environment? How can these affect natural food webs?

3. List three reasons why space to bury wastes is an issue.

4. Science is both a process and a product. What are elements of the process of science as it is currently practiced?

5. What are the products of scientific inquiry? List some specific examples of those that benefit society.

6. How effective are the practices of burning and burying in dealing with societal wastes?

7. Why must scientists have open minds toward new evidence?

8. Why do scientists frequently present their findings to other scientists?

9. How does science affect individuals who are not scientists?

10. How are the methods used by scientists also used by all of us in our everyday lives?

11. What is the role of data in answering a scientific question?

12. What is the difference between a question that can be addressed by science and one that cannot? Give some examples from the *Mobro* issue.

Congress

The Congress is a planning session for the roles you will play during the Forum, a meeting of the River City Town Council. During the Congress, you will identify your own points of view, take sides, and develop the level of expertise you will need for the Forum.

The setting for this role play is the hypothetical town of River City, located somewhere near you, with a population of 30,000. The town is trying to decide how to dispose of local waste. You will represent one of the groups that has a stake in the decision to be made by the Town Council.

You will need to identify the possible points of view for this issue and reach a consensus about both the nature of the issues and possible resolutions. This is an opportunity for you to take an individual, personal stand and decide which issues you wish to respond to. You may also propose recommendations to be sent to others who are potentially involved, such as organizations and government bodies.

Procedure

1. In preparation for the upcoming Town Council Meeting, organize into factions and interest groups. Your teacher will provide descriptions of the various roles for the Council meeting and help you to distribute yourselves evenly in the groups. Decide which group you would like to represent. The possible groups interacting at the Town Council will be:

   ◆ Members, River City Town Council (an odd number of members so that a no-tie decision can be reached)
   ◆ Planners, River County
   ◆ Sales Managers, Garbo-burn Incineration Company
   ◆ Sales Representatives, Covermeup Sanitary Landfill Company
   ◆ Members, River County Citizens Association

- ◆ Members, River County Business Association
- ◆ Corporation Executives, Clean-River Recyclers, Inc.
- ◆ Members, River County Environmental Coalition

2. With your group, gather information from which you will argue your side at the Town Council. Try to anticipate what the other participants' arguments will be. Compile the evidence for your position, focusing on biological evidence. Determine what you might need to say to counter the others' arguments, and decide what additional information might be needed. You should plan to enter the council meeting as experts on your views. Use all resources you have available, particularly results from your Guided and Extended Inquiries.

3. Your group will have a choice of two methods of presentation to the Council: a brief letter to the Council that will be read at the meeting by a council member; or a five-minute oral presentation at the meeting by a member of your group. Begin your preparations for one of these now. Your teacher will share with you evaluation criteria for what you are to prepare.

RIVER CITY TOWN COUNCIL MEETING

This Forum is a role play of the River City Town Council Meeting. Town Council meetings are examples of our democratic process in action. Your teacher will have given you cards that define your role at this important meeting. Since your actual local settings will vary, your teacher will also describe the nature of the meeting, the ground rules, and the expected timing to make the setting as realistic as possible. Each of your groups will be represented in some way at the meeting. Since each group has a vested interest in convincing the Council of its views, a highly effective letter or presentation is important.

The Problem to Be Addressed by the Town Council

River County's landfill is filling up. The Town Council must decide how to deal with this problem. Some members of the community want to develop a new landfill site; others suggest alternative waste management methods. The current landfill is located 3 km north of River City on county property. Obviously, the county must eventually approve the plan proposed by the Town Council. A nearby river, Big Creek, has cut a valley almost 15 m deep and 0.8 km wide. Big Creek runs toward the town. Much of the valley is covered with old-growth trees. A number of very nice houses have been built along the valley, including near the landfill area, taking advantage of the wonderful views of the river and trees out of the back windows.

Many nearby cities are worried that the groundwater may be polluted by leachates. The Covermeup Sanitary Landfill Company has proposed two new sites for landfills, each costing approximately $2.5 million to develop. The first site is privately owned farmland, 8 km northeast of River City, near the headwaters of Willey's Ford and Big Creek. The second site is 6 km directly east of the city, on property owned by the county.

If a new landfill is built, it will generate up to $250,000 per year in income for the county. Garbo-burn Incineration Company has offered to collect and transport River City's waste to its plant 80 km west of the city. It will charge the city $1.5 million per year. Garbo-burn plans to use mass-burn incineration and recover energy from the waste. The Clean-River Recyclers propose to develop and implement a program of consumer separation and curbside pickup of recyclable wastes. The cost of waste collection will remain the same as currently charged by the county, $10 per month per home and $50 per month for each business. The composition of River City's waste is as follows:

Paper	.33.0%
Glass	.11.0%
Metals	.12.0%
Food waste	.12.0%
Yard waste	.20.0%
Plastics	.6.0%
Textiles/wood	.3.0%
Other inorganics	.3.0%

The Town Council must decide how to solve the problem. During a hearing, each group will have five minutes to state its case to the Council.

The River City Town Council Meeting

Each group has five minutes to present its case. After the last group has finished, the Council has allotted five minutes for questions and discussion of the issues. Afterwards the Council must adjourn to closed session to decide what type of waste management system it will recommend to the County. The Council must then present the plan to the various interest groups, explaining how and why it reached its decision. After the meeting, discuss the following questions:

1. What trade-offs were made to solve the problems?
2. What information proved most useful in determining the choice of waste management systems?
3. Outline what steps were taken in the decision-making process.

Summary of Major Concepts

1. Wastes produced by our society present environmental challenges. Our personal decisions and actions directly influence waste production.

2. A trash audit is a systematic analysis of societal waste.

3. Most trash will tend to decompose and dehydrate over time if environmental conditions are right.

4. Matter occupies space and has mass. Matter cannot be destroyed but can be changed into different forms. Since wastes are matter, simply burying them does not make them go away.

5. Matter is made up of many different kinds of atoms. Different combinations of atoms make different molecules.

6. Some atoms and molecules react to form new molecules or compounds. These reactions can be expressed by chemical equations.

7. Matter tends to be cycled in the ecosystem. A good example is the carbon cycle.

8. Energy is the capacity to do work. Energy can take many forms.

9. Both aerobic respiration and fermentation extract energy from food and produce carbon dioxide. An additional product of fermentation is alcohol. An additional product of respiration is water. Organisms that respire aerobically are able to extract much more energy from food than are organisms that ferment.

10. Science is a process of inquiry and the knowledge that is gained through inquiry. Scientific knowledge changes with new discoveries.

11. The direct results of inquiry are called data. Data help us to understand the natural world.

12. Living things possess unique characteristics. All organisms exhibit structural organization, use energy and matter, reproduce, respond to stimuli, pass their genetic information on to successive generations, grow and develop, maintain internal stability, and evolve over time.

13. Photosynthesis and respiration are complementary processes in the carbon cycle. Waste and other products of each of these processes are used in the complementary process.

14. Biological knowledge is used by society on a regular basis. Learning biology is useful in today's highly technical world. Many interesting occupations require learning science.

15. Various organisms in compost help to decompose it.

16. Among the characteristics of science are reserved judgment, an open mind, curiosity, and a willingness to present new findings to others.

17. Science affects all people in many ways. Knowing about science is useful to everyone.

18. Many questions about our tangible world can be addressed by science. Most questions about what we believe outside the natural world cannot be addressed by science.

Suggestions for Further Exploration

Dindal, D.L. 1990. *Ecology of Compost.* State University of New York. Syracuse, NY.

An inexpensive booklet published by the College of Environmental Science and Forestry at the State University of New York. Contains clear directions for constructing and maintaining a compost pile. Illustrations include line drawings of a food web of the compost pile.

Hammond, A., Ed. 1993. *The 1994 Information Please Environmental Almanac.* Houghton Mifflin, Boston.

A yearly series compiled by the World Resources Institute. Provides updated data on global environmental issues.

Lavies, B. 1993. *Compost Critters.* Dutton Children's Books, New York.

An elementary-level book containing color photographs of some common compost pile inhabitants. "Describes what happens in a compost pile and how creatures, from bacteria and mites to millipedes and earthworms, aid in the process of turning compost into humus."

Rathje, W. & Murphy, C. 1992. *Rubbish!: The Archeology of Garbage.* HarperCollins, New York.

Describes the study of today's solid waste from an archeological perspective. Researchers' findings have often been contrary to people's beliefs about what is in landfills.

Rathje, W. 1991. Once and future landfills. *National Geographic,* 179(5), 116–119.

A National Geographic *article that includes illustrations of components found in landfills. Discusses actual versus perceived contents in landfills.*

USDA CSREES. *Home•A•Syst.,* 2006. http://www.uwex.edu.homeasyst

This nation-wide program includes customized versions for most states. Home•A•Syst helps you identify waste and pollution-related risks in your home and guides you to take preventative or remedial action.

World Resources Institute. 1994. *World Resources 1994–95: A Guide to the Global Environment.* Oxford Press, New York.

A biennial publication of the World Resources Institute in Washington, D.C. Provides information on the environment and development. Includes data on many topics, including populations, energy, materials, and water.

Videos

The Environmental Revolution. Program 1: Race to Save the Planet. 1990. WGBH Science Unit. The Annenberg/CPB Collection, Washington, D.C.

This 60-minute video is the beginning of a series that looks at the relationship of humans to their environment. Narrated by Meryl Streep, these programs include people from every continent discussing the restoration of damaged resources.

The Environmental Revolution. Program 8: Waste Not, Want Not. 1990. WGBH Science Unit. The Annenberg/CPB Collection, Washington, D.C.

One of a series of videos narrated by Meryl Streep, this program includes information on garbage barges, toxic waste dumping, and overflowing landfills. Alternatives to disposal are included.

All *living* ORGANISMS

What governs InterConnections between

TWO

ECOSYSTEMS

EARTH

ultimately

terrelated and

ANTE

NISMS?

nitial Inquiry

EVERYTHINGISCONNECTED

Setting

Figure 2.1

The Tennessee Copper Basin.

Imagine thousands of acres of land without visible life. You might picture the surface of the moon or a large desert on the earth. Or you could picture the Copper Basin in southeastern Tennessee (Figure 2.1). There, copper companies began removing and processing tons of ore more than 130 years ago. After taking the ore from the ground, the companies extracted copper by smelting the ore outdoors. This process produced large amounts of sulfur dioxide fumes that escaped into the air, causing acid rain. The deadly rain fell over thousands of acres, destroying all living things.

Now imagine that you live in a community in the Copper Basin. What would life be like? What could you do if you saw this destruction going on while you lived in the community?

The Copper Basin Video

View the short documentary video on the Tennessee Copper Basin. As you watch it, think about the following questions. After watching the video, participate in a class brainstorming session and talk about the questions.

◆ What issues does the video raise?

◆ What problems can you identify?

◆ What do you need to know that might help you solve the problems in the Copper Basin?

◆ If an expert were available for questions, what would you ask?

◆ How would you decide what type of expert you need?

After this discussion, record your thoughts in your *BioLog*. Think about what happened in the Copper Basin. Organize into groups of four or more students. Each group will be assigned several of the following statements for analysis. Working in your group, decide whether each statement is true or false. Explain your reasoning. Use resources such as the Copper Basin Fact Sheet on pages 76–77, the video you have just seen, maps, and photos such as Figure 2.2 on page 74 to help you.

1. For more than 100 years, companies removed copper from the area.

2. Copper was the major product of the mines.

3. The smelting of copper ore occurred in the Copper Basin.

4. Most Copper Basin residents worked for the copper companies.

5. Smelting produced sulfur dioxide fumes.

6. Most of the trees in the Copper Basin were cut to provide fuel for the smelting process.

7. The sulfur dioxide fumes from the smelting process killed all remaining vegetation.

8. The Copper Basin covers more than 30,000 acres (12,145 hectares), with a central area of 7,000 acres (2,843 hectares).

9. After copper mining ended, the Copper Basin was completely bare of vegetation.

10. Because of the lack of vegetation and the heavy rainfall, all of the topsoil in the Copper Basin eroded away.

11. The eroded soil accumulated downstream in reservoirs and rivers. Because of these sediments, some segments of these streams have no aquatic life.

12. Almost none of the types of original vegetation now grow in the Copper Basin.

13. Animals that were native to the Copper Basin before mining began are not present now.

14. Plants are growing again in some areas of the Copper Basin after intensive reconditioning of the soils.

15. The environment is not healthy for people living in the Copper Basin.

16. The copper companies that were responsible for the destruction of the Copper Basin ecosystem are no longer active.

17. Revegetation will restore the original forest plants.

18. People who lived in the Copper Basin were mostly in favor of the revegetation efforts.

Figure 2.2

The Isabella Mine and Mill was the hub of Copper Basin mining activity.

Sediment that had eroded from the bare hills clogged local streams and reservoirs.

Record your group's decisions in your *Log*. Compile data from all groups in the class. Discuss those questions on which you do not agree.

Brainstorming

After viewing the video, think about the Copper Basin ecosystem. An ecosystem is made up of all the living things in an area and the nonliving environment that supports them. As a class, discuss the consequences of the destruction of the Copper Basin ecosystem. Focus on the political, social, and economic factors that have resulted from the destruction. Try to cover many sides of this environmental issue. Consider the following questions, for example:

◆ Who is responsible for the Copper Basin disaster: only the copper companies or other groups as well?

- How did the almost total loss of plants affect animals and other organisms in the Copper Basin?
- Who benefited from the mining, and how did they benefit?
- Did anyone, at the time, understand the magnitude of the consequences?
- Does it really matter, nearly a century later, who is to blame?
- What normal human factors were involved in the decisions that led to this disaster?
- How did the loss of almost all vegetation affect the lifestyles of Copper Basin residents?
- What can we learn from this event as we enter the 21st century?
- How did the accumulation of sediment in local streams and reservoirs affect the decision to completely revegetate the Copper Basin?

After you have shared your observations and ideas with your classmates, enter your thoughts into your *Log*.

Restoring Vegetation

What is being done to restore vegetation in the Copper Basin? Virtually all of the plants were destroyed, and the fertile topsoil was lost to erosion. Can this valuable topsoil ever be replaced? How can new plant growth be encouraged? Look at the revegetation efforts listed on the fact sheet (see pages 76 and 77). Why was the choice of plants important?

As they planned the revegetation of the Copper Basin, foresters had to think about biomass production. Biomass is the total mass of a defined group of organisms in an ecosystem. Foresters and other scientists investigated which types of plants would produce the most biomass (Figure 2.3). Since the Copper Basin soil had lost all organic material and many of the nutrients that are needed for plant growth, foresters had to find plants that could grow well under these poor conditions. They also explored ways to improve the soil itself and experimented with using other organisms to help the newly planted trees survive and grow. Ectomycorrhizae, which are fungi that wrap themselves around pine tree roots (Figure 2.4), proved to be particularly useful. These fungi accumulate soil nutrients and make organic molecules that the pine trees then share. This helps the trees to live in soil that lacks other organic material.

Figure 2.3

Plants that have been used to revegetate the Copper Basin include sycamore trees such as this seedling.

Figure 2.4

An ectomycorrhizal fungus on pine tree roots.

THE COPPER BASIN FACT SHEET

Climate and Vegetation

Average annual precipitation: 58 inches

Mean monthly temperatures: Range from 37°F (January) to 75°F (July)

Native vegetation: Mixed hardwood and pine forests

Copper Basin native vegetation.

Mining Activities

1843: Copper is discovered by a gold prospector.

1850: The first copper mine (Hiwassee Mine) opens.

Copper smelters.

1854: The first open-air copper smelters are built along the banks of Potato Creek.

Forests are cut down to fuel the copper smelters.

Open-air roasting of copper ore releases sulfur dioxide fumes, which create acid rain.

1861–1863: The demand for weapons during the Civil War stimulates copper production.

1876: Trees outside the Basin are cut and floated downriver to fuel the smelters after most of the trees in the Basin have been used.

1880s: Mining and smelting cease, owing to lack of rail transport to the mining sites.

1890: Mining and smelting resume after construction of the Marietta and North Georgia Railway.

The Ducktown Sulphur, Copper, and Iron Company starts production.

A by-product of manufacturing is sulfur recovered from the smelting process.

1904: Development of a new copper-smelting technique by the Ducktown Sulphur, Copper, and Iron Company ends open-air roasting of ores.

1907: The impact of the sulfur dioxide fumes on the vegetation reaches its greatest extent.

The affected area covers 32,000 acres (50 square miles) 23,000 of which are totally without vegetation.

Copper Basin at the height of devastation.

The Tennessee Copper Company begins production of sulfuric acid, using recovered sulfur dioxide gases from the copper smelters.

Revegetation Activities

1934: The first revegetation efforts begin at the margins of the Copper Basin.

1939: The Tennessee Copper Company and the Tennessee Valley Authority (TVA) begin the first extensive tree-planting programs.

Tree planting in the Copper Basin.

1941: The TVA establishes a Civilian Conservation Corps (CCC) Camp in the Copper Basin. CCC workers plant hardwood trees, shrubs, and pine trees including:

- Loblolly pine (*Pinus taeda*)
- Shortleaf pine (*Pinus echinata*)
- Virginia pine (*Pinus virginiana*)
- Pitch pine (*Pinus rigida*)
- Black locust (*Robinia pseudoacacia*)

1941–1946: The TVA begins an experimental program to identify the best plants to revegetate the Basin. The study reaches the following conclusions:

- Pitch pine had the best survival rate.
- Loblolly pine had the best rate of growth.
- Virginia pine had better-than-average growth and survival rates.
- Shortleaf pine had poor survival and growth rates.
- Weeping love grass produced the best ground cover.
- Other useful plantings included switchgrass (*Panicum virgatum*) and shrub lespedeza (*Lespedeza bicolor*).

1945: The TVA submits a comprehensive plan for revegetation to the Tennessee Copper Company.

1934–1949: More than 2,800,000 trees and shrubs are planted in the Copper Basin.

1946: Open-range grazing of cattle and deliberate burning, used to clear the land, were stopped.

1954: The Tennessee Copper Company hires a professional agriculturist to continue revegetation.

1950–1960: Kudzu (*Pueraria lobata*) is introduced to slow erosion but is soon recognized as a competitive threat to trees and a winter fire hazard.

1960s: Japanese fleece-flower (*Polygonum cuspidatum*) is planted to slow erosion, although no one knows how compatible it is with native pines. Loblolly and pitch pines are the preferred plantings through 1969.

Although it did help to control erosion, planted kudzu became a nuisance in the Copper Basin.

1963: The Cities Service Company purchases the Tennessee Copper Company.

1970s–1980s: More than 500,000 trees are planted each year.

1970s: The Cities Service Company experiments with the following soil improvement methods:

- Subsoiling (breaking up soil to improve water penetration)
- Application of fertilizer tablets to improve soil before planting

1973: The Cities Service Company and the U.S. Department of Agriculture Forest Service start a five-year research project to test the effects of the following soil practices:

- Deep subsoiling, with application of fertilizer and lime
- Applications of solid sludge to replace missing organic matter in the soil
- Planting pine seedlings along with specific fungi
- This study concluded that pine seedlings treated with *Pisolithus tinctorius*, a type of fungus, grow more rapidly than do untreated seedlings.

1978: Fertilizer (300 lb per acre) is applied from helicopters.

1980s: The Soil Conservation Service implements revegetation and surface water control techniques.

Helicopters applied fertilizer over wide areas of the Copper Basin.

1984: An intense revegetation program begins.

Its goal is to completely revegetate the Copper Basin by the year 2000. By this time, the situation in the Basin can be described as follows:

- The exposed mineral subsoil is compacted, infertile, and acidic (pH 3.8–5.0).
- Groundcover is either sparse or nonexistent.
- 12,612 acres are remain in need of revegetation.
- 2,295 acres of the Copper Basin remain completely bare of vegetation.

1984–1996: The TVA and the resident chemical company continue to cooperate in a plan to completely revegetate the Copper Basin.

7,865 additional acres are reforested.

100 acres near the Ducktown Museum will remain completely bare for environmental education programs.

The Copper Basin before (above) and after (below) the intensive reforestation and fertilization.

Determining Biomass

Biomass is the total amount of matter in an organism. From where does the biomass of an organism such as a plant come? Under what conditions is biomass more quickly produced? How does soil type affect plant growth and biomass production?

In this activity, you will compare the biomass of two types of plants, grown in three types of soil.

Plant Types	Soil Types
◆ Corn	◆ Soil from your local area
◆ Lima beans	◆ Soil from your compost pile
	◆ Soil such as that found in the Copper Basin

Because your goal is to study the effects of soil characteristics on growth, you must keep other variables, such as light and water, the same. Do not fertilize these plants. Observe the effects of growth in the existing soil conditions, with nothing extra added.

MATERIALS

- Three corn seeds and three lima bean seeds per student or group, soaked for at least 24 hours
- Six small plastic containers
- Soil to fill two of the small containers with each of the following: local soil, compost, and soil such as that found in the Copper Basin
- Balance that will mass to ±0.01 gram

Procedure

Before you begin, read the safety note on page 79.

1. Gather your soil samples from safe, secure areas. Consult your teacher to obtain soil such as that found in the Copper Basin. Predict what will happen when you plant the seeds in the three different soils. Record and explain your predictions in your *Log*.

2. Determine what conditions of light, water, and temperature the plants need to grow and how often you will take care of these needs.

3. Record the mass of each of your soaked seeds in your *Log*. (Figure 2.5 shows you a format for recording data.) You can compute averages later.

Day	Plant/Seed Type	Seed Masses (grams) in Each Soil Type		
		Local Soil	Compost	Copper Basin
0	Corn			
0	Bean			
last day	Corn			
last day	Bean			

Class Data:	Mean Plant Mass (grams) after 20 Days of Growth		
Basin	Local Soil	Compost	Copper Basin
Corn			
Bean			

Figure 2.5

Sample mass data table for Guided Inquiry 2.1.

4. Fill your containers with soil. Fill two containers with compost, two with local soil, and two with soil similar to that found in the Copper Basin. Keep hands away from face, and wash hands when finished. Punch small holes in the bottom of each container to drain water. Label the containers.

5. Plant a corn seed in each type of soil and a lima bean seed in each type of soil. Plant the seeds about 1 inch deep. Moisten the soil. Keep it moist, but don't soak it.

6. Try to choose environmental conditions (light and temperature) that you think will produce plants with the greatest biomass possible in two to three weeks. All of your plants must experience the same environmental conditions. This means that you are controlling these conditions. In your *Log*, explain why this control is important to the experiment and your final conclusions.

7. Record in your *Log* a description of the environment in which your plants will be growing. Describe the air temperature, location, watering schedule, and number of hours of light the plants receive each day.

8. In your *Log*, make a data table like the one in Figure 2.6 on page 80. Enter your day zero data for mass and height.

Figure 2.6

Sample height data table for Guided Inquiry 2.1.

Height in Centimeters of Seedlings in Three Soil Types

Day	Plant/Seed Type	Plant Heights (centimeters) in Each Soil Type		
		Local Soil	Compost	Copper Basin
0	Corn			
0	Bean			
1	Corn			
1	Bean			
2	Corn			
2	Bean			

etc. (Leave room in the *Log* for 20 days total, probably an entire page.)

Class Data: Basin	Mean Plant Height (centimeters) after 20 Days of Growth		
	Local Soil	Compost	Copper Basin
Corn			
Bean			

During the next two to three weeks:

9. Each day, note any differences among the plants.

10. Each day, measure the height, in centimeters, of each plant. Record these data in your *Log*. You will collect, interpret, and analyze final data later, as part of Guided Inquiry 2.8.

Interpretations: Complete the following as homework:

1. Identify your independent variables—the causes of change—in this experiment.

2. Identify other variables that should be kept constant (controlled). Why do you have to keep these variables constant?

3. Identify the dependent variable in your study. This is the effect or result of the experiment. How did you measure the dependent variable? How often did you measure it?

4. On the basis of your responses to the three preceding instructions, write a hypothesis for this experiment. This should be an "If . . ., then . . ." sentence, with the "if" representing your independent variable(s) and the "then" representing your dependent variable(s).

5. Why is it a good idea to calculate the average or mean values of height and mass for each type of plant?

Applications: Respond to the following in your *Log:*

1. Determine which of the natural environmental characteristics of the Copper Basin contributed most to soil erosion. Investigate the potential for similar erosion problems in your own community.

2. Which characteristics of Copper Basin soil make it unsuitable for plant growth? Use information from the Copper Basin Fact Sheet and your own observations to answer this question.

BIOprediction

Can the Copper Basin Be Returned to Its Original State?

The Copper Basin was to be completely replanted by the year 2000. Was this goal achieved? How similar is the replanted vegetation in the Basin to the surrounding forests? What do you think will happen to the Copper Basin in the next 20 years?

Making Biomass

Plants and animals use different energy sources to make biomass. Animals get the organic materials that they need for growth and metabolism from the foods they eat. That is why animals are called consumers. Plants and some microorganisms are known as producers because they make the organic molecules that they require for growth and metabolism from inorganic nutrients. They use energy from the sun for this process of photosynthesis.

The yellow leaves of this pine seedling indicate a nitrogen deficiency.

Plants must have water, nutrients, and light for growth. Light is the energy source for photosynthesis (Figure 1.27 on page 38). Plants get most of their water from the soil. Plants obtain inorganic nutrients such as phosphorus (P), nitrogen (N), potassium (K), calcium (Ca), and iron (Fe) from the soil or other growth medium. Carbon dioxide (CO_2) from the atmosphere provides the carbon atoms that plants use to make sugars during photosynthesis. 🌍

The Role of Light and Pigments in Photosynthesis

Sunlight energy is made up of light of many wavelengths. What is the relationship between the way in which a plant uses light and the colored pigments that the plant contains? Can you isolate and identify these pigments?

In Part A of this inquiry, you will investigate the composition of light. In Part B, you will explore the types of colored pigments that are found in plants.

Before you begin, read the safety note on page 83.

MATERIALS

- Prism
- White paper
- Light source
- Green, red, and blue light filters made of cellophane or other material
- Green plant leaves (Spinach works well.)
- Chopping knife or mortar, pestle, and sand
- 95% acetone or ethanol
- Cardboard with a slit cut into it
- Chromatography paper or coffee filters, cut to fit inside test tube
- Pencil, ruler, and paper clip
- Suction bulb and micro-pipette or narrow cylindrical wooden stir rod
- Glass bottles or beakers
- Glass test tubes with stoppers
- Chromatography solvent (nine parts petroleum ether and one part acetone)

Part A: The Composition of Light

Procedure

1. Shine a light through the prism onto a sheet of white paper, as shown in Figure 2.7. Adjust the light until you see a spectrum of colors on the white paper. Record in your *Log* the names of the colors and the order in which they appear.

2. Hold each of the colored filters, one at a time, between your light source and the prism. Observe the changes in the spectrum on the white paper. Record the colors of light that you see.

3. Try using combinations of two or more filters. How does this affect the spectrum that is created?

Figure 2.7

Alignment of the prism, light source, filters, and paper to investigate the composition of white light.

Part B: Paper Chromatography of Plant Pigments

Procedure

1. Chop the green plant leaves into small pieces, and soak them overnight in a solvent such as acetone or ethanol. Some of the plant pigments, the color-producing molecules, will be extracted into the solvent. Or, instead of chopping the leaves, grind them with a mortar and pestle, using a little sand and solvent. This will make a more concentrated extract.

2. Lightly draw a pencil line 2 cm from the bottom edge of the chromatography strip.

3. Using a suction bulb and micropipette or narrow cylindrical wooden stir rod, place a drop of pigment extract in the center of this line. Allow the spot to dry. Then add eight to ten more drops of extract to this spot, allowing the extract to dry between each drop. Keep the spot small.

4. Bend the paper clip to make a hook at one end. Embed the opposite end of the paper clip in the bottom of a test tube stopper.

5. Add chromatography solvent to fill a test tube to the level of about 1 cm.

6. Suspend the strip of chromatography paper from the paper clip hook on the stopper, as shown in Figure 2.8 on page 84. Insert the paper strip into the test tube so that the pigment spot is near the bottom of the tube but does not touch the solvent.

SAFETY NOTE

- Acetone, petroleum ether, and, to a lesser extent, ethanol are flammable. Keep them away from flames. Consult with your teacher on safety guidelines before use.
- Avoid inhaling the vapors.
- Be certain that the room is well-ventilated.
- Wear **goggles** and **gloves**.

Figure 2.8

Experimental apparatus for paper chromatography of plant pigments.

— Test tube stopper

— Test tube

— Chromatography paper

— Pigment spot

— Pencil line

— Chromatography solvent

7. Place the test tube in an upright position for 10 to 15 minutes to let the pigments separate.

8. Stop the separation by removing the strip from the test tube when the chromatography solvent seeps to the top of the paper strip.

9. Allow the paper strip to dry. When it is dry, use a pencil to circle each of the different color bands. Each color band is a different photosynthetic pigment. Tape the dry chromatogram in your *Log*. Label the colors.

Interpretations: Respond to the following in your *Log*:

1. How did combining filters affect the spectrum that was created in Part A?

2. What colors of pigment did you find?

3. What was the pattern of pigment bands produced from the plant extract?

4. What colors (wavelengths) of visible light would you expect this plant to absorb?

5. What colors (wavelengths) of visible light can this plant use for photosynthesis?

6. What does this inquiry tell you about what makes green plants appear green?

Applications: Respond to the following in your *Log*:

1. How would this activity help you to decide what color windows to use in a greenhouse?

2. Suggest a hypothesis that explains why the photosynthetic parts of plants are green.

3. What color lights are commonly used for indoor plants? Why? Explain your answer.

Light Energy Is in the Form of Waves

Sunlight is a form of energy called electromagnetic energy, which consists of wavelike disturbances in electrical and magnetic fields. These electromagnetic waves have various heights and lengths, just like ocean waves. Types of radiation are identified in terms of their wavelengths, the distances between individual crests of each wave. Wavelengths vary from very long radio waves (longer than one meter) to very short gamma rays (less than 10^{-3} nanometers wavelength). Figure 2.9 shows the wavelengths of different types of radiation.

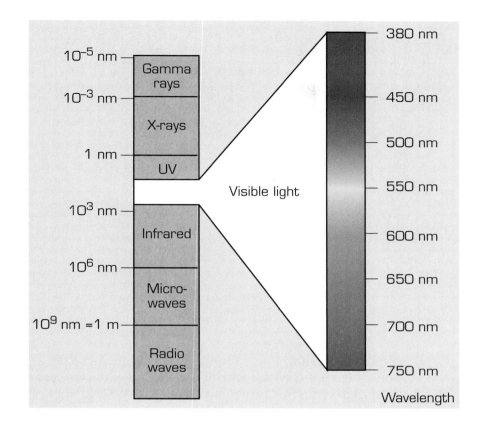

Figure 2.9

The electromagnetic spectrum.

Energy and Wavelength: A Demonstration

Waves with shorter wavelengths have more energy than do waves of longer wavelengths. You can demonstrate the relationship between wavelength and energy by using a jump rope and some of your own energy.

You and a partner hold the ends of an eight- to ten-foot rope, as if you were preparing to jump rope. Your partner simply holds one end, and you create waves in the rope by shaking it gently up and down. Start with slow, long-wavelength waves; then increase the intensity to make fast, short-wavelength waves.

Watch the wave crests as they travel along the length of the rope. Which type of wave needed more energy input from you? The amount of energy you had to use to make a wave illustrates the energy the wave contains.

Visible Light

The human eye is sensitive to wavelengths of radiant energy between about 380 and 750 nanometers. These wavelengths are called visible light. Although it may appear white, it is really made up of a spectrum of colors. When visible light encounters matter, the light is either reflected, absorbed, or transmitted (see Figure 2.10 on page 86). Pigments absorb visible light. The color of a pigment is determined by the type of light that it reflects or

Figure 2.10

Light is either reflected from, absorbed into, or transmitted through a solid object such as this leaf.

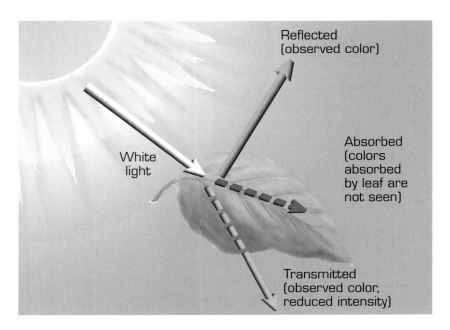

Figure 2.11

A chlorophyll molecule.

Magnesium

Nitrogen

Carbon

Oxygen

Hydrogen

transmits. For example, a green pigment transmits and reflects green light, which is why it looks green to our eyes. A green pigment absorbs red and blue light. A black pigment absorbs all visible light, and a white pigment reflects all colors of visible light.

If you want your plants to absorb the most energy from the sun, what colors of visible light should you provide? How can you determine which types of light are best for photosynthesis?

Photosynthetic Pigments

Photosynthesis takes place in organisms that contain a special pigment that can harvest light energy. This green pigment that absorbs light and allows plants to photosynthesize is chlorophyll (Figure 2.11). All photosynthetic cells contain chlorophyll, which converts light energy into chemical energy for use by the cell. The first step in the light reaction of photosynthesis (Figure 1.27 on page 38) is absorption of light energy by chlorophyll molecules. The four nitrogen atoms and the central magnesium atom are essential to the functioning of this molecule. This in part explains why nitrogen and magnesium are essential plant nutrients.

Other pigments that can harvest light are found in many plants and microorganisms. These accessory pigments absorb light energy and transfer the collected energy to chlorophyll molecules. Since these pigments differ in color, they absorb different wavelengths of light. Carrot roots, for example, contain orange pigments called carotenoids. Red seaweeds and blue-green algae contain red and purple pigments called phycobilins.

Organisms having accessory pigments can use a wider range of light colors for photosynthesis. Figure 2.12 (below) shows the light wavelengths that are absorbed by various photosynthetic pigments. Green chlorophyll pigments absorb red and blue light. Yellow and orange carotenoids absorb blue-green light. The purple and red phycobilin pigments absorb green and yellow light.

Oxygen Production

Indirectly, photosynthesis provides food for humans and other consumers. It is also a major source of the molecular oxygen in the earth's atmosphere. More than 3.5 billion years ago, primitive photosynthetic cells began releasing molecular oxygen to the atmosphere (see Figure 2.13). These primitive photosynthesizers produced the oxygen that made possible the evolution of diverse, oxygen-requiring organisms—including humans.

Figure 2.13

Primitive photosynthetic organisms.

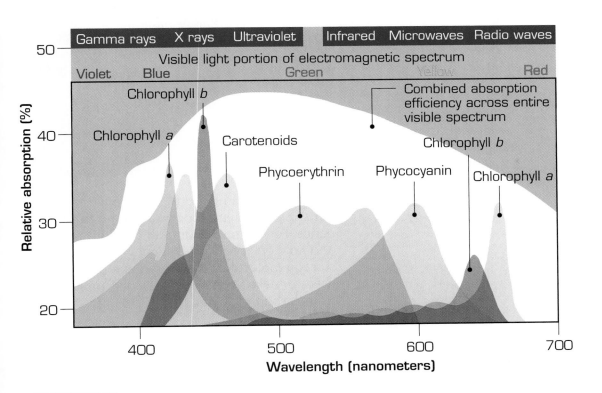

Figure 2.12

Chlorophyll, the primary photosynthetic pigment, and accessory pigments in plants absorb light.

Photosynthesis and Energy Transformations

Energy is the capacity to do work, and it exists in two forms: active energy, or motion, and potential energy, or stored energy. For example, an apple that is attached to a tree branch has potential energy. When it falls, this potential energy is changed into the energy of motion, sometimes called kinetic energy. Fossil fuels represent potential energy until they are burned, producing kinetic energy as heat.

FIRST LAW OF THERMODYNAMICS: Energy is not created nor is it destroyed during conversion to another form.

SECOND LAW OF THERMODYNAMICS: The energy that is available to do work decreases during successive energy conversions, resulting in an increase in the randomness (entropy) of energy within the system.

In the process of photosynthesis, plants convert light energy (sunlight) to chemical energy (sugars). Plants use these sugars for growth, the production of biomass, and metabolism. Plants store within their cells any sugars that they do not need for growth. Usually, these are stored in the form of starch. Humans and other consumers use these stored carbohydrates as food sources.

Metabolism is a collective term to describe the chemical and physical reactions that occur in living organisms. When organisms take in energy sources, as a plant absorbs light energy or animals consume foods, they convert it to metabolic energy. The organisms use this energy for growth and maintenance. For example, plants absorb light energy and convert it to stored sugars and energy storage molecules. The stored energy is then used to make carbohydrate (sugar) molecules from carbon dioxide (Figure 2.14).

Light energy

Plant cells

CO_2

Metabolic energy

Sugars

Starch (storage)

Consumption by animals

Plant growth

Starches are also metabolized for plant growth

Figure 2.14

The flow of energy and matter during photosynthesis.

Can a Lake Explode?

It seems impossible, but this is just what happened in 1986 in Lake Nyos in Cameroon in central Africa: Gases from the lake formed a deadly cloud over the valley. In the hundreds of villages dotting the nearby valley, all living organisms, including people, animals, trees, and other vegetation, died. A few days later, scientists visited the area and investigated. The scientists pieced the information together to discover what really happened in this valley (Figure 2.15).

Figure 2.15

Lake Nyos after the explosion.

Carefully read the findings and the tentative conclusions of the scientists:

- The victims were overwhelmed by a cloud of poisonous gas.

- The gas came from Lake Nyos.

- Lake Nyos lies in a volcanic crater.

- A slow buildup of carbon dioxide occurred deep within the lake.

- Carbon dioxide is still found deep within the water of the lake.

- A landslide may have occurred near the lake.

- The landslide could have churned up and released the carbon dioxide gas.

- Vegetation was destroyed only on the southern side of the lake.

- Most scientists believe that more deadly gas could be released from Lake Nyos in the near future.

- Most villagers have decided to remain in the valley.

Respond to the following in your *Log*:

1. If you lived near Lake Nyos, would you leave your village? Why or why not? What additional information would you need to make a decision?

2. If you decided to leave, where would you go? What would you need?

3. If you decided to remain in the valley, what immediate concerns would you have? How could you protect yourself?

4. According to the scientists, another release of this deadly gas is likely to occur in the very near future. Should people be forced to leave the valley?

BI🌐occupation

Kathy Stecker: Environmental Quality Management

Kathy Stecker is an environmental quality manager for the South Carolina Department of Health and Environmental Control. Her job is to help people assess and restore the health of South Carolina's lakes.

When asked about a "typical day" in her job, Ms. Stecker hesitates. "Every day is so different," she says. "I spend a good bit of my time answering inquiries regarding water quality from the public and other government agencies."

She described a typical project, which began when a group of homeowners around a 600-acre lake needed help in determining why the lake had become covered with aquatic weeds. As often happens before expert help is requested, the homeowners had attempted their own aquatic plant control. They tried using herbicides, chemicals that kill certain plants, in an effort to get rid of the weeds. Not only did the herbicide treatments fail to get rid of the weeds, they created even more water quality problems.

When Ms. Stecker studied the lake, she found that exotic plants had been brought in, probably on the propellers of boats moved from other lakes. These plants caused a thick layer of organic sediment to form on the bottom of the lake. Ms. Stecker helped the homeowners to understand the source of the weed problems and to come up with ways to

restore the lake. Her recommendations included dredging the lake bottom to remove plants, roots, and the organic sediment or adding plant-eating fish to the lake. But her main job was to educate the local residents and lake users about how to avoid bringing more exotic plants to the lake.

When asked about the best part of her job, Ms. Stecker replies, "Talking to people, answering their questions. Often they go off and learn more on their own and begin to take an attitude of stewardship [a feeling of responsibility] toward their lake." The hardest part of her job involves the uncertainty of funding. Shifting government priorities from one year to the next may mean less money for environmental work.

The educational requirements for her job included a Bachelor of Science degree in natural sciences or a related field and several years of experience in related jobs. High school students who are interested in a career in the environmental quality field should enroll in college courses in natural sciences or environmental health. Ms. Stecker highly recommends volunteering to work on research projects with state agencies or university faculty. She says, "This not only gives you experience that can make you a valuable employee in the future, but it also helps you see if this is something you really want to do."

Nitrogen Fixation

Plants need nitrogen to make essential compounds such as chlorophyll and proteins. What are the sources of nitrogen for plants? How is nitrogen made available to plants?

In this activity, you will look for bacteria in the root nodules of clover or other plants that harbor nitrogen-fixing bacteria. Although you cannot actually see the chemical reactions in nitrogen fixation, you can observe the nodules where this process takes place, and you can observe the bacteria that carry out this process.

MATERIALS

- Nodule from the root of a legume such as clover, alfalfa, or bean
- Slides and coverslips
- Toothpicks
- Methylene blue in dropper bottle
- Compound microscope

Procedure

1. Squash the nodule between two microscope slides.
2. Clean one microscope slide. Discard the outermost covering of the nodule. Save the nodule contents on the other slide.
3. With a toothpick, push the nodule contents to the center of the slide and spread them out.
4. Place a drop of methylene blue in the center of the contents. Mix it with the toothpick, and cover the contents with a coverslip.
5. Examine the nodule contents under high power. If the dye density is too great to see any contents, remove the coverslip, add a drop of water, and view again. The nitrogen-fixing bacteria are rod-shaped structures. They are very small but numerous.
6. Make a sketch in your *Log* of the whole nodule and of the bacteria.

Interpretations: Respond to the following in your *Log*:

1. What was stained most densely with the methylene blue?
2. Where are the bacteria inside the root nodules?
3. What is the benefit of the nitrogen-fixing bacteria being located in the roots?
4. Write a chemical equation to represent nitrogen fixation (nitrogen gas to ammonia). Consult Figure 2.16 on page 92 for information.

SAFETY NOTE

- Methylene blue will stain hands and clothing. Wear latex gloves and aprons or lab coats.
- Take care not to break slides when squashing root nodules. Place a folded paper towel on the slide and press down on the towel to avoid cutting your finger if the slide breaks.

Figure 2.16

The nitrogen cycle.

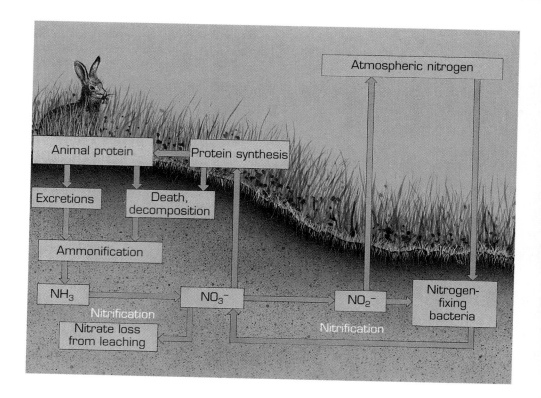

5. Write a chemical equation to represent the change from ammonia (NH$_3$) to nitrites (NO$_2^-$) and from nitrites to nitrates (NO$_3^-$). Consult Figure 2.16 for information.

Applications: Respond to the following in your *Log*:

1. Why would farmers rotate a corn crop, which requires much nitrogen for growth, with a clover or bean crop?

2. If all nitrogen fixation in the world stopped, how would this affect you?

3. Evaluate this statement: "All bacteria are bad because they are harmful to humans."

4. Where in the environment is nitrogen most abundant? What chemical form does it take?

5. What chemical form of inorganic nitrogen is most abundant in soils?

Where Do Plants Get Nitrogen?

Plants need nitrogen to produce essential molecules such as proteins and chlorophyll. But where do plants get their nitrogen? Air contains much more molecular nitrogen (N$_2$) than any other gas. However, plant cells cannot use this form of nitrogen. If nitrogen is combined with oxygen in the form of nitrates (NO_3^-) and nitrites (NO_2^-), it can be used by plants. How, then, are these forms of nitrogen produced?

Plants depend on nitrogen-fixing organisms, such as certain bacteria and blue-green algae, to change nitrogen from gaseous form into nitrates and nitrites (Figure 2.16). These molecules are used by plants to produce biomass, which is then consumed by animals or broken down by decomposers. Another nitrogen-containing molecule, ammonia (NH_3), is produced. Other bacteria in the soil convert ammonia to nitrites and nitrates. Still other bacteria break down these molecules to liberate nitrogen gas to the atmosphere. This interaction of organisms and processes is called the nitrogen cycle (Figure 2.16).

In plants such as clover, peanuts, and alfalfa, nitrogen-fixing bacteria such as *Rhizobium* live inside root nodules (Figure 2.17 and Figure 2.18). The microbes take in N_2 and provide nitrogen in a usable form for these plants. Foresters in the Copper Basin used *Lespedeza* plants to improve the nitrogen content of the soil. Farmers grow both clover and alfalfa to increase the nitrogen content of agricultural soils, especially when they want to plant crops that need large amounts of nitrogen. Many farmers alternate plantings of nitrogen-rich crops such as alfalfa and nitrogen-poor crops such as corn. Alternating planting is called crop rotation. This plan maintains the nutrient quality of the soil. 🌏

Figure 2.17

Rhizobium *bacteria [dark spots] in plant root nodules.*

Figure 2.18

Soyben root nodules.

Mapping Your Ecosystem

What is your personal territory? Where do you exist for most of your life? Can you visualize all the places you visit in a 48-hour period? In this activity, you will investigate the environment in which you live and the resources that you use. Scientists call the area required by an animal to secure food, shelter, and mates and to raise offspring the "home range" (Figure 2.19). You will now find your own home range and the home range of your classroom. Let's define your home range as the area in which 90 percent of your daily activities take place.

Figure 2.19

Where do these animals call home?

MATERIALS

- For urban or suburban areas, a city or local area street map; for rural areas, a county road map. You may instead use a highway map or a computer mapping program such as *Street Atlas USA* (DeLorme Mapping).

- Sheet of tracing paper or acetate
- Pencil
- One projection acetate for the class discussion

Procedure

1. Create and keep a record of your exact location and activities over a two-day period. Mark these locations on the map of your local area. Place a small X at each place you have been for each hour (on the hour) for 48 hours. After you have recorded data for 48 hours, your map should show all locations you have occupied.

2. In your *Log*, keep a general record of activities at each location on the map. Identify which activity occurred at which location.

3. In your *Log*, keep a record of all the food you consumed during the two-day period. Record the quantity of each food item consumed (for example, ten potato chips, one cup of cereal, four ounces of meat, and so on). Include everything that you eat— snacks as well as meals. You will use this 48-hour record of your food intake later, for Guided Inquiry 2.6, so record it accurately in your *Log* now.

4. Use the Xs on the map to identify your home range (the entire area that you have traveled within).

5. Cover your map with a sheet of tracing paper or acetate, and draw a boundary around the area on the map that includes all of your marks. The boundary should follow established roadways and may not cut through buildings or open lots.

6. As a class, establish two reference points on the map, such as large intersections or buildings that are on all of your maps.

Interpretations: Respond to the following in your *Log*:

1. The map on the tracing paper or acetate is a boundary map of your home range. Get together in groups of four to combine maps. Each group member should place his or her boundary map on top of the previous one, with the reference points aligned. Place another sheet of tracing paper or acetate on top of the pile and trace all of the outside range lines from all four maps. Do this against a window surface or an overhead projector so you can see through the four individual sheets. The boundary of the group map includes the home ranges for all four group members. Record your observations about this group home range in your *Log*.

2. Using your group maps as the basis for a class discussion, determine the boundary of the home range for the entire class. Present your group's boundary map to the class. One member of each group should mark the group's boundary map on an acetate map that is large enough to include all possible group boundaries. The resulting boundary map will define the classroom home range.

Your teacher can display this map on an overhead projector. Record your observations about the group home range in your *Log*.

3. Develop some general categories, such as going to school, eating, sleeping, shopping, and recreation, for your activities list. This should help you to recognize the kinds of activities you perform within your home range. Compare your personal home range to the class home range.

4. What organisms share your home range with you? What kinds of resources are available in your home range? Resources include energy, water, shelter, food, and open space. Add these resources to your map, along with any important physical characteristics of the land, including rock types and watersheds. This becomes your biomap.

5. Where does the waste from the class home range system go? Find out by doing a little research. Label these locations on your map.

Applications: Respond to the following in your *Log*:

1. Locate your class home range on at least two maps, such as a larger regional map, a picture of the earth from space (Figure 2.20), a world map, or a United States biome map (Figure 2.21). Record your observations.

2. Record the information you learned about your home range.

3. Determine the biome in which you live. Compare the characteristics of your biome with those of some of the major biomes described in Appendix I.

Figure 2.20

A view of the earth from space.

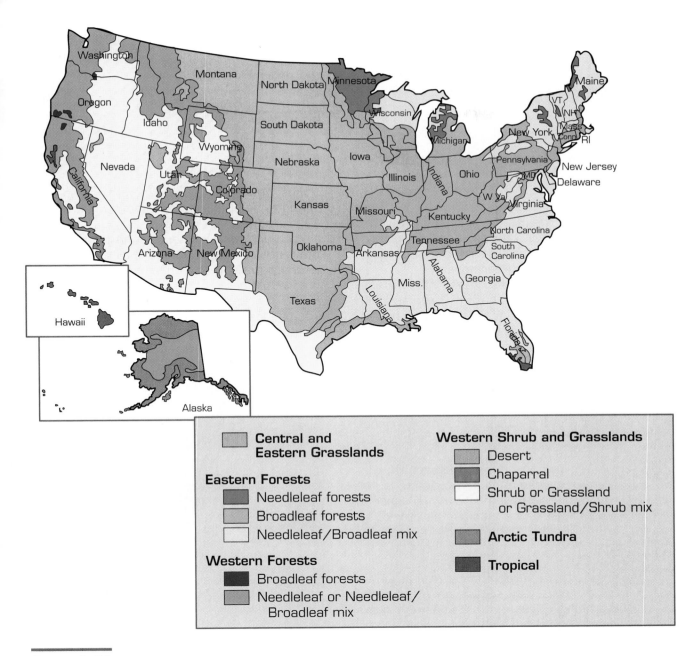

Figure 2.21

The natural vegetation of the United States.

BI🌐occupation

Rudy Mancke: Naturalist

Meet Rudy Mancke, a naturalist and host for educational television's popular program *NatureScene*. As the host of this award-winning show, Mr. Mancke leads viewers on nature walks through some of the most beautiful areas of our country.

Mr. Mancke is the creator of *NatureScene*. He grew up loving nature. "I started with bugs and snakes as a youth, then became interested in plants, rocks, and fossils when I was in high school," he said. "I tried to be in the woods whenever possible. I was so curious, I read everything I could about nature. There were so many questions and so much to learn. The most difficult thing about growing up was reconciling science with my religious training. As time went on, I saw less and less conflict."

After graduating from high school, Mr. Mancke earned an undergraduate degree in biology. He has been both a high school biology teacher and a museum curator of science. One day, when he was leading a field trip, he was taped for a segment on the evening news. The segment was so successful that the television station asked him to do more. *NatureScene* grew out of this beginning. "Now I have the best job in the world," he says. "We travel all over and help bring an understanding of nature to our audience. To be a naturalist, you simply have to be extremely interested in all of nature, not just one part. And you have to be interested in the connections between things. You must have an open mind and be willing to be surprised by what you find. That's the way science is."

A student who is interested in a career like Mr. Mancke's should take all the science courses available in high school. The next step would be an undergraduate degree in biology, ecology, or environmental science. You can learn more about *NatureScene* locations on the interactive site: *http://cfmedia.scetv.org/naturescene*

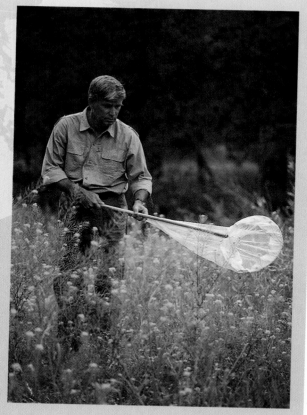

Trophic Scavenger Hunt

Where does food energy come from? What happens to energy that organisms use? See the simple food chain illustrated in Figure 2.22. Corn, a photosynthetic plant, is the producer because it makes the food that it needs using energy from the sun. The mouse occupies a second level in the food chain. It is a primary consumer or herbivore. The snake and owl are secondary and tertiary consumers or carnivores.

How much of the solar energy that plants capture is actually available to organisms that eat plants? If a snake eats the mouse, how much of the original energy of the corn is available for use by the snake? Food levels represent the amount of energy available for the ecosystem. These are usually referred to as trophic levels. For this activity, assume that you can estimate the total energy in a trophic level by the number of organisms that occupy that level.

In this activity, you will participate in a scavenger hunt to find the producers and consumers in your ecosystem. You will observe how the producers and consumers interact. You will also discover the relative amount of energy available to the next level in a food chain.

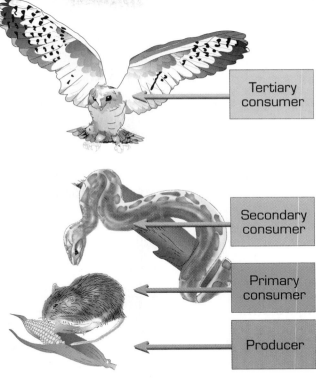

Figure 2.22

A simple food chain. Can you identify the trophic levels?

MATERIALS

- A watch with a second hand
- A sample area outside the classroom (about 10 meters × 10 meters). Locate an area that is as natural as possible.
- Field guides to identify organisms
- Colored construction paper
- Graph paper (optional)
- Scissors
- Tape

Procedure

1. Prepare in your *Log* a data table as shown in Figure 2.23.

Figure 2.23

Sample data table for Guided Inquiry 2.5.

Number of Individuals Found in School Sample Area		
Trophic Level in Sample Area	Group Counts (numbers of individuals)	Class Averages (numbers of individuals)
Producer		
Herbivore		
Carnivore		
Scavenger		

2. Write a hypothesis that expresses what you expect to observe about this ecosystem on the basis of the different organisms that you find.

3. Form teams of four. Two members of each team will be responsible for producers, one for herbivores, and one for carnivores.

4. Prepare for a 10-minute scavenger hunt. Your teacher will tell you which area to explore. Follow your teacher's instructions for field trip safety.

5. Describe in your *Log* what you believe you will find in your area.

6. Make sure your entire team understands the following rules for the scavenger hunt:

   ◆ All teams will make their observations in the same 10m × 10m area.

   ◆ Teams will have exactly 10 minutes for observations and counting.

   ◆ Each member of the team will count as many individual organisms from the assigned trophic level as possible within the sample area. Duplicate observations do not count.

- Don't make assumptions about the trophic level of an organism. For example, just because you find an insect on a leaf doesn't mean that it is a herbivore. When in doubt, observe it, make a decision, and then ask your teacher.

- For the sake of simplicity, you can count each blade of grass or each tendril of ivy as a single organism. If there are repeated patterns of a plant, such as blades of grass, that cannot be counted quickly, count only one section of the area and multiply the number in the smaller section by the total area.

7. Collect data for your trophic level for 10 minutes. Identify the organisms, and make a note of their locations within the area.

8. When you return to the classroom, one person in class will draw on the chalkboard a table similar to the one you used in your *Log*. Record your group's data on this table. Find the class average for each trophic level.

9. Using different colors of construction paper, cut a rectangle representing the number of organisms that your group found at each trophic level. Let each organism be represented by a paper area of 1 square millimeter or 1 square centimeter. (You could also use a square on a page of graph paper.) Label each trophic level.

10. Construct a trophic level pyramid. Tape your rectangles together with producers at the bottom, herbivores on top of producers, and so on. Your diagram should resemble Figure 2.24.

11. Compare your pyramid with those of other groups and note any differences.

Trophic Levels

Tertiary consumers

Secondary consumers

Primary consumers

Producers

◄ **Energy content** ►
(can be estimated by biomass or number of organisms)

Figure 2.24

A sample trophic level pyramid.

Interpretations: Respond to the following in your *Log*:

1. By what fraction (in powers of 10) does the number of organisms decrease as you move up from one level to the next? Make a rough estimate.
2. Which trophic levels are missing from your food pyramid?
3. List some other names for secondary consumers and tertiary consumers.
4. How would you explain the ratio of producers to consumers that you found?

Applications: Respond to the following in your *Log*:

1. Where would you locate humans on the trophic pyramid?
2. On which level of the food pyramid would you find a vulture?
3. Where would you locate decomposers on the trophic pyramid? Which other organisms do they affect?

Trophic Levels

A trophic level diagram like the one you created or the one in Figure 2.24 illustrates how much energy can be transferred from level to level. The diagram also shows you that there is less biomass at each higher level. Because the trophic level diagram forms a pyramid-like shape, it is often called a food pyramid or ecological pyramid. Understanding trophic levels allows you to predict what might happen when there are too many or too few organisms at a particular level.

A food web or a food chain shows you how energy moves from the sun, to be transformed step by step, first by producers (plants), then by primary consumers (the plant eaters or herbivores), then by secondary consumers (animal eaters or carnivores), and so on. An organism can get its energy from more than one trophic level. Omnivores, for example, eat both plants and animals. Bears, pigs, and humans are all omnivores.

The organisms in a food web interact with each other and with the environment. Energy and matter are passed from one organism to another and used for metabolic processes and growth. The result is a community of interacting organisms. A community is the total of all organisms in an ecosystem, such as a forest, a log, an area of soil, a compost pile, a tiny pool of water, or a lake.

Each community of organisms has a unique trophic structure, which is described by its energy transfers. As you have seen, these structures represent available energy, but they also show the relationships among the different life forms. 🌍

Trophic Pyramids

The English ecologist Charles Elton was the first to display trophic structures in the form of pyramids. Elton created pyramids by drawing blocks for the organisms at each trophic level and then stacking them. The sizes of the blocks depended on features that could be counted or measured, such as numbers, biomass, or energy. Producers, which get their energy and biomass by using light or chemical energy, are always placed at the base of the pyramid because in nature they form the base of the food chain. Consumers get the energy they need to increase their biomass from other organisms. Therefore they are placed in higher tiers of the trophic pyramid.

Where are humans in a trophic pyramid? Does placement depend on diet? Do vegetarians occupy a different trophic level than meat eaters do?

You can display the trophic structure of a community in several different ways, depending on which feature of the community you are measuring (Figure 2.25). Each feature can be depicted in pyramid form. For example, you might use a pyramid to illustrate:

◆ the number of organisms at each trophic level;

◆ the total biomass (wet weight, dry weight, caloric value, or other measure of the total quantity of living organisms) at each trophic level;

◆ the rates of energy flow, in the form of food, through the food chain.

Ecological pyramids are just one example of how scientists use diagrams or models to help communicate ideas or enhance understanding.

How Do We Study Ecosystems?

You can study ecosystems by looking at three basic features:

◆ Major structural features such as the dominant species, life forms, or indicators

Grassland in summer
- Top carnivore
- Secondary consumers
- Consumers
- Producers

Number of organisms

Pyramid of numbers

Wisconsin Lake
- Secondary consumers
- Consumers
- Producers

Biomass
(grams dry weight/square meter)

Pyramid of biomass

Silver Springs, Florida
- Top carnivore
- Secondary consumers
- Consumers
- Producers

Energy flow
(Kcal/square meter/year)

Pyramid of energy flow

Figure 2.25

Trophic pyramids can be used to show biomass, number of organisms, or energy levels.

- ◆ Physical conditions of the ecosystem
- ◆ Functional characteristics such as the type of metabolism or dominant activity that takes place in the area (for example, photosynthesis, respiration, agricultural production, urban landscaping)

Ecosystem Functioning

How does an ecosystem function? That depends on how the organisms interact with physical conditions such as soil or water supply. A single species, or perhaps a group of species, can shape the ecosystem. These organisms, called dominants, may be the most numerous, or they may have the greatest biomass. Dominants may occupy the most space, they may make the greatest contribution to the flow of energy, or they might influence the rest of the community in some other way.

An ecosystem can also be drastically affected by small changes or by organisms that are not dominants in the ecosystem. For example, the fungus that causes the chestnut blight completely changed the makeup of hardwood forests in the eastern U.S. When European settlers first set foot on American shores, chestnut trees dominated the eastern forests. The chestnut blight fungus was discovered in a Japanese plant exhibit at the New York Botanical Gardens in 1904. Forty years later virtually every chestnut tree in the United States was dead (Figure 2.26). Now the only remnants of the chestnut are rare sprouts from dead tree trunks. Once the chestnut trees were gone, other trees took over their place in the ecosystem, which changed the species composition of the forests. Similar processes continue to occur. Gypsy moths and spruce budworms have affected hardwood and spruce forests. The first major damage due to gypsy moths was noticed in 1890. Western spruce budworm reached a peak, in terms of damage to the forests, in 1987. Both of these insects eat the leaves from the trees; without leaves, the trees are unable to photosynthesize, and they die. A severe gypsy moth infestation can destroy every leaf on a tree. Spruce budworm outbreaks have lasted for more than 25 years.

On the other hand, some organisms that aren't very numerous can help to maintain diversity among more numerous organisms. These organisms are called keystone species. For example, in the zone along the U.S. Pacific Ocean coastline, the starfish *Pisaster* is a keystone species because it preys on the dominant organism in the ecosystem, the mussel *Mytilus* (Figure 2.27).

Figure 2.26

A blight-infested chestnut tree in the early 1900s.

Figure 2.27

Pisaster *predation on* Mytilus.

Because the starfish keeps mussel populations small, there are more resources and space for 15 other types of animals. If the starfish were not present, the ecosystem could maintain only eight other types of organisms.

Introduced Exotics

Organisms that are introduced into an ecosystem where they are not native are called exotics. Such introductions can have drastic effects on the ecosystem. Zebra mussels are aquatic organisms that were native to western Russia. After canals were built in the 1700s and 1800s to connect bodies of water, the zebra mussels spread throughout Europe. In 1988, zebra mussels were discovered in the U.S. Great Lakes (Figure 2.28). They probably came from Europe in the bilge water of boats. They have spread rapidly and may soon be the dominant organism at the bottom of many lakes and streams. The presence of zebra mussels changes the way many aquatic ecosystems function because these organisms outcompete many native species for food and living space. They also restrict human uses of water by clogging pipes used to remove water for drinking, power generation, or industrial use.

Have you ever emptied the water from an aquarium into a lake or stream? This seems harmless enough, but you might have introduced a nonnative plant or animal into the water. This exotic, like the zebra mussel, might have an undesirable effect on the ecosystem of the lake or stream.

Zebra Mussel Sightings Distribution
Dreissena polymorpha

- Zebra mussel occurrences
- ☆ Zebra mussels trailered overland on boat hulls

Map produced by the U.S. Geological Survey, Gainesville, Florida, June 13, 2005.

Figure 2.28

This map shows the distribution of zebra mussels (Dreissena polymorpha) within the United States.

How can you predict the effects of adding or removing organisms from an ecosystem? How can you recognize such disturbances and their effects? How else do humans affect the ecosystems in which they live (Figure 2.29)? 🌏

Guided Inquiry 2.6

How Much Land Do You Need?

All organisms use energy. But how much energy does an organism need to stay alive? Producers, called autotrophs, use energy from the sun to make food. Consumers, or heterotrophs, obtain their energy from the food they eat. Thus energy moves from its source in the sun to the photosynthetic producers, which transform light energy into chemical energy (food), and eventually to the consumers. This process is outlined in Figure 2.30.

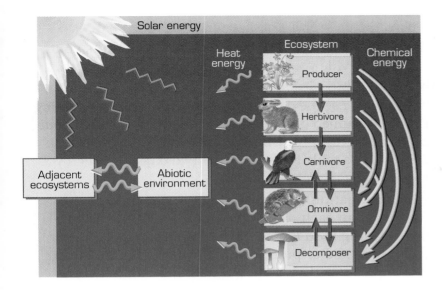

Figure 2.30

Energy flow in an ecosystem.

How much energy do you think a human requires? How much energy do you use? How different are the amounts of energy needed to produce the food for various types of diets? In this inquiry, you will calculate the amount of land area that you need to support your food energy needs for one year.

Food energy is usually measured in units of kilocalories. One kilocalorie is defined as the amount of heat energy needed to raise the temperature of one kilogram of water by 1°C. The food Calorie that diet books and food labels refer to is a kilocalorie (1,000 calories). Note that this food Calorie is always written with a capital C.

MATERIALS

- Food consumption information from Guided Inquiry 2.4
- Pencil
- Data collection sheets
- Computer and spreadsheet software program (optional)

- Food Calorie counter (See Appendix J, and use available books or computer programs.)
- Calculator

Procedure

1. Predict how much land area (in square meters) you think you would need to provide you with food for one year. Record this estimate in your *Log.*

2. Retrieve from your *Log* the data from Guided Inquiry 2.4 regarding the food you consumed during a 48-hour period. Create in your *Log* or on a computer spreadsheet a table similar to the one in Figure 2.31. Make a table for each of the two days for which you have food records.

3. Record the information about your food intake onto these tables. Try to assign each food to one or more of the listed categories. Reading food labels will be important as you try to assign some mixed or processed foods. For example, most salad dressings can be divided about half and half between vegetable oil and sugar. Potato chips may contain more fat than potato starch. Count everything that you ate, including snacks. Estimate the quantity of individual foods as ounces, cups, or pieces. (This is important.) Consult Appendix J for some hints.

4. Calculate the amount of Calories in each of the foods that you ate. Nutrition guides that include Calorie estimates are available as books, computer programs, and on sites such as the USDA's: www.mypyramid.gov that calculates Calories and nutrients for the food you eat and helps you set up a personal fitness plan.

5. Add the Calorie amounts for each food to determine the total number of Calories that you ate during your 48-hour data collection period.

6. To determine your average daily intake, divide the total number of Calories consumed for the two days by 2. Multiply this amount by 365 to estimate the total number of Calories you consume during a year. Record this value in your *Log.*

7. Create a table similar to the one in Figure 2.32 (see page 110) in your *Log* or on a computer spreadsheet. Use this table and your Calorie data to determine the amount of land required to support you. Determine your annual consumption of each type of food, and divide each of the values by the yield. Add all of the values in the square-meters-of-land column to arrive at the total land required to support you. Add the values in each subgroup (C3 plants, C4 plants, and animal products).

8. Calculate a class average for the square meters of land required to support each of you for one year. Are you surprised? How does this compare to your prediction? Record your responses in your *Log.*

Ecosystems

You Are What You Eat*

Food	Breakfast	Lunch	Dinner	Between Meals	Total
Bread					
Wheat cereal					
Citrus fruits					
Orange juice					
Coffee					
Tea					
Peanut butter					
Rice or rice cereal					
Potatoes					
Carrots, other vegetables					
Apples, other fruits					
Vegetable oil					
Margarine					
Beet sugar					
Cane sugar					
Soft drinks					
Corn cereal					
Sweet corn					
Milk					
Cheese					
Eggs					
Chicken					
Pork					
Beef					
Tuna					
Perch					
Shrimp					
Total	**Your 24-hour gross energy intake** _____ **kcal**				

*Record kilocalories (= Calories) if possible. If not, record servings or weights, and later convert to kilocalories.

Figure 2.31

How Much Land?

Food	Your Annual Consumption (Cal./year)	Yield (Cal./m²/yr)	Square Meters of Land Required to Support You (Consumption ÷ Yield)
C3 Plants			
Bread	_____	650	_____
Wheat cereal	_____	810	_____
Oranges, grapefruit	_____	1000	_____
Frozen orange juice	_____	410	_____
Coffee	_____	4	_____
Tea	_____	40	_____
Peanut butter	_____	920	_____
Rice or rice cereal	_____	1250	_____
Potatoes	_____	1600	_____
Carrots	_____	810	_____
Other vegetables	_____	200	_____
Apples	_____	1500	_____
Pears, peaches	_____	900	_____
Vegetable oil	_____	300	_____
Margarine	_____	300	_____
Beet sugar	_____	1990	_____
C4 Plants			
Cane sugar	_____	3500	_____
Soft drinks	_____	3500	_____
Corn cereal	_____	1600	_____
Sweet corn	_____	250	_____
Animal Products			
Milk	_____	420	_____
Cheese	_____	40	_____
Eggs	_____	200	_____
Chicken	_____	190	_____
Pork	_____	190	_____
Beef (feedlot)	_____	130	_____
Frozen fish fillets	_____	2	_____

Figure 2.32

9. Calculate the amount of land that is required to support five billion people at your level of Caloric intake. How much productive land is available on the earth? Is it enough?

Interpretations: Respond to the following in your *Log:*

1. How many Calories did you consume during one day?
2. How many square meters of land do you need to support your average daily Caloric intake for one year?
3. How many square meters of land are needed to produce the food for an individual who consumes 3,000 Calories a day? How much productive land would be required to support five billion people at this level of Caloric intake? How does this value compare to the one you calculated in step 9 (above).

   There are one millon (10^6) square meters in one square kilometer. Convert your answer in #2 to square kilometers.
4. If you can have two harvests per year on your land, how much land is needed to support you for one year?
5. Assume that each of your family members consumes the same number of Calories as you do. How much land would you need to support your family for a year?
6. Assume that each of your classmates consumes the same number of Calories as you do. How much land is needed to support your class for one year?

Applications: Respond to the following in your *Log*:

1. Describe an area near your school or home that is about the size needed to provide food for your class for one year.
2. Describe areas in your community that would be large enough to support (a) you, (b) your family, and (c) your class.
3. Japan had a human population of about 128 million in 2006. Its people enjoy one of the highest standards of living in the world. The entire country has an area of 374,744 square kilometers. Only 13 percent of this land is suitable for growing food crops. If each person needs 3,000 Calories a day, how much land would be needed to support the population of Japan?
4. Compare the amount of land per person in Japan to the amount of land you need to support your Caloric intake. How do these estimates differ?
5. How do you suppose the Japanese survive with so little land?
6. How does the number of calories you consume compare to what you need?

Figure 2.33

Per capita consumption of grain, meat, and dairy products in the U.S., Italy, China, and India.

Human Calorie Consumption

Humans have the same biological energy needs as do other animals. We need energy to grow to adulthood, to maintain our bodies, and to reproduce. Much of the energy we consume in the form of food is used to maintain our bodies' metabolic processes. Adult humans require 11 (female) to 12 (male) Calories per day to maintain each pound of their body mass (24–26 Calories per kg). The 2,000 Calorie diet referred to on most food labels would maintain an adult male weighing about 168 pounds (76 kilograms) or an adult female weighing about 181 pounds (82 kilograms).

Individuals in industrialized societies consume more food than humans in the rest of the world do. Look at Figure 2.33. How does total food consumption and the amount of each type of food vary in these countries? Individuals in industrialized countries consume 45 percent of the world's beef and veal. In these countries, annual consumption of beef and veal is 27 kilograms per person. Compare this with the 4.3 kilograms consumed in a year by each individual in developing countries. North Americans currently consume approximately 130 percent of their basic Calorie requirements. What if everyone on the earth consumed this much food? What is the result of taking in more food than you need? 🌐

Guided Inquiry 2.7

Revisiting Life in the Compost

Remember the compost columns and pile that you set up in Guided Inquiry 1.2? Each one is a model ecosystem. When you examined the microscopic life in your compost pile at the end of Unit 1, the compost was only about three weeks old. A lot has happened in your compost since then. Now is a good time to examine the whole range of organisms in your pile. You will probably find a host of microorganisms, such as bacteria and fungi, as well as macroorganisms, such as worms and insects.

MATERIALS

- Compost
- Plastic beaker or other tall container to measure 50 to 100 milliliters
- Cheesecloth or window screening
- White enamel or plastic pan (approximately 8 × 13 inches)

- Distilled water
- Forceps
- Compound and dissecting microscopes
- Alcohol solution and a plastic jar (optional)

Procedure

1. Take a sample (about 50 to 100 milliliters) from the center of your compost pile.

2. Place the compost sample on the window screening or cheese-cloth in the white pan.

3. Gently pour distilled water over the compost, washing the soil and smaller particles out and retaining the larger particles and macroorganisms on the screen.

4. Using forceps, place each organism, one at a time, on the stage of a dissecting microscope. Observe the smaller organisms on a microscope slide using a compound microscope.

5. Sketch each organism in your *Log*. (If possible, group similar organisms, and draw only a representative of each type.)

6. Compare your drawings to those in the compost food web (Figure 1.30 on page 43) and in Figure 2.34 on page 114. Which of the pictured types of organisms did you find? List these in your *Log*.

7. Count each type of organism you find.

SAFETY NOTE

- Wear **safety goggles.**
- Wear **gloves** and a **surgical mask** when handling compost.
- If you are allergic to molds, discuss your involvement with your teacher before beginning.
- Alcohol can be flammable and irritating to eyes and other tissues. Follow teacher's instructions for use of fire equipment and assure adequate ventilation of the room.
- Wash hands before leaving the lab.

Figure 2.34

How many of these common organisms can you find in your compost?

8. (*Optional*) Preserve all of the organisms by covering them with 70 percent alcohol solution and storing them in a dark place in a plastic sealed jar. Save this sample for Guided Inquiry 8.4.

9. Dispose of debris and clean up as indicated by your teacher.

Interpretations: Respond to the following in your *Log:*

1. What organisms are most common in your sample? How do you explain this?

2. What organisms do you believe are very abundant, even though you cannot observe them with the available instruments?

3. Make a diagram that includes all the organisms you observed in your pile. Draw arrows to indicate the direction of food energy flow. Research the feeding habits of some of the organisms, using *Compost Critters* by Bianca Lavies (1993) or a similar resource.

4. How do the organisms in your sample compare with those found by other students?

Applications: Respond to the following in your *Log:*

1. Research how each of the compost organisms that you found functions in the process of decomposition.

2. What forms of life might you expect to find in a compost pile in a garden?

Collecting and Analyzing Your Biomass Data

Let's return now to the biomass experiment that you set up in Guided Inquiry 2.1 at the beginning of this unit. Your corn and bean plants have grown and are ready to be measured. Remember, you wanted to find out how soil type affected biomass production. You can use the techniques that you learned as a basic tool to explore the following:

What can be done to make it possible for plants to grow again in the Copper Basin?

MATERIALS

- Plants grown in Guided Inquiry 2.1
- Balance
- Water
- Paper towels
- Gloves
- Dust mask

Procedure

1. Gently pull the six plants out of the soil, keeping the roots intact. Wash off the soil particles. Gently pat the roots dry with a paper towel.

2. Mass each plant to determine the wet biomass. Record these biomass values in a table in your *Log.*

3. As a class, record all of your collected biomass data in a single table.

4. From this class table, calculate the mean value for the biomass of the corn and of the bean plants grown in each of the three types of soil.

5. Construct a histogram of class data in your *Log.* Figure 2.35 on page 116 shows a sample histogram.

SAFETY NOTE

- It is best to wear **surgical gloves** and a **mask** when handling soils that may be rich in molds and fungi.
- Wash hands before leaving the lab.

Figure 2.35

A hypothetical sample histogram of plant biomass. You should not expect your plants to produce these results.

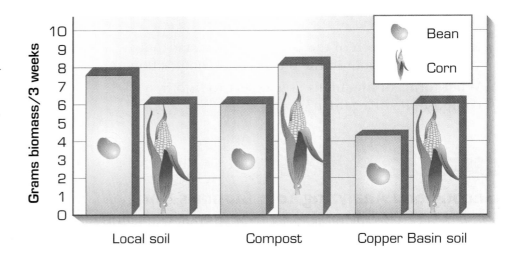

Interpretations: Discuss the following questions in your group. As homework, write responses in your *Log*:

1. Compare the data on the different soil and plant types in your histograms. What trends are evident?
2. What is the origin of the new mass accumulated by the plants? What is being added to the plants that is not readily visible?
3. What is taken into plants and what is given off by the plants as they grow?
4. Comment on the experiment's design. Review the independent, dependent, and controlled variables.
5. What variables could you not control, even though you may have tried?
6. Write a definition of a controlled experiment.
7. Describe an experiment that would test one idea that you generated during this inquiry.

Applications: Respond to the following in your *Log*:

Most of the mass of an organism is, of course, water. Assume that 90 percent of your seeds and resulting plants are water. Calculate their dry masses. Use a table like Figure 2.36 for your final dry mass estimations.

Figure 2.36

Sample table for dry biomass of plants in different soils from Guided Inquiry 2.8.

	Copper Basin	Compost	Local	Average for All Soil
Corn				
Bean				

Self-Check 1

By the time you complete most of the Guided Inquiries in this unit, you should have some understanding of ecosystems and how they operate. This self-check is designed to help you find out how much you understand.

Form groups of four students. Each student in your group should select and answer three of the following questions. No two people in a group should choose the same question. As resources, use the work you did on the Guided Inquiries, your *Log* notes, and books in the classroom or library. Your teacher will guide you if you need help. You may want to work in advance on some answers as homework.

1. What have you learned from the Copper Basin experience about the removal and use of natural resources?

2. How is light important for photosynthesis?

3. What is the relationship between light and chemical energy?

4. What happens to the energy that is transformed in photosynthesis?

5. What are the reactants and the products of photosynthesis?

6. How does photosynthesis cause mass to increase in plants?

7. State the first and second laws of thermodynamics, and describe an example of how they are applied to living systems.

8. Describe the components of an energy pyramid.

9. Explain the shape of an energy pyramid.

10. What happens to energy as it flows through an ecosystem?

11. Explain the concept of an ecosystem.

12. Describe examples of natural and artificial ecosystems.

When everyone in your group has reasonable answers to his or her questions, come together as a group and let each member share answers with the entire group. As a group, you should then discuss and evaluate the completeness of each answer and modify it as necessary. Everyone in the group should eventually have a complete set of answers to all questions.

During the Guided Inquiry activities, you collected data from a number of sources. Now each of you need to produce an abstract. This abstract should include organized presentations of the data from each experiment, your interpretations of the data, and your suggestions for what needs to be investigated next. Include graphs, as appropriate, as part of your presentation. See page 62 for some ideas.

Present your abstract to your group. Each presentation should take about five minutes.

After you have discussed your presentations, brainstorm with your group a specific problem to investigate further and solve. The problem that you choose may be a continuation of the Copper Basin scenario. You may choose to investigate a local land or water degradation case and find possible solutions. If you are still investigating topics from Unit 1, consider incorporating the work you did for that unit as the problem you select.

As a class, identify additional inquiries needed to explore the problem. Then choose, individually or as members of a small group, one or more inquiries to fully design and carry out on your own. If you work with a group, be sure each member is assigned a specific part of the experiment. Your extended research on these inquiries will help in finding resolutions to present to the class at the Congress.

This is your opportunity to further explore ecosystem topics that especially interest you. You may extend your studies of the Copper Basin ecosystem or apply what you have learned about ecosystem damage and restoration to a local situation. If you have decided to continue with the Copper Basin scenario, then your Extended Inquiries will further investigate that problem. A number of other investigations are suggested here. If you prefer to investigate a local problem, the suggestions here will provide direction, but you should tailor your project to your local environment and needs.

Extended Inquiry 2.1

The Lorax

Do you think it is possible to use so much of a resource that no more is available? Can use or overuse of another species cause that species to become extinct? Can environmental resources be wisely used so that there will always be something left for the future?

MATERIALS

- *The Lorax* by Dr. Seuss (book or video)

Procedure

Read the book or watch the 30-minute video of the Dr. Seuss story *The Lorax*. Identify, through discussion, the major events and themes in the story, both obvious and hidden. Think about how *The Lorax* relates to the Copper Basin scenario. In your *Log*, write your thoughts and reflections on the story.

Interpretations: Respond to the following in your *Log*:

1. Briefly describe what happens in *The Lorax*. Include descriptions of the activities of the Once-ler, the Lorax, the Truffula trees, the Brown Bar-ba-loots, Thneeds, the Once-ler's relatives, and the last Truffula seed.
2. Why do the animals have to leave this ecosystem after the Truffula trees are destroyed?
3. Whom might each of the characters in the story represent in your own community?
4. Why don't you ever see the face of the Once-ler?

Applications: Respond to the following in your *Log*:

1. Describe a real-life situation that has occurred in your community or in your state that resembles the story of *The Lorax*.

2. Some people think that this story is just propaganda. Discuss why they might think that way. What do you think?

3. Are there identifiable "good guys" and "bad guys" in this story? Where do the people who purchase and use Thneeds fit on a good-to-bad scale?

4. How could you save the Truffula ecosystem without completely ending the cutting of Truffula trees?

5. (*Optional*) Graph the change in the number of species over time, and compare it to the decrease in Truffula tree abundance.

Extended Inquiry 2.2

Stomate Research

Stomates are openings in the leaves of green plants (Figure 2.37). They open and close to allow carbon dioxide to enter the leaves and oxygen to go out into the atmosphere. Plants also lose water vapor through open stomates. Environmental factors such as air temperature and humidity may affect the number of stomates on a leaf or the amount of time the stomates are

Microscope photo of stomate with scale superimposed.

Pore

Epidermal cells of lower leaf surface

Guard cells

Figure 2.37

Stomates in the epidermis of a leaf.

open. Plants that live in hot, dry climates usually have fewer stomates, especially on the upper surfaces of the leaves.

Count the stomates on a leaf surface according to the following procedures. Then develop and conduct a research project about stomate density, that is, how closely the stomates are spaced on the leaf surfaces.

MATERIALS

- Fresh green leaves
- Forceps
- Compound microscope
- Microscope slides and plastic coverslips
- Water

Procedure

1. Tear the leaves at an angle so the edges show a white or colorless area projecting beyond the green leaf. This is the epidermis. Note in your *Log* whether it is the upper or lower epidermis.

2. Use forceps to remove a portion of the epidermis for microscope viewing.

3. Count the number of stomates in a microscope field. Refer to Appendix D to review how to calculate the area of a microscope field.

4. Using this information, calculate the density of stomates on the leaf epidermis. Record this in your *Log*.

Interpretations: Record the following information in your *Log:*

1. Describe and draw in your *Log* a single stomate that you observed. Record the type of leaf from which this stomate was obtained. See Appendix G for hints on making scientific drawings.

2. How many stomates did you count in a single microscope field? Be sure to note the magnification you used.

Applications: Design your own Inquiry to investigate some aspect of stomate density. For example:

◆ Compare the stomate density on the upper and lower surfaces of leaves from a single plant.

◆ Explore the number and arrangement of stomates on leaves from bean and corn plants.

◆ Explore the number and arrangement of stomates on the upper or lower surfaces of leaves from plants grown in different environments (for example, at various temperatures or humidities).

Investigating an Ecosystem

Ecological systems may be named for their major physical, biological, or functional features. For example, biologists often refer to forest ecosystems, soil ecosystems, or pond ecosystems. They also talk about urban or agricultural ecosystems.

In this inquiry, you will survey an ecosystem. This is one of the fastest ways to observe ecological systems. This activity is best done as homework.

MATERIALS

- Plastic gloves
- Magnifying glass or hand lens
- Tongs
- Small plastic bags
- Taxonomy books and guides
- Plant presses and insect collection materials
- *BioLogs*

- Consult with your teacher concerning poisonous or allergy-causing plants to avoid.
- Avoid stinging, biting insects (e.g., bees, hornets) and ticks, lice, and some spiders; they can be toxic or infection vectors.

Procedure

1. Identify a small but well-defined area to study. For example, choose an area of a park or yard that is 5–10 square meters.
2. Identify the most visible features of the area.
3. Classify the ecosystem by its dominant features, plants, animals, and physical features.
4. Give a descriptive name to this area, perhaps based on the dominant life forms or physical activities of the area (such as forest ecosystem, urban ecosystem, agricultural ecosystem, or school ecosystem).
5. Estimate the area of your ecosystem in square meters. Estimate the size of the larger ecosystem of which it is a part.
6. Identify the dominant living components, or communities, of the ecosystem. If you cannot immediately identify the name of an organism, give it a descriptive name and write enough information in your *Log* for later identification.
7. If possible, collect representative samples of the living components of the community and preserve them for reference.

Interpretations: Respond to the following in your *Log*:

1. Review the information on typical biomes in Appendix I, and identify the biome in which your study area is located.

2. Biomes are essentially determined by two physical factors: precipitation and temperature. What are the characteristic rainfall and temperature patterns in your biome? For example, does it rain all year or only during a portion of the year? Does the temperature vary greatly during the year, or is there only a small difference in temperature between winter and summer?

3. What are the dominant plants? How did you decide that they were dominant?

4. What are the dominant animals? How did you decide that they were dominant?

Applications: Respond to the following in your *Log*:

1. Biomes can also be characterized by graphs of temperature and precipitation called climatograms. Figure 2.38 shows several climatograms that are typical of different biomes. Which is closest to your biome? Explain why.

2. Make a climatogram, such as those in Figure 2.38, for the biome in which you live.

3. In which biome would you like to live? What makes it desirable?

4. Which biome(s) probably contain the greatest number(s) of humans? Why?

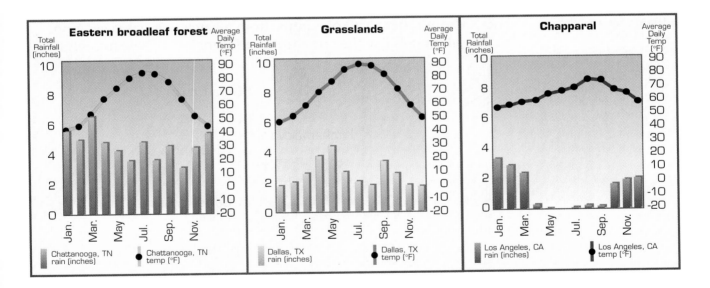

Figure 2.38

Climatograms describe a biome's environmental conditions by displaying mean monthly precipitation and temperature. These data are available at:
http://www.met.utah.edu/html/normrain.html
http://www.met.utah.edu/html/normtemp.html

Extension Studies on the Copper Basin

Investigate one or more of the following characteristics of the Tennessee Copper Basin. As you design and implement each study, create and answer your own Interpretations and Application questions.

1. Copper Basin Soils

Select one of the following variables. Design and perform an experiment that examines the effects of that factor on plant growth.

- ◆ A variable that you think might influence plant growth
- ◆ Acidity (pH level) of the soil
- ◆ Soil water capacity (the amount of water the soil can hold)
- ◆ Soil particle size
- ◆ Diversity of organisms in the ecosystem
- ◆ Amount of humus in soil

2. Copper Basin Diversity

Alcohol is flammable and irritating to the eyes and other human tissue. Follow the directions provided for use by your teacher.

Design and perform an experiment that examines the differences in biodiversity in the soil of the Copper Basin, or a similarly bare area of ground, and a sample of soil from an area with vegetation. Use the simulated Copper Basin soil remaining from Guided Inquiry 2.1, or collect soil from a local area that lacks vegetation. (See your teacher for assistance.) Use another local soil sample from an area that has vegetation. Set up soil funnels like the one shown in Figure 2.39. These funnels help

Figure 2.39

A soil funnel for collecting soil microorganisms.

to drive soil invertebrates into collecting jars of 70 percent alcohol. Then, using a microscope or hand lens, count the numbers and types of organisms you find in each type of soil. Identify the different types of organisms, or simply draw or describe them. Design a table in which to record the results of your data. What conclusions can you draw about the differences between bare or Copper Basin soil and vegetation-covered soil?

3. How to Restore Copper Basin Soil

Design and perform an experiment that examines how changes to the Copper Basin soil affect plant growth. Possible additions to the soil might be:

◆ Nitrogen (as ammonium nitrate) fertilizer
◆ Phosphorus (as phosphate) fertilizer
◆ Organic material (compost from your compost pile)

4. Library Research

For the Copper Basin or another area such as Sudbury, Ontario, Canada, research one or more of the following topics:

◆ Land degradation due to wind or water erosion
◆ Land restoration
◆ Acid rain or soil pH in general
◆ Strip mining
◆ Ore mining and processing

Whichever of these extensions of your Copper Basin research you choose, you should do the following:

◆ Maintain notes on your research in your *Log*.
◆ Prepare a report for the class. This report can be oral or written, a poster, a scrapbook, or another form of communication.

Extended Inquiry 2.5

Local Problems

Select a local problem to investigate. Consider one of the following projects:

◆ Survey the organisms in a specific ecosystem.
◆ Research the use of lichens as indicators of air pollution.
◆ Research leaf yeasts as indicators of air pollution.
◆ Find out how local water quality testing is done.
◆ Investigate ecosystem characteristics such as seed germination, plant growth, and trophic levels.

Non-Point Source Pollution

To envision non-point source (NPS) pollution, just think about what happens each time it rains. Water flows over lawns, agricultural fields, parking lots, buildings, and all other natural and human-made structures. As the water flows, it picks up dirt, trash, nutrients, small organisms, and toxic wastes. All of this runoff eventually pours into lakes, streams, rivers, and oceans or seeps into the groundwater. Thus all of our water sources are affected by this pollution (Figure 2.40).

Why should we worry about this? NPS pollution accounts for more than half of the water pollution in the United States. Environmental protection regulations that have been enacted since the 1970s have effectively reduced point source contamination from industrial plants and sewage treatment facilities. Non-point source pollution is far more difficult to control because the sources are so diffuse.

What is the ultimate source of NPS pollution? *You* are! Every time you wash your car or fertilize your lawn, you contribute to the problem. This doesn't mean that you need to completely change your lifestyle. Responsible and educated personal decisions can drastically reduce NPS pollution and improve the quality of the water that we all use.

Phosphorus is an important component of NPS pollution. Humans and human activities are responsible for most of the phosphorus in runoff. The per capita amount of phosphorus that is generated in the biome depends on the amount and type of food that the population consumes and the amount of household waste flushed through the system. For example,

Figure 2.40

Non-point sources of pollution.

Exhaust from furnaces and factories

Sewage (treated and untreated)

Discharge of detergents

Street and lawn runoff

Agricultural runoff (from manure and cultivation)

Car exhaust

Natural runoff

Ecosystems

soaps and detergents that contain phosphorus increase the total amount of phosphorus in household wastewater. Most states have banned the use of phosphate detergents to reduce phosphorus NPS pollution.

You can estimate the amount of phosphorus contributed by each person in your biomap area. Multiply the number of people by the amount of phosphorus that one person produces. Several studies in North America and Europe found that the domestic sewage (excrement plus household wastes) produced by one person each year contains approximately 0.80 kilogram of phosphorus. 🌐

Studies on Non-Point Source Water Pollution

Where does non-point source water pollution occur in your community? For this inquiry, explore the types and sources of NPS pollution in your community.

Procedure

1. Look for potential problems of runoff into local lakes and streams.

2. When there is a rainstorm, observe and note in your *Log* the actual sites where most of the runoff occurs.

3. Prepare a report that describes existing and potential NPS problems.

4. As a class and/or with representatives of your community, brainstorm methods for reducing non-point source pollution.

Interpretations: Respond to the following in your *Log*:

1. Define the watershed drainage area, and identify the rivers and streams that receive the runoff.

2. Identify the types of water pollutants that are associated with the land uses and activities on the watershed. Which of these materials drain into the river through a pipe, and which travel through the soil and materials of the watershed?

Applications: Arrange one of the following expeditions:

1. Take a field trip to observe point and non-point source pollution problems in your community. If a field trip is not possible, seek a representative of an appropriate local or state agency to discuss this issue in person or by phone.

2. Take a trip to a sewage treatment facility to learn about how your municipal wastes are handled. Determine how the wastes are treated (primary, secondary, or tertiary treatment) and where the treated wastes are discharged.

What if all government air and water quality standards were eliminated? What standards would individuals, industries, and municipalities maintain? Who would decide what level of quality was appropriate?

Energy in Biomass

How much energy is in biomass? How much energy did your bean and corn plants from Guided Inquiry 2.8 acquire? For this inquiry, you will calculate the energy coming into an ecosystem and its conversion into biomass. You will investigate and compare two different photosynthetic pathways for that energy conversion.

MATERIALS

- Calculator
- Data from Guided Inquiry 2.8 on page 115

Procedure

1. Calculate the biomass of the corn and bean plants in Calories, as shown in Figure 2.41. Assume that the energy value of plant material equals 4 kilocalories per gram of dry weight. (4 kilocalories per gram is the Caloric value for both carbohydrates and proteins.)

Figure 2.41

Calculation of Calorie biomass from Guided Inquiry 2.8.

	Average (all soils) Wet Biomass (per plant)	×	4 Calories Per Gram	=	Energy Content (in calories)
Corn					
Bean					

2. Read "C3 and C4 Pathways." Then use this information to help you analyze your data. Respond to the following questions in your *Log*:
   a. Which plants—beans or corn—were able to produce more energy biomass?
   b. Which plants—beans or corn—use C3, and which use C4 photosynthesis pathways?
   c. Does this mean that one type of plant is more efficient than the other? Explain.
   d. How could the differences in efficiency be related to C3 or C4 pathways?
   e. If you had to live for an extended period of time on either corn or bean seeds, which would you choose? Why?
   f. What else did you learn from this experiment?
   g. What questions remain?
   h. How could you design an experiment that would answer one of your remaining questions?

C3 and C4 Pathways

C3 Plants

Plants use carbon dioxide (CO_2) from the atmosphere for photosynthesis. Many plants can't photosynthesize when they have too little carbon dioxide.

Plants that need higher concentrations of CO_2 are called C3 plants; a sugar that contains three carbon atoms is the first molecule formed in the dark reaction of photosynthesis. In C3 plants, photosynthesis stops when carbon dioxide concentrations in the leaves drop just a little below normal. The beans that you grew in Guided Inquiries 2.1 and 2.8 are C3 plants.

Why do carbon dioxide concentrations decrease? Plants obtain gases through openings in the leaf surfaces known as stomates. (See Extended Inquiry 2.2, page 120.) When plants are subjected to very hot, dry conditions, stomates close. This action prevents water loss from the leaves. When the stomates close, carbon dioxide from the atmosphere can't enter the leaves. Oxygen (O_2) produced in photosynthesis builds up in the leaves.

C3 plants don't photosynthesize when there is too little carbon dioxide or too much oxygen. On very hot, dry, sunny days, or in the dry tropics, photosynthesis is likely to stop. These plants could continue to photosynthesize under these conditions if they had a method for using low concentrations of carbon dioxide.

C4 Plants

C4 plants are so named because the first sugar that is formed in photosynthesis has four carbon atoms. One example of a C4 plant is corn (Figure 2.42). C4 plants have a distinct advantage over C3 plants when they are grown under hot, dry, sunny conditions. In C4 plants, the molecule that first attaches to carbon dioxide is extremely efficient in using carbon dioxide, even at low concentrations. Thus C4 plants have an advantage when carbon

Figure 2.42

Corn is a C4 plant.

Figure 2.43

Beans are C3 plants.

dioxide is in low supply. They also have an advantage in dry climates in which stomates must be kept closed for much of the day to retain water. Under these conditions, carbon dioxide from the atmosphere cannot get into leaves.

Think about where and when corn grows. What does its being a C4 plant (see Figure 2.43) say about its usual growing conditions? Beans and most other broad-leaved plants are C3 plants. What growing conditions should be best for beans? How does this information affect your interpretation of the plant biomass you obtained in Guided Inquiry 2.1, "Determining Biomass," on page 78, and Guided Inquiry 2.8, "Collecting and Analyzing Your Biomass Data," on page 115? 🌏

Extended Inquiry 2.8

Networking to Acquire Information

Consider networking with other high school students in the United States who are working on the Copper Basin problem. Networking is an excellent technique for comparing ecosystems. Perhaps you can set up a conference on the Internet to share data. Or you might network via telecommunications or by regular mail. A good technique for mail networking is to prepare boxes containing samples of the items in your ecosystem and then exchange boxes with students in other parts of your state or the country.

Self-Check 2

ow that you have completed several Extended Inquiries, you should have some additional understanding about ecosystems and related issues in your community. You should also have new insights about how science works in society. This self-check is designed to help you find out how much of the material you understand.

Form groups of four students. Each student in your group should select and answer two of the following questions. No two students in a group should answer the same question. As resources, use the work you did on the Guided Inquiries and Extended Inquiries, your *Log* notes, and books in the classroom or library. You may want to work in advance on some answers for homework.

1. What is a variable, and why are we concerned with variables in scientific experiments?

2. Explain the relationship between cause and effect variables.

3. What purposes do controls serve in an experiment?

4. Compare the amount of land that is needed to feed an affluent American with the amount that is needed to support an Asian farmer at a minimal level.

5. Why must humans protect and preserve environmental resources that are used for human benefit?

6. Why would organic farming, which does not rely on intensive fertilizers, be less stressful to the soil?

7. Explain the role of each of the following processes in the quest for knowledge: predicting, hypothesizing, collecting data, organizing data, analyzing data, and inferring from data.

8. Why is communicating new findings to peers an important part of science?

Congress

This Congress is a planning session for the Forum, which is an imaginary court case about the Copper Basin. In this Forum, a coalition of conservation groups has instituted a class action suit against the copper company that was involved in the devastation of the Copper Basin.

With the help of your teacher, each student will choose a participant role from the list of characters. Decide which person you would like to represent. You will need to be well prepared for your day in court. Remain as true as possible to the character you are playing, but you can invent details and think of your own arguments as the case progresses.

Research your role by consulting your *Log*, reading reference material, or interviewing people in your community. Become knowledgeable about your point of view. This preparation may require several days of work outside of the classroom.

With your group, compile information in a briefing document to argue your side at the trial. Focus on the biological evidence. Present your position to your group for initial feedback. Anticipate your opponents' positions and arguments. How will you counter your opponents' arguments?

Cast of Characters

Defendants:

◆ Copper industry, CEO (Chief Executive Officer) of Copper, Inc.

Plaintiffs:

◆ Coalition of local environmental groups
◆ Active member, Sierra Club

- Active member, National Wildlife Federation
- Active member, Audubon Society
- Active member, Nature Conservancy

Defense:
- Local attorney, with up to three assistants

Prosecution:
- Local Assistant District Attorney, with up to one assistant

Jury:
(Fill completely if the class is large enough; half this number is still adequate.)
- Foreperson, homemaker with children (male or female)
- Member, postal worker
- Member, sheep rancher
- Member, commercial artist
- Member, high school principal
- Member, homemaker
- Member, computer programmer
- Member, nurse
- Member, restaurant owner
- Member, incinerator operator
- Member, unemployed
- Member, day laborer

Judge:
- District Circuit Judge, former district attorney

Expert Witnesses:
- Forester
- Economist
- Agricultural engineer
- Metallurgist
- Watershed analyst
- Botanist
- Biologist (played by your teacher)
- Chemist
- Sociologist
- Hydrologist

A DAY IN COURT

This will be a standard courtroom setting. Everyone must be well prepared, as courtroom time is very limited. (A criminal trial will commence in this courtroom in exactly one hour.) The prosecution has 15 minutes to present the case to the court, including the calling of witnesses. The defense also has a total of 15 minutes. The judge must give the jury appropriate instructions to be objective and to reach a decision in no more than 15 minutes. The foreperson of the jury announces the verdict. The judge then issues the sentence and/or fines or releases the defendants, if they are found not guilty.

Your teacher will give you the evaluation criteria for the Forum.

Homework

Reflect on the arguments presented at the trial, and respond to the following in your *Log*:

- ◆ Why do you think the jury reached its decision?
- ◆ What evidence was most convincing?
- ◆ If this trial were held again, what additional evidence would you seek?
- ◆ How might this new evidence change the jury's decision?

Summary of Major Concepts

1. The devastation of the Tennessee Copper Basin is an example of humans using the environment without considering the long-term results.

2. Biomass is a measure of the total amount of living matter in a system.

3. Light energy from the sun is captured by plants during photosynthesis, transformed to chemical energy, and stored as carbohydrates. Photosynthesis uses carbon dioxide and water, releases oxygen, and produces sugars. As plants grow, they increase in mass primarily because of the carbon dioxide taken from the air and water taken from the ground, both of which have been reconfigured into carbohydrates.

4. Energy can be neither created nor destroyed. It can be transformed from one form to another, such as from solar to chemical energy. The flow of energy through an ecosystem is inefficient. Most of the energy is lost as heat.

5. The element nitrogen cycles through producers and consumers in an ecosystem. Nitrogen is important for growth because it is an essential component of proteins.

6. An ecosystem contains interacting populations of organisms and their nonliving environment.

7. An energy pyramid shows the decreasing amounts of energy that are available to producers, primary consumers, and secondary consumers as energy flows through the ecosystem.

8. Because of principles based on the energy pyramid, a relatively large amount of land is required to support the food needs of one human.

9. Science tries to identify cause-and-effect relationships. In experiments, this is often done by manipulating an independent variable and measuring the dependent variable.

10. Communication of experimental results is an important part of the scientific process. Findings are upheld (or overturned) by scrutiny from peers.

11. Cause variables are those that make something happen. Effect variables are the results that are produced by causes.

12. Controls are the parts of an experiment that are kept the same so that whatever results occur can be explained by one cause variable.

13. The home range of an animal describes the geographic area where that animal lives, eats, and reproduces.

14. There are many reasons to protect and preserve our environment. One important reason is to make sure the earth's resources will be available to future generations.

15. Inquiry usually involves processes such as predicting, hypothesizing, collecting data, organizing data, analyzing data, and inferring from data.

16. Compost changes significantly over time, both in size and in the types of organisms that inhabit it.

Suggestions for Further Exploration

Baskin, R.M. 1991. *How Many Calories: How Much Fat?: Guide to Calculating the Nutritional Content of the Foods You Eat.* Consumer Reports Books, Yonkers, N.Y.

Includes tables of fat and caloric content of foods.

Clay, G. 1983. Copper Basin cover-up. *Landscape Architecture,* 73(6), 49–55, 94.

Looks at historical record of Copper Basin environmental injury and reclamation efforts.

———. 1990. *Food values: Calories.* Harper & Row, New York.

Contains tables of caloric content of foods.

Geisel, T.S. (Dr. Seuss). 1971. *The Lorax.* Random House, N.Y

A classic children's story that illustrates environmental injury caused by overusage of materials in an ecosystem. Also available on videotape.

Global Lab Project. 1991. *Leaf Yeasts as Bioindicators of Air Quality.* Technology Education Research Corporation.

Global Lab Project. 1991. *Lichen Investigations.* Technology Education Research Corporation.

Gore, A., 1993. *Earth in the Balance: Ecology and the Human Spirit.* Penguin Books, New York.

An overview of the state of global ecology aimed at the general public. Includes examples of citizen involvement in improving ecosystems.

Lavies, B. 1993. *Compost Critters.* Dutton Children's Books, New York.

Describes what happens in a compost pile and how creatures, from bacteria and mites to millipedes and earthworms, aid in the process of turning compost into humus.

Ludyanskiy, M.L., et al. 1993. Impact of the zebra mussel, a bivalve invader. *BioScience,* 43(8), 533–544.

A technical article detailing the life cycle and chronology of the invasion of the exotic organism Dreissena *(zebra mussel). Includes negative environmental and industrial impacts and control strategies.*

Muncy, J.A. 1986. *A Plan for Revegetation Completion of Tennessee's Copper Basin.* Technical Note B59, Land Reclamation/SCOAP Program, Division of Land and Economic Resources, Tennessee Valley Authority, Norris, Tennessee 37828.

Odum, E.P. 1993. *Ecology and Our Endangered Life-Support Systems,* 2nd ed. Sinauer Associates, Inc., Sunderland, Mass.

This ecology textbook for beginning college students is designed to be a guide to principles of modern ecology. Emphasizes causes of, and long-term solutions to, environmental problems rather than quick-fix treatments.

Perry, R. 1991. Calculating and comparing the plant diversity indices. In: *Natural History and Ecology of Homo Sapiens.* The Woodrow Wilson National Fellowship Foundation. Princeton, N.J.

Population Reference Bureau. 2006. *World Environment Data Sheet.* Population Reference Bureau, Washington, D.C.

A poster suitable for classroom research. Contains information on energy, calorie supply, decreases in forest cover, and safe water for many of the countries on each continent. This and other up-to-date population information is available on the website: http://www.prb.org

Quinn, M.-L. 1988. Tennessee's Copper Basin: A case for preserving an abused landscape. *Journal of Soil and Water Conservation,* 43(2), 140–144.

Presents the argument that the environmentally injured landscape should be preserved. Local opinion considered the area an integral part of local and state history, and some believe that the area should stay unvegetated as a reminder of dangers of industrial development.

———. 1991. The Appalachian mountains' Copper Basin and the concept of environmental susceptibility. *Environmental Management,* 15(2), 179–194.

Briefly reviews the site's physical setting, industrial history, and environmental history. Looks at the Copper Basin environmental degradation from the perspective of the interaction between humans and nature.

World Resources Institute. 1995. *World Resources 1994–1995.* Oxford University Press, New York.

Internet Resources

http://www.mypyramid.gov

The USDA developed this interactive website to display recommendations for a healthy diet and to allow individuals to create personalized fitness plans and track daily nutrition.

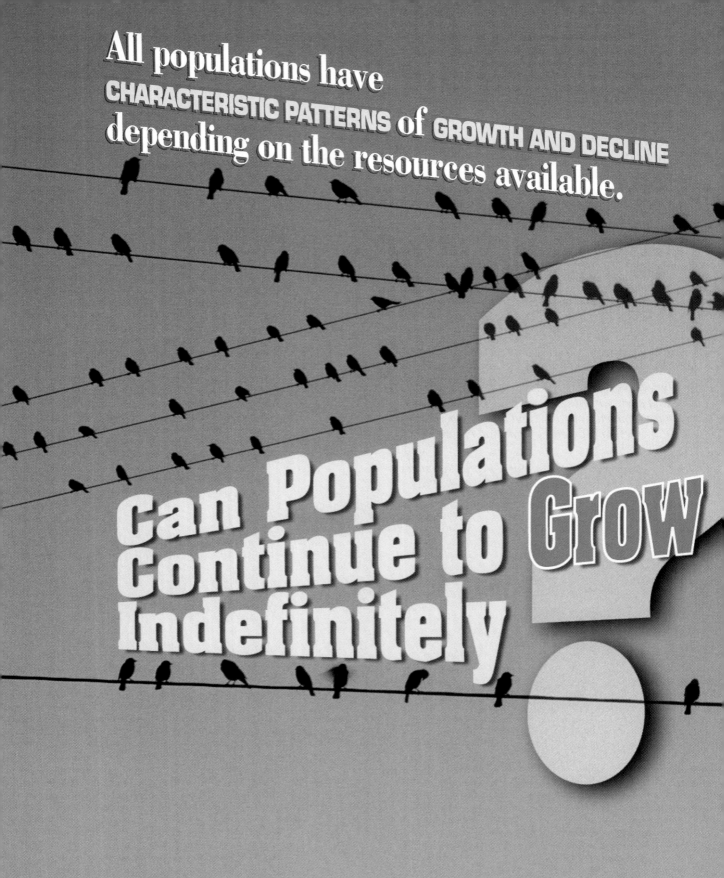

All populations have **CHARACTERISTIC PATTERNS of GROWTH AND DECLINE** depending on the resources available.

Can Populations Continue to Grow Indefinitely?

THREE

POPULATIONS

nitial Inquiry

Are there limits to the growth of populations on the earth?

WORLD POPULATION

Setting

The video on world population, adapted from Zero Population Growth's *World Population* (1990), depicts for you the history of the increase and distribution of humans on the earth during approximately the past 2,000 years. It also illustrates some important biological events in the history of human population growth.

As you watch the video, ask yourself:

◆ What questions does the video raise?

◆ What problems can you identify?

◆ What do you need to know to solve these problems?

The video gives you a lot of information in just a few minutes, so you'll probably want to watch it several times. Once you have grasped the material, try to answer the above questions in your *BioLog*. Then write your responses to the following questions:

◆ What patterns in the rate of population growth did you see?

◆ When did the growth rate seem to accelerate?

◆ Where on the earth did population explosions occur?

◆ Why do you think the explosions occurred where they did?

Brainstorming

Meet in small groups to discuss your answers to the above questions. After this discussion, think about what you might need to know about populations and how they grow. Create a list of questions to address these needs.

In Unit 2, you explored some of the interconnections within ecosystems. Humans are a species within world ecosystems. How does the video help you to appreciate the potential impact of the human species within an ecosystem?

To understand populations, you first need to know how to talk about them. You need to learn the language of population biology. Then you need to conduct experiments with populations. What does the term *population* mean to you? In how many ways can you define it? How does the meaning change when different people use it in different contexts? Record these thoughts, and list some examples of populations to illustrate each meaning in your *Log*. Now you are ready to begin the first Guided Inquiry.

What Is a Population?

A population is a group of individuals of the same species that lives in the same geographic area. A species is a distinct type of organism. Members of the same species have similar anatomical features and can interbreed to produce fertile offspring.

How do we identify a distinct population? The way we group individuals into a population can depend on the scale at which we view them. For example, it is simple to talk about an isolated, local population, such as the human population of an isolated island (Figure 3.1), the population of fleas on a dog, or the population of monarch butterflies that migrate to Mexico each winter (Figure 3.2 on page 142). Each of these populations is composed of organisms of a single species. They are isolated because of their location (island

Figure 3.1

Geographic isolation has contributed to the diversity among human populations.

Figure 3.2

Monarch butterflies.

or dog) or because of their particular behavior (butterfly migrations). Other populations, however, have limits that are more difficult to define. Humans, for instance, all belong to the same species. We are all *Homo sapiens*. In some respects, then, we are all part of one single, enormous population. We could call this population "humans on the planet earth," but we are spread out into many smaller populations that might or might not interact.

A group of different populations that lives in the same geographic area forms a community. Populations within a community may share common resources and may interact. Just how much interaction occurs among the species in a community is a lively and much-discussed topic in population biology. Interactions seem to be more common among organisms within a community than among organisms that live in different communities.

Look at the cartoon in Figure 3.3, and try to find other cartoons about populations and communities. In your *Log,* describe what you know about the words *community* and *population.*

COMMUNITY INTERACTIONS

Figure 3.3

My Own Population

How can you grow a population on your own? What does a population need to keep it alive and to reproduce more individuals?

In this activity, you will set up a new population and care for it. Your teacher will assist you in choosing one of several small, rapidly growing organisms for your study, such as bacteria, algae, protists, yeast, mealworms, duckweed, Fast Plants®, flour beetles, or fruit flies. One of these organisms, the fruit fly, is pictured in Figure 3.4. Choose organisms that can complete several reproductive cycles within the time period of your study.

Figure 3.4

Many small organisms such as this fruit fly can easily be grown in the classroom.

Learn about the needs of your population before you begin. For example, what will the organisms of your population eat? Guidelines on how to maintain various populations in your classroom are provided in Appendix K. Additional resources are listed at the end of this unit.

Choose organisms that will be easy to monitor for changes in population size. Guided Inquiry 3.2, on page 147, describes how to recognize and evaluate changes in the size of your population.

This first Guided Inquiry simply starts your population growth experience. Try to maintain your population as long as possible, at least throughout this unit and, if you can, for the rest of this school year.

MATERIALS

- Organisms to grow
- Culture containers (baby food or other jars for fruit flies or organisms grown in liquid, trays for flour beetles, pots and soil for plants)
- Food for the organisms
- Dissection microscope (for insects or tiny plants such as duckweed)
- Compound microscopes (for microscopic organisms such as algae, bacteria, and yeast)
- Gloves

Guided Inquiries

Figure 3.5

Create a table similar to this one in your Log or on a computer spreadsheet.

Procedure

1. Choose an organism to grow. Your teacher can tell you which organisms are available or practical for classroom use. Select an organism that will grow quickly in just a few weeks.

2. Work independently or in groups of two to four; or work as a class, as directed by your teacher, to study and maintain one large population in the classroom.

3. As you set up your population, record observations in your *Log* about your population's appearance (color, shape, smell, activity level of the individuals, etc.) and the environment surrounding it (room temperature, light, food available, moisture, etc.).

4. Create a table, such as the one in Figure 3.5, in your *Log* or on a computer spreadsheet to record data about your population. The first column should be the date on which you sampled the population. Also include columns for the number of organisms in the population and their appearance, environmental factors, and other relevant information. Refer to Appendix E for assistance in making a data table. You will use these data in Guided Inquiry 3.6 to make graphs and reports describing the growth of your population.

Sample date	Population size	Observations on the appearance of organisms	Environmental characteristics	Comments

5. Determine how many individuals are in your population on this first day that it is established. How you do this depends on the type of organism that you are growing.

   ◆ If you have only a few organisms in your population, count all of them. Record this in your *Log* as the population size on Day 0.

   ◆ If your population consists of many organisms, you won't be able to count all of them. Instead, count all of the individuals in a small subsample of the total population. The best way to do this is to select a defined area or volume of the total population living space and to count all of the individuals in this small subsample. Refer to "How to Sample Populations," on page 151, for assistance in working with these populations.

6. Continue taking care of your population for as long as you can or at least until you complete this unit. Monitor the growth of your population every few days for at least several weeks. After that, monitor it weekly. Every time you measure the population size,

record your data in the table in your *Log*. Also record your obser-vations about the population and its environment.

Interpretations: Respond to the following in your *Log:*

1. Describe the physical appearance of one individual in the population that you are caring for. List the charac-teristics that you will use to identify a single individual as your population grows in number.

2. How did you decide which environmental conditions would be best for the population that you are caring for?

Applications: Do the following as homework:

Learn more about the organisms that you are caring for in this Inquiry. Use library or other resources to prepare a short report about your selected organism. Record the information that you find in your *Log*. This information must include the proper scientific name of your organism, where it is found in nature, and its growth requirements. The report that you develop from this information will be a part of the Conference abstract that you will prepare after completing the Guided Inquiries.

How Are Populations Described?

The most basic way to describe a population is by its size, either the actual size or an estimate. For example, you could describe the population of your classroom by counting the number of individuals in the room. This is a direct count, or census. However, you could also multiply the number of individuals in your classroom population by the number of classrooms in the school to determine the size of the school population; this is an esti-mate. In Guided Inquiry 3.2, "Studying Populations," you will learn to count and estimate population size.

Another useful way to describe a population is its density, the number of individuals in a given area or volume (Figure 3.6). For example, the number

Figure 3.6

Population density can be expressed in terms of either area or volume.

Trees per hectare

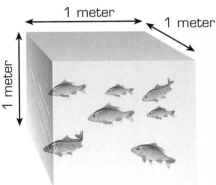

1 meter

1 meter

1 meter

Fish per cubic meter

A

B

C

Figure 3.7

(A) Algae appear to be randomly distributed in lake water.
(B) These insects display a clumped distribution.
(C) Agricultural crops are often uniformly distributed in fields.

Figure 3.8

How is your perception of the distribution of these fish altered by viewing them at different levels of magnification?

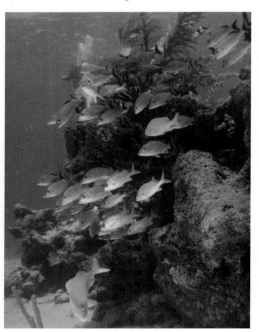

of trees per hectare is a tree population density. The density of fish in a farm pond is described in terms of the number of fish per cubic meter of pond volume.

A third characteristic, population distribution, describes the way in which individuals are distributed within their geographic boundaries (Figure 3.7). There are three basic distribution patterns. One pattern is seen when individuals of a population are found together in clumps or groups. In another, organisms are spread evenly throughout an area in a uniform distribution. Farm fields provide excellent examples of uniformly distributed organisms. Corn and other agricultural crops (including trees) are often planted to have uniform distribution in the fields. A third type of distribution is called random because it does not follow any apparent pattern.

Our perception of population distribution is affected by the scale of our view. For example, schools of fish display a clumped distribution, but fish within a school keep approximately even distances between each other—they are uniformly distributed within the school (Figure 3.8).

In your *Log*, describe some biological populations that naturally exhibit each of the distribution patterns (clumped, uniform, and random). 🌐

Studying Populations

What is the best way to study populations? After you have completed this Inquiry, you'll know how to study population density and distribution patterns. You will look at two sample populations: the population of students in your school and the population that you started growing in Guided Inquiry 3.1. Remember to record all your observations and calculations in your *Log*.

Part A: Studying Population Density

If you have only a few organisms in your population or if the individual organisms are large enough, count them directly. This will be your population census. If you have many organisms or if they are microscopic or move around too rapidly to count, you may need to estimate the population size. To do this, you will take a subsample (a small part of the total population), count it, and then use this direct count to make the population estimate. To go from a direct count of a subsample to an estimate of the total population size, you must know the relationship between the size of the subsample and the total population size.

For example, let's say that you are growing yeast cells in a 100 milliliter water environment (Figure 3.9). Take a 0.1 milliliter subsample and, using a microscope, count all the yeast cells in that subsample. Since 100 milliliters is 1000 times larger than 0.1 milliliter, the yeast population size estimate would be calculated as 1000 times the number of yeast cells that you counted in the subsample.

Figure 3.9

Counting a measured subsample of this yeast culture allows you to estimate the total population size.

Use pipette to transfer sample to slide

Determine what fraction of the total volume of the beaker solution is contained in the sample

Using the sample volume, the beaker solution volume, and the number of individuals counted in the sample, calculate the total population estimate

Yeast population in a beaker

Count yeast cells in the sample

Figure 3.10

Counting a measured subsample allows you to estimate population.

Another example is a plant population growing in a 0.16 m² tray (Figure 3.10). Choose a 100 cm² section of the tray and count all of the plants in it. Since 0.16 m² is 16 times as large as 100 cm², multiply the direct count of the plants in the subsample by 16 to estimate the number of plants in the entire population.

MATERIALS

- The population that you established in Guided Inquiry 3.1
- Instruments and supplies for measuring the size of your population's living space (such as rulers)
- Instruments and supplies for counting the number of individuals in your population (such as microscopes, slides, coverslips, forceps, and pipettes)
- Calculator (optional)

Procedure for Estimating the Size and Density of Populations

For students in your school:

1. Count the number of students in your classroom.
2. Find out the number of classrooms in the school building.
3. Use this information to estimate the number of students in the total school population. Record this estimate in your *Log*.
4. Find out how many students actually go to your school.

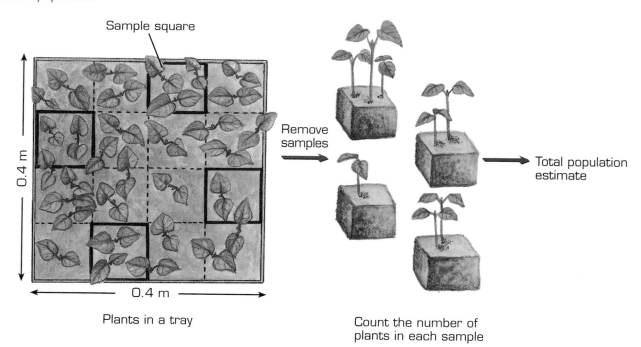

Sample square

0.4 m

0.4 m

Plants in a tray

Remove samples

Count the number of plants in each sample

Total population estimate

5. Compare your estimate to this actual number.

6. Measure the dimensions (length and width) of your classroom.

7. Using your previous count of the number of students in the classroom, calculate the density of the population in your classroom by counting the number of students in the classroom and dividing by the number of square meters of floor space.

8. Record this information in your *Log*.

For your own population:

1. Count or estimate the number of individuals in the population that you established in Guided Inquiry 3.1.

2. Measure the area or volume of your population's living space. Use volume if the organisms are not confined to a surface. Such organisms might include fish in an aquarium or fruit flies in a jar.

3. Calculate or estimate the population density (number of individuals per unit area or volume) of your population.

4. Record this information in your *Log*.

5. Repeat Steps 1 through 4 periodically throughout this unit (and as long as possible through the school year) to determine the size and density of your population.

Part B: Studying Population Distribution

The distribution of individuals in a population may determine how and when these individuals interact. It also may reflect the distribution of required resources or other amenities of life. In this part of the Inquiry, you will describe the distribution of individuals in your population. Are they evenly distributed or are they clumped? What features of the environment or the organisms themselves might explain this distribution?

MATERIALS

- The population that you established in Guided Inquiry 3.1

Procedure for Estimating Population Distribution

For students in your school:

Look around your classroom. How are your classmates distributed around the room? Describe their distribution as clumped, uniform, or random.

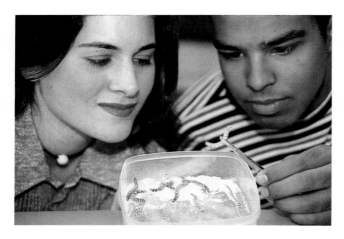
These students are counting the number of organisms in their population.

For your own population from Guided Inquiry 3.1:

1. Describe the distribution of your population. Draw a picture of this distribution in your *Log*. Describe the distribution of your population as clumped, uniform, or random.

2. Experiment with changing the environment of your population to find out whether you can change its distribution. You might make the living space more complex by adding barriers or other objects; or you might change light, temperature, or other conditions.

Interpretations: Respond to the following in your *Log:*

1. How would you explain the way in which the organisms in your population from Guided Inquiry 3.1 and the students in your classroom are distributed?

2. Does their distribution fit one of the categories exactly? Does it ever change? What could cause a change in population distribution?

3. How would you calculate the density of your population from Guided Inquiry 3.1 and the entire school population?

Applications: Respond to the following in your *Log*:

1. What is the value of knowing the number of individuals in a population?

2. If someone tells you that 150,000 humans are present, what else do you need to know to make this information useful?

3. To calculate population density, you need to know the number of individuals and the area or volume of space. However, when studying a large population, such as humans in the United States, you might need additional information to understand how crowded the conditions might be. List three variables that might be useful.

4. Find the human population of (a) your town or city, (b) your county, and (c) your state.

5. Find the area of (a) your town or city, (b) your county, and (c) your state.

6. Using the data from 4 and 5, calculate the human population density per square mile of your town or city, county, and state.

7. Why is it useful to know the distribution of a population, especially a large population?

How to Sample Populations

What do you do if you want to know how many individuals are in a population? You count them, obviously. This is easy enough if you're working with the population of goldfish in a fish tank, but it is rarely practical in nature.

Census Taking

To count all the organisms in a population, you take what is called a census. When you counted all the students in your classroom in Guided Inquiry 3.2, you conducted a census. Every 10 years, the United States Census Bureau tries to make a complete census of all of the people living in the United States. Imagine how hard this must be. To accomplish this task, thousands of temporary census workers (Figure 3.11) are hired. (You can learn more about the United States census on the Bureau of the Census home page at http://www.census.gov)

Some populations are nearly impossible to count. Can you imagine trying to count each fish in the Pacific Ocean or all the trees in the Amazon rain forest?

Sampling

Population biologists know all about the difficulties of taking an accurate census, so they most commonly use estimates of population size. They count a small sample of the population and then use their knowledge of the population distribution to estimate the approximate size of the entire population. This is just what you did in Guided Inquiry 3.2 when you counted the number of students in your classroom and then used that number to estimate the number of students in your school. But how do you know where and how to sample a population?

When estimating something like population size from observations of subsamples, you must be sure that the subsample represents the total population. What if the sampling area that you choose happens to have no organisms in it, even though there were organisms in other areas? If this were your only sample, you would incorrectly estimate the size of your population as zero. To avoid this problem, take several subsamples

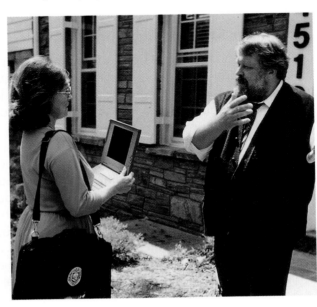

Figure 3.11

A U.S. census taker.

from different areas in your population's living space, and then average the counts from these subsamples to get a truly accurate estimate of total population size.

Suppose you wanted to determine the total number of trees in New York City's Central Park (Figure 3.12). The park covers 3.4 km². Rather than running madly through the park trying to count all the trees, you could mark off a small area (let's say 0.1 km²), count the trees in that area, and then multiply (in this case by 34) to estimate the tree population of the park. How accurate would this approach be? What if the area you chose to look at had lots and lots of trees? What if it were a grassy area with few trees? How could you make sure that your population sample was representative of the entire population?

Figure 3.12

The patchy distribution of trees in Central Park might present problems if you wanted to estimate the total number of trees in the park.

Techniques for Sampling Populations

One method for sampling a population is called the quadrat method. To use the quadrat method, construct a grid of equal-sized boxes on the area you want to study, and count the populations in some of the squares in the grid (see Figure 3.10 on page 148). These squares are called quadrats. You must know the area of each quadrat and its relationship to the total area. Choose the quadrats randomly. To find the population density of a quadrat, all you have to do is divide the number of individuals in that quadrat by the area of the quadrat. To find the total population density for the entire area, calculate the average of the population density values for all of the selected quadrats, and then multiply this average by the total number of quadrats. In Figure 3.10, there are few enough plants that you can count each of them. How does this census compare to your estimate? What factors might cause a difference between your population estimate and the census results? What would be the best way to select the quadrats?

The quadrat method works well for counting things that don't move around. But what if you want to sample actively moving organisms? You can use the mark-and-recapture method (Figure 3.13). Catch some individuals of a population, and mark them so that they can be identified later on. Then release these marked individuals back into the population. Later, catch more individuals. The number of previously marked individuals that are recaptured is used to estimate the total number in the population. When using this procedure, you must assume that both capture procedures are totally random, that is, each individual in the population has an equal chance of being caught. You also assume that the population size remains constant; there can't be any organisms entering or leaving the population during the time period of the surveys.

Suppose you caught, marked, and released 10 beetles in a local forest. When you returned a few days later, you caught 10 beetles. Four of those beetles were marked, so you knew that they had been caught and released during the previous sampling. Assume that it is as easy to capture marked beetles as unmarked beetles. Therefore you recaptured 4 of the ten, or 40 percent of the marked beetles. The 10 beetles that you originally caught and marked represented 40 percent of the population. You might conclude that the total population of beetles was 2.5 times greater than the original number of beetles that you marked. You could then estimate that the forest beetle population was 25 individuals. 🌐

Figure 3.13

On the first day, all beetles that are captured are marked. During the next capture, 4 of the 10 beetles captured have a mark. The entire beetle population can therefore be estimated as 25 beetles.

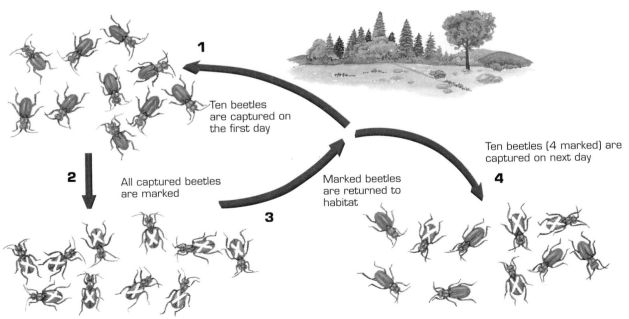

1 Ten beetles are captured on the first day

2 All captured beetles are marked

3 Marked beetles are returned to habitat

4 Ten beetles (4 marked) are captured on next day

My Family in 100 Years

How fast will your future family grow? This growth depends on several factors. At what age will you begin to have children? How many children will you have? What about other factors? In this Inquiry, you will calculate the number of direct descendants of several hypothetical families to illustrate how family size and the time between generations can make a difference for the family and society.

In these examples, only females are represented. This is a method used by population biologists to simplify calculations. You will start each family with a female and assume that all children are females. The final number of descendants will thus represent the maximum possible growth in numbers for each family.

MATERIALS

- Set of family cards
- Colored paper or colored paper squares
- Scissors
- Staplers or tape
- Meter stick
- Markers
- Calculators (optional)
- Sample family graph
- Chart paper for graphs

Procedure

1. Form small groups. Each group will graph the descendants for one family. Your teacher will give each group the necessary family information.

2. Using this family information, graph the data for "your" family. Your family will start with one person beginning at time 0 on the graph. Your family begins having children at the time indicated on your family card.

3. Calculate the number of descendants in each successive generation given the conditions outlined on your family card. Calculate the descendants for 100 years unless your card tells you otherwise.

4. Select one color of paper, and cut squares to represent your descendants. These squares should be no larger than 1.5 cm by 1.5 cm.

5. Set up and label a graph with the family name and years. Use the sample family graph in Figure 3.14 as a model.

6. Staple or tape the appropriate numbers of descendants in the corresponding years on the graph. Show the descendants for 100 years unless your card tells you otherwise.

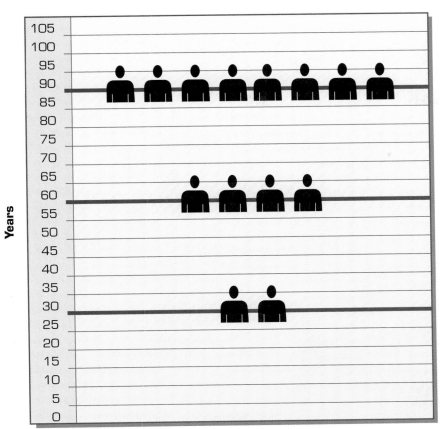

Figure 3.14

Use this sample to guide your graphing of the population size of your family over the next 100 years.

Years (y-axis)

Sample Family

2 children per family
Women have their first children at age 30

Interpretations: Respond to the following in your *Log*:

1. How does the number of descendants in your family compare to those of the other families in the class after 100 years?

2. Which appears to have a greater impact on the final population size of a family: the number of children in each generation or the time between generations?

Applications: Do the following as homework:

1. Explore the impact of family size on the population growth rate in one or more countries. Consult resources such as the *World Population Data Sheet* or other references for the necessary data.

2. How can individual behavior affect a community and society?

How Important Is Population Control?

China is a nation of 1.3 billion people, more than one-fifth of all the people on the earth. This population inhabits a land area about the size of the United States. Along the way to becoming the most populous nation on earth, China has experienced dramatic changes in fertility patterns. A brief recounting of China's recent history can help you to begin to understand its population situation.

As the most populous nation on earth, China is attempting to curb growth in its population size.

Since the end of World War II, China has experienced enormous political, social, economic, and population changes. The end of that war was also the end of nearly a century of foreign control.

In 1950, at the start of the Great Leap Forward period in China's history, the total fertility rate, the average number of children that a woman has in her lifetime, was 5.8 children per woman. Hardships suffered during this period greatly decreased the fertility rate, to 3.3 children per woman by 1961. As hardships diminished, the fertility rate increased, to 7.5 children per woman by 1963.

A decision was made to attempt to improve the standard of life for the people of China by slowing the rate of population size increase. To accomplish this, population control policies were instituted. These involved delaying of marriages, sterilization, methods of contraception, and pregnancy termination. Improvement of the status of women in China, by giving them better opportunities for education, employment, and reproductive health care, was a major component of these programs.

By 1979, when China's total fertility rate was 2.8 children per woman, the republic started a campaign to promote one-child families. The social consequences of this government program continue to be very controversial, both in China and in other nations. But there is no question about the success of this program in slowing population growth. The total fertility rate in 2003 was at 1.7 children per woman. At this rate, China will have 1.4 billion people in 2050. The new concern is now to care for a rapidly aging population.

Respond to the following in your *Log*:

1. How can the standard of living for a people be related to the population density?

2. Record your personal thoughts about this issue in your *Log*, and discuss them with your classmates.

Frank and Ernest

DON'T GET TOO CLOSE -- HE'S OVERPOPULATED, YOU KNOW.

THAVES 1-31

Population Growth

Population growth, or increase in population size, can be determined by calculating the number of individuals originally in a population, plus the number of individuals entering the population, minus the number of individuals leaving the population. (See first equation below.) Individuals enter a population when they are born (births) or move into the population (immigration). Individuals leave a population when they die (deaths) or move out of a population (emigration). Net migration is the difference between emigration and immigration. Net migration can have a positive or a negative value on population size. When we talk about populations, we use the symbol N to stand for the population size. For example, $N = 150$ means that there are 150 individuals in a particular population. The equation for calculating a new population size (N_t) is:

New population size		Size of original population		Births	Deaths		Immigration	Emigration
N_t	$=$	N_o	$+$	B	$- \quad D$	$+$	I	$- \quad E$

The primary factors affecting population size are the number of individuals who are born, who die, or who enter (immigrate into), or leave (emigrate from) the population.

Because most populations change over time, we need a way to describe how rapidly N is increasing or decreasing. We refer to a change by using the greek letter Δ (delta). The formula for calculating the absolute change (ΔN) in population size from the beginning to the end of any time period is:

Change in population size over time		Births	Deaths		Immigration		Emigration
ΔN	$=$	B	$- \quad D$	$+$	I	$-$	E

What if you want to know the rate at which a population is increasing or decreasing over a given period of time? You describe the percentage of change in population size over time as the population growth rate (G). A rate is always described as a change over a designated period of time.

For example, you can calculate the changes in the size of the U.S. population in 1991 as follows:

Absolute population change in individuals	=	Births in 1991	−	Deaths in 1991	+	Net migration in 1991
ΔN	=	B	−	D	+	$(I-E)$
2,669,000	=	4,084,000	−	2,157,000	+	742,000

Notice that the net migration $(I-E)$ is into the United States, as is evidenced by ceremonies such as that in Figure 3.16. The rate of growth (G) of the U.S. population in 1991, expressed as a percentage of the population size midway through the year, is calculated as follows:

$$\frac{\Delta N}{\text{Total population}} \times 100 = \text{Population growth rate in years}$$

$$\frac{4,084,000-2,157,000+742,000}{252,177,000} \times 100 = 1.06\% \text{ per year}$$

From this calculation, we see that the United States' population increased by 1.06% in 1991. The growth rate in 1991 was therefore 1.06% per year.

Figure 3.16

New Americans recite the oath of allegiance at Ellis Island.

Models of Population Growth

You can also talk about the total growth rate of a population by describing the impact of a single individual on population growth during a unit of time. An individual affects population growth by giving birth, by dying, or by migrating into or out of a population. The total growth of the population is influenced both by the number of individuals in the population (N) and by the contribution of each individual (r). This is described as an individual's intrinsic rate of increase.

Another way to think about the rate of population growth (G) is to consider the intrinsic ability of each individual in the population to reproduce:

Population growth rate	=	Intrinsic rate of increase	×	Population size
G	=	r	×	N

The intrinsic rate of increase (r) can be thought of as an individual's potential reproduction rate. For example, each of the families in Guided Inquiry 3.3 had a specified constant rate of reproduction (Figure 3.17 on page 160). The fastest rate of population growth was exhibited by the Norako family, in which each individual produced three offspring over a generation time of 15 years. In contrast, the Brown family, in which each individual produced only one child over a generation time of 35 years, had the lowest rate of population growth.

Figure 3.18 (on page 160) shows an example of an extreme case of population increase, called exponential growth. Even though the growth rate stays the same, the actual number of individuals in a population may

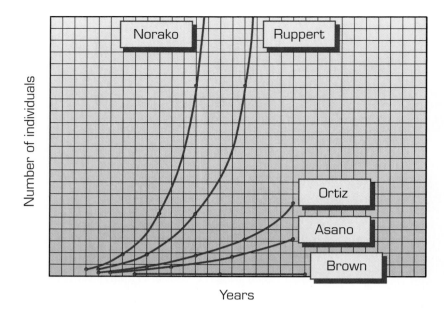

Figure 3.17

Individual reproduction rates greatly affected the growth rates of the families in Guided Inquiry 3.3.

continue to increase because there are more individuals and each individual continues to reproduce at the same rate. Which of the families in Guided Inquiry 3.3 demonstrated a growth pattern that most resembled exponential growth?

In nature, exponential growth can rarely be kept up over a long period of time. You will see it most often in small populations in environments with abundant resources. This happens sometimes when a population colonizes a new living area, as when you introduced the first organisms in your own population into a new living space or culture medium. However, in nature, population growth usually slows down or stops as it approaches some environmental limits. Food, water, light, oxygen, lack of living space, predators, competition, or a specific chemical or nutritional deficiency can limit the growth of populations.

Do the following in your *Log*:

Compare the pattern of growth of the population that you established in Guided Inquiry 3.1 to the graph of exponential growth.

Figure 3.18

In this graph of exponential growth, as the population size increases, the graph curves upward over time.

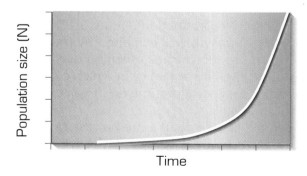

BIOoccupation

Kimberly Crews: Demographer

Have you noticed that the nightly news often features a story about the birthrate or the total population of another country or the world? Where do you think the news programs get their information? Often, they turn to a professional such as Kimberly Crews.

Kimberly Crews is a demographer (from the Greek word *demos* meaning "people") for the Population Reference Bureau (PRB). The PRB is a private, nonprofit educational organization that works to increase public awareness of the role that population plays in shaping the nations of the world. As a demographer, Ms. Crews studies the features of human populations. These might include statistics about a population's size, growth, birthrates, and density, for example. Looking at population trends can help communities to make decisions about their future.

In her role as a demographic educator, Ms. Crews travels throughout the United States conducting training workshops. These workshops are for teachers who are interested in teaching their students about human populations. She also collects statistics on population trends in the United States and the rest of the world. Ms. Crews uses this information to design materials to teach about human populations.

"There is no typical day," Ms. Crews says when asked about her job. "Some days I am reviewing audiovisual materials or writing and researching the answers to questions people ask about populations. Other days I am providing training workshops to teachers or helping to write a high school biology textbook."

Ms. Crews began working at the PRB when she was 23 years old. Since that time, her job has taken her throughout the United States as well as Canada and Europe. Because of the interdisciplinary nature of demography, Ms. Crews works with a variety of subjects and grade levels. She must have a knowledge of biology, economics, environmental science, geography, history, home economics, mathematics, and sociology. Her education for this job includes a bachelor's degree in secondary education and a master's degree in demography.

When asked what she would recommend to high school students who are considering demography or population education as a career, Ms. Crews recommends coursework in environmental science, statistics, and applied math before going on to college.

The best part of her job, according to Ms. Crews, is "talking to people, telling about new content, and seeing them understand—the light comes on!" She adds that one of the biggest challenges of working with people in population education programs is that "people don't know enough about population trends and how these trends can affect their own lives. They just don't see how it can affect them!"

Predator-Prey Simulation

How are populations affected by predator-prey relationships? What can be the influence of the numbers of predators on a prey population and vice versa? Census data show the numbers of individuals in a population at any given time. A simulation, however, permits you to observe changes over several generations within one class period.

This simulation illustrates how predator-prey interactions affect population sizes. Our example uses wolves and rabbits (Figure 3.19) in a board game (Figure 3.20).

MATERIALS

- Sixty, 6.0 cm × 6.0 cm squares cut from stiff colored paper: the wolves
- 400, 2.0 cm × 2.0 cm squares cut from a different color of cardboard: the rabbits
- One sheet of green paper (approximately 43 × 28 centimeters): the meadow
- Graph paper

Figure 3.19

Rabbits can be an important component of wolves' diets.

Procedure

1. Read the following rules of the game:
   - ◆ The game contains a meadow and stacks of reserve cards for wolves and rabbits. Active wolves and rabbits are taken from this reserve.
   - ◆ The meadow is the playing field.
   - ◆ To start the game, the rabbit managers distribute three rabbits evenly on each meadow. The rabbit managers add active rabbits by spreading them evenly in the meadow and remove rabbits as they are caught.

Figure 3.20

Commercial version of the game board for Guided Inquiry 3.4.

- ◆ The wolf managers throw active wolf cards and add or remove active wolves from the meadow.

- ◆ All animals that are removed from the meadow are placed back in the reserve stacks.

- ◆ The following represents one round of the game and produces one generation:

  a. The wolf managers toss each active wolf square into the meadow in an effort to catch rabbits. The toss must leave a wolf manager's hand outside the meadow area. (This prevents just dropping the wolf onto the rabbit.) As long as the wolf square touches a rabbit square, that rabbit is considered to be caught.

  b. Each wolf that can catch three rabbits with one toss has enough energy to reproduce, so the wolf managers double the surviving wolf population in the next round.

  c. After the caught rabbits are removed, the remaining rabbit population is doubled for the next round.

  d. If a wolf cannot catch three rabbits in a round, the wolf starves and is removed from the meadow by the wolf managers.

- ◆ If there are no surviving rabbits, a new round is begun with three new rabbits, which immigrate into the meadow.

- ◆ If there are no surviving wolves, a new round is begun with a new wolf, which immigrates into the meadow, and double the number of rabbits left at the end of the last round.

2. Play the game in groups of four. Work in pairs. One pair manages the prey (rabbit population), and the other pair manages the predators (wolf population).

3. Begin the game with one wolf and three rabbits. Record these numbers as rabbits and wolves in the meadow. Continue to record their counts at the beginning of each round for the 25 generations in the game.

4. One of the wolf managers should toss a wolf card into the meadow in an attempt to land on at least three rabbits. Probably, the first wolf catches fewer than three rabbits and starves. There will be no surviving wolf or new baby wolf. (How do you explain this?)

5. The rabbit managers should double the rabbit population and place them in the meadow.

6. Complete the data table for this generation.

7. The wolf managers toss a new wolf into the meadow.

8. If the wolf catches three rabbits, remove three rabbits, add a wolf, and double the remaining rabbits for the next round. If the wolf was unsuccessful, begin the next round with a new immigrant wolf, and continue to double the remaining rabbits.

9. Continue additional rounds. Eventually, the rabbit population will increase to a level that allows the wolf to catch three rabbits in a single toss. If the wolf catches three rabbits, it not only survives but also reproduces. It has one baby wolf for each three rabbits that it catches. Therefore if it catches six rabbits, it will have two babies.

10. Continue to play the game for up to 25 generations, recording data at the beginning of each generation. By this time, your meadow may look like the one on the right in Figure 3.20. Toss as many wolf cards as are in their populations.

11. Graph your data using the number of individuals as the dependent variable and the number of generations as the independent variable. Use a separate line on the same page for rabbits and wolves.

Interpretations: Respond to the following in your *Log:*

1. Study your graph lines for the two populations. How are the wolf and rabbit populations related to each other? How do the sizes of each population affect each other?

2. Under what modifications can both populations continue to exist indefinitely?

3. What do you think would happen if you introduced an additional predator, such as a coyote, which requires fewer rabbits to reproduce?

4. What would happen if you introduced another type of rabbit, one that could run faster and escape its predators? (In the game, you could give the new type of rabbit a chance to escape by tossing a coin after it is caught and letting it live if you got heads.) Which type of rabbit would predominate after many generations of predation?

Applications: Respond to the following in your *Log:*

1. How does this simulation relate to the human population and its interaction with its environment? Are there any predator-prey relationships?

2. What predator-prey relationships have you observed in your community?

3. If a population biologist visited your classroom, what are some questions about the human population you could ask?

Limiting Factors and the Carrying Capacity

What do the individuals in a population need for growth and reproduction? Every population needs an energy source, water, living space, and specific nutrients. As populations grow larger, they consume more of these resources. This consumption eventually limits population growth. Suppose the amount of available resources remains fixed. The larger the population, obviously, the fewer resources are available for each individual because more and more individuals are competing for the resources. Each individual needs a certain minimum amount of resources just to be able to survive. As fewer resources are available, reproduction may be difficult. Therefore populations with more individuals may have lower growth rates.

Malthus's Essays

The probable consequences of population numbers increasing faster than resources can be provided to support them were formally discussed by an 18th century English economist, Thomas Malthus (Figure 3.21), who wrote several essays on the natural laws of population growth. Malthus stated that since "food is necessary to the existence of man . . . [and] that the passion between the sexes is necessary . . . [then] the power of population is indefinitely greater than the power of the earth to produce subsistence." He concluded that "Population, when unchecked, increases in a geometrical ratio. Subsistence increases only in an arithmetic ratio. This implies a strong and constantly operating check on population from the difficulty of subsistence."

In other words, population size will always be limited by the amount of food that is available to feed the individuals of the population. These essays greatly influenced later scientists as they studied the ways in which animal

Figure 3.21

Thomas Malthus.

populations survived and increased. Most important, Charles Darwin cites these as the inspiration for his book *On the Origin of the Species,* in which he describes the natural processes leading to evolutionary changes in organisms.

Carrying Capacity

Population growth slows when the number of individuals in the population cannot be adequately supported by the available food supply. In the early stages of population growth, when there are few individuals and abundant resources are available, population size increases exponentially. As the population increases in size, each individual has fewer resources to devote to reproduction; therefore population growth rates decrease. When the number of individuals in the population is at the maximum that can be supported by the available food supply, the population size stops increasing. This maximum population size is known as the carrying capacity of the population in this environment.

Figure 3.22 shows the changes that occur when population growth is affected by limiting factors. Carrying capacity is the maximum number of individuals of this species that the resources in this environment can support. The carrying capacity will be different for various species and even for the same species in different environments. This is because the types and amounts of limiting factors will vary. At first, the population grows faster and faster, and the carrying capacity has little effect on the actual population growth rate. As resources are used up, though, the population grows more slowly. It eventually reaches a level at which the population size equals the carrying capacity.

A Closed System

For a population to continue, it must have resources. But if the resources are used up entirely, all of the individuals in the population will eventually die. This is what would happen in a completely closed system, one that has no input of resources and no immigration of new organisms into the population. Think, for example, of your kitchen in summer. You have lots of fresh fruit on the counter—peaches, apples, and bananas. You also have swarms of fruit flies that come in on the fruit and use it as a convenient food source. You find yourself swatting more and more of the creatures until the fruit is eaten or taken away. When the fruit is gone, the fruit flies die, and the population falls to zero (Figure 3.23).

Figure 3.22

Population growth slows when resources become limiting.

Figure 3.23

When resources—in this case fruit—are used up, the population dies.

Figure labels:
- Fruit Flies in My Kitchen (Summer 1996)
- Fruit remains in kitchen
- Fruit is removed from kitchen
- Fruit containing fruit flies is put in kitchen
- Last remaining fruit flies die
- Fruit fly population size (N)
- Time (days)

Stability

The fruit flies' cycle of rapid growth and death is dramatic, but most populations in nature achieve some level of the stability shown in Figure 3.24. Think of a population of house sparrows near your home. As these birds were first introduced or immigrated into your neighborhood, the population grew in size. But as food and space to live became scarce, population growth slowed down. Since the amount of food and space, possible predators, and even exposure to disease can vary slightly from year to year, the population does not maintain a steady number of individuals, but rather fluctuates, increasing and decreasing over the years at a size somewhere near the carrying capacity. This population pattern continues unless there is a drastic change in the environment.

Law of the Minimum

The 19th century German chemist Justus Liebig determined that populations are limited by the least abundant essential factor. This is the law of the minimum, which is illustrated in Figure 3.25 on page 168.

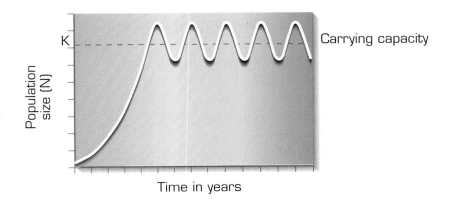

Figure labels:
- K
- Carrying capacity
- Population size (N)
- Time in years

Figure 3.24

Population size fluctuates because of resource availability and predation.

BIO*thoughts*

Imagine what would happen to the cockroach population if cockroaches were never stepped on, had an unlimited supply of food, and were immune to all insecticides.

Organisms will grow until they use up all of any one essential material. Even though other materials are present in abundance, the lack of one essential material will stop or severely impair growth. For example, your garden will not grow if it gets no water, even if you provide plenty of fertilizer. Water is the limiting resource in this example. The unique set of resources or environmental limitations that regulate the size of a population are known as limiting factors. Every population experiences a slowing or stopping of growth as these essential limiting factors run out. Each population has a different set of limiting factors that affect its growth.

In your *Log,* describe the limiting factors for your study population.

BIOprediction

The carrying capacity of the human population depends on what happens to the populations of other organisms. Humans rely upon other organisms for food, medicine, buildings, clothing, and virtually everything else that we need to survive. However, human use of other organisms can prevent these other organisms from maintaining stable population sizes. Therefore the maximum number of humans these populations can support will eventually decrease.

In 1994, humans harvested 101 million tons of fish, which was essentially the same amount that they harvested in 1993. This is just about the maximum amount of fish that can be harvested if the fish populations are to be maintained at their current size. If humans consistently overfish by removing more fish than can be replaced in the course of normal fish population growth, how will this eventually affect the carrying capacity of humans on the earth?

We don't know the carrying capacity for humans on the earth. Estimates range from fewer than one billion people to more than 1,000 billion.

Respond to the following in your *Log:*

- What factors would you use to calculate the carrying capacity for humans on the earth?

- How might your choice of factors affect your calculation?

- How might technological and medical advances affect the carrying capacity for humans on the earth?

Population Demographics

When demographers want to make predictions about the future growth of a population, they first estimate its total size. They next seek to gather information about the age-sex structure of the population. The age-sex structure is the proportion of people of each age by sex. Demographers want to know the proportion of people in a population who are at the age at which they can have children. They also need to know how many people are in the ages at which death rates are high. The average age of a population affects the population's rate of growth.

Populations grow primarily by an excess of births. Rapidly growing populations usually have high birthrates. For example, look at a country like Kenya, where 50 percent of the population is younger than 15 years of age (Figure 3.26 on page 170). In Kenya, even if the fertility rate could be instantly reduced to just two children per couple, the younger half of the population would still replace itself within a couple of generations. This is because the birthrate, the number of children born to *all* women during a year, would remain high. The number of deaths would still be low during this period because of the relatively small number of people in the oldest age groups. Therefore even if fertility declined, the high birthrate would assure that population size would continue to increase for at least a few more generations.

The U.S. population is growing much more slowly than that of Kenya (Figure 3.27), but a large proportion of the U.S. population is still of reproductive age and younger. So even though the fertility is low, about two children per woman, the U.S. population will continue to increase. The age-sex structure is important because it determines not only the needs of the population, but also the potential for future growth of the total population and the increase of specific age groups. 🌐

Figure 3.26

With so many young people at or approaching reproductive age, Kenya will continue to have a high birthrate for many years.

Figure 3.27

Graph of population size change (1900–2000) for Kenya and the United States.

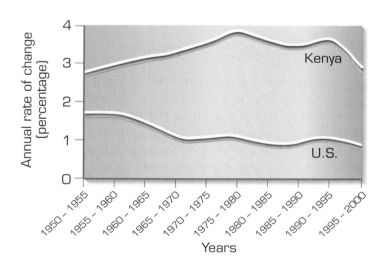

Populations

Pyramid Building (Demography of Populations)

In this Inquiry,* you will study some data on the populations of several countries, looking at the age and sex distribution. Then you will construct your own population pyramid.

MATERIALS

- Population pyramids below and on page 172 showing age and gender distribution for Kenya and the United States
- Population data tables on page 173 showing age distribution and gender for the
- United States, Japan, Brazil, Kenya, China, and Austria
- Graph paper, 4 squares to the inch, or 0.5 centimeter grid (4 pieces per student)
- Current *World Population Data Sheet*

Procedure

1. Examine the population pyramids for Kenya and the United States (Figure 3.28 below and Figure 3.29 on page 172). Notice that each pyramid has two separate columns of numbers, one for the male population and one for the female population. This is called a double histogram. Look at the base of each figure. Can you see that the two histograms for each gender are joined at their bases to make the double histogram for the total population? Designing the graph this way enables you to compare gender differences at each age level. You can also make comparisons between countries.

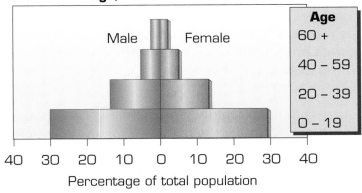

Kenya Population Pyramid (1995)
Age/Sex Distribution

Figure 3.28

The age-sex pyramid for Kenya.

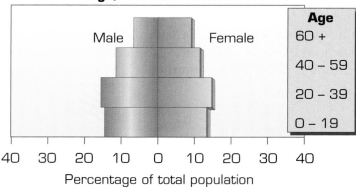

Figure 3.29

The age-sex pyramid for the United States.

United States Population Pyramid (1995)
Age/Sex Distribution

Male   Female

Age
60 +
40 – 59
20 – 39
0 – 19

40 30 20 10 0 10 20 30 40

Percentage of total population

2. What are the three variables for each graph? What are the age group intervals for the ages given at the right of the graph? Record this information in your *Log.* Look at the numbers at the bottom of each graph. These indicate what percentage of the total population is male or female.

3. Describe the differences in shape between the two pyramids. What can you infer from these shape differences?

4. Consult a reference such as the *World Population Data Sheet,* and decide what factors other than the age-sex distribution might affect future population size.

5. Examine the pyramids for Kenya and the United States again, and read the description of each.

6. Now it's time to construct your own population pyramids. Use the population data for Brazil, Austria, China, and Japan in Figure 3.30. Draw your pyramids on graph paper. Use as much of the graph page as possible for each of the four countries. Your graphs will be similar to the ones for Kenya and the United States, using the same variable intervals for the ages and the same labels.

7. Identify the four graphs you just made as depicting either rapidly growing or slowly growing populations. How did you decide?

8. A country that has a rapidly growing population has a relatively high birthrate. Examine the pyramids for all six countries, and study their differences. Record your findings in your *Log.*

Interpretations: Respond to the following in your *Log:*

1. What might be some of the reasons for the different shapes of these pyramids?

Population in Thousands of Individuals (1995 data)

United States					Japan			
Age Group	Male	%	Female	%	Male	%	Female	%
0 – 19	38,977	14.7%	37,050	14.1%	14,835	11.8%	14,096	11.3%
20 – 39	41,277	15.7%	41,081	15.6%	17,604	14.1%	17,064	13.6%
40 – 59	29,935	11.4%	31,273	11.9%	18,129	14.5%	18,267	14.6%
60 +	18,477	7.0%	25,345	9.6%	10,837	8.7%	14,262	11.4%
Total	128,666	48.8%	134,749	51.2%	61,405	49.1%	63,689	50.9%
Total	263,415				125,094			

Brazil					Kenya			
Age Group	Male	%	Female	%	Male	%	Female	%
0 – 19	34,237	21.2%	33,852	21.0%	8,300	29.8%	8,157	29.2%
20 – 39	26,480	16.4%	26,567	16.5%	3,719	13.3%	3,698	13.3%
40 – 59	13,802	8.6%	14,112	8.7%	1,363	4.9%	1,415	5.1%
60 +	5,856	3.6%	6,478	4.0%	568	2.0%	664	2.4%
Total	80,375	49.8%	81,009	50.2%	13,950	50.0%	13,934	50.0%
Total	161,384				27,884			

China					Austria			
Age Group	Male	%	Female	%	Male	%	Female	%
0 – 19	218,356	17.9%	202,216	16.5%	973	12.2%	913	11.5%
20 – 39	228,745	18.7%	214,202	17.5%	1,325	16.6%	1,235	15.5%
40 – 59	126,582	10.4%	117,202	9.6%	990	12.4%	991	12.4%
60 +	54,870	4.5%	59,289	4.9%	604	7.6%	940	11.8%
Total	628,553	51.5%	592,909	48.5%	3,892	48.8%	4,079	51.2%
Total	1,221,462				7,971			

Figure 3.30

Population (in thousands) age-sex distribution in the United States, Brazil, China, Japan, Kenya, and Austria (1995 data).

2. What is the relationship between the shapes of the pyramids and the birthrates?

3. What proportion of the population in each country is at or below an age at which reproduction is possible?

4. Describe the unique features of the pyramid for each of the six countries.

Applications: Respond to the following in your *Log:*

> *1.* What can you infer about the population future of Kenya?
>
> *2.* What can you infer about the population future of the United States?

You will probably have to do some research before you can answer these questions. Work in small groups to find out everything you can about each country's natural, scientific, and economic resources.

Population Growth in Kenya and the United States

Kenya's pyramid has a wide base and a narrow top (Figure 3.28). This is typical of a "young" or rapidly growing population. In these populations, high birthrates add more and more people to the lowest bars of the pyramid and, in turn, shrink the relative proportion of people at the oldest ages. Improved health care means that more people survive to reproductive age and guarantees continued growth for several generations. When these people give birth, they will widen the base of the pyramid further. This shape is common in many developing countries that have experienced improvements in life expectancy but continue to have high birthrates. It reflects both a history of rapid population growth and the potential for future rapid growth.

The age-sex pyramid for the United States is typical for a slowly growing population. The United States has had declining birth and death rates for most of this century. As the birthrate declines, fewer people enter the lowest bars of the pyramid. As life expectancy increases, a greater percentage of the people born survives to old age. As a result, the population is said to be aging. This means that the proportion of older people in the U.S. population has been growing. This trend was interrupted by a period of exceptionally high birthrates after World War II. This period, which lasted from 1947 to 1964, is referred to as the baby boom. After 1964, birthrates continued to fall. Members of the baby boom generation have by now had their own children (Figure 3.31). Are you one of these children? These children of the baby boomers are represented by the slightly widening base of the pyramid. Therefore, even though the birthrate is lower than ever before, the United States population continues to grow. 🌍

Figure 3.31

These baby boom parents have begun their contribution to the 1980s—1990s baby boomlet.

Population Age Structure

Demographers study the structure of human populations. Any factor that affects how long people live or the rate at which they reproduce will determine a population's age structure. Age structure, in turn, determines the future size of a population. Why? Births are more likely to occur to the young and deaths to the old.

Let's look at an example. Imagine a population with a large number of children and young adults. Probably, this population will have many new families, many births, and relatively few deaths. Obviously, it will also have a high rate of growth. Now imagine a different population in which half the people are over the age of 50. This population will form fewer new families and have fewer births but a higher number of deaths. The rate of growth here is likely to be low; it might even be negative.

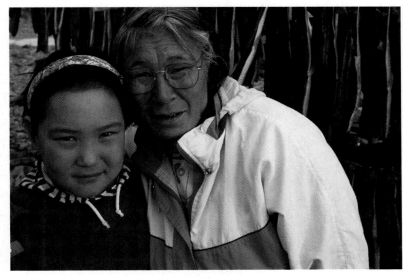

The aging of the world population will present many challenges for the young, who must provide support and health care for the elderly.

Look at Figure 3.30 and the population pyramids that you drew. They show how birthrates, death rates, and generation time affect the population age structure. Examine the age distribution of males and females in the United States population. The baby boom group is shown mostly in the age class of 20 to 39 in the graph. The aging of the so-called boomers has affected everything in our society. During the 1950s and 1960s, for example, more houses were built and schools had to expand to accommodate the growing families. When baby boomers entered the work force, they created huge competition for jobs because so many people were applying for the same positions. After a decrease in the birthrate during the 1970s, the baby boomers reached reproductive age, and the birthrate increased. Their children formed a baby boomlet in the 1980s and 1990s.

As health care improves, the entire population of the world is aging. Even in the less-developed countries, improved access to antibiotics has reduced the death rate at all ages. These triumphs of modern medicine provide a mixed blessing. With an average expected lifespan of 83 years and a declining birth rate, societies must look for ways to support the ever-increasing proportion of the population who are elderly. 🌍

Frank and Ernest

Copyright (c) 1994 by Thaves. Reprinted with permission.

How Much Has My Population Grown?

How much has your population grown since you set it up? It is now time to check the population that you established in Guided Inquiry 3.1. Using techniques you learned in previous inquiries and readings in this unit, estimate or count the size of your population today and determine the distribution of your population. You should repeat this census every few days until you complete this unit and then at least weekly throughout the life of your population.

MATERIALS

- Populations established in Guided Inquiry 3.1
- Dissection or compound microscopes, as needed to view the population
- Instruments to sample and observe your population (pipettes, microscope slides and coverslips, forceps, etc.)

Procedure

1. Make a table similar to the one in Figure 3.32 in your *Log* for your population. You may not use all columns in the table.

Figure 3.32

Set up a data table like this one in your Log.

Date population was sampled	Population size	Births	Deaths	Net change in population size

2. In your *Log*, graph the changes in population size from the first day that you started it (in Guided Inquiry 3.1) until today. Be sure to include the date you established the population and today's date. Add values that are appropriate to your population to the Y axis (population size). Allow for continued growth of your population when you set up this axis. Continue to plot the growth of your population each time you sample it. A sample graph is shown in Figure 3.33.

3. Calculate the growth or decline of your population using the following information. Perform each of these calculations for your own population, from the date it was established until today.

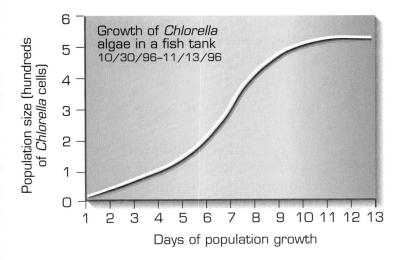

The absolute change in population size describes the change in numbers over a certain period of time (see page 158). You might not be able to count the actual number of individuals being born, dying, or migrating into and out of your population, but you can combine all of these effects into one measure of population size change from day to day.

For example, say that a population started with 10 individuals on day 1 and grew to 100 individuals by day 10. Calculate the absolute change (growth or decline in your population) from day 1 to day 10:

Absolute change	=	Population size on day 10	−	Population size on day 1
90 individuals	=	100 individuals	−	10 individuals

Calculate the percent change in population size:

$$\text{Percentage change} = \frac{\text{Absolute change from day 1 until day 10}}{\text{Population size on day 1}} \times 100\%$$

900%	= 90 individuals /10 individuals

Calculate the average daily change in population density:

$$\text{Average change in population density} = \frac{\text{Population on day 10} - \text{Population on day 1}}{\text{Total number of days}}$$

$$9 \text{ individuals per day} = \frac{100 \text{ individuals} - 10 \text{ individuals}}{10 \text{ days}}$$

Estimate the average rate of growth (or growth rate). This will allow you to compare the change among several different populations.

4. Record your calculations in your *Log*. Summarize your population growth by completing the following statement:

My population grew by _____ individuals /day
from day #_____ to day #_____.

What should you do with your population at this point? You should continue to maintain your population if you plan to examine it in more detail later, in Extended Inquiry 3.5, or in another study later in the year.

Interpretations: Respond to the following in your *Log:*

1. Describe the overall pattern for the growth of your population. What has contributed to this pattern?

2. What was unexpected about the growth of your population?

3. If you continue to feed and maintain your population, what would you predict about its future population growth pattern, assuming that its living space remains the same?

Applications: Respond to the following in your *Log:*

Suppose you wanted to maintain a modest population of some organism at home as a hobby, such as the hamster shown in Figure 3.34. What have you learned from growing your own population in this unit that would make this hobby more successful?

Figure 3.34

Raising hamsters can be an interesting and enjoyable hobby.

Self-Check 1

By the time you have completed the Guided Inquiries and read the information in this unit, you should be able to answer the following questions, which will test your understanding of the concepts developed by these activities. Working in groups of four, distribute the questions among members of the group. Once everyone has answered the assigned questions, review all responses as a group, modifying answers as necessary. Be sure that each member of the group has a final set of responses to the questions.

1. Create a definition of a population that includes the words *individuals, interbreed, geographic area,* and *species*.

2. Describe the differences between population and community.

3. Describe how you would grow and maintain a population.

4. What are the variables in determining population density? What are the units for density?

5. Describe the patterns in which populations can be distributed.

6. Write an equation for changes in population size that takes into account births, deaths, emigration, and immigration.

7. How is the population growth rate calculated and what units are used?

8. What is a census? How can population size be estimated without a census?

9. Explain the differences between the quadrat and mark-and-recapture methods of sampling a population.

10. What are some indirect methods of assessing relative population growth?

11. Describe some commonly seen patterns of population growth over a long period of time.

12. What is a possible pattern of population numbers when there are predator-prey relationships?

13. What is carrying capacity?

14. What are typical limiting factors on population growth?

15. Define birthrate. How does it compare to measures of fertility?

16. How can population pyramids be used to predict future changes in population size?

Conference

As you completed the Guided Inquiry activities in this unit, you collected all kinds of information about populations. You should be able to explain some of the information you discovered and to make connections between that information and real communities. In this Conference, you'll have a chance to choose your best work, just as you did in Units 1 and 2, and present an abstract.

What exactly is an abstract? It's just a summary of research or experiments you've done, condensed so that you can quickly share it with others. Scientists write abstracts as a way of sharing information efficiently. It's the same in your classroom. You want to let the class know what you've discovered, sharing your new knowledge quickly and concisely. You should aim for your abstract to be one typewritten page or two handwritten pages long.

Think back to the beginning of this unit, when you watched the video. You brainstormed then, jotting down questions that the video raised. At the Conference, you'll want to focus on what you have learned that helps you to answer those initial questions. Here are a few questions you should be able to answer now:

1. What did you learn about populations?
   a. Which limiting factors affected populations?
   b. What kinds of growth patterns did you discover?
   c. How were your organisms distributed? How did their distribution change during your study?
   d. What were the growth rates?
   e. What was the carrying capacity? How did you alter the carrying capacity?
   f. How did the population use the available resources?

2. How does your experimental population compare with the human population?

   a. What kinds of predictions can you make for the human population in the future?

   b. How are the characteristics and dynamics of the human population like those of other populations?

3. What additional information would you like to have to fully understand populations and population growth?

Procedure

1. Work with one other student. Look back over the work you did in the Guided Inquiries in this unit. From which Guided Inquiry did you learn the most? What was the most important thing you learned? Together, choose a Guided Inquiry that you will write up.

2. Prepare a written abstract of this Inquiry.
   Begin with the following:
   ◆ The title of the Guided Inquiry
   ◆ The particular question or hypothesis you were investigating
   ◆ The procedures you followed

3. Respond to the following:

   a. What did you learn from the Inquiry?

   b. How does what you learned relate to the rules of population growth?

   c. What else do you need to know to answer the question that you posed?

   d. What sort of Extended Inquiries would help you to find out what you need to know?

   e. Explain the research plan for your new Inquiry.

4. Revise your abstract to make it concise; one typewritten page is best. Once it is finished, get together with the authors of three or four other abstracts. Present your abstract to this larger group and ask for suggestions. How does your abstract make a contribution to the class's knowledge about populations? How can you improve your abstract?

5. You and your partner should now talk about the changes you want to make. For homework, each of you should revise the abstract.

ow you are ready to continue your population investigations by focusing on one or more topics of special interest to you. Read through the Inquiries that follow, but remember: They are only suggestions. You can select one or more of them, or you can design your own investigation. Your teacher can also make suggestions. You may work alone or in a group. Just be sure you consult with your teacher before you begin your work.

Extended Inquiry 3.1

No Island Is an Island

Barbados is a tropical island in the West Indies that is often visited by American vacationers. Located about 500 kilometers north of the border between Venezuela and Guyana in South America, Barbados has beautiful sandy beaches and lots of sun (Figure 3.35). Barbadian teenagers enjoy surfing, skin diving, sunning, and listening to a unique blend of calypso and reggae music called *Bejan.* Barbados was once under British rule but is now independent. Although Barbadians have long been independent from Britain, they still practice some British customs. Imagine wearing neat brown and white uniforms to school every day in a tropical country or driving on the left side of the road in a car that has the steering wheel on the right side.

Although Barbados might seem like utopia, Barbadians have a very serious problem: Their population is becoming too large for the tiny island to support. Reliance on local production, waste disposal and treatment, fresh drinking water, and enough space for all to work and live are now major concerns.

Imagine that you are a high school student in Barbados. You are just beginning to understand the island's problem, and you begin to think you should do something about it. But first, you must decide whether the problem is real. If it is, you will want to learn more about this pressing environmental challenge. Finally, you must decide what you, as one individual, can do. What can you do to prevent the island from being seriously endangered?

Procedure

Use the data from the Barbados Fact Sheet on page 184 and other available resources to respond to the following.

1. Examine a world map and locate Barbados, West Indies. How would you fly there? Describe the route in your *Log.* Investigate what the normal stopovers at airports along the way would be.

2. Using the dimensions of Barbados on the Fact Sheet, estimate the total land surface of the island. Remember that the island is not a square or rectangle.

3. Calculate the density of the human population on the island per square kilometer. Calculate the density of the U.S. population, using data from the Population Reference Bureau's *World Population Data Sheet.* The area of the United States is approximately 3,612,000 square miles, or 9,355,080 square kilometers. Compare the population densities of the two countries. Record these calculations in your *Log.*

Figure 3.35

The beaches of Barbados are visited by many vacationers.

4. Using the 1992 net population growth rate for Barbados shown in Figure 3.36 on page 185, and assuming that the growth rate remains constant, calculate its populations for (a) the year you will graduate from high school, (b) the year you would expect to have a child your age, and (c) the year you would expect to retire from your job. Record these calculations in your *Log.* What do these calculations indicate?

5. Using the data from the Barbados Fact Sheet on page 184 and those in Figure 3.36 on page 185, compare the net rate of increase of each country with Barbados. (A "minus" migration rate means emigration out of the country.)

Interpretations: Respond to the following in your *Log:*

1. Given the data you have examined, how would you assess the population situation on Barbados? What appears to be unique about this island? What is the problem?

2. If the Barbadian government asked you to make recommendations based on your knowledge, what would you say?

3. In what realistic ways is Barbados not an island entirely on its own?

Applications: Respond to the following in your *Log:*

1. In what ways is the population situation in Barbados similar to the situation in your community? In what ways is it different?

2. In what ways is the population situation in Barbados comparable to that of the world?

Barbados Fact Sheet

History of the People:

Barbados was probably named by Portuguese sailors in reference to bearded fig trees. An English ship visited in 1605, and British settlers arrived on the uninhabited island in 1627. Slaves worked the sugar plantations but were freed in 1834. Self-rule came gradually, with full independence proclaimed on November 30, 1966. British traditions have remained.

Geography:

SIZE: 166 square miles (430 square kilometers). Barbados is a small triangular island extending 32 kilometers from northwest to southeast and ringed by coral reef with a coastline of 97 kilometers.

LATITUDE: 59° to 60°W   LONGITUDE: 13° to 14°N

CAPITAL: Bridgetown

NEARBY LAND: 160 kilometers east of Saint Vincent; 320 kilometers northwest of Trinidad.

Climate:

Tropical with an average annual temperature of 26.5°C. The mean annual rainfall is 1,420 millimeters. There is a hot and rainy season from June to December when temperatures range from 23°C to 30°C and humidity is high. Northeast trade winds blow steadily during the dry season from December through May.

Economy (1990–1992 figures):

A per capita income of $6,500 has given Barbados one of the highest standards of living among the small island nations of the Caribbean. Historically, this island's economy was based on sugarcane and other agricultural products. The current economy has diversified to include manufacturing and tourism. The tourist industry is the major employer of the labor force and the primary source of foreign exchange.

INFLATION RATE: (consumer prices) 3.4%   UNEMPLOYMENT: 18%

MAJOR INDUSTRIES: Tourism, sugar, light manufacturing, component assembly for export.

IMPORTS: Foodstuffs, consumer durables, raw materials, machinery, crude oil, construction materials, chemicals.

EXPORTS: Sugar and molasses, electrical components, clothing, rum, machinery, and transport equipment.

AGRICULTURE: Accounts for 10 percent of Gross National Product; major cash crop is sugarcane; other crops: vegetables and cotton; not self-sufficient in food.

Flying fish for sale in a market.

Population Characteristics (1990s):

POPULATION: 256,000 (July 1994)

POPULATION GROWTH RATE: 0.24% /year

BIRTHRATE: 15 births/1,000 population/year

RATE OF NATURAL INCREASE: 0.7%

DEATH RATE: 8 deaths/1,000 population/year

NET MIGRATION RATE: 6 emigrants/1,000 population/year

INFANT MORTALITY RATE: 22 deaths/1,000 live births/year

LIFE EXPECTANCY AT BIRTH: 73 years male, 78 years female

TOTAL FERTILITY RATE: 1.8 children per woman

LITERACY: 99% age 15 and over who have attended school

BIRTH, DEATH, AND MIGRATION RATES/1000 PERSONS/YEAR, 1995

COUNTRY	Birth Rate	Death Rate	Migration Rate	Population Growth Rate
Barbados	15.45	8.27	−4.82	0.24%
USA	15.25	8.38	3.34	1.02%
Germany	10.98	10.83	2.46	0.26%
Niger	54.80	20.80	0.00	3.40%
Brazil	21.16	8.98	0.00	1.22%
India	27.78	10.07	0.00	1.77%
Australia	14.13	7.37	6.33	1.31%

Figure 3.36

Population data for various countries for comparison to Barbados.

Population Growth in My Town

Do you live in a small town? Do the people in your town tend to stay put, living and dying where they were born? Does your town have a local cemetery where most of the residents are buried when they die? Does it contain gravestones from early in your town's history? If so, you have a chance to do an interesting study. Visit the cemetery and take some notes. Look at birth and death dates, life spans, and gender. The gravestone may even tell you if the cause of death was war or illness. What was the population growth pattern over a period of 50, 75, or 100 years or even longer? What major historical events may have had significant impact on the population numbers? How has the life span changed over the years? How much has the town grown?

As an alternative, visit city hall. Birth and death records there are an additional source of information. In addition, you can talk to senior citizens who know the town well or find data in back issues of the local paper.

Put the data into some kind of form. Create graphs showing the number of individuals born or dying each year. The X axis will be for years; the Y axis will be the number of individuals. Or make a histogram of life spans. Here the X axis is life span categories such as <10 years, 10–20 years, and so on; the Y axis is number of individuals. A computer data management program can help you to analyze your data and create the graphs.

Revisiting the Video

How would you describe human population growth? At what time in recorded history did human population growth rates change most dramatically? When did the world population reach greatly accelerated or exponential growth? To answer these questions, you will revisit the Unit 3 video segment, examine Figure 3.37, and discuss questions about the history of population growth. Because this very short video is packed with information, you may want to view it several times.

Procedure

1. Watch the video again to get a feel for the pattern of human population growth.

2. Watch a second time (and a third if needed) and describe:

    a. what happened to the population in the years 200, 400, 600, 800, 1000, and 2000.

    b. the major historical events in these years.

3. Create a line graph of world population changes throughout history using the data in Figure 3.38.

Interpretations: Respond to the following in your *Log*. Review the video again if you need to.

1. What did the sound in the video symbolize?

2. When did you begin to notice a large increase in population growth? In what year does the growth begin?

3. What specific historical events, scientific advances, or societal changes may have contributed to that population growth? What limiting factors may have contributed to these changes in population growth?

4. Slight decreases in the population size occurred at several points. In what part(s) of the world did you notice decreasing population size? What biological events, such as those in Figure 3.39, in those time periods may have contributed to the population size decreases?

5. In which country did the most population growth occur? Choose a time period, and determine which parts of the world experienced the most growth during this time period.

Figure 3.37

Each dot on this map represents a population of 1,000,000 people.

Reprinted courtesy of Zero Population Growth, Inc.

1990

6. What areas of the world are likely to remain relatively unpopulated by the year 2020? Why?

Applications: Respond to the following in your *Log:*

1. How rapidly has your community (town or city) been growing?

2. How might projected world population growth affect your community during your lifetime?

3. In a paragraph in your *Log,* summarize the main ideas of the video.

YEAR	POPULATION (IN MILLIONS)
1	170
200	190
400	190
600	200
800	220
1000	265
1100	320
1200	360
1300	360
1400	350
1500	425
1600	545
1700	610
1800	900
1850	1211
1900	1625
1950	2515
2000	6251
2050	8062

Figure 3.38

Use these data to make a graph of world population changes throughout history.

Reprinted courtesy of Zero Population Growth, Inc.

A — **CELLS FIRST DISCOVERED**

B — **DARWIN SAILS**

C — **CHROMOSOME DISCOVERED**

D — **DNA DISCOVERED**

Figure 3.39

Do you recall when the pictured biological events occurred? How did they affect the human population?

Extended Inquiry 3.4

Continued Investigations on Your Own Population

What will happen if you change one of the living conditions (variables) of the population that you started in Guided Inquiry 3.1? What if you change habitat size, resource use and allocation, or environmental factors? How will the change affect carrying capacity?

After reviewing the safety notes on page 144, try these activities with samples taken from your own population:

◆ Remove a sample of your population, and place it in a separate container. Omit one essential factor from the sample, such as food, water, or light. Continue to care for your main population as you always have. Monitor the changes in population size in the sample, and compare it to your main population.

- Remove a sample of your population, and place it in a separate container. Vary the amount of one essential factor, such as food, water, light, or specific food. Don't provide any food for a few days or weeks, for example, and then add food. Monitor the population size throughout the starvation and refeeding periods.

- Remove a sample of your population, and place it in a separate container. Add an appropriate predator or competitor. Monitor the population size until one population is extinct in the container.

Extended Inquiry 3.5

The Last Days of Easter Island

Today, Easter Island (Figure 3.40), in the Pacific Ocean, contains about 2,100 people and more than 200 massive stone statues. The archeological evidence indicates that the population on the island was once much larger. What happened? The August 1995 issue of *Discover* magazine contains a fascinating article that attempts to explain the history of the island.

If this mystery fascinates you, find the article and read it. Write a brief report containing the following:

- A summary of the article

- Your interpretation of why the island is now so sparsely populated

- The connection between this story and the possible future of planet earth

Figure 3.40

These statues are evidence of a great population on Easter Island. Why did so many inhabitants leave?

Participate in the Monarch Watch

Each fall, millions of monarch butterflies (Figure 3.41) begin one of the most spectacular migrations in nature, a 3,000-mile journey from their summer breeding grounds to their remote winter habitat on mountaintops in Mexico. What guides them to roosts they have never seen? How do they find their way? How do monarchs from Colorado to New England all find the same roosts each year? What are the secrets of the monarchs?

We know where the migration begins and where it ends. But we don't know how the monarch accomplishes this amazing migration. We're curious about the answers, but curiosity is not the only reason we are seeking clues to the mystery.

Knowledge serves as our best guide in preserving and protecting our natural resources. As our knowledge of the monarch increases, so does our ability to ensure that future generations will enjoy this magical flight.

The Monarch Watch has two parts: tagging and observation. You can join in one or both aspects of the program. Your teacher can give you more information about the Monarch Watch, or you can look it up on the Internet at *http://monarch.bio.ukans.edu*

Figure 3.41

Migrating monarch butterflies.

Self-Check 2

Now that you have completed at least one of the Extended Inquiries, you are ready to find out how well you understand populations by working through the following questions and activities. Work in groups of four, assigning three different questions or chores to each person. Once you have answered your questions, get back into your group to review all the responses. The group should evaluate each response and modify it if necessary. Be sure that each member of the group has a final set of responses. If you find that you need help getting answers to some of the questions, consult your teacher.

1. Design an experiment to study the environmental factors affecting population growth.

2. Why are graphs an effective method of communicating population growth patterns?

3. What are the differences between what a straight line and curved line shows in a graph of population size over time?

4. Explain in population terms the status of the human population on the earth. Describe an example of a human population that has probably reached its carrying capacity. What can be done to permit that population to exceed its carrying capacity? What should be done?

5. Why is human population growth such an issue today? What are some consequences of human overpopulation?

6. Describe a career that requires knowledge of populations and population growth principles.

7. What is the value of keeping records for research that takes a long time and generates a lot of data?

8. What is the role of constructing a graph in understanding the results of an experiment?

9. What are usually the independent and dependent variables in a graph of population growth?

10. What are among some independent variables that could affect a population growth experiment?

11. How does the amount of resources available for one individual change as population size increases but resource availability does not? What can happen between individuals in such cases?

12. What is the carrying capacity of a population? What factors might cause a change in carrying capacity?

EXPLORING FUTURE SCENARIOS

Sometimes when scientists want to help others picture what they think could happen, they create a scenario. This is a story with details that helps envision the possible outcomes of an event, given certain assumptions. In this Congress, you will be part of a group that presents a scenario of a growth pattern for humans on the earth.

Setting

The United Nations is trying to make some long-range plans for the next half century. There are many very important global areas that require advance planning. Among these are health care and disease, international peace, human rights, education, nutrition, and equitable distribution of natural resources. Obviously population growth is a major variable that will affect all of these areas. But, what kind of world population growth pattern is most likely in the future?

The UN is seeking input from knowledgeable sources through delegates in every country. Your biology class has been asked for your best prediction of world population growth over the next fifty years. To accomplish this in the most systematic way, you will need to consider some future population growth scenarios and determine which is most likely.

Procedure

1. Your class will form four groups. Each group will consider a different population growth scenario. The four possible scenarios are listed below. Each are represented by a graph presented earlier in this Unit.

◆ Continued growth without limits (Figure 3.18)

◆ Maintenance of a stable population size (Figure 3.22)

♦ Growth and eventual decline (Figure 3.23)

♦ Fluctuation about a carrying capacity (Figure 3.24)

2. Choose a group/scenario in which you are interested and for which you feel you could find supporting evidence. Please refer to the figures listed for a graphic representation of your scenario.

3. In your groups, elect a chair, a recorder, and a facilitator. The remaining members will be brainstormers and data gathers.

4. Each group will study a scenario, gather supporting evidence for it, and construct a briefing to present to the entire class. Try to draw from your learning experiences in Unit 3. Consider and include information on the following:

   a. A projection of actual population numbers over the next 50 years.

   b. An explanation of why this scenario is a reasonable outcome.

   c. Possible limiting factors to the growth rate.

   d. An estimate of the possible carrying capacity of the U.S. in 50 years.

   e. An estimate of the possible consequences of this scenario.

5. Convene the entire class as a Congress. Each group will have ten minutes to present its scenario and corresponding briefing. The entire class will then vote on which they think is the most likely scenario for the future 50 years. Members of a group are free to vote for a scenario other than the one represented by their group. The most convincing scenario will be the one sent by your class to the UN delegation.

Homework

As homework, reflect upon the deliberations of this class Congress. Make a statement in your *Log* about the scenario you personally think is most likely, and explain why it is the most reasonable one to you.

The United States Congress is beginning debate over a bill for an amendment to the Constitution that would limit net population growth to 0.8 percent per year for the next 50 years beginning in the year 2000. Each state would establish its own mechanisms for limiting population growth; however, immigration into the state from other states or countries could not be limited. Immigration laws would be established by the federal government and by the respective states in separate legislation.

Procedure

1. Working in small groups, determine the following:
   a. What number of new individuals would constitute 0.8 percent per year?
   b. How might your state limit net population growth to this level?
   c. How could we limit immigration into the US overall?
2. Your group should debate another group about the following:
   a. How will these limitations impact different groups in society?
   b. What other laws would have to be changed to support this amendment?
   c. What are the ramifications of this amendment?
   d. How practical, ethical, and legal is this amendment?
3. Finally, take a class vote on the bill. This represents your informed, class opinion over this amendment.
4. Record in your *Log* the outcome and what you believe to be reasons for this vote. Give your personal thoughts on how limited population growth could best be accomplished.

Summary of Major Concepts

1. A population is a geographically isolated group of individuals that interbreeds. A population is composed of only one type of organism (one species).

2. Population density is the number of individuals in a given area or volume. Population distribution tells how individuals are located within a designated area.

3. Populations increase in size by growth or immigration. They decrease in size by death or emigration.

4. All populations have much the same basic needs as do individuals for food, shelter, space, and the opportunity to reproduce.

5. A census is a count of all of the individuals in a population. Large populations may be estimated by sampling of portions of the organisms' territory.

6. When populations grow under conditions of unlimited resources, the growth pattern becomes geometric. Geometric growth causes population numbers to rise very rapidly. This pattern is indicated by a curved or J-shaped graph line.

7. Population growth rate can be expressed as the percentage increase in organisms per year. Changes in the numbers of a population can also be expressed by the equation

$$\Delta N = B - D + I - E$$

8. A community consists of closely interacting populations of different species in an ecosystem.

9. Graphs are effective methods of communicating population growth because they illustrate patterns visually.

10. Eventually, most populations stabilize and fluctuate over periods of time, depending on environmental pressures. One such pressure is predator-prey relationships.

11. Limiting factors are independent variables that regulate the size of a population.

12. Carrying capacity is the maximum number of individuals of a species that the environment can support.

13. The human population could exceed the carrying capacity of the earth. The local carrying capacity is already exceeded in some isolated areas, such as Barbados and most of our large metropolitan areas. These areas must import food and other resources to support their local population.

14. When one does an experiment over long periods of time, accurate records of observations are essential.

Suggestions for Further Exploration

Bodanis, D. 1992. *The Secret Garden: Dawn to Dusk in the Astonishing Hidden World of the Garden.* Simon & Schuster, New York.

This delightful book includes many color pictures, often enlarged up to 2,000 times, of the inhabitants of an average back yard. It includes discussion of interactions among the populations living there.

Cohen, Joel. 1992. How Many People Can Earth Hold? *Discover*, 13 (11), 114–20.

Includes a discussion on Malthus' theory of population growth, projections from the United Nations' Population Division, and the economic considerations of population growth.

Gallant, R. 1990. *The Peopling of Planet Earth: Human Population Growth Through the Ages.* Macmillan, New York.

Examines the impact of human population growth from the origin of the species to the present day.

Gorham, E. An ecologist's guide to the problems of the 21st century. 1990. *The American Biology Teacher*, 52(8), 480–483.

Discusses the ecological problems seen by late 20th-century ecologists, such as population growth, energy glow, community regulation, the role of diversity, and behavior.

Matthews, R.W., Koballa, T.R., Flage, L.R., and Pyle, E.J. 1996. *WOWBugs*. Riverview Press, Athens, GA.

Winckler, S. 1990. *Our Endangered Planet: Population Growth*. Lerner Publications, Minneapolis, MN.

Written at a middle-school level, this book studies the effects of uncontrolled population growth on the global environment. It discusses the often dangerous pressures on natural resources, wildlife, air, water, and living space.

World Population Data Sheet. Population Reference Bureau, Inc., Washington, DC.

Produced annually by the Population Reference Bureau, the Data Sheet lists "all geopolitical entities with populations of 15,000 or more and all members of the UN." Data are listed for population, birth and death rates, doubling time, infant mortality rate, and life expectancy.

Videos

Powers of Ten. (1978) Pyramid Film & Video, Santa Monica, CA.

A popular nine-minute video that illustrates differences in magnitudes. Starting at a picnic by a lake, it transports the viewer outward toward edges of the universe and in to the level of atoms.

Internet Resource

Population Reference Bureau Web Site. URL: http://www.prb.org/prb/

Provides timely, objective information on U.S. and international population trends. Web sites change frequently; therefore use a search engine to look for this and related sites.

U.S. Census Bureau World Wide Web Site. URL: http://www.census.gov

Provides up-to-date U.S. population information including special reports and a daily estimate of the U.S. population.

The Body's Mechanisms

WORK TO

KEEP

CONDITIONS

OF LIFE

C O N

FOUR

HOMEOSTASIS: THE BODY IN BALANCE

S T A N T.

?

What causes an organism's system to get out of balance?

nitial Inquiry

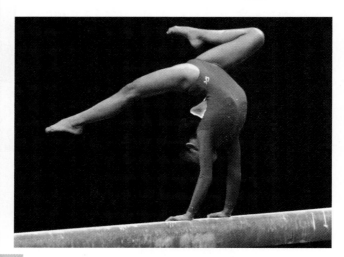

How do body functions stay in balance? What happens when they don't?

WHAT IS BALANCE AND HOW IS IT MAINTAINED?

Setting

To perform well in their chosen sports, athletes must maintain a balance within their internal physiological systems—the muscles, skeleton, nervous system, and so on. At the same time, the activities of sports training themselves threaten to disrupt the body's physiological balance. Many other activities besides sports can affect the internal balance. Scientists use the word *homeostasis* to describe a process or system that is in balance.

Complex multicellular organisms such as humans can monitor and control important functions of the body. When body temperature gets too high, for example, specialized body sensors detect the temperature change and initiate mechanisms to cool the body. When disease organisms invade the body, the immune system acts to inactivate them. These and other processes help to keep living organisms functioning properly.

Homeostasis: The Body in Balance

The Video

You will begin this unit by watching a video about students engaging in sports. Their activities would not be possible if their bodies did not maintain or restore homeostasis. Yet these and other activities threaten homeostasis. As you watch the video, try to detect potential threats to homeostasis.

As you watch the video, focus on these four questions:

◆ What seems to be out of balance in the organisms in this video?

◆ What are the signs that some imbalance is occurring in these organisms?

◆ What could cause the apparent imbalance?

◆ How could the imbalance be corrected or prevented?

Brainstorming

In small groups, discuss the above questions and try to agree on answers. Then discuss the following questions, and record your responses in your *Log*:

◆ What is balance?

◆ What is being done to keep a proper balance?

◆ How do you know that monitoring and control are occurring?

◆ How do organisms other than humans maintain balance in their body functions (Figure 4.1)?

Figure 4.1

What internal balance must animals maintain to live outside in winter and summer?

What Is Balance?

Conditions of the body's internal environment that need to be regulated include temperature, blood pressure, and salt concentration. Changes can sometimes cause these conditions to increase or decrease. Balance results when these conditions are held constant. Think of a circus performer who balances a pole on the end of his nose. He moves constantly, adjusting his position to keep the pole upright and on the tip of his nose. Like the circus performer, your body works to maintain balance in the face of changing conditions.

An organism is in balance when it can maintain vital conditions such as body temperature, fluid volume, and nutrient concentrations. During exercise, muscles use large amounts of nutrients, especially sugar, as well as oxygen. Waste products of cellular respiration (such as carbon dioxide) build up quickly. The internal chemistry of the human body is temporarily out of balance during strenuous exercise. The body needs to replace the sugars and oxygen that it uses and get rid of carbon dioxide and other wastes. To reestablish homeostasis in this situation, the heart and breathing rates increase, bringing the needed oxygen and sugar to the internal environment. Exercise also increases body temperature. The body responds by increasing perspiration to step up heat loss and lower body temperature. Body temperature remains relatively constant because heat gain is balanced by heat loss.

Monitoring and Control

How does the body know what to do to establish balance? When body temperature rises, for example, internal sensors that monitor temperature alert the brain. The brain responds by generating a series of internal signals that activate processes to increase heat loss. These processes include perspiration and flushing the skin with blood. The sensors continue to report the internal temperature to the brain. Actions and reactions continue until the temperature is normal.

A home heating and cooling system can be used as a model to illustrate homeostasis (Figure 4.2). The system contains a device to monitor temperature, the thermostat, and devices to control the temperature, a furnace and an air conditioner. (A heat pump may serve for both heating and

Figure 4.2

A room thermostat is a model of a homeostatic mechanism.

Homeostasis: The Body in Balance

cooling.) When the house becomes too cool, for example, the thermostat turns on the furnace. The temperature begins to rise. When the temperature reaches the desired level, the thermostat turns off the furnace.

Your body's temperature regulator uses a similar mechanism to maintain temperature. Specialized cells in the brain act as a thermostat. The body can increase heat loss by perspiration and by increasing the flow of blood to the skin. The body can increase heat gain by lowering blood flow to the skin and by shivering, which generates heat quickly.

Transport Processes Maintain Homeostasis

Many of the adjustments that maintain homeostasis in the body involve the transport of materials such as water, salts, sugar, and nutrients throughout the body. Several processes are used to transport materials. These include diffusion, convection, and active transport.

Diffusion is the random motion of atoms and molecules that takes place in all substances. As they move, atoms and molecules tend to become evenly distributed (Figure 4.3). There is a redistribution of atoms and molecules from areas of high concentrations to areas of low concentrations. Diffusion occurs quickly over small distances and very slowly over larger distances. For example, a small molecule in water might move 1 micrometer (10^{-6} meter) in 1 millisecond but only 1 centimeter (10^{-2} meter) in 1 day. Much of the transport of materials at the cell level is by diffusion. You will investigate diffusion in Guided Inquiries 4.1 and 4.2.

Convection is the mass movement of materials by what we normally call flow. Much of the movement of molecules that we observe combines actions of diffusion and convection (Figure 4.4). The heart is a muscular pump that causes the blood to flow. The movements of the chest muscles and diaphragm cause air to flow into and out of the lungs. Convection allows materials to be moved in bulk rapidly over distances greater than a millimeter.

Active transport differs from diffusion in that it uses organismal energy to move molecules. The required energy is usually in the form of ATP (adenosine triphosphate), which is produced during metabolism. Whereas diffusion causes molecules to move from more concentrated areas to less concentrated areas, active transport can move molecules from less concentrated areas to more concentrated areas. 🐾

Figure 4.3

The dye eventually becomes evenly dispersed because of random molecular movement.

Water

Dye molecules

Figure 4.4

Both diffusion and convection act to distribute this dye in the water.

Guided Inquiry 4.1

Diffusion

How do molecules move between cells? This Inquiry models molecular movement so that you can observe the process of diffusion. You will examine diffusion of a mild acid in agar, a carbohydrate that is extracted from brown seaweed. (Agar and other seaweed carbohydrates are used to thicken foods such as pudding and ice cream.) You will experiment with various amounts of acid and various-sized cubes of agar gel to explore the following questions:

- ◆ How do the amount of acid and the size of the agar cube affect diffusion?
- ◆ How does the relationship between surface area and volume affect diffusion?

The agar cubes that you will use in this Inquiry contain phenolphthalein, a chemical that is pink in the presence of a base and colorless in the presence of an acid. When you place an agar cube into an acid solution, the acid diffuses into the gel, causing the phenolphthalein to become colorless. You can see how far the acid has traveled into the agar block by measuring the width of the colorless zone.

This Inquiry has two parts. Part A examines the effect of a solution's concentration on diffusion. Part B examines the relationship of surface area and volume to the amount of diffusion. Work in groups of at least four students. Two group members will set up Part A, and the other two will set up Part B. All group members will make observations for both parts of the Inquiry.

MATERIALS

- A wax marking pen or water-proof marker
- Seven small beakers, jars, or plastic cups
- HCl solutions: 5 percent, 0.5 percent, 0.05 percent, and 0.005 percent
- A block of phenolphthalein agar
- A knife or dental floss to cut the agar
- Four plastic spoons
- A clock or watch that measures seconds
- Paper towels
- A metric ruler
- Safety goggles, gloves, and apron

Part A: Concentration

Concentration describes the amount of a substance in a given volume. You will explore the effect of the concentration of a diffusing substance on the distance traveled by the substance in a set time.

Procedure

1. Use the marking pen to number four beakers 1 to 4. Place 100 milliliters of hydrochloric acid (HCl) solution in each beaker as follows: Beaker 1: 5 percent HCl; Beaker 2: 0.5 percent HCl; Beaker 3: 0.05 percent HCl; Beaker 4: 0.005 percent HCl.

2. Cut four cubes, 3 centimeters on each side, from the agar block. They should be nearly identical. Wear gloves, and be careful not to damage the cubes as you handle them.

3. Using the plastic spoons, place each cube in a different beaker. Begin timing immediately. Let the cubes remain in the solutions for 6 minutes.

4. In your *Log,* write a hypothesis about how the concentration of the acid solution affects the rate of diffusion.

5. Remove all cubes from the beakers at the same time. Place each cube on a paper towel. Slice each cube open across the colored area with a knife or dental floss. Measure the thickness (in millimeters) of the colorless edge (that area that is not pink) on the cut face of each cube. Refer to Figure 4.5. Create a data table in your *Log* like the one in Figure 4.6, and record your data.

6. For each solution, record the distance (in millimeters) that the acid traveled in 6 minutes. You will not calculate a rate (millimeters per minute) here because the distance traveled by a diffusing substance is not proportional to time.

Figure 4.5

Trim your cube of phenolphthalein agar after it has been in an acid solution for 6 minutes.

Beaker Number	HCl Solutions	Distance (mm) traveled (thickness of colorless edge) in 6 minutes
1	5%	
2	0.5%	
3	0.05%	
4	0.005%	

Figure 4.6

Sample data table for Part A.

Part B: Relationship of Surface Area to Volume

In this part of the Inquiry, you will explore the relationship of the surface area and the volume to the rate of diffusion.

Procedure

1. Use the marking pen to number three beakers 1 to 3. Place 100 milliliters of 5 percent hydrochloric acid (HCl) solution in each beaker.

2. Cut three different-sized agar cubes from the agar block. For example, you might make one cube 3 centimeters on each side, one 2 centimeters on each side, and one 1 centimeter on each side. Record the sizes in a data table like Figure 4.7.

3. Using plastic spoons, place each cube in a different beaker. Let the cubes stay in the solutions for 6 minutes. While you wait, calculate the surface area and volume of each cube:

   Surface area of a cube = Length × Width × 6

   Volume = Length × Width × Height

   Record this information (in cubic centimeters) in your data table.

4. Construct a hypothesis about the effect of cube size on the depth to which the acid penetrates in 6 minutes.

5. After 6 minutes, carefully remove all three cubes from the beakers and place them on a paper towel. Cut away the cleared edges of each cube so that you are left with only the pink portions.

6. Measure the dimensions of each remaining pink cube (in millimeters). Record these values in the data table in your *Log*. Calculate the surface areas and volumes of the pink cubes, and record them in your *Log*.

Figure 4.7

Sample data table for Part B.

Beaker Number	Dimensions of original cube	Dimensions of pink cube	Surface area of original cube	Surface area of pink cube	Volume of original cube	Volume of pink cube	SA/V ratio of original cube	SA/V ratio of pink cube
1								
2								
3								

Interpretations: Respond to the following in your *Log*:

1. Check your data for diffusion in Part A. How does the distance traveled in 6 minutes differ among the four cubes?

Homeostasis: The Body in Balance

2. Construct a bar graph (histogram) of your results for Part A. Label the horizontal axis with the different concentrations of HCl (the independent variable). Label the vertical axis with the distance traveled in 6 minutes (the dependent variable). Refer to Appendix L for assistance in constructing graphs. Give your graph an appropriate descriptive title.

3. How did the concentration of HCl affect diffusion into the cubes? What conclusions can you draw from your data? How are these conclusions different from your conclusions about the distance traveled?

4. Compare the amounts of pink agar that you observed in each cube at the end of the experiment in Part B. Calculate the ratio of surface area to volume for each cube. Record this information in your *Log*. Calculate the volume of each remaining pink cube as a percentage of the original volume of the cube. Record this information in your *Log*.

5. Construct a bar graph (histogram) or scattergram that shows the relationship between the volume of each remaining pink cube as a percentage of the original volume of the cube and the original cube's surface area to volume ratio. Use the ratio as the independent variable (horizontal axis) and the percentage volume of the pink cube as the dependent variable (vertical axis). Refer to Appendix L for assistance in constructing graphs.

6. What interpretations can you make from your histogram about the effect that the surface area to volume ratio has on diffusion?

7. Was the acid penetration distance different in each cube? In which cube was diffusion the most complete? How can you explain this?

Applications: Answer the following in your *Log*:

1. How might the limits of diffusion affect living organisms? How could an organism rely on diffusion alone as a mechanism to expel wastes and gain nutrients?

2. Most cells are no larger than 0.01 centimeter on a side; some are much smaller. What did you learn from this experiment that might explain why most cells are not very large? What exceptions are there to this rule? What challenges exist for the cell in Figure 4.8 for exchange of materials such as oxygen and carbon dioxide?

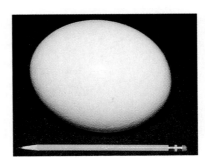

Figure 4.8

An ostrich egg is one of the largest cells in the world.

How Particles Diffuse

Diffusion is the simplest transport mechanism in living organisms. The process occurs because all molecules have energy, which makes them move. As molecules bump into one another, they change directions randomly. No energy from the cells themselves is required. However, diffusion alone cannot meet the needs of cells to transport materials, especially in very large cells, such as the ostrich egg in Figure 4.8.

◆ Diffusion is effective only over minute distances.

◆ Sometimes the rate of diffusion is insufficient for material transport needs.

◆ Material that moves into or out of a cell is consumed as it reacts with other substances in the cell or is used by cellular metabolic processes.

As you observed in Guided Inquiry 4.1, particles diffuse from areas where they are more concentrated to areas where they are less concentrated. In Guided Inquiry 4.1, the concentration difference was greatest between the agar cube and the 5 percent acid solution. More molecules of acid from this solution diffused into the agar, but the distance that these molecules penetrated into the agar was the same as that in the less acidic solutions.

Diffusing particles or molecules can enter an object, such as the agar cube, only through its surface. Objects with a small surface area to volume ration (S/V), like your largest cube, have a long distance between their surface and their center. Objects with a large S/V, like your smallest cube, have a shorter distance between their surface and center. This is why a greater percentage of the original volume of the larger cubes remained pink after immersion in the acid solution. 🌐

Figure 4.9

The fact that this cross-section of a Norway spruce needle is clearly composed of cells means that it was once living.

What Is a Cell?

A cell is the basic unit of life (Figure 4.9). It is defined as an organized entity that can survive and reproduce. The term *cell* was applied by the 17th-century English microscopist Robert Hooke. He and other early users of microscopes devised three generalizations about cells:

◆ All organisms are composed of cells.

◆ The cell is the basic unit of life.

◆ New cells arise only from cells that already exist.

Characteristics of Cells

Cells are the building blocks of all organisms. Every cell potentially can:

◆ copy genetic (hereditary) information,

◆ make new cell components,

◆ make and use energy-rich compounds,

◆ enclose its internal contents within a boundary that separates the contents from the external environment, and

◆ regulate the passage of materials into and out of the cell.

Cell Boundaries

Although the external boundaries of cells may differ, depending on the type of cell, all cells are surrounded by a layer called the cell membrane. The cell membrane acts not only as a barrier, but also as the site for active transport of nutrients into the cell and waste products out of the cell. In fact, the cell membrane plays the most important role of any cell component in maintaining a balance between the internal and external environments of the cell.

The Cell Membrane

The cell membrane is made up of two layers of lipid molecules that form a flexible "sandwich" called a lipid bilayer (Figure 4.10). Each lipid molecule has an electrically charged (polar) head region and an uncharged (nonpolar) tail. The polar heads on both sides of the membrane are in contact with watery environments: the fluid outside of the cells and the watery cytoplasm inside the cell. Both of these environments, like the lipid molecule heads, are electrically charged. Proteins embedded within and on the bilayer perform a variety of jobs in the membrane. For example, some act as bridges or pumps that move substances into and out of the cell.

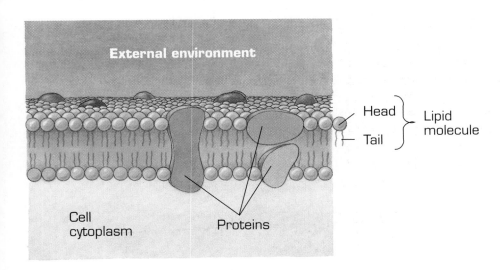

Figure 4.10

The cell membrane is a lipid bilayer with embedded and surface proteins.

Figure 4.11

This bacterium, like all prokaryotes, does not have a membrane-bound nucleus.

The cell membrane is called a selectively permeable membrane because it allows some types of molecules to pass through while blocking others. For example, water and oxygen molecules pass through the cell membrane easily, as do uncharged molecules such as small lipids. Charged atoms and large molecules, such as glucose, have a much harder time getting through the cell membrane. However, these molecules may pass through channels or be actively transported across membranes by proteins.

Distinctions among Cells

There are two main types of cells: prokaryotes and eukaryotes. The primary difference between prokaryotes and eukaryotes is the way the cells package their genetic material and internal functions. In eukaryotic cells, the genetic material is enclosed in a membrane-bounded nucleus. Eukaryotic cells also contain membrane-bounded compartments called organelles. Prokaryotes lack a membrane-bound nucleus and organelles, though they do have most of their genetic material concentrated in a nuclear area.

Prokaryotic Cells

Prokaryotic cells are usually much smaller than eukaryotic cells. Bacterial cells, for example, are prokaryotes (Figure 4.11). Most prokaryotic cells are only a few micrometers in diameter, whereas eukaryotic cells are usually 10 to 1,000 micrometers in diameter. Prokaryotes are believed to be the first organisms to have evolved on earth, approximately 3.5 billion years ago.

The basic components of a prokaryotic cell are shown in Figure 4.12. Most prokaryotes have both cell walls and cell membranes. The cell walls provide protection and maintains the shape of a bacterial cell. Prokaryotic

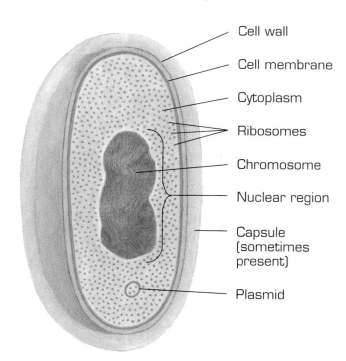

Cell wall

Cell membrane

Cytoplasm

Ribosomes

Chromosome

Nuclear region

Capsule (sometimes present)

Plasmid

Figure 4.12

The structure of a prokaryote cell.

cell walls have a unique chemical composition different from the walls of other cells, such as plants. The cell wall may be covered with a sticky protective layer, called a capsule. Though the cell may contain internal membranes, it lacks membrane-bounded compartments. Small spherical structures called ribosomes are scattered throughout the cytoplasm. Proteins are made on the ribosomes. Some prokaryotes also have specialized membranes within the cytoplasm that are used for respiration and photosynthesis. The genetic material usually is concentrated into a nuclear region but is not contained in a membrane. The cell also may contain additional hereditary material: small circular structures called plasmids.

Eukaryotic Cells

Eukaryotic cells contain a membrane-bound nucleus and other membrane-bounded compartments called organelles. Because the organelles have various functions, membranes allow the different processes that are involved to be separated from each other within the cell. All plant and animal cells are eukaryotic.

The major organelles in plant and animal cells are identified in Figure 4.13. The nucleus contains the genetic material of each cell. The mitochondria are the cell's powerhouses where cellular respiration takes place and ATP (adenosine triphosphate) is produced. The sphere-shaped structures in the cytoplasm are ribosomes. Proteins are synthesized on the ribosomes. In eukaryotic cells, ribosomes may be bound to layers of folded membranes called the endoplasmic reticula (ER). These ER are called rough ER because their surface appears rough in electron microscope photos. Endoplasmic reticula without ribosomes are called smooth ER.

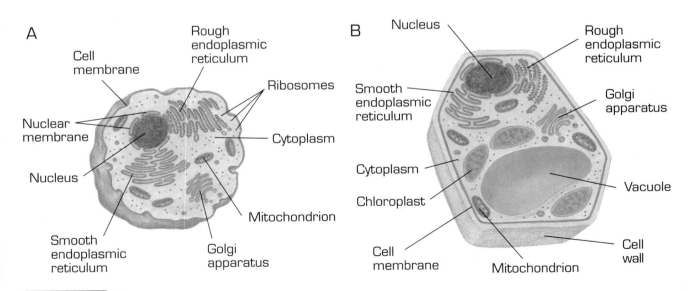

Figure 4.13

Animal (A) and plant (B) cells are eukaryotic. Which parts do they have in common? Which parts are different?

Rough endoplasmic reticula and related membranous organelles such as the Golgi apparatus are important for several reasons. Within their membranes, these organelles synthesize proteins and other cell materials, package them, and ship the materials to other locations in the cell or its external environment. For example, smooth ER has enzymes bound to the inner surface of its membranes that help in synthesizing carbohydrates and lipids that are used to produce such products as the sex hormones.

Although animal and plant cells are similar, there are several important differences between them.

Animal cells do not have walls. Some animal cells, such as those that make up organs, live in environments that have about the same salt concentration as the inside of the cell. The cells of your body, for example, are bathed in a fluid part of your blood that has a salt concentration similar to that of the interior of the cells. In this environment, your cell membranes can maintain homeostasis, since there is no strong concentration gradient between the inside and outside of the cells. Other body cells may be exposed to environmental conditions that are unlike the interior of a cell. To maintain homeostasis, these cells must use energy to actively transport molecules across the cell membrane, thereby maintaining a balance between the concentrations of certain molecules inside and outside the cell. If the cell were not able to maintain this balance, it could burst or shrink as large quantities of molecules, mostly water, move inside or outside the cell membrane.

Plant cells contain all of the internal structures that animal cells have. In addition, plant cells contain chloroplasts and are encased by a cell wall. Chloroplasts are the organelles in which photosynthesis takes place. Chlorophyll, which you studied in Unit 2, is contained in chloroplasts. All plant cells have cell walls made of rigid layers that encase the cell membranes and their contents. The major component of the plant cell wall is cellulose (see Figure 1.23 on page 35). Cell walls and the pressure exerted on the wall by the cell contents make it possible for plants to stand erect.

Figure 4.14

A photo of Tobacco mosaic virus.

Viruses Are Not Cells

Viruses (Figure 4.14) have some of the characteristics of life but are not cells. They are one of the smallest infectious agents. A virus is composed mostly of proteins and genetic material. Proteins form the protective coating that encases the genetic material. This protein coat is called the capsid. The capsids of some viruses look like geodesic domes and can be less than 0.1 micrometer in diameter. Some viruses also have a membrane layer outside the capsid called an envelope. The envelope is similar to the cell membrane and contains additional viral proteins.

Viruses replicate (make more viruses) by infecting a cell and using the cell's own materials and processes (energy, protein synthesis, and other molecules) to make new viruses. When a virus infects a cell and replicates, it usually damages or kills the cells that it has invaded as new viruses are released to infect other cells. Among the many diseases that viruses cause are colds, influenza, chicken pox, measles, mumps, hepatitis, herpes, and AIDS.

If viruses are not cells, are they alive? Scientists have discovered other, even smaller, entities that have some of the characteristics of living things. How would you define life? 🐾

Osmosis

Some molecules easily diffuse through cell membranes, as shown in Figure 4.15. Other molecules cannot pass through at all or must be moved through the membrane by active transport. Therefore cell membranes are said to be selectively permeable.

Water moves easily through cell membranes because it is a small molecule. The direction and amount of its movement is regulated by the concentration of dissolved substances inside and outside of the cell. The movement of water across cell membranes is a special case of diffusion called osmosis. 🐾

Figure 4.15

Small molecules, such as CO_2 and H_2O, diffuse through membranes. Larger molecules, such as starch, do not.

Guided Inquiry 4.2

Maintaining Water Balance

How does a cell maintain just the right amount of water inside? How does water get into a cell? In this Inquiry, you will find out how water, a molecule that is critical to life, moves into or out of a cell by the process of osmosis. The cell membrane lets the liquid part of a solution move across it, but some of the dissolved substances cannot. Therefore osmosis occurs as a result of differing concentrations of water on the two sides of the membrane.

In this Inquiry, you will observe the movement of water into and out of animal cells (Part A) and plant cells (Part B). You will also investigate factors that affect the concentration of water inside a cell.

Figure 4.16

The internal structure of a bird egg. The yolk of this unfertilized egg is a large single cell.

Part A: Animal Cells

Unfertilized bird eggs (Figures 4.8 and 4.16) are some of the largest cells in the world. Actually, the yolk of the egg is the cell; and the external membranes, egg white, and shell are accessory coverings. If the egg is fertilized, the yolk is transformed into both the embryo and its food source. The "white" part of the egg, the albumen,

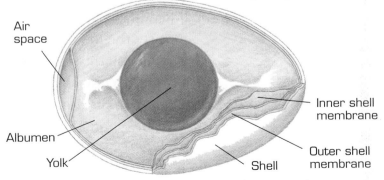

Air space · Albumen · Yolk · Inner shell membrane · Outer shell membrane · Shell

contains a protein. The albumen is enclosed by a membrane that lies just under the shell. The shell is made up of calcium carbonate ($CaCO_3$), the same molecule that is in your bones and teeth.

In this part of the Inquiry, you will observe the effects of osmosis, diffusion of water across the egg's shell membrane. You will also determine some factors that affect this movement.

MATERIALS

- One uncooked chicken egg
- A balance
- A graduated cylinder
- 100 milliliters of vinegar or other 3 percent acid solution
- A 200-milliliter beaker (with wax or plastic sealing film)
- 100 milliliters of corn syrup
- Distilled water
- Safety goggles

SAFETY NOTE

Raw eggs are known sources of *salmonella*. Wear **safety goggles** and **gloves** when handling eggs and solutions. Wash your hands at the end of each procedure on pages 212 and 213.

Procedure: Day 1

1. Describe in your *Log* the appearance of your egg.
2. Determine its mass, and record this information in your *Log*.
3. Gently submerge your egg in a jar of vinegar (about 100 milliliters). You may cover the container to prevent evaporation of the vinegar and to minimize the odor in the classroom. Leave the egg in the vinegar for 2 to 3 days.
4. Predict what will happen to the shell and the egg in the vinegar. Record your prediction in your *Log*.
5. Go on to Part B, "Plant Cells." Complete Part B and return to Part A on Day 3.

Procedure: Day 2

Observe your egg but do not disturb it.

Procedure: Day 3

1. Gently remove the egg from the jar.
2. Rinse the egg and gently pat it dry.
3. In your *Log*, describe the egg's appearance, and record its mass. Answer the following questions:
   - How did the mass change?
   - How accurate was your prediction?
4. Dispose of the vinegar, and wash the jar.
5. Measure approximately 100 milliliters of corn syrup into your jar, and place your egg back in this container. Leave it overnight.
6. In your *Log,* record a second prediction about the egg.

Procedure: Day 4

1. After 24 hours, remove the egg from the corn syrup.
2. Rinse the egg, and describe its appearance in your *Log*.
3. Determine its mass, and record the data in your *Log*.
4. Describe the appearance of the syrup remaining in the jar.
5. Dispose of the syrup, and wash the jar.
6. Consider your second prediction. How accurate was it? Explain in your *Log*.
7. Measure 100 milliliters of distilled water into the jar, and place the egg back in this container. Let the egg remain in the distilled water overnight.
8. Make a prediction about what will happen to the egg after it is submerged in distilled water. Use Figure 4.17 to help you make this prediction.

Procedure: Day 5

1. After 24 hours, remove the egg from the water.
2. Determine the mass of the egg.
3. Describe the appearance of the egg.
4. Measure the amount of water now in the jar. Record this value in your *Log*.
5. Consider your third prediction. How accurate was it?

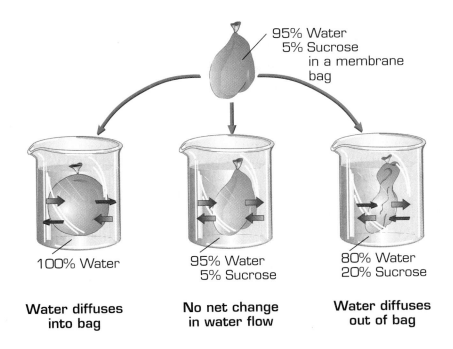

Figure 4.17

This animal membrane filled with a 5-percent sucrose solution will gain water when placed in pure water and will lose water when placed in a more concentrated sucrose solution.

Interpretations: Respond to the following in your *Log*:

1. Evaluate your predictions. How had your egg changed after you soaked it in vinegar? In syrup? In distilled water? In a table, summarize the changes that you observed.

2. How had each of the solutions in the jar changed after soaking the egg?

3. How can you account for the changes that you observed?

4. Explain why your egg reacted differently in each of the solutions.

5. What property of the cell was demonstrated in this series of experiments?

6. What other solutions might cause this egg cell to change? Design an experiment that would alter the egg in the same way that the corn syrup solution did.

7. How does Figure 4.17 compare to what happened to your egg in Guided Inquiry 4.2?

Applications: Respond to the following in your *Log*:

1. Some people sprinkle table salt on slugs in their gardens. On the basis of your results from Part A, what do you think salt does to slugs?

2. How does salt "cure" meat to preserve it, as in beef jerky?

3. Why would a long-distance runner drink liquids that contain salts? Look at the ingredients in sports beverages in the grocery store. What sorts of molecules do these ingredients supply?

Part B: Plant Cells

For this part of the Inquiry, you will be working with a freshwater plant called *Elodea* (Figure 4.18). Its leaves are only two cell layers thick, so you can observe the cells under a microscope and clearly see their structure. You can also observe some of the activities of individual cells. The parts of the cell that you may expect to see are shown in Figure 4.19. You will observe the normal *Elodea* cell and then see what happens when the environment around it is changed.

In your *Elodea* cell (Figure 4.19), you should be able to identify the nucleus, the chloroplasts, the cell membrane, and the cell wall. Depending on your view of the cell, you may observe that most of the cell contents appear to be compressed along the inside of the cell membrane. This is because most of the interior of *Elodea* cells, as in most plant cells, is taken up by a fluid-filled sac called a vacuole. In this part of the Inquiry, you will observe water loss from the vacuole.

Figure 4.18

Elodea *is a freshwater plant that is often planted in aquaria.*

Homeostasis: The Body in Balance

Figure 4.19

The internal components of an Elodea *cell as seen under a microscope.*

Labels (top to bottom):
Cell wall
Cell membrane
Cytoplasm
Chloroplast
Vacuole
Nucleus

MATERIALS

- An *Elodea* leaf
- A clean microscope slide and coverslip
- A dropper bottle of salt water
- Distilled water
- A microscope

Procedure: Begin this activity on Day 1 of Part A.

1. Place the *Elodea* leaf on the clean slide, and cover it with a drop of distilled water and a coverslip.

2. Observe the cells first on low power and then on high power. In your *Log*, sketch one or two cells while you view them under the high-power objective. Scan the entire leaf to see whether all of the cells look alike.

3. Remove the coverslip, and add a drop of salt water. What do you think will happen to the cell now? Replace the coverslip, and again observe the cells, first on low power and then on high power. Sketch one or two cells while you look at them under the high-power objective. Record any changes. Scan the entire leaf to see whether all of the cells look alike. Did the cell change in the way you expected?

4. Remove the coverslip, rinse the leaf, and then flood the leaf with distilled water. Predict what will happen to the cell now. Once again, replace the coverslip, and observe the cells first on low power and then on high power.

5. Sketch one or two cells as you look at them under the high-power objective. Record any changes that you see in the cells now that they are no longer covered with salt water.

6. Scan the entire leaf to see whether all of the cells look alike. Was your prediction correct?

Interpretations: Respond to the following in your *Log*:

1. Describe how the cells changed during this experiment.

2. What do you think might have caused this change?

3. How might this ability to adjust allow the cells to survive and stay healthy?

Applications: Respond to the following in your *Log*:

1. If you used a lot of table salt on slugs in your garden, how could it affect the plants in the garden?

2. What happens to raisins or other dried fruits in break-fast cereals when you pour milk over them? How do you explain this change?

3. Why would you be thirsty after swimming in the ocean's salty water?

How Do Plant Cells Stand Up?

When a plant has sufficient water, its cells swell and press against the interior of the cell walls. The amount of this internal stress, known as turgor pressure, determines how erect or wilted a plant appears. Erect plants exhibit higher turgor pressure. Wilted plants have low turgor pressure; they do not have enough water for their cell membranes to press against the cell wall interiors (Figure 4.20). Animal cells, which have only a delicate cell membrane enclosing the cell contents, may burst from water pressure. Plant cells, because of their strong cell walls, usually do not. 🌏

Figure 4.20

Lack of turgor pressure in a wilted plant can be inferred from the shriveled appearance of its cells.

Erect stem

Wilted stem

Food Preservation

Single-celled microorganisms, like all other organisms, must have water for cell growth and metabolism. Understanding the techniques of food preservation is a good way to review the requirements of most cells for growth. In addition to nutrients, all cells require:

◆ water and salts in the correct concentrations for that cell,

◆ an optimal temperature within a fairly narrow range, and

◆ the correct pH level.

When undesirable microorganisms begin to grow on food, we say that the food has "gone bad," or has "spoiled." Methods of food preservation (Figure 4.21) alter cellular water balance, pH, or temperature to remove microorganisms and to keep them from growing on food. These methods accomplish one or more of the following:

◆ They kill the microorganisms present.

◆ They reduce the number of microorganisms present.

◆ They create environmental conditions that make it difficult or impossible for the microorganisms to reproduce.

Drying and Salting

One preservation method is to dry foods until their water content is very low. The microorganisms that live on the food cannot grow without water, so the food is preserved safely until it is rehydrated. Fruits such as raisins (which are dried grapes) and prunes (which are dried plums) are preserved in this way.

Adding extra salt to foods is another preserving method. It is often used in addition to drying. The extra salt creates an environment in which water moves out of all of the affected cells, not only of the food but of any microorganisms existing on the food. Thus the organisms are killed or are unable to grow. Beef jerky is prepared by drying and salting the meat. Ham is sometimes preserved by coating it in layers of salt or sugar.

High concentrations of sugar in foods have the same effect as high concentrations of salt. When you make jams and jellies from fruits and added sugar, the concentration of sugar is calculated to limit the growth of microbes.

Heating and Freezing

Heat is another simple and effective technique for preserving food. Canned foods, for example, are preserved by heating them to a temperature high enough to kill most microorganisms.

Figure 4.21

Can you tell what methods were used to preserve each of these foods?

Pasteurized milk is heated to a temperature that is hot enough to kill disease-producing microorganisms but not all bacteria. Therefore pasteurized milk can still spoil. Canned or ultrapasteurized milk has been heated until all bacteria are killed.

The process of pasteurization is named after the French scientist Louis Pasteur. In 1850, he demonstrated that microorganisms cause food to spoil. He also developed a process for killing the microbes in liquids by heating. This is the process that we now know as pasteurization, which is almost universally used to preserve milk.

Freezing works as a method of food preservation because most microorganisms cannot grow on frozen food. However, freezing does not necessarily kill microorganisms, so thawed food can spoil quickly. At the very least, the microorganisms' growth rate is lessened, since they grow and divide more slowly at lower temperatures. That is why food lasts longer when it is stored in a refrigerator or another cold place.

Pickling

Pickling involves placing food in a solution in which some harmless microorganisms grow and produce acids. The low pH (high acidity) of the solution keeps other microorganisms, including harmful ones, from growing. As a consequence, pickled foods (such as sauerkraut and dill pickles) can be stored for months at room temperature. Many pickled foods are also high in salt or sugar, which helps to preserve them without refrigeration. 🌐

Balance of Water and Salts

To survive, cells must maintain a balance of water and salt. The cells of multicellular organisms such as humans are bathed in a fluid environment called extracellular ("outside of the cell") fluid that contains water and dissolved molecules such as salt. This fluid allows multicellular organisms to exist, and even thrive, in dry and constantly changing environments.

Kidneys Help to Maintain Homeostasis

In humans and other animals, kidneys (Figure 4.22) maintain homeostasis by adjusting the amount of water and dissolved substances in the extracellular fluid, including the blood. Specialized kidney structures called nephrons function by first filtering everything out of the blood except blood cells and large proteins. They then pump back into the blood just the right amounts of the specific substances that are needed to maintain homeostasis.

Substances that are not pumped back into the blood (such as nitrogenous wastes, toxic chemicals, some salts, and some water) are sent through the ureters to the bladder for excretion to the outside.

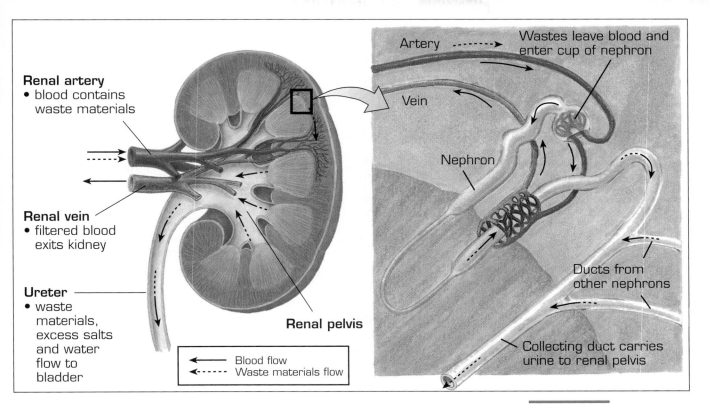

Renal artery
- blood contains waste materials

Renal vein
- filtered blood exits kidney

Ureter
- waste materials, excess salts and water flow to bladder

Renal pelvis

← Blood flow
←----- Waste materials flow

Artery ----→

Vein

Wastes leave blood and enter cup of nephron

Nephron

Ducts from other nephrons

Collecting duct carries urine to renal pelvis

Figure 4.22

The human kidney filters wastes from the blood.

Kidney Disease and Dialysis

When the kidneys don't function well, abnormal amounts of dissolved substances and liquids in the blood cause an imbalance. Harmful or toxic molecules may build up in the blood as a result. Individuals who have severely damaged kidneys must, therefore, have their blood cleaned of contaminants and excessive solutes by means of an artificial kidney in a procedure called dialysis (Figure 4.23). People with kidney failure need dialysis to survive.

An artificial kidney passes the patient's blood through a dialyzer, a chamber with very small channels surrounded by thin membranes. Blood is on one side of the membrane, and dialyzing fluid is on the other. Unwanted substances diffuse from the blood into the dialysis fluid, which then is collected in a waste container

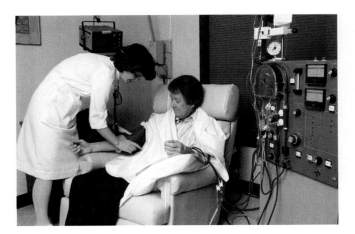

Figure 4.23

Dialysis is a routine procedure for some people who have kidney disease.

Blood flows from patient's artery into the artificial kidney

Cleansed blood flows from the artificial kidney into patient's vein

Gas bubbles removed

Dialyzer

Fresh dialyzing solution

Constant temperature bath

Used dialyzing solution

Figure 4.24

Principles of the artificial kidney.

and discarded. After blood leaves the dialyzer, the gases are removed from the blood. It is then returned to the patient and passes through the lungs to be oxygenated before it is pumped through the body. Figure 4.24 is a schematic of an artificial kidney.

Although patients with kidney disease can be kept healthy for a long time, kidney dialysis does present problems. People with failing kidneys must use the artificial kidney for 4 to 6 hours, three times a week. This can be very inconvenient and time-consuming. Patients are also threatened by possible infections and blood clots that the artificial dialysis process may cause.

The Human Urinary System

Maintaining a balance of water, salts, and other materials is crucial not only to survival at the cellular level, but also to the organism in general. An organism can get rid of excess or potentially dangerous molecules through a process called excretion. One of the ways in which waste materials leave the body is by the urinary system. The human urinary system includes the kidney, ureter, urinary bladder, and urethra (Figure 4.25). 🌐

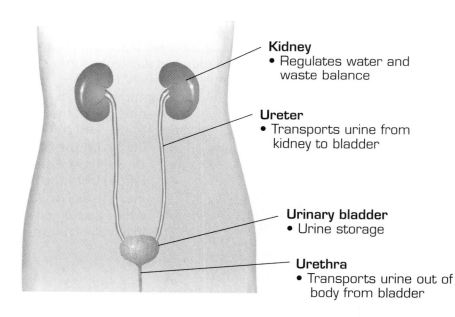

Kidney
• Regulates water and waste balance

Ureter
• Transports urine from kidney to bladder

Urinary bladder
• Urine storage

Urethra
• Transports urine out of body from bladder

Figure 4.25

The urinary system in humans rids the body of dissolved wastes.

Homeostasis: The Body in Balance

BI🌐occupation

Belfondia Pou: Medical Student

Belfondia Pou uses his knowledge of biology every day in his life, both directly and indirectly. Belfondia, known to his friends and family as "Bell," is finishing his fourth year of medical school. Bell grew up in Waynesboro, Mississippi, and graduated from high school near the top of his class of 125 students. He first became interested in medicine when he was a young boy. His mother worked at a local hospital, and he often came to visit her at work. Bell liked the working relationships that the doctors had with their patients. After completing medical school, Bell intends to enter family practice.

Bell knew at the age of eight that he wanted to be a doctor. He began to realize his goal in high school when he had the opportunity to discover more of what the medical field was all about. "I enjoyed all of the sciences," says Bell, "biology, chemistry, earth science, and physics, because they stimulated my mind."

One of the things that Bell has noticed most about his experience in medical school is how his past experiences and his earliest biology classes gave him a strong foundation for learning anatomy and other aspects of medicine. "I remember a biology class I had in high school. We were studying the workings of the human heart, but, of course, none of us had ever really seen one. When I came to medical school and saw my first cadaver, I thought, 'Oh my gosh, this is what they were talking about in high school. This is what they were trying to get across.' Those kinds of early experiences were embedded in my brain, and I could actually apply them at the hospital."

Bell said of his high school biology teacher, "She saw something at an early stage and pushed me hard to advance. To this day, I am grateful that she did that. She pushed me to do my best work, and it paid off."

Bell looks forward to the day when he has his own family practice clinic somewhere in the South. The study of biology has helped Bell to realize his dream of becoming a doctor. He says that the gratification he gets from healing a patient is like none other. His advice to students who are interested in a medical career? "Try to take as many science courses as you can. Don't steer away from them because they sound complicated. You'll find that the more complicated they are, the more you'll learn. It's that simple."

Ingestion and Digestion of Food

All organisms take in food and excrete waste. Large animals such as humans have specialized organs for ingesting, digesting, and excreting the food they eat. How do smaller organisms ingest and digest food?

Paramecium (Figure 4.26) is a single-celled microorganism that is

Figure 4.26

A Paramecium cell.

commonly found in freshwater ponds. Because it is not capable of photosynthesis, it must eat to live. *Paramecium* provides a simple model of how organisms ingest and digest food. How does this tiny creature capture food, take it in, and transport food throughout its body? In this Inquiry, you will observe *Paramecium* as it feeds on yeast cells that have been dyed red.

MATERIALS

- Petroleum jelly
- Slides and coverslips
- A dropper
- *Paramecium* culture
- Methyl cellulose solution
- Stained yeast solution
- A microscope

Procedure: Day 1

1. Make a circle (about 1 centimeter in diameter) of petroleum jelly on the slide to contain a drop of liquid.

2. With a dropper, place one drop of the *Paramecium* culture on the slide in the middle of the circle (Figure 4.27). Add one drop of

Figure 4.27

Place one drop of the Paramecium *culture on the slide in the middle of the circle.*

Toothpick dipped in petroleum jelly

A

Add 1 drop of *Paramecium* culture

B

Add 1 drop of methyl cellulose

C

Add 1 drop of yeast solution

Cover with coverslip

D

methyl cellulose. This helps to slow the movement of the organisms and makes them easier to observe.

3. Add one drop of stained yeast solution to the culture drop on the slide. Gently add a coverslip to the slide.

4. Look at the slide under low power. Locate a slow-moving *Paramecium,* and observe it under high power. Continue observing that organism until it ingests a yeast cell. There may already be yeast cells inside the organism.

5. Draw a sketch of the *Paramecium.* Include any parts that are involved in the ingestion of food, and draw any other parts you can find.

6. Refer to Figure 4.28 for help in identifying the parts of the *Paramecium* that you observed and drew. Try to determine the following:

   a. How does *Paramecium* use its cilia?

   b. Through what parts of the *Paramecium* does food travel?

   c. How is food prepared for digestion?

   d. How are digestive wastes excreted?

Procedure: Day 2

1. Repeat steps 1 through 5 from the Day 1 procedure.

2. Observe a single food vacuole as it forms, and follow its movement within the organism. Note any changes that occur inside the vacuole as it moves.

3. Observe a different vacuole as it forms, and follow its movement. Compare the movement of this second vacuole to the movement of the first one that you observed.

Interpretations: Respond to the following in your *Log*:

1. Why did you use stained yeast cells?

2. How can you distinguish between the most recently formed food vacuole and one that was formed earlier?

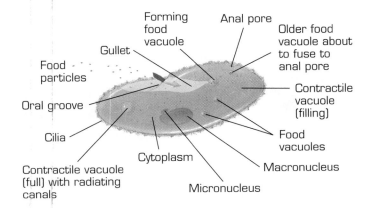

Figure 4.28

Internal structures of a Paramecium *cell.*

3. Illustrate the movement of the food vacuoles within a *Paramecium*. How do you account for this movement?

4. What might a color change within a food vacuole indicate?

5. Why is it necessary for nutrients to circulate within an organism?

Applications: Respond to the following in your *Log*:

1. Compare and contrast the way in which a *Paramecium* ingests its food and the way in which you ingest your food.

2. Describe a possible method of nutrient transport for the following kinds of multicellular organisms: plants, worms, and humans.

3. React to this statement: "Only larger organisms have complex and specialized structures." Explain your reaction to this statement on the basis of the observations that you made during this Inquiry.

Paramecium as a Research Model

Researchers often use protozoa such as *Paramecium* to study human physiology on a smaller, more convenient scale. You may have noticed many similarities between *Paramecium* and larger animals, such as humans. For example, the oral groove may be compared to a human mouth and esophagus, since it is used solely to capture food and bring it into the body for digestion. Similarly, the food vacuoles are like little stomachs where digestion takes place. The contractile vacuoles are like kidneys, since they maintain the organism's osmotic balance. There are many other interesting similarities between single-celled creatures and humans. However, although both animals have digestive systems that share the same functions, *Paramecium* uses organelles, and humans use multicellular organs. 🌐

Human Digestive System

Figure 4.29 shows the human digestive process. Food enters the digestive system through the mouth. Chewing breaks the food into smaller pieces, which are more easily digested and swallowed. Some digestion of starch takes place in the mouth as enzymes in saliva act on food particles. Chewed food then moves through the esophagus to the stomach. Some

Frank and Ernest

Copyright (c) 1996 by Thaves. Reprinted with permission.

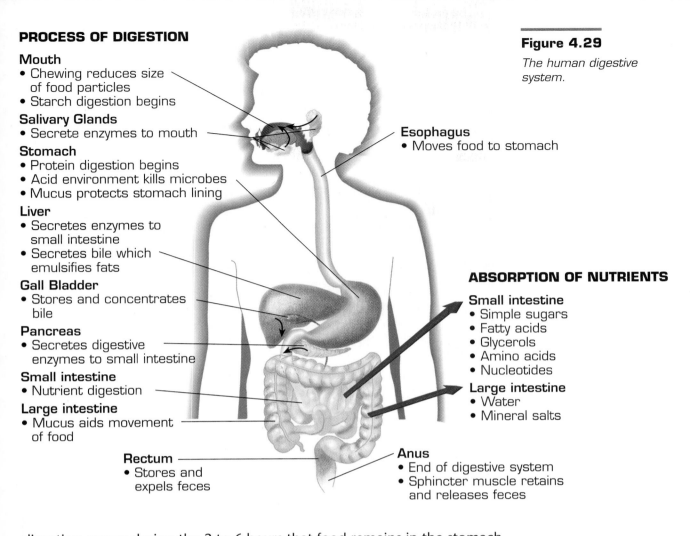

PROCESS OF DIGESTION

Mouth
- Chewing reduces size of food particles
- Starch digestion begins

Salivary Glands
- Secrete enzymes to mouth

Stomach
- Protein digestion begins
- Acid environment kills microbes
- Mucus protects stomach lining

Liver
- Secretes enzymes to small intestine
- Secretes bile which emulsifies fats

Gall Bladder
- Stores and concentrates bile

Pancreas
- Secretes digestive enzymes to small intestine

Small intestine
- Nutrient digestion

Large intestine
- Mucus aids movement of food

Rectum
- Stores and expels feces

Esophagus
- Moves food to stomach

Figure 4.29

The human digestive system.

ABSORPTION OF NUTRIENTS

Small intestine
- Simple sugars
- Fatty acids
- Glycerols
- Amino acids
- Nucleotides

Large intestine
- Water
- Mineral salts

Anus
- End of digestive system
- Sphincter muscle retains and releases feces

digestion occurs during the 2 to 6 hours that food remains in the stomach. Most of the rest of digestion occurs in the small intestine. This is also the place where food is broken down and nutrients are absorbed by the body. Undigested food passes through the large intestine or colon, is stored in the rectum, and leaves the body through the anus. 🌍

Guided Inquiry 4.4

Metabolism of Sugars

A simple sugar is called a monosaccharide. Glucose is a simple sugar. Its formula is $C_6H_{12}O_6$. An example of a more complex sugar, called a disaccharide, is sucrose: $C_{12}H_{22}O_{11}$. Disaccharides are two monosaccharides linked together by a chemical bond. Do organisms get more energy from monosaccharides than they do from disaccharides? Which sugars seem to contain the most energy? What about a more complete food source, such as molasses (which contains vitamins and minerals, as well as sugars)?

In this Inquiry, you will observe the growth of yeast as it uses either a monosaccharide, a disaccharide, or a more complex food. The monosaccharide that you will test is glucose, the disaccharide is sucrose, and the complex food is starch. You will measure the production of CO_2 to indicate metabolic activity. CO_2 is one of the products that is released as sugars are broken down. You will calculate the rate at which yeast metabolizes these various foods.

MATERIALS

- Four fermentation tubes
- A marking pen
- 10-percent solutions of glucose, sucrose, and starch
- A dropping pipette
- Yeast suspension
- Water
- A metric ruler

Procedure

1. Number the fermentation tubes 1 to 4.
2. In your *Log*, prepare a data table like the one in Figure 4.30.

Figure 4.30

Sample data table for Guided Inquiry 4.4.

Tube Number	Contents	Amount of Gas Produced (mm)	Volume of Gas Produced (mm³)	Observations
1				
2				
3				
4				

SAFETY NOTE

- Wear **safety goggles**.
- Wash hands at the end of the procedure.

3. Fill test tube 1 three-fourths full of glucose solution. Place five drops of yeast suspension in the solution. Place your thumb over the opening of the tube, and tip the tube so that the glucose and yeast mixture fills the closed end of the tube. (If you are using a test tube instead of a fermentation tube, invert a small test tube into the large test tube and tip the assembled tubes so that the glucose solution fills the small tube and sinks to the bottom. You may have to place your thumb over the mouth of the large tube to keep the solution from spilling as you tip it to fill the smaller tube.) See Figures 4.31 and 4.32.

4. Assemble tubes 2 and 3 in the same way, filling tube 2 with sucrose and 3 with starch solution.

5. Fill test tube 4 three-fourths full of water. Place five drops of yeast suspension in the water.

Homeostasis: The Body in Balance

Large
vial
(inverted)

Small
vial
(filled)

Figure 4.31

Assembly of fermentation tubes for Guided Inquiry 4.4.

Figure 4.32

As yeast grows, it produces gas.

6. Construct a hypothesis that predicts how much carbon dioxide the yeast will produce from each of the three food sources. Enter your hypothesis in your *Log*.

7. Put the tubes in your test tube rack, and set them aside overnight.

8. The next day observe the contents of the tubes. Without disassembling the fermentation setups, measure the amount of gas trapped in each tube. Record the height (in millimeters) of the gas in each tube. Calculate the volume of gas in each tube using the equation for the volume of a cylinder (Volume $= \pi r^2 \times h$). Record this information in the data table in your *Log*.

9. What was the volume of gas that the yeast produced from each food per hour during the experiment? Record this information in your *Log* data table.

Interpretations: Respond to the following in your *Log*:

1. Create a histogram to summarize your data.

2. Evaluate your hypothesis, and explain your evaluation.

3. What conclusions can you make about the ability of yeast to metabolize the foods that you provided?

4. One of the sugars in the experiment was a monosaccharide, and one was a disaccharide. How do your results reflect the differences in the complexity of the sugar being metabolized? How do you explain your results when using starch?

Applications: Respond to the following in your *Log*:

1. Wine and beer are both products of fermentation. They also contain a lot of calories. What is the source of these calories?

Figure 4.33

Left to right:
red blood cell, platelet,
white blood cell.

2. Although termites eat wood, they have no enzymes to digest wood. How can you explain this apparent discrepancy? If necessary, do some research on how termites get energy.

Internal Transport Mechanisms

The survival and growth of an organism depend not only on its ability to obtain and use food, but also on its ability to transport needed nutrients throughout its body. The process of diffusion is useful for transporting molecules over short distances but is inefficient for long-distance transport. All organisms except the very smallest have systems for convectively transporting dissolved nutrients, gases, and wastes throughout the body. In humans and other large animals, this convective transport is accomplished by the circulatory or cardiovascular system.

Blood is the primary medium in which dissolved nutrients, gases, and waste products are transported. Human blood is a suspension of several types of cells in a liquid called plasma (Figure 4.33). The body of an average-size human adult contains about 4 to 6 liters of blood. About 55 percent of this volume is blood cells. The rest of the volume is plasma.

There are two main types of blood cells: red blood cells, which transport oxygen, and white blood cells, which are important components of the immune system. Platelets, which aid in blood clotting, are fragments of cells produced in the bone marrow. 🌐

Guided Inquiry 4.5

Circulation in a Goldfish

How do complex multicellular organisms, such as the goldfish shown in Figure 4.34, get rid of carbon dioxide waste products that result from the breakdown of nutrients?

Figure 4.34

How does this goldfish supply nutrients to and transport wastes away from each of the cells in its body?

Homeostasis: The Body in Balance

MATERIALS

- Water from a fish bowl
- A petri dish bottom
- Two wads of absorbent cotton
- Two microscope slides
- A dip net
- A goldfish
- A dropping pipette
- A compound microscope
- A transparent metric ruler

Procedure

1. Put a small amount of water in a petri dish. Saturate a thin wad of absorbent cotton with water from the fish bowl, and place it in the petri dish. Place one of the microscope slides in the petri dish next to the cotton wad (see Figure 4.35). Carefully place the goldfish on the cotton wad in the petri dish so that the tail rests on the microscope slide. Place thick, wet cotton on the fish, especially over the gill areas, to keep the goldfish moist. Place the other slide on top of the tail. The fish may move its tail, disturbing the slide. Simply reposition the slide and start over.

2. Use your pipette to drip water on the cotton pads from time to time. This will help to keep the fish healthy.

3. Carefully place the petri dish on the stage of your microscope, and position it so that the tail is over the hole in the stage. Focus the microscope on a thin part of the tail. You should see large, thick vessels. Of these larger vessels, those that contain blood moving away from the heart are arterioles. Branching from the arterioles are smaller vessels called capillaries. These are the smallest vessels that you can see. Cells move in single file through the capillaries (Figure 4.36 on page 230).

Thick wet cotton

Slides

Thin wet cotton

Figure 4.35

Setup for Guided Inquiry 4.5.

Endothelial cells

Red
blood cells

Figure 4.36

*Blood cells flowing
through capillaries.*

4. With your transparent metric ruler, measure the diameter of an arteriole at the point where it divides into two capillaries. Measure the diameter of a capillary. Appendix D will remind you how to calculate the diameter of your microscope's field of view. What is the ratio of the diameter of an arteriole to the diameter of a capillary? Record your measurements in your *Log*.

5. Observe the red blood cells moving through the capillaries. Describe the size and shape of these cells and the way in which they pass through the capillaries.

6. Capillaries empty into venules, which carry blood back to the heart. Calculate the ratio of the diameter of an arteriole to that of a venule. Construct a ratio of the diameter of venules to capillaries.

7. Record the rate of the movement of red blood cells in arterioles, venules, and capillaries. To do this, count the number of red blood cells passing through each of the blood vessels in a specified period of time.

8. Sketch what you see of the fish tail in your field of view. Use arrows to indicate the direction of blood flow, and record the approximate number of blood vessels that you see.

Interpretations: Respond to the following in your *Log*:

1. Compare the rate of blood flow among arterioles, venules, and capillaries.

2. From your diagram (Step 8), compare the thicknesses of the arteriole wall and a capillary wall. How do these differences relate to the functions of the arteriole wall and the capillary wall?

3. From your diagram (Step 8), compare the average distance between arterioles with the distance between capillaries. How do the differences relate to their functions?

4. Summarize your observations of the capillary circulation in the tail of a goldfish. Discuss the ability of the circulatory system to transport materials to and from the tissues of the body.

Applications: Respond to the following in your *Log*:

1. William Harvey first demonstrated the one-way circulation of blood in 1616, but it was not until 1661 that Marcello Malpighi first described the network that connects arteries and small veins. Why do you think Malpighi's discovery was so important?

2. In some forms of heart disease, the aortic valves do not close properly between heartbeats. Predict what would happen to the blood pressure and heartbeat of a patient who had this condition.

3. Heart disease is still the primary cause of adult death in the United States. Conduct some research to find out why. Explain which factors people cannot control and which factors they can control.

The Human Circulatory System

The cardiovascular system in humans and other complex animals is composed of the heart, the blood, and blood vessels of different sizes and types. In the human circulatory system (Figure 4.37), the heart, a muscular organ, pumps blood under pressure into vessels known as arteries, which carry blood to all parts of the body. The walls of arteries are thick and are composed of several layers (Figure 4.38 on page 232). Between the inner and outer layers of simple cells is a layer of muscle cells and elastic fibers. These allow arteries to expand and contract as blood flows through them and as blood pressure rises and falls with each beat of the heart. After traveling through the arteries, blood is transported through a series of successively smaller diameter vessels: the arterioles and capillaries. Some capillaries are so narrow that blood cells must pass through them in single file. You observed this phenomenon in Guided Inquiry 4.5.

It is in the capillaries that blood cells exchange nutrients, gases, and wastes with the cells of the body tissues. Capillaries are uniquely suited for this exchange process because their walls are only one cell thick. The arterial system terminates in the capillary beds Where oxygen and nutrients diffuse to the cells and where carbon dioxide and waste diffuse from the cells to the capillaries.

Blood leaves the capillary beds by way of venules, which converge to form the larger veins. The venous system of blood vessels transports blood back to the heart. The walls of veins are much thinner and less muscular than are the walls of arteries. By acting as one-way doors, valves in the veins of the arms and legs help to maintain blood flow toward the heart and prevent the blood from flowing backwards. 🖐

Artery

Vein

Heart

Figure 4.37

The human circulatory system.

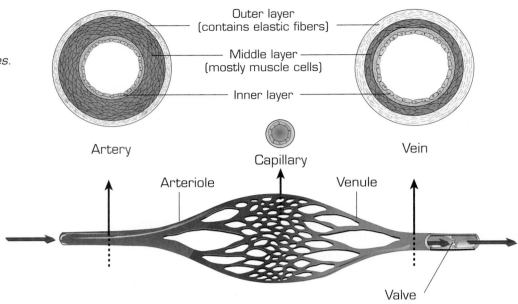

Figure 4.38

Comparison of veins, arteries, and capillaries.

Outer layer
(contains elastic fibers)

Middle layer
(mostly muscle cells)

Inner layer

Artery

Capillary

Vein

Arteriole

Venule

Valve

Effects of Exercise on Pulse and Breathing Rates

How does your body adjust to changes in your activity level or conditions in your environment? In this Inquiry, you will observe changes in the rate at which blood and gas transport takes place. You can measure changes in blood transport rate by measuring your pulse rate. You can estimate your gas transport rate by measuring your breathing rate and the amount of carbon dioxide in your breath.

Before you begin, list some factors in your *Log* that you think would affect your pulse and breathing rates. How would the same factors affect different people? How do you think your body senses and responds to changes in pulse and breathing rates?

MATERIALS

- A clock that measures seconds
- A 200-milliliter flask
- Water
- A dropper
- Phenolphthalein solution
- Safety goggles
- A marking pen
- 0.04 percent NaOH in a dropping bottle
- Two soda straws
- A sphygmomanometer, digital finger or cuff type (optional)

Procedure

1. Construct hypotheses about how various levels of human exercise will affect:

   ◆ pulse rate,

   ◆ breathing rate,

   ◆ the amount of CO_2 produced by respiration, and

   ◆ blood pressure.

   What is the independent variable for each situation? What are the dependent variables? Write an explanation in your *Log*.

2. Work in pairs. One person will be the subject, and the other will be the experimenter. Design an experiment to test your hypotheses. Include a wide range of activity, from resting quietly to running in place. Use the measuring techniques below for pulse rate, breathing rate, and CO_2 production.

   ◆ *Pulse rate*:   Lightly place two fingers (not your thumb) on the inside of your wrist near the bone at the base of your thumb (Figure 4.39). Alternatively, place the fingers on the side of your neck, just below the jaw. Once you feel the pulse, count the number of pulses in 15 seconds. Multiply this number by 4 to get the pulse rate as beats per minute.

   ◆ *Breathing rate*:   Visually count the number of breaths taken in 30 seconds. Convert this to the number of breaths per minute.

   ◆ *CO_2 production*:   Fill two 200-milliliter flasks half full with tap water. Add three drops of phenolphthalein to each flask. If the water doesn't turn pink, add sodium hydroxide (NaOH) to the water drop by drop until you obtain a light pink color. Label one flask as the control. Insert a straw into the other flask (Figure 4.40), and blow gently into the water for 1 minute. (You may need to take one or two breaths; the total exhalation

Figure 4.39

Monitor your pulse rate at your wrist or neck.

Figure 4.40

The setup for measuring CO_2 production.

time, though, should be 1 minute.) Exhaled carbon dioxide dissolves in water to create an acidic solution. (Water and carbon dioxide react to form carbonic acid.) As the pH of the solution drops below 8, the phenolphthalein in the solution loses its pink color. Add NaOH to the flask, drop by drop, and swirl gently to mix. Count the number of drops it takes to restore the original pink color, comparing the color of the water to that in the control flask.

3. Once your teacher has approved your experiment plan, you can begin. Take turns with your partner collecting data. Each of you should use a fresh straw for the CO_2 production experiment. Record the data in your *Log*.

4. If a digital finger or cuff sphygmomanometer (Figure 4.41) is available, you can also measure your blood pressure. Watch carefully your teacher's demonstration of how to use the sphygmomanometer. Then take turns measuring your partner's blood pressure. Blood pressure is expressed as a fraction, such as 120/80 mm Hg.

Interpretations: Respond to the following in your *Log*:

1. Graph your data. Because the scales and units of the three independent variables are likely to be different, make a graph for each dependent variable. You might want to make a histogram.

2. Contribute to a class scattergram for each dependent variable that is similar to the ones you constructed. Use dots for all data points on the class graph. Elect a classmate to draw a straight, thick line that runs through most of the dotted region, representing a best fit of the data.

3. On the basis of the graphs of class data, explain how your hypothesis is either supported or rejected.

4. Describe any differences that you perceive between:

   ◆   your data and those of the class,

   ◆   data of males and females, and

   ◆   data of athletes and nonathletes.

5. Why are the resting pulse and resting breathing rates important in this activity?

Figure 4.41

This digital finger sphygmomanometer measures blood pressure.

Applications: Respond to the following in your *Log*:

1. Why does the heart of an overweight person work harder than the heart of someone who is thinner?

2. Suppose an Olympic runner has a resting pulse rate of less than 50 beats per minute. A couple of minutes after winning the 5000-meter run, the runner was able to speak to reporters without taking heavy breaths. How do you explain this?

3. Optional homework: Find your resting pulse rate as you lie on your back. Then place an ice pack on the top half of your face. (First place a wash cloth over your face to protect it from the ice.) After 30 seconds, take your pulse and record it.

4. Research the physiological mechanisms in the human body that regulate pulse rate, breathing rate, and carbon dioxide output. How is this information related to your hypothesis?

Heart Rate, Blood Pressure, and Respiration

You have a pulse because your heart pumps blood intermittenly by contracting and exerting pressure. The most muscular region of the heart, the left ventricle, provides the pressure that pushes the blood out. (Figure 4.42 shows a diagram of the human heart.) After blood exits the left ventricle, it enters a large artery called the aorta. The aorta branches off into smaller arteries and arterioles and finally to capillaries.

You can measure your pulse most easily in one of two places: the carotid artery in your neck just below your jaw or the brachial artery running into your wrist just below the palm of your hand (see Figure 4.39). You might have seen detectives in mystery movies feel for the pulse on the carotid artery of the neck to determine whether a victim is still alive.

Heart Rate

Your heart rate is an indirect measure of how fit you are. A normal heart rate is between 75 and 90 beats per minute, but athletes can easily have a heart rate below 50. Heart rate is also an indication of body size, but, oddly enough, larger animals have slower heart rates. For example, hummingbirds have heart rates averaging 200 beats per minute, whereas an elephant's heart rate is only 35. You can easily train your heart to beat more slowly through exercise. Any exercise that causes your heart rate to increase for short periods of time also strengthens your heart, leading to a slower resting heart rate.

Blood pressure is not as easy to change as heart rate, but increases in body fat can cause blood pressure to rise. Anxiety can also cause high blood pressure. Some families have a genetic tendency toward high blood pressure, also called hypertension. When blood pressure gets too high, kidney failure, heart attacks, and other problems can result. Doctors can help to regulate blood pressure by prescribing medication and/or diet and exercise programs.

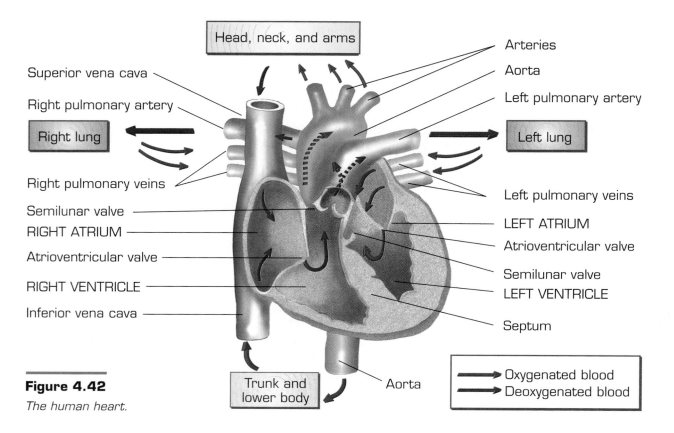

Figure 4.42

The human heart.

Labels in figure:
- Head, neck, and arms
- Superior vena cava
- Right pulmonary artery
- Right lung
- Right pulmonary veins
- Semilunar valve
- RIGHT ATRIUM
- Atrioventricular valve
- RIGHT VENTRICLE
- Inferior vena cava
- Trunk and lower body
- Aorta
- Arteries
- Aorta
- Left pulmonary artery
- Left lung
- Left pulmonary veins
- LEFT ATRIUM
- Atrioventricular valve
- Semilunar valve
- LEFT VENTRICLE
- Septum
- Oxygenated blood
- Deoxygenated blood

Blood Pressure

Blood pressure rises and falls with each heartbeat as the heart contracts and then relaxes. The systolic pressure is the maximum pressure of the blood in your arteries as the left ventricle of your heart pumps blood into the arteries. The diastolic pressure is the minimum pressure in the arteries of your body when the heart is resting between heartbeats. When you have your blood pressure taken, the systolic blood pressure is written in the numerator, and the diastolic pressure is written in the denominator. For example, a desirable blood pressure such as 120/80 means 120 millimeters of mercury (mm Hg) systolic pressure and 80 mm Hg diastolic pressure. A millimeter of mercury, or mm Hg, is a unit of pressure; 760 mm Hg is equivalent to 14.7 pounds per square inch (atmospheric pressure at sea level).

One way to measure blood pressure is to use an inflatable cuff attached to a pressure gauge (reading in mm Hg). The cuff is wrapped around the upper arm and then inflated with air until it stops arterial blood flow. As air is released from the cuff, blood begins flowing through the arteries in spurts. The person who is measuring blood pressure listens with a stethoscope for the tapping sound the blood makes as it reenters the artery. At that time, the number on the gauge that coincides with this sound is the systolic pressure. When more air is released, blood flows continuously, and the tapping sound disappears. At that time, the person again observes the number on the gauge. This provides a measure of the diastolic pressure. Blood pressure in a healthy adult is about 120 mm Hg systolic and 80 mm Hg diastolic. A finger sphygmomanometer can also be used by wrapping the finger cuff snugly around the first finger. Remove any rings that you may be wearing or use your second finger. Most finger sphygmomanometers now have digital read-out, and many even inflate the cuff automatically.

Respiration

The breathing rate is controlled by the balance of the blood gases oxygen and carbon dioxide in the body tissues. To understand why and how the involuntary action of breathing occurs, it is important to understand the process of respiration, which is the exchange of these gases between the body and the external environment. The parts of the human respiratory system are shown in Figure 4.43.

When you inhale, you take external air into your body. This is aided by the action of two sets of muscles: one set acts on the ribs, and the other, the diaphragm, controls the size of the cavity the lungs sit in. When you breathe in (inhale), your diaphragm and rib muscles contract. The rib cage expands as it moves upward, while the diaphragm moves downward. As a consequence, the volume of the chest cavity increases, decreasing air pressure in the lungs.

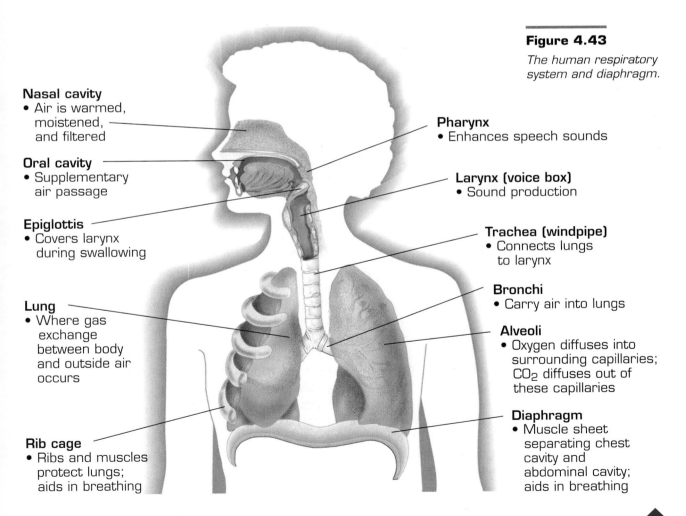

Figure 4.43

The human respiratory system and diaphragm.

Nasal cavity
• Air is warmed, moistened, and filtered

Oral cavity
• Supplementary air passage

Epiglottis
• Covers larynx during swallowing

Lung
• Where gas exchange between body and outside air occurs

Rib cage
• Ribs and muscles protect lungs; aids in breathing

Pharynx
• Enhances speech sounds

Larynx (voice box)
• Sound production

Trachea (windpipe)
• Connects lungs to larynx

Bronchi
• Carry air into lungs

Alveoli
• Oxygen diffuses into surrounding capillaries; CO_2 diffuses out of these capillaries

Diaphragm
• Muscle sheet separating chest cavity and abdominal cavity; aids in breathing

Figure 4.44

Oxygen that is inhaled into the lungs diffuses into the fine capillaries that surround the alveoli and is transported to the rest of the body in the blood.

Air moves from the external environment, where the pressure is higher, to the lungs, where the pressure is lower. The air that you inhale moves into the lungs and travels through a series of smaller and smaller branching air tubes, at the ends of which are tiny air sacs called alveoli. The alveoli (Figure 4.44) have thin walls leading to the body and are the site of gas exchange between the blood and inhaled air. After picking up what has just been inhaled, the blood transports gases and other materials to the body tissues.

When you breathe out (exhale), the rib and diaphragm muscles relax, and the volume of the chest cavity decreases, increasing the air pressure in the chest cavity. The amount of air that you move in and out with each breath is only a small fraction of the air your lungs could hold. The total amount of air that your lungs can hold is called your lung capacity.

Have you ever wondered why you can't hold your breath for a really long time? Once you have exhaled, you must inhale because your body responds to the change in blood gases as you hold your breath. A high blood level of carbon dioxide signals your brain to stimulate the rib and diaphragm muscles, forcing you to inhale. Your involuntary breathing rate is controlled by the relative concentrations of two gases, oxygen (O_2) and carbon dioxide (CO_2), in your body tissues. Metabolism, the sum of all the chemical processes in your cells and tissues, results in the production of carbon dioxide. When the carbon dioxide concentrations in your body tissues are high, your breathing rate increases so that you can expel the carbon dioxide via your lungs. As you increase your breathing rate, you increase the oxygen concentration in your blood, resupply the tissues with oxygen, and reduce the carbon dioxide concentration in the blood. 🐾

BIOthoughts

Your pulse rate will drop if you apply an ice pack to your face. This is similar to a response known as the mammalian diving reflex. Have you ever heard of people who survived after being submerged in near-freezing bodies of water? You would expect these people to die, especially after being under water for up to an hour, unable to breathe. It seems miraculous, but some people (though not all) actually survive. Explain in your *Log* why this may happen.

Homeostasis: The Body in Balance

BIOissue

Should We Sacrifice Baboons to Save Humans?

Hearts and other organs from baboons and other animals can be, and sometimes are, transplanted into humans. Why? Because human donor organs are very scarce, and unless a transplant is done soon, the affected human will die of heart or kidney failure. Baboons and chimps have a close enough tissue match that the human body does not reject their organs easily. Baboon bone marrow is being used experimentally as a treatment for AIDS.

The transplant procedure, of course, means that the baboon or chimp must die. Some people in the medical community see this as a viable alternative when a human organ is not available. Imagine the different points of view, depending on who you might be. If you were the person dying of heart or kidney failure, you would probably feel that the life of a human is more important than that of a baboon. If you were a baboon or chimp and could think about the choice, you might feel differently.

Scientists who support the use of animals for donor organs say that it is comparable to raising cattle or pigs for their meat. They say that if primate-to-human transplantation becomes common, then these animals could be raised like livestock. Do you agree with this proposal?

Is it appropriate to take the life of one organism to save another? Should we sacrifice baboons to save humans? Record your thoughts in your *Log*.

Hemoglobin

Human red blood cells contain hemoglobin, a complex protein molecule that carries oxygen molecules. Oxygen diffuses through the lung alveoli into the blood and attaches to these hemoglobin molecules. Each hemoglobin molecule can carry up to four molecules of oxygen. Once the oxygen is attached to the hemoglobin molecules, the blood cell is said to be oxygenated. When oxygenated blood reaches body tissues that have too little oxygen and too much carbon dioxide, the hemoglobin releases the oxygen molecules.

They then diffuse to the tissues. At the same time, the tissues release carbon dioxide, which diffuses into the blood plasma. Some is transported as bicarbonate ions (HCO_3^-), and some attaches to the hemoglobin. A bicarbonate ion is formed in the blood from the breakdown of carbonic acid (H_2CO_3), which is formed when carbon dioxide combines with water:

$$CO_2 + H_2O \Longleftrightarrow H_2CO_3 \Longleftrightarrow HCO_3^- + H^+$$

Carbon dioxide   Water   Carbonic acid   Bicarbonate ion   Hydrogen ion

As more carbon dioxide is released into the blood, the blood pH level decreases. This chemical change in the blood causes the hemoglobin to release more oxygen to the tissues. As you can see, tissues that originally have the most carbon dioxide and the least oxygen receive the most oxygen from the blood. This is another way the body maintains homeostasis.

The Endocrine System and Hormones

Complex organisms regulate their metabolic processes by using enzymes and hormones. But the nervous system, which is made up of specialized cells that transmit signals throughout the body, also regulates metabolic processes. The nervous system is often called the quick message system of humans and other complex animals. When you step on a nail and draw back quickly or when you blink your eye, your nervous system is involved. (You will learn more about the nervous system in Unit 6.)

If the nervous system is the quick message system, the endocrine system is the slow message system. Although the nervous system and the endocrine system respond at different speeds, they interact extensively. Most complex animals, including humans, have endocrine systems. The endocrine system is composed of tissues and glands that secrete hormones that regulate body functions, thereby helping to maintain homeostasis.

Hormones have various functions and play an important role in growth, reproduction, and the body's response to stress. Certain hormones affect target organs that control the blood's concentration of important molecules such as water, sodium, and glucose. Also, particular body processes, such as menstruation in women, may be regulated by several different hormones. Figure 4.45 shows the locations of the endocrine glands in the human body and lists their major secretions and functions. Notice how widely dis-

Frank and Ernest

Copyright (c) 1993 by Thaves. Reprinted with permission.

Homeostasis: The Body in Balance

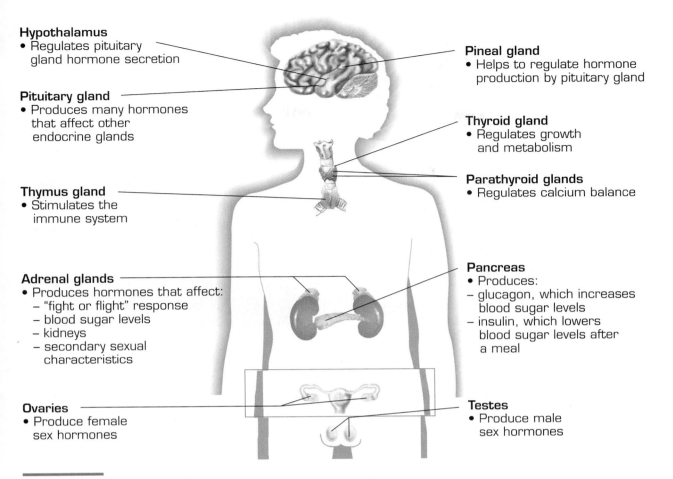

Hypothalamus
• Regulates pituitary gland hormone secretion

Pituitary gland
• Produces many hormones that affect other endocrine glands

Thymus gland
• Stimulates the immune system

Adrenal glands
• Produces hormones that affect:
  – "fight or flight" response
  – blood sugar levels
  – kidneys
  – secondary sexual characteristics

Ovaries
• Produce female sex hormones

Pineal gland
• Helps to regulate hormone production by pituitary gland

Thyroid gland
• Regulates growth and metabolism

Parathyroid glands
• Regulates calcium balance

Pancreas
• Produces:
  – glucagon, which increases blood sugar levels
  – insulin, which lowers blood sugar levels after a meal

Testes
• Produce male sex hormones

Figure 4.45

The endocrine system.

persed the endocrine glands are.

Many of the hormones that the body produces are classified as steroid hormones. (The term *steroid* describes their chemical nature.) Some steroids, including progesterone (normally produced by the ovaries), can be manufactured and sometimes are prescribed by physicians to treat health problems. However, some athletes and body builders (Figure 4.46) take steroids to increase their muscle mass, a practice that is dangerous and illegal. Over-the-counter use of steroids is banned by the National Collegiate Athletic Association and body-building organizations. Why? Along with building muscle, steroid overuse has been linked to sterility, impotence, and some cancers. 🌏

Figure 4.46

A body builder can develop muscle mass without using steroids.

BIOoccupation

Carmen Fignole: Paramedic

Carmen Fignole (pronounced "fee-nyo lay") is an emergency medical services paramedic. Born in Haiti, she grew up in New York City before moving to a coastal resort town in the southeastern United States. Ms. Fignole began her career in emergency medicine as an emergency medical technician (EMT) in the late 1980s after instruction at a local technical college.

When she worked as an EMT, Carmen performed general first aid care, basic life support, bandaging, and splinting during emergency ambulance calls. After Ms. Fignole had been an EMT for two years, her employer paid to send her to the local technical college for more advanced paramedic training. As a paramedic, she can perform more extensive advanced life support and cardiac care for emergency patients.

Directions (called protocols) for patient care in emergencies are established ahead of time by the physician who is the medical director of the emergency medical services. However, every situation is different. Ms. Fignole must be able to solve problems under stressful situations. For example, she might need to splint a broken arm when none of the splints on the ambulance fits the arm. She must make modifications so that the arm can be immobilized quickly with as little discomfort as possible to her patient.

At Ms. Fignole's station, the paramedics work one 24-hour shift and then are off for 48 hours. The day begins with a thorough check of the ambulance and its equipment inventory. A typical shift includes 10 emergency calls

that range from dry runs (injuries that are not serious enough that anyone needs to be transported) to head-on automobile collisions. Ms. Fignole might have to reassure a frightened 85-year-old woman who has fallen in her bathtub. On another call, she might have to crawl under a wrecked car at 4 a.m. to reach a trapped teenager.

When asked what qualities a prospective emergency services professional should have, Ms. Fignole said, "You should love change, be adaptable to new situations, and be able to switch gears quickly. However, the most important thing is that you truly like people—even when they aren't at their best."

She recommends to high school students, "If you are interested in becoming an EMT or paramedic, take all of the biology and anatomy courses you can, and volunteer at local hospitals and emergency services. After high school, enroll in a technical college that has a two-year EMT program or a four-year degree program."

The Transmission of a Contagious Disease

Remember the last time you caught a cold (Figure 4.47)? Did you know at the time just how you contracted the cold? How could it have been prevented?

Most contagious diseases are caused by bacteria, viruses, or protozoa and are spread by direct contact with someone who is infected or by indirect contact, as with water or objects contaminated by an infected person's body fluids or wastes (blood, saliva, feces).

The spread of Acquired Immune Deficiency Syndrome (AIDS) has caused a great deal of concern. Human immunodeficiency virus (HIV), the virus that is believed to cause AIDS, attacks and weakens the immune system. HIV is transmitted from one person to another by the exchange of body fluids.

How do contagious diseases spread so fast? This Inquiry simulates the spread of a contagious disease.

Figure 4.47

Some contagious diseases can be spread by airborne droplets.

MATERIALS

- A test tube containing 10 milliliters of fluid
- Test solution

Procedure

1. Obtain from your teacher a test tube that contains a clear solution. One student in the class has an "infected" test tube. You will not know who this is.

2. Exchange test tube fluid with a classmate in the following way: Pour the contents of your tube into the tube containing the contents of the person with whom you wish to exchange. Mix the two contents together by gently moving the tube back and forth. Then pour half of the combined contents back into the empty tube.

3. Record the name of the person with whom you exchanged fluids.

4. After everyone in class has made the first exchange, exchange tube contents three more times, each time with a different student. Try to select persons randomly for the exchange. Record their names.

5. Add one to two drops of test solution to your tube. If the fluid turns pink, then you have been "infected."

6. Empty and wash the test tubes, and return them to the designated place. WASH YOUR HANDS!

SAFETY NOTE

- Wear **goggles**.
- Treat all materials as if they are hazardous.

7. Record the names of all students who were "infected" with the mock disease-causing organism.

Interpretations: Respond to the following in your *Log*:

1. What percentage of students were infected after three exchanges?

2. Predict the number and percentage of students in the class who would be infected after four exchanges.

3. Analyze the data as to who became infected and who did not. Use investigative logic to identify the source of the "infection." Try to trace the path that the disease followed from one student to another.

4. On the basis of this activity, describe the relationship between the number of contacts a person has and the possibility of contracting an infectious disease.

Applications: Respond to the following in your *Log*:

1. HIV type B is the viral strain that is thought to be responsible for the AIDS epidemic in the United States. Explain what this Inquiry might suggest about the spread of HIV B in the United States.

2. A new, very contagious strain of HIV (HIV E) was discovered in Thailand. It appears to be spreading primarily through unprotected heterosexual intercourse, and an estimated 22 percent of the Thai population is now infected. How do you account for this rapid spread of HIV E?

3. How could HIV E be a threat to people in the United States?

The Immune System

How do organisms protect themselves from disease? What happens when agents of infection, toxins (poisons), or other physiological and/or anatomical conditions threaten an organism's survival? Animals respond to invasion by foreign material in many ways. The immune system is one important line of defense. The immune system is made up of cells that are scattered throughout the body. Even though they are spread out, the cells all react to specific foreign molecules. Figure 4.48 illustrates the roles of the specialized cells of the human immune system.

Antigens and Lymphocytes

Anything that causes an immune response is called an antigen. Antigens can be agents of infection, such as bacteria and viruses; they can be proteins or polysaccharides; and they can even be the body's own cells, such as cancer cells.

White blood cells are the immune system's primary defense against foreign antigens. Lymphocytes are one type of these cells. There are two major

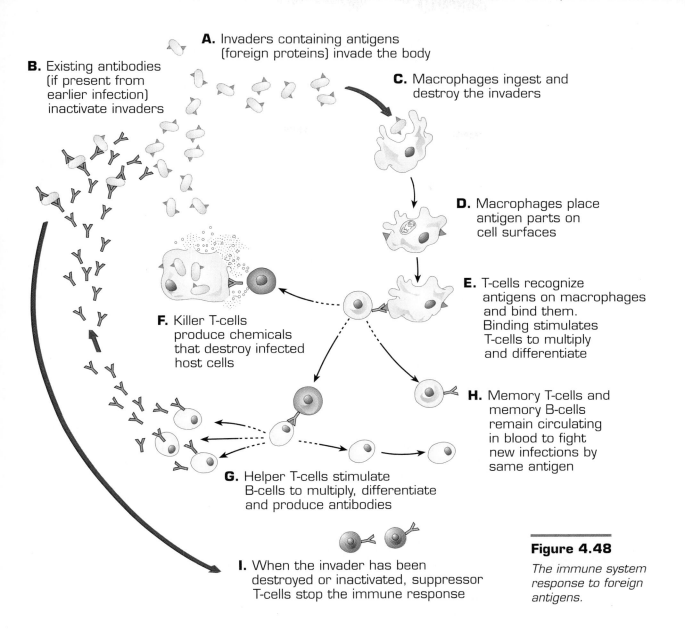

A. Invaders containing antigens (foreign proteins) invade the body

B. Existing antibodies (if present from earlier infection) inactivate invaders

C. Macrophages ingest and destroy the invaders

D. Macrophages place antigen parts on cell surfaces

E. T-cells recognize antigens on macrophages and bind them. Binding stimulates T-cells to multiply and differentiate

F. Killer T-cells produce chemicals that destroy infected host cells

G. Helper T-cells stimulate B-cells to multiply, differentiate and produce antibodies

H. Memory T-cells and memory B-cells remain circulating in blood to fight new infections by same antigen

I. When the invader has been destroyed or inactivated, suppressor T-cells stop the immune response

Figure 4.48

The immune system response to foreign antigens.

groups of lymphocytes: B-cells, which develop in the bone marrow, and T-cells, which develop in the thymus gland. B-cells produce proteins called antibodies, which recognize and bind to specific antigens. Because there are many different antigens, there are many different antibodies. When an antibody recognizes and binds a specific foreign antigen, the antibody inactivates the antigen or foreign cell. Also, other white blood cells (macrophages) become attracted to the area. T-cells do not produce antibodies. However, T-cells recognize foreign agents and respond by attacking and killing or inactivating those agents. There are four types of T-cells: helper T-cells, killer T-cells, suppressor T-cells, and memory T-cells.

The Immune Response

When a foreign invader (antigen), such as a virus, a bacterial cell, or a protein, enters the body, two things can happen. Either antibodies bind to the antigen and inactivate it, or the large white blood cells known as macrophages will ingest the antigen. One problem with the immune response is that it takes some time for B-cells to make antibodies. The first time a foreign antigen enters the body, there will be no antibodies to make it inactive. Memory B-cells come into contact with the antigen and "remember" it the next time it is present in your body. At that time, the B-cell (known as a memory cell) starts producing large quantities of antibody to neutralize the invader. On the other hand, macrophages can ingest the antigen the first time it invades. Thus macrophages are on the front line of your immune response.

How does a macrophage help in fighting invaders? First, the macrophage digests the foreign agent and places some of the agent's proteins (antigens) on its cell surface. Helper T-cells recognize these antigens on the surface of macrophages and bind to the antigen. This binding stimulates helper T-cells to multiply. The new army of helper T-cells produces chemicals that stimulate killer T-cells to attack and destroy the invader. Helper T-cells also stimulate B-cells to produce antibodies to inactivate the antigen.

Immunization

Immunization, sometimes called vaccination, uses the immune system's memory of previous invaders. When you are immunized against a disease, you are given a form of the organism that stimulates the immune system without actually causing the disease. Then if you become infected by that organism in the future, the memory T- and B-cells will respond quickly, and you probably will not get the disease. Effective long-term vaccines against many childhood diseases such as measles, mumps, rubella, diphtheria, whooping cough, tetanus, and chicken pox are now available. Before vaccination, these diseases were quite common, and some were responsible for the deaths of many children. Vaccines can virtually eradicate a disease. For example, the vaccine against smallpox was so effective that there has not been a case of smallpox anywhere in the world since 1980. The World Health Organization has declared that smallpox is eradicated.

AIDS

A healthy immune system is powerful and effective in preventing disease. However, some diseases, such as AIDS, destroy the defense mechanisms that should be destroying them. The HIV virus that causes AIDS infects and destroys helper T-cells. These cells, which are so important in fighting invaders, are the actual targets of the viral infection.

HIV has a spherical capsule encased by an envelope and a cone-shaped core that contains the genetic material. Protein molecules extend outwards from the envelope (Figure 4.49).

HIV attaches to the receptor sites of the T-cell lymphocytes (Figure 4.50). Once attached, the T-cell engulfs the virus, creating another problem for

Figure 4.49

An electron micrograph of HIV.

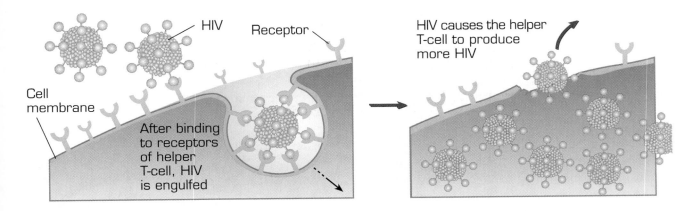

Cell membrane

HIV

Receptor

After binding to receptors of helper T-cell, HIV is engulfed

HIV causes the helper T-cell to produce more HIV

the immune system. Antibody production requires a blueprint of the invader. The protein coat of the virus hides inside the very cells that are assigned as sentries for invading antigens. Here, inside the T-cells, the virus replicates slowly, eventually killing the T-cells.

Without a functioning immune system, most individuals with AIDS die from infections caused by viruses, fungi, or bacteria; or they may develop cancers. There is no cure for AIDS yet and no vaccine (Figure 4.51). Existing treatments work to stop the virus from reproducing. However, scientists are working to find ways to help the immune cells that are not infected to resist the virus, and they are trying to produce an effective vaccine. The best defense against AIDS is to avoid contact with body fluids of an infected person.

Immune System Reactions

The normal immune system is vital to homeostasis, health, and well-being. However, in some individuals, the immune system reacts or overreacts in a way that causes problems. In someone with allergies, for example, the immune system produces excess amounts of antibodies. Most people do not produce antibodies to pollens and dust, but some individuals do. The result is a variety of allergic responses such as asthma (narrowing of the air passages in the lungs), hay fever (nasal and sinus congestion), or hives (skin reaction). The antibodies that are produced in an allergic response cause cells to release chemicals, such as histamine, that produce itching, a runny nose, and watery eyes. Drugs called antihistamines counteract the histamine to help relieve the symptoms of an allergy. 🌐

Figure 4.51

Preventing the spread of AIDS is the best defense against the disease.

STOP AIDS...

BIOprediction

Horrors in *The Hot Zone*

The Hot Zone, a book by Richard Preston, tells a terrifying true story about three closely related strains of extremely deadly and contagious viruses. Both *Ebola zaire* (Figure 4.52) and *Ebola marburg* have their genetic origins in the Lake Victoria region of Central Africa, where HIV is also believed to have originated. *Ebola marburg*, like HIV, is believed to have had its origins in monkeys. Although *Ebola marburg* is extremely deadly to monkeys, it apparently does not harm humans. But *Ebola zaire* and another strain, *Ebola sudan*, are deadly to humans. *Ebola zaire* kills approximately 90 percent of people who are exposed to it, and *Ebola sudan* kills 50 percent. The primary cause of death from *Ebola* viruses is severe hemorrhaging (bleeding) throughout the body, followed by actual liquification of vital organs.

Scientists understand little about how *Ebola* spreads. After infecting and nearly destroying a small population, these viruses seem to disappear, sometimes for many years. In the 1980s, *Ebola zaire* wiped out 50 villages north of Lake Victoria and then disappeared for more than 10 years. Although they examined many wild animals, virologists could not locate the virus. Scientists speculate that *Ebola* may mutate frequently, resulting in new strains of the virus that may be more or less dangerous. *The Hot Zone* describes a situation in the late 1980s when a virus—believed to be *Ebola marburg*—killed hundreds of monkeys that had

Figure 4.52

An electron microscope view of the Ebola *virus from the Centers for Disease Control and Prevention (CDC).*

been imported to a holding facility in Reston, Virginia. Some of the human caretakers became sick and later died of what appeared to be other causes. But scientists still do not know whether these people were infected by the virus. Both *Ebola zaire* and *Ebola marburg* undoubtedly still exist in nature, particularly in Africa. *Ebola marburg* has made it to the United States, but will it appear again?

Once again, consider whether a virus is alive. Does the behavior of a virus meet the characteristics of life described earlier in this unit? In your *Log*, list your reasons for deciding that a virus is or is not alive.

Antibiotic-Resistant Bacteria

Antibiotics are substances that inhibit the growth of bacteria or even kill them. Many antibiotics prevent bacteria from building cell walls. Usually, antibiotics do not damage human cells because these drugs damage only prokaryotic and not eukaryotic structures and metabolic processes.

Before the 1940s, when antibiotics such as penicillin began to be produced commercially, bacterial diseases killed millions of people every year. Diphtheria, scarlet fever, tuberculosis, pneumonia, bacterial meningitis, food poisoning, and blood poisoning were among the many diseases that killed children and adults. Alexander Fleming discovered penicillin in 1928; shortly thereafter, many more antibiotics were discovered, developed, and marketed. The days of deadly bacterial infections seemed to be over.

Even in the early days of antibiotic use, scientists found that a few bacterial cells could survive antibiotic treatment. These cells were identified as being resistant to the antibiotic. Because the potential for resistance to antibiotics is carried genetically in bacteria, billions and then trillions of resistant bacteria could be produced by the division and multiplication of one cell. Over time, particularly if an antibiotic were used frequently, the only bacteria that survived would be those that were resistant to the antibiotic (Figure 4.53).

The number of antibiotic-resistant bacteria has increased steadily since the 1940s. Antibiotics are widely used in the cattle and poultry industries, for example, increasing the number of antibiotic-resistant bacteria in the environment. In humans, doctors sometimes prescribe antibiotics to treat viral diseases, perhaps at the insistence of patients who demand medication, even though antibiotics are useless against viruses. Because of this misuse, we now have populations of extremely dangerous bacteria that are resistant to virtually every antibiotic that is made.

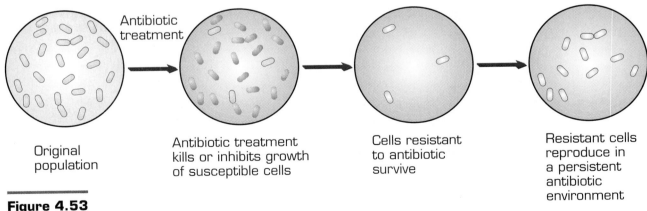

| Original population | Antibiotic treatment kills or inhibits growth of susceptible cells | Cells resistant to antibiotic survive | Resistant cells reproduce in a persistent antibiotic environment |

Figure 4.53

The development of antibiotic-resistant bacteria.

Should Parents Send Sick Children to School?

On Wednesday morning, eight-year-old Marci Baker woke up with a few red spots on her abdomen. Her mother immediately recognized them as symptoms of chicken pox. Marci attends John Howell elementary school. Her school had made no announcement about an outbreak of chicken pox. Two weekends ago, Marci attended a citywide Brownie Scout cookout. The incubation period (the time between exposure to the virus and the appearance of symptoms) for chicken pox is approximately two weeks.

Respond to the following in your *Log*:

1. What can Marci's mother do to help control the spread of the disease?
2. What should Marci do?
3. If other children who have chicken pox continue to attend school, should Marci also return?
4. What obligations do Marci and her parents have in relation to other Brownies and students at Howell school?
5. Should Marci be given antibiotics?
6. If other students want to avoid getting chicken pox, what could they do?

Self-Check 1

When you have completed the Guided Inquiries and readings in this unit, you should have some understanding of the mechanisms that maintain homeostasis. This self-check is designed to help you find out how much you understand. Divide the questions among your group and work on a subset individually. Then check and share your responses with your group. Your teacher will guide you if you need help. After you discuss your responses with your group, revise them and write your final answers for all questions in your *Log*.

1. Explain why homeostasis (a stable internal environment) is essential for the efficient functioning of an organism.

2. Give examples of at least three factors that affect the rate of diffusion.

3. Name two factors from your diffusion experiments that did not affect the rate of diffusion.

4. Explain how the surface area and volume of a cell limit the maximum size of cells.

5. Explain why osmosis is a special type of diffusion.

6. Explain why cells must constantly regulate their internal osmotic pressure.

7. Identify the types of cells that have a cell membrane. Explain how the cell membrane helps materials to enter and exit the cell.

8. Describe three generalizations about cells (the cell theory).

9. How does the excretory system get rid of substances such as urea from the body?

10. Explain the processes of ingestion, digestion, and transportation. Describe three examples of structural adaptations that are used to accomplish each of these processes.

11. Why does a complex multicellular organism need a circulatory system? How do a heart, arteries, veins, and capillaries serve this need?

12. How do lungs help to maintain homeostasis?

13. What are the effects of varying body activity on breathing and pulse rate?

14. Give three examples of how to preserve food against bacterial growth.

15. Give examples of organisms that (a) carry out cellular respiration and (b) carry out photosynthesis.

16. Explain what causes infectious diseases and how they are transmitted.

Conference

In this Conference, you will get together in small groups to share what you now know about homeostasis. Refer to your *Log* for your responses to the questions posed during the Brainstorming session at the start of this unit. Consider how the Guided Inquiries and readings addressed these basic questions about balance. Respond again to these four questions, incorporating what you have learned from the Guided Inquiries. How have your answers changed? List any additional questions that you have about balance.

Review the video and as you are watching, record a list of the questions that the video raises. In your group, make a composite list of issues and questions raised by the video. Next, review your *Log* notes about the Guided Inquiries. Discuss within your group any questions or issues that arose from each Guided Inquiry. List each question and issue on a chart or blackboard. Under each question or issue, list what you know and what you need to know if the issue is not resolved or the question is not answered.

Include in your list of issues and questions the words, *fluid, temperature, nutrients,* and *waste removal.* Then, relate your understanding of homeostasis and these words to what you have learned in the three prior units, "Matter and Energy for Life," "Ecosystems," and "Populations."

Reconvene as an entire class to present your annotated list of questions and issues. Decide how you want to share your knowledge and ideas with your classmates. This could be in the form of a poster session, a class presentation, reporting to a small group, or another method approved by your teacher.

As a class, compare the questions and issues presented by each group and prepare a condensed list of topics for further study. One or more of these topics can be used as Extended Inquiries.

Washing Your Hands of Bacteria

Body parts that are exposed to the environment—your hands, for example—touch objects that are likely to contain many kinds of bacteria. In fact, right now your hands are probably home to several different species of bacteria. This is one reason why you wash your hands before eating a meal (Figure 4.54). Does it help to use soap? Does the kind of soap or detergent matter? Does how long you scrub or rinse matter? In this Inquiry, you will explore these questions and will see what kinds of bacteria live on your hands.

Figure 4.54

What is the most effective way to wash your hands of bacteria?

MATERIALS

- Four sterile petri dishes containing sterilized nutrient agar
- Masking tape
- Paper towels
- Soaps
- Markers

Procedure

1. Select someone from your group who will be the subject of your study of bacteria on the hand.

2. Decide on different exposure conditions for each of four plates. Some recommended conditions are:
   - without washing hands at all,
   - washing quickly with soap and water and drying hands with clean paper towels,
   - washing as a surgeon might, rubbing your hands together with soap and water for at least 30 seconds and drying with clean paper towels,
   - a fourth condition decided by your group.

3. Construct in your *Log* a hypothesis for each of your exposure conditions. The hypothesis should relate the exposure condition to the amount of bacterial growth expected.

4. Do not open the petri dishes until you wish to expose them intentionally. When you want to expose a plate:

   a. lift the top of the plate from one side,

   b. gently drag a finger across the top of the agar layer from one end of the plate to the other without breaking the surface of the agar,

   c. close the top,

   d. tape the sides of the plate so that it will not reopen, and

   e. label the plate with the exposure conditions and your team name.

5. Now expose each plate to the labelled condition.

6. Place the four plates in a warm, dark area for 48 hours.

7. After 48 hours, sketch four circles on one page in your *Log* under the heading "Data for Extended Inquiry 4.1." Label each circle with the exposure condition. Sketch the amount of resulting bacterial growth, and describe its appearance.

8. Dispose of your plates as directed by your teacher.

Interpretations: Respond to the following in your *Log*:

1. Describe the differences among the bacteria growth on the four plates.

2. Describe the extent to which each of your hypotheses appears to be supported.

3. Explain the differences in bacterial growth on your plate.

Figure 4.55

In Extended Inquiry 4.1, you expose agar in a petri dish to bacteria from your hand.

Homeostasis: The Body in Balance

Applications: Respond to the following in your *Log*:

1. Under what conditions would you wash your hands in the future to get rid of bacteria?

2. Why do you think surgeons wash with soap and water for at least 30 seconds?

3. Hypothesize what happens to bacteria under longer exposure to soapy water. Ask your teacher for a further explanation.

4. Figure 4.54 shows a surgeon who is washing her hands. She will next put on sterile surgical gloves. How do you think that surgeons dry their hands?

Lung Volume

In this exercise, you will use a simple spirometer to measure your tidal volume, your vital capacity, and the expiratory reserve volumes of your lungs. You can compare this to the other lung volumes.

MATERIALS

- Disposable mouthpieces
- A bag or tank spirometer, calibrated in liters
- A rubber band

Procedure

1. In your *Log,* write predictions about the differences (if any) in lung volumes that you expect to observe between various groups such as male and female students, athletes and nonathletes, and smokers and nonsmokers. In your *Log,* record class data and identify each piece of data in terms of these groups.

2. Attach a disposable mouthpiece to your spirometer. Note any special instructions for the particular spirometer that you are using. Remove air from the spirometer (see Figure 4.56).

3. Sit quietly for a couple of minutes to establish a resting breathing rate. After a normal inhalation, expel one normal breath into the mouthpiece. Be careful not to exhale through your nose. Hold your nose if necessary.

Figure 4.56

This tank spirometer can be used to measure lung volume.

4. When you have completed one normal exhalation, immediately position the spirometer to prevent any of the exhaled air from escaping.

5. Following the instructions for the spirometer that you are using, read the air volume in the bag. This is your lungs' tidal volume. Record your tidal volume in your *Log*.

6. Remove the air from the spirometer. Repeat steps 2 to 4; but this time, exhale normally before exhaling into the bag. Force all of the air that you can into the spirometer. This extra exhalation is your lungs' expiratory reserve volume. Record this value in your *Log*.

7. Remove the air from the spirometer as before. Repeat Steps 2 to 4; but this time, inhale as much air as you can and then exhale into the spirometer as much as you can. Measure the volume as before, and record the vital capacity of your lungs in your *Log*.

8. Calculate your inspiratory reserve volume by adding the tidal volume to the expiratory reserve volume and subtracting the total from the vital capacity.

9. Finally, remove your disposable mouthpiece, and attach a clean one. Have your partner do Steps 1 to 8.

Interpretations: Respond to the following in your *Log*:

1. Compare the vital capacities of male and female students. Report any difference as percentages. Compare the data with your prediction. What factors do you think contribute to any differences?

2. Compare the vital lung capacities for athletic and nonathletic students. Report any differences as percentages. Compare the data with your prediction and explain.

3. What evidence would you need to show that vital capacity can be increased?

Intense, long-term training can increase an athlete's vital lung capacity.

Applications: Respond to the following in your *Log:*

1. How do your results compare with "normal values" as presented in physiology texts?

2. How do diseases such as asthma, cystic fibrosis, chronic bronchitis, and emphysema affect lung capacity? How does this affect an organism's ability to exchange gases?

Lung Volume

How much air do your lungs hold? Does this change if you forcibly inhale or exhale? Is there always some air remaining in your lungs? If so, how much?

The amount of air that you normally breathe in and out is called the tidal volume of the lungs. You may be aware that even after exhaling normally, you can force considerably more air out of your lungs. This extra volume of air is called the expiratory reserve volume. Similarly, the inspiratory reserve volume is that volume of air that can be forcefully inhaled after a normal inhalation. The maximum amount of air that can be exhaled with a full breath makes up what is called the lungs' vital capacity. Even after you exhale as much air as possible, some air remains in the lungs. This volume is called, appropriately enough, the residual volume. 🌐

Extended Inquiry 4.3

The Effects of Temperature on the Heart Rate of Earthworms

Can the external environment affect the internal temperature of an earthworm? If so, will it change the rate at which the worm carries out bodily processes such as circulation? In this Inquiry, you will determine how a change in the temperature of an earthworm's environment affects the worm's blood flow. Figure 4.57 shows an earthworm similar to the one you will study in this Inquiry.

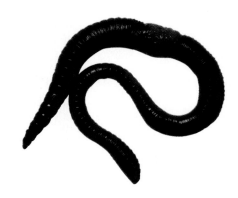

Figure 4.57

How does an earth-worm maintain home-ostasis?

MATERIALS

- Paper towels
- Tap water
- A rectangular pan (about 30 centimeters long)
- An earthworm (a large, healthy night crawler)
- A laboratory thermometer
- Ice
- A warm water bath
- A clock to measure seconds

Procedure

1. Place a moist paper towel on the inside bottom of the pan.

2. Place the earthworm in the pan, dorsal (top) side up. You can identify the dorsal side because it is much darker and rounder than the ventral (bottom) side. Moisten the worm with a few drops of room temperature tap water. Your setup should look like the one shown in Figure 4.58.

3. Find the dorsal blood vessel that runs directly down the crown of the worm's dorsal surface. Find a place where you can most easily see the actual pulsing of the blood vessel. Take a trial count of the number of heartbeats in 1 minute.

4. Construct a hypothesis that relates the temperature of the worm's environment to the pulse rate of the dorsal blood vessel.

5. Expose the worm to at least five different temperatures. The water can range from nearly freezing to warm, but don't expose the worm to hot temperatures. It will die at temperatures above 45°C. Mix warm and cold water to get the temperatures you want. Then add the water to the aluminum pan to a depth of 1 to 2 centimeters. The exact temperatures don't matter, but it is important to use a wide range of temperatures.

6. Working in pairs, determine the worm's pulse rate per minute under each temperature condition. Let the worm adjust to each temperature for at least 3 minutes before you begin counting. Place the thermometer in the pan so that the bulb is submerged. Read the temperature just before you count the pulse rate. Pour off the water, and let the worm breathe for at least 2 minutes between each change of water.

7. When you finish collecting data, return your worm to the place designated by your teacher. You can also turn the worms loose in a garden or in your class compost pile.

Figure 4.58

Setup for Extended Inquiry 4.3.

8. Construct a scattergram to help interpret your data. Refer to Appendix L for instructions on making a scattergram. Place the independent variable on the horizontal axis and the dependent variable on the vertical axis. Each intersection of a temperature and

a corresponding heartbeat rate is represented with one solid dot. Which factor is the independent variable, and which factor is the dependent variable?

9. As you examine your dots, try to see whether there is any evident pattern. A pattern is usually indicated by a clustering of the dots. If possible, draw a best-fit curve on top of the dots to help you see a relationship if there is one. One indication of no relationship in a scattergram is when the dots are fairly evenly distributed over the entire graph.

Interpretations: Respond to the following in your *Log:*

1. Was your hypothesis supported? Explain.

2. Why is it important to wait a few minutes between different temperatures before counting the pulse rate?

3. Why did you have to pour off the water to let the worm breathe?

4. What is the experimental advantage of starting with either the coldest or the warmest temperature and working gradually in the other direction instead of skipping around to different temperatures?

5. Describe any patterns that the dots or curve on your graph revealed, and relate these changes to temperature maintenance in the earthworm.

6. What are some flaws or sources of error in this experimental procedure?

Applications: Respond to the following in your *Log:*

1. When water on your skin evaporates, heat energy is absorbed into the water molecule. Why do you sweat if it means losing water from inside the body?

2. An earthworm cannot regulate its own body temperature. In contrast, humans and other warm-blooded animals can self-regulate body temperature. What results might you have obtained if you had performed this procedure on a warm-blooded animal?

3. When humans are exposed to a very cold environment without enough cover, their body temperature may decrease. If this decrease in body temperature is great enough, they may suffer from hypothermia (low body temperature), which is a life-threatening condition. Why would hypothermia be dangerous for you but not for an earthworm?

4. Some human surgical procedures require that the body temperature be decreased to the point of hypothermia. Why might this surgical hypothermia be a useful technique?

Metabolism of Germinating Pea Seeds

Recall from the introductory video that some of the athletes were warming up before their events. What do you think is the purpose of warm-ups? Is there an optimum temperature at which muscle cells function? What about the cells of other organisms? For example, how does temperature affect the functioning of plants?

In this Inquiry, you will test for the production of carbon dioxide during cellular respiration in seeds of a plant. Find out whether the products of plant cellular respiration are the same for other organisms. Does plant cell respiration depend on temperature?

CO_2 dissolves in water and reacts with it to produce carbonic acid (H_2CO_3). You can use a number of indicator solutions that change color in the presence of an acid to detect its presence. Phenol red is such an indicator. It is red if the solution is basic and light yellow if the solution is acidic.

MATERIALS

- Three test tubes
- A marking pen
- Distilled water
- 0.04 percent phenol red indicator solution
- Nonabsorbent cotton
- A soda straw
- Ten germinating pea or bean seeds (moistened for 24 hours)
- Ten nongerminating pea or bean seeds (dry)
- Two rubber stoppers to fit the test tubes

SAFETY NOTE

- Be careful not to draw the phenol red solution into your mouth.

Procedure: Day 1

1. Label three test tubes A, B, and C and fill each approximately one-fourth full of distilled water. Place eight drops of phenol red indicator solution into each tube.

2. Place a wad of nonabsorbent cotton about half or two-thirds of the way into two of the tubes. The cotton should not touch the liquid in the bottom of the tubes. Use just enough cotton to provide support for the seeds you will put into the tubes.

3. Place ten germinating seeds into tube A. Place ten nongerminating seeds into tube B. Stopper both tubes snugly. Stopper tube C without putting any seeds in it. Set the tubes aside in a vertical position until the next day. Your setup should look like the one in Figure 4.59.

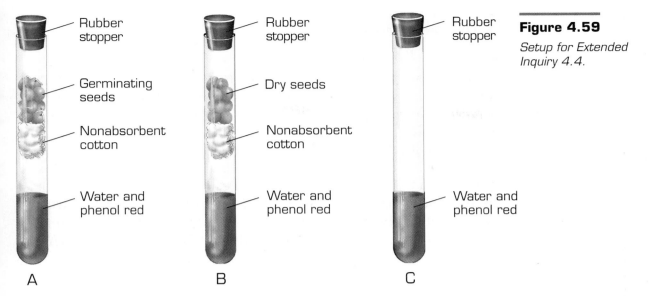

A   B   C

Figure 4.59

Setup for Extended Inquiry 4.4.

Labels for tube A: Rubber stopper, Germinating seeds, Nonabsorbent cotton, Water and phenol red

Labels for tube B: Rubber stopper, Dry seeds, Nonabsorbent cotton, Water and phenol red

Labels for tube C: Rubber stopper, Water and phenol red

4. Construct a hypothesis about which of the three tubes will exhibit respiration. Explain why you think this will happen.

Procedure: Day 2

1. Use the soda straw to blow gently into the solution in tube C for 1 minute. Do not blow so hard that you expel solution from the tube. Observe any changes in the solution, and record your observations in your *Log*.

2. Observe tubes A and B for any color changes. Record your observations in your *Log*, and complete your analysis.

Interpretations: Respond to the following in your *Log*:

1. Compare and contrast the color changes in each of the three tubes. What do these color changes indicate?

2. What do the data suggest about your hypothesis?

3. What evidence is there of CO_2 production by the dry seeds? What evidence do you have that the dry seeds are indeed alive? How might you be able to detect CO_2 production in dry seeds?

4. What was the experimental purpose of the tube with no seeds?

Applications: Respond to the following in your *Log*:

1. How do greenhouses help to meet the needs of plants?

2. Suppose you want to start a garden. Early in the spring, you germinate seeds in a flat box that contains soil. Then you can plant the seedlings rather than the seeds into the ground. Where would you want to keep the germinating seeds? Why?

3. When would you plant the seedlings in your garden? Why?

Enzymes: A Look at Amylase

Enzymes are proteins that help to increase the rate of chemical reactions. Most enzymes work by bringing or keeping reactants together until the product of the reaction is formed. During this process, the enzyme is not consumed or destroyed. After the reaction is complete, the enzyme is ready to do the same thing again.

Organisms use digestive enzymes to help break down food. In this Inquiry, you will investigate an enzyme called amylase. The name of this enzyme explains its function. Enzyme names usually begin with a word denoting the molecule that they act on and end with the suffix -*ase*. In this case, the enzyme amylase is specific for the breakdown of starch; *amyl* refers to starch, and -*ase* denotes an enzyme.

Starch is a polysaccharide; *poly* means "many," and *saccharide* refers to sugar. A simple sugar such as glucose is called a monosaccharide, which means one sugar unit. Many glucose units are linked together to form the long chain of a polysaccharide such as starch. Figure 4.60 illustrates the structures of mono-, di-, and polysaccharides.

MATERIALS

- A dropper bottle of iodine-potassium iodide (IKI) solution
- Salt solution
- Two test tubes
- 100 milliliters of 0.1 percent starch solution
- 10 milliliters of 5.0 percent fungal amylase solution
- Glucose solution
- A 500-milliliter beaker
- A graduated cylinder
- A sheet of white paper
- A Celsius thermometer
- A timer or access to a clock that measures seconds
- A hot plate
- A water bath

SAFETY NOTE

- Wear **goggles**, **gloves**, and **aprons**.
- IKI is toxic. Avoid getting it on your skin. It will also stain clothing.
- Dispose of your solutions as directed by your teacher.

Part A: Identifying IKI Reactions with Test Solutions
Procedure

1. You will use a solution of iodine-potassium iodide (IKI) as an indicator that a chemical change has occurred. IKI reacts with certain types of molecules. In this Inquiry your first assignment will be to discover what types of molecules those are.

2. During this Inquiry, be sure to wash all glassware between uses. Read the entire procedure before you start.

3. Design a data table similar to the one in Figure 4.61 below in your *Log*.

4. Put five drops of IKI solution in a test tube, and carefully note its color.

5. Measure 10 milliliters of one of your test solutions, and pour it into the graduated cylinder. Record the color of this solution in your data table.

6. Pour the 10 milliliters of solution from the graduated cylinder into the tube containing the IKI. Adding the test solution to the IKI in this way rapidly and thoroughly mixes the solutions. Did the color change? Record your observations in your data table.

7. Clean the test tube and graduated cylinder and repeat Steps 3 to 5 with each of your test solutions. Record your observations of the color change in each solution. Be sure to wash the tube and graduated cylinder after each testing.

A

B

Figure 4.60

The structures of simple and complex carbohydrate molecules.

Glucose is a monosaccharide. It occurs in ring (a) or linear (b) forms

Sucrose is a disaccharide

Starch is a polysaccharide composed of many glucose units.

 Each is a single glucose molecule

Test Tube Number	Test Solution	Color before Adding IKI	Color after Adding IKI	Observation of Reactions
1	Salt Solution			
2	Glucose Solution			
3	Starch Solution			
4	Other			

Figure 4.61

Data table for Part A of Extended Inquiry 4.6.

8. In the data table in your *Log*, note the solutions to which the IKI solution reacted.

Part B: Temperature Effects on Amylase Activity
Procedure

1. Set up a water bath to maintain a temperature of approximately 65°, 55°, 45°, 35°, 25°, or 15° Celsius, as assigned by your teacher. Each student team will have a different temperature. Record this temperature in your *Log*. Maintain this temperature during the course of this experiment.

2. Make a hypothesis about the effects of temperature on amylase activity. Record this hypothesis in your *Log*.

3. Place five drops of IKI solution in a test tube.

4. Measure 15 milliliters of starch solution, and pour it into the test tube containing the IKI solution. Record the color of this solution in your *Log*. Rinse the graduated cylinder.

5. Measure 1 milliliter of the fungal amylase solution into a second test tube.

6. Immerse both test tubes in the water bath, and let them sit for 3 minutes. This allows both solutions to come to the same temperature as the water bath. Place the entire setup on white paper to more easily monitor any color changes.

7. Pour the starch-IKI solution into the amylase solution and immediately begin timing.

8. Return the test tube to the water bath. Predict what will happen to the starch and what color changes you will observe.

9. Record the time that it took for a color change to occur. What might cause this change?

10. Repeat your experiment one more time at the same temperature. If any reaction has not run to completion within 20 minutes, you may stop that reaction.

11. Graph your data. Be sure to label both axes. Title your graph, and make sure the title reflects the information available from the graph.

12. Get together with your class, and record all data collected for all temperatures on the blackboard. Record this information in your *Log*.

Interpretations: Respond to the following in your *Log*:

1. Which of the solutions that you tested in Part A reacted with the IKI solution? Describe this reaction. Write a statement about the type of molecule that reacts with IKI solution.

2. To what extent do the data collected in Part B support your hypothesis about the effects of temperature on amylase activity? Explain.

3. What advantages does this enzyme activity give to the fungus?

4. Amylase is found in many different organisms, including plants, animals, fungi, and microorganisms. On the basis of your observations of the optimal temperature range for amylase activity, make some predictions about the organism that produced the amylase and its environment.

5. Your body should maintain a temperature that is warmer than your typical environment. Why is this an advantage?

Applications: Respond to the following in your *Log*:

1. Would a snake or a rat be more likely to outmaneuver the other on a cold winter day? How can you explain your answer?

2. What occurs physiologically when you warm up before doing strenuous exercise? Why is this important?

3. How do enzymes in warm-blooded animals help digestion to work more efficiently?

How Enzymes Help to Maintain Balance

For homeostasis, an organism's internal body temperature must remain within a certain range. Why is this so important? One reason is because organisms must maintain the internal temperature range in which their particular enzymes can function optimally. Enzymes are biological catalysts; they speed up chemical reactions among the molecules in living cells. In fact, most chemical reactions in a cell are catalyzed by enzymes. If the body temperature is too low, enzyme activity will be slowed. If the body temperature is too high, the enzyme activity will be increased. At very high temperatures, the enzyme, since it is a protein, could be destroyed.

Some enzymes increase the rate of a reaction by a million. In other words, a reaction that takes only 1 minute with an enzyme would require almost 2 years without the enzyme! One extraordinary enzyme, carbonic anhydrase, increases the rate of an important reaction in your body by a factor of more than 10^7 (10 million). This enzyme takes carbon dioxide gas from your cells and converts it to bicarbonate, which dissolves in the blood. In this form, carbon dioxide is transported to the lungs and exhaled.

How Enzymes Work

How do enzymes work? Where do they get their catalytic power? Enzymes have the ability to hold specific chemicals, called substrates, in a particular position that allows these chemicals to react efficiently. By holding the substrate or substrates, the enzyme also stabilizes the chemical reaction. Imagine how difficult it would be to slice an apple precisely in half if it were hanging on a string. Now imagine how much easier and faster it would be if the apple were held in a clamp and marked by that clamp so that one quick chop with a knife would neatly cleave it in half. This illustrates how some enzymes work.

Enzymes are highly specific, much as a key is specific for a lock. They are specific not only for the types of chemical reactions they catalyze, but also for the substances that can participate in that reaction. For example, amylase specifically catalyzes the breakdown of starch, a polysaccharide, into maltose, a disaccharide. Figure 4.62 shows how an enzyme interacts with a substrate (the molecule that is acted on) to help form a product. The enzyme attaches to a molecule (the substrate) to form an enzyme-substrate complex. While the enzyme and substrate are attached, the substrate is chemically altered to produce new products.

The concentration of enzymes in cells where they are manufactured is regulated. Because it takes energy to make an enzyme, cells usually make only the amount of enzyme they need when they need it and when the enzyme will work properly.

Enzymes function best within a narrow range of conditions, including salt concentration, pH, or temperature. These requirements guarantee that the enzymes will function only when appropriate. For example, if the organism's body temperature is not in the appropriate range, the enzymes will not work efficiently.

Review what you have learned about food preservation methods. How might these methods affect enzyme functioning?

Figure 4.62

Enzymes serve as reaction sites for molecules that are acted upon.

Substrate A

Active site

Enzyme

I.
Substrate binds to active site of enzyme

Enzyme-substrate Complex

II.
Substrate reacts

Products

B   C

III.
Products are released

Enzyme Examples

Let's look at some examples of enzymes at work. Commercial meat tenderizer powder is really an enzyme called protease that helps to break down some of the protein in meat. It damages the structure of the meat and makes it easier to chew. Papain, an enzyme that is found in papaya fruit, is a natural source of protease. What do you think would happen if you put fresh papaya in gelatin, which is an animal protein?

An enzyme that is important for milk digestion is lactase. It converts the sugar in milk, a complex sugar called lactose, to two simple sugars. Some people lose this enzyme as they grow older and cannot properly digest milk; they are said to be lactose intolerant. This characteristic, lactose intolerance, is considered to be a genetic trait. In the United States, 8 percent of all adults with Caucasian ancestry, 70 percent of individuals with African ancestry, and 85 percent of those with Japanese ancestry are lactose intolerant. Can you hypothesize why these differences may exist? 🌍

Figure 4.63

The albumin in a chicken egg can stimulate an immune response in susceptible humans.

Albumin

Extended Inquiry 4.6

The Antigen-Antibody Reaction

In this Inquiry, you will explore the immune response in chicken eggs. The white part of a chicken egg (Figure 4.63) contains a protein called albumin. Albumin can act as an antigen. Antigens stimulate immune responses and the production of antibodies. Which antibodies does albumin react with? How specific are these reactions?

MATERIALS

- A petri dish with agar
- A small section of soda straw
- A selection of solutions made from six different foods
- A permanent marker
- A toothpick
- Chicken egg albumin antibody

Procedure: Day 1 (Set up the experiment)

1. Label your dish as shown in Figure 4.64 on page 268.
2. Center your dish over the right side of Figure 4.64, and punch out the holes exactly as they are in the figure. Use the piece of straw to punch the holes. Throw the agar plugs away.

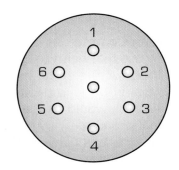

Figure 4.64

Setup for Extended Inquiry 4.6.

3. Into the six outer wells, gently place enough solution to fill the well. You may pick any of the selections provided. Be careful not to overfill the wells or mix any of one solution with another. Make a note in your *Log* about which sample you poured into each numbered hole.

4. Ask your teacher to add the unknown antibody to the center well.

5. Keeping the plate absolutely level, put on the cover, and put masking tape around two sides to seal the plate closed. Store the plate as indicated by your teacher.

6. Construct a hypothesis about how the chicken egg albumin will react to the various solutions you placed in the six holes on the perimeter of the plate.

Procedure: Day 2 (Collect the data)

1. Carefully examine your petri dish. Look for any evidence of antibody-antigen reaction between the center well and any of the outer wells. Record your observations.

2. Compile class data for all of the original food samples.

Interpretations: Respond to the following in your *Log*:

1. Analyze your hypothesis. Why did reactions take place for some foods and not others?

Applications: Respond to the following in your *Log*:

1. When might an immunology lab use this technique? What are some limitations of this technique?

2. Imagine that a patient has symptoms of a disease that is carried in the blood. The doctors cannot identify the disease. What would you advise the doctors to do? Be specific in your response, and describe a procedure.

3. While visiting a foreign country, you ate a piece of strange and exotic fruit, you were stung by an insect, and you inhaled some pollen from a native tree, all at the same time. You begin to show signs of allergic response. How could an allergist decide which of the three—the fruit, the insect, or the pollen—triggered this response? Describe the procedure that the allergist might follow.

Individual Research Projects

Following is a list of 12 different research projects related to the learning experiences of this unit. For an Extended Inquiry, select one or more that explore further your selected focus.

1. Research the topic of nutrition, and develop a personal definition of proper nutrition. Design a restaurant around a theme of good nutrition, plan a menu for this restaurant, and create a TV commercial or print advertisement to promote your restaurant.

2. Use the library or the Internet to research the Project Biosphere 2 in Arizona. Look into the philosophy behind the project. How has the project actually turned out? Look at both the positive and negative results.

3. Design and create a self-sustaining closed ecosystem. You will need to do some research to determine the approximate needs of various organisms.

4. Design an experiment to test responses to environmental change of organisms that are larger than brine shrimp and isopods.

5. Write and illustrate a short children's book with a theme that focuses on some aspect of homeostasis. Be sure that the material you present is correct. Write at a level that is appropriate to your target audience.

6. Create a video or write a skit that discusses balance within the body.

7. Research a disease or condition that throws the body out of balance. Some interesting examples are anorexia, bulimia, steroid abuse, and diabetes. Your report should include an interview with a health care professional and be as up-to-date as possible.

8. Interview a doctor or nurse about fever. In what situations would the doctor recommend that a fever be treated? When might the doctor refrain from prescribing drugs to treat a fever? What is the physiological basis for these decisions? What are the benefits of fever?

9. Investigate one of the following "chilly" topics: cryogenics, freezing embryos, sperm banks, or lowering the body temperature during surgery.

10. Watch the film "Forever Young," "Lorenzo's Oil," or "Late for Dinner." Conduct research to find out whether the scenario in

the film is plausible. If the events could happen, what would be the impact on society? Write a report on your results.

11. Investigate different types of organisms that inhabit different climates and their mechanisms for maintaining homeostasis in their particular environment.

12. Analyze your own diet nutritionally, using the information provided on food labels.

Self-Check 2

Now that you have completed several Extended Inquiries, you should have some additional understanding of homeostasis. This Self-Check is designed to help you find out how much of the material you understand. Check your knowledge and skills by answering these questions and recording them in your *Log*. Divide the questions among your group; then work on your questions as homework. Check your answers with your group. Your teacher will guide you if you have difficulty. After you discuss the responses with your group, revise your answers and write final answers in your *Log*.

1. What happens to bacteria when you wash your hands with soap? Explain the effects of soap and the amount of time the bacteria are exposed to the soap.

2. What effect does external temperature have on the circulatory system of organisms that do not maintain a constant body temperature?

3. Explain why organisms such as mammals maintain a very constant body temperature.

4. How does an organism's ability to exchange gases with its external environment affect its homeostasis?

5. Why is an organism's ability to protect itself against pathogens, toxins, and other conditions that threaten its survival crucial to its homeostasis?

6. Explain why highly contagious diseases can spread quickly through a population.

7. Describe an immune system in general terms.

8. Give three examples of how enzymes illustrate homeostatic mechanisms.

9. Define the role of enzymes in cell metabolism.

10. Describe the chemical reactions for cellular respiration, photosynthesis, and fermentation.

11. Distinguish between independent and dependent variables, and give an example of each.

12. Explain in general terms the purposes of experiments.

13. Explain why controls are needed in experiments.

14. Explain the components and use of a scattergram.

15. What are the characteristics of a good hypothesis?

16. How does scientific research benefit your community?

In this Congress, you will consider the health, academic, and other benefits of physical education courses as you prepare a statement to be delivered to your local school board. You will convene in small groups and as a whole class to design and refine your group presentation. As you work on this presentation, use the information and skills you gained in this unit to support your statements regarding physical education classes. The following setting serves as the impetus for your presentation to the school board.

Setting

Your local school district is growing. The district needs more school facilities, including a new gymnasium for the physical education program. Tax money for schools is limited. Some members of the community are pressuring the school board to prioritize and perhaps even reduce school expenditures.

Your local school board has just received a proposal from a parent group to eliminate physical education (PE) as a course in kindergarten through grade 12. The letter from this group is shown on page 274. The group members believe that PE is an expense that has little to do with academics. Their proposal means that there would be no PE classes at any grade level. All of the PE teachers would be reassigned to teach academic subjects. The group recommends keeping interscholastic football, basketball, and baseball strictly extracurricular activities for athletically talented students.

The school board has requested comments from parents, teachers, administrators, and students. The board has made it clear that it will seriously consider input from all groups and is especially interested in the views of students. You must examine all aspects of this issue to prepare for the school board meeting. The board meeting will be the Forum for this unit. Just as you did for the Copper Basin trial, you will need a full set of notes and a brief that contains all the information you need to consider.

Congress

Parents Coalition FOR Better Education

....

President of the School Board
1234 Address
Some City, State, Zip

Dear President:

The Parents Coalition for Better Education (PCBE) has met regularly for more than a year seeking to design school programs that will provide the best education for our children, the future citizens and leaders of this city. We are also concerned with rising costs of education. This letter represents the first of a series of proposals to improve education and curb spending.

The PCBE recommends eliminating physical education as a formal instructional requirement in grades K–12. We support this recommendation because:

1. PE does not serve a strong academic purpose and reduces by one hour per day the time students have for basic studies such as mathematics, reading, and science.

2. Students expend a great deal of energy during PE, making them tired in their other classes.

3. PE frequently encourages loud behavior, which spills over into the school hall or classes that follow PE classes.

4. PE causes students to get hot, sweaty, and dirty. As a result, the schools must provide showers and other facilities. This is an additional expense to the taxpayer.

5. Students have numerous opportunities for exercise outside of school. We do not need to subsidize this effort during school.

Elimination of PE would not require that anyone be fired. We can reassign the PE teachers to other school duties. The savings could exceed $500,000 a year eventually. This money could be better spent on more necessary academic expenses.

We would like to present our case before the next school board meeting and see the issue brought to a vote.

Sincerely,

Carla T. Millikin
Radna Thompson

Carla T. Millikin and
Radna Thompson

For:
The Parents Coalition for Better Education

Procedure

1. Hold a class meeting to clarify the proposal, specifically the following:
   - What do you think the proposal means?
   - How would it affect students?
   - What might be the various points of view?

2. Break into small groups, and identify some of the issues. Each group will focus on one advantage and one disadvantage of the

proposal. In all cases, try to take into account what you have learned about homeostasis in this unit. Use your teacher as a source of information.

Think of possible merits of eliminating PE classes, such as:

◆ How much money would be saved?

◆ How would eliminating PE create a better learning environment at school?

◆ What resources in the community, such as a YMCA or YWCA, serve the same function as PE classes?

Think of possible disadvantages of eliminating PE classes, such as:

◆ Would only school athletes be getting regular exercise?

◆ What are the benefits of everyone taking PE?

◆ Are there other long-term benefits to taking physical education beyond regular exercise? What else do students learn in PE class?

◆ What are the potential costs of not having physical education classes?

◆ How does PE benefit the learning environment at school?

3. Convene as a whole class. Each group should report its findings.

4. Volunteer for one of the roles to be played at the school board meeting. Your teacher will help to make assignments. These roles are:

◆ Two students, each representing one side

◆ Chairperson and four members of the school board

◆ Three members of the parents group

◆ The district superintendent, who attends board meetings

◆ The district director of finance

◆ Two district physical education teachers

◆ One district biology teacher (to be played by your teacher)

If your biology class is large enough, you may add the following roles:

◆ The district director of facilities

◆ The school's head football coach

◆ The school's head girls basketball coach

◆ Two concerned parents who are not part of the parents group

◆ An active audience (can be played by the remainder of the class)

THE SCHOOL BOARD MEETING

In this Forum, you will role play the school board meeting during which the issue of physical education classes is debated. As you play your assigned roles at this meeting, use appropriate information to support your position on this issue. For example, one of the two student presentations should emphasize the effects of physical education classes on overall health and fitness. In contrast, the district director of finance should present the economic aspects of the issue. Some of the roles will require integrating information from various aspects of the issue. For example, parents certainly want to have healthy children, but they also want them to have the best possible overall education.

Setting

The meeting occurs at the local school board meeting site. Board members and district administrator representatives are seated in front, facing the audience. There is a stage or space between the board seats and the audience for presenters to speak. Since physical education has become a very controversial issue, the building is packed with people from the community. The board has already received a written proposal from the Parents Coalition for Better Education to abolish physical education. The board has agreed to let one member of the committee make a public statement in favor of its proposal. The board will also solicit comments from members of the community.

A Suggested Procedure for the Forum

1. The school board meeting will begin promptly at the beginning of class. Each formal presentation is limited to three minutes, and each comment is limited to one minute.

2. A member from the Parents Coalition for Better Education makes a formal presentation.

3. The director of finance comments in favor of the proposal.

4. The superintendent comments in favor of the proposal.

5. A student who advocates eliminating PE makes a formal presentation against the proposal using the word *homeostasis*.

6. A student who advocates keeping PE speaks in favor of the proposal using the term *homeostasis*.

7. A concerned parent makes a presentation against the proposal.

8. A physical education teacher makes a presentation emphasizing lifelong physical fitness.

9. A high school biology teacher makes a presentation against the proposal that emphasizes the need for a well-balanced physiology.

10. Other comments follow from coaches, other parents, other members of the Parents Coalition for Better Education, or others in the audience. Most speak in favor of the proposal.

11. The board discusses the matter in front of the audience for about five minutes.

12. The board votes and declares its decision and rationale. The meeting is adjourned.

In your *Log*, summarize the events at the board meeting, the decision that the board made, and the reason for the decision.

Summary of Major Concepts

1. Homeostatic mechanisms ensure a stable internal environment for bodily functions. This commonly applies to factors such pH, blood pressure, and body mass.

2. Diffusion is the random thermal movement of atoms and molecules. As they move, these atoms and molecules tend to become distributed evenly throughout the space that they occupy. There is a redistribution of atoms and molecules from areas where they were highly concentrated to areas where they were initially less concentrated.

3. Diffusing molecules move at a rate that depends on the size of the molecule, the nature of the medium, and the temperature. Increasing the concentration of molecules does not make them move faster but can affect how many molecules move.

4. Because diffusion is fast over very small distances, it is adequate for the transport of materials at the cell level. Organisms accomplish large-scale movement with convective transport systems, which use pumps such as the heart and lungs to produce fluid flow.

5. Osmosis is a special case of diffusion. It describes the movement of water through a selectively permeable membrane.

6. All cells have a cell membrane. The cell membrane is made of proteins in a double layer of lipids. The membrane helps to select what goes into and out of the cell.

7. Complex organisms digest food to simpler forms (amino acids, sugars, fatty acids, and glycerol) that can enter the circulatory system.

8. Enzymes are catalysts in the cell that speed up chemical reactions, such as digestion.

9. A cell is the basic unit of life. Cells function more or less independently. Only cells can produce more cells.

10. All organisms need a source of energy to survive. During photosynthesis, plants capture sunlight energy and store this energy in carbohydrates. This process uses CO_2 and H_2O and produces O_2. Nonphotosynthetic organisms and plants carry out cellular respiration to extract usable energy from food. This process uses oxygen and produces carbon dioxide and water.

11. Protein metabolism produces ammonia, which is changed by the liver to the less toxic compounds urea and uric acid. These are then filtered out by the kidney and become part of the urine.

12. Complex multicellular organisms need a circulatory system to efficiently transport nutrients and wastes. There are often specialized circulatory structures to aid in circulation.

13. The lung is an example of a specialized structure that helps to make oxygen available to the tissues and expel carbon dioxide.

14. Most organisms operate most efficiently with a narrow temperature range, in part because their body enzymes function best only at certain temperatures. Highly specialized organisms, such as mammals, frequently use energy to keep the body warmer than the external environment. Most organisms, however, take on the temperature of the external environment.

15. Most common diseases are infections that are caused by organisms or particles called pathogens. Many very dangerous pathogens, such as HIV, are transmitted by direct body contact or exchange of body fluids.

16. Organisms such as vertebrates have an elaborate immune system with many lines of defense against pathogens.

17. Hormones are chemicals that regulate metabolic processes in specific areas of the body.

18. Scientists do experiments to learn the cause-and-effect relationships between variables in the natural world.

19. Independent variables are those that can be manipulated or changed by the investigator. These are also called cause variables. The data in an experiment represent the dependent variables. These are also called results or effects.

20. If there is more than one independent variable in an experiment, it is difficult to identify the cause of the outcome. For this reason, experiments are designed to control for other variables except the one under study.

Suggestions for Further Exploration

Caldwell, M. 1992. Resurrection of a killer. *Discover*, 13 (December), 58–64.
Discusses why we should not forget about tuberculosis.

Caldwell, M. 1993. Why we don't have an AIDS vaccine. *Discover*, August, 61–67.

Corner, T.R. 1992. Ecology in a jar: Bacterial growth in the Winogradsky column. *The Science Teacher,* 59(3), 32–36.
Illustrates method of studying anaerobic bacteria in the classroom. Includes materials, procedure, and background information on development of the Winogradsky column.

Flannery, M.C. 1993. Looking at the cell once again. *The American Biology Teacher*, 55(2), 118–121.
Discusses new information from cell research including mitochondria from the male, cell cycle, and nuclear structure.

Hart, S. 1994. The drama of cellular death: Scientists discover genes that set the balance between survival and self-destruction of cells. *BioScience*, 44(7), 451–455.
Discusses programmed cell death, which is hypothesized to play a crucial part in keeping cell populations in line "by killing off unneeded new cells while allowing others to differentiate."

Joklik, W.K., et al. 1993. Why the smallpox virus stocks should not be destroyed. *Science*, 262, 1225–1226.
In 1979, the world was declared free of smallpox. Immediately thereafter, the research world began discussing the possibility of destroying their existing stocks. This article argues against this, since there is the possibility of reemerging infectious agents.

Levine, A.J. 1992. *Viruses*. Scientific American Library, New York.
A detailed look at the composition and life cycles of viruses.

Mahy, B.W.J., et al. 1993. The remaining stocks of smallpox virus should be destroyed. *Science*, 262, 1223–1224.
In 1979, the world was declared free of smallpox. Immediately thereafter, the research world began discussing the possibility of destroying their existing stocks. This article argues for this, since there are so many new infectious diseases to be researched.

Preston, R. 1994. *The Hot Zone*. Random House, New York.
This book tells the spellbinding story of the 1989 outbreak of the Ebola virus. Set in Zaire, Africa, and an Army research facility outside of Washington, D.C., this true story points out the potential impact of previously unknown viruses as they enter human populations.

Rosenthal, A. 1991. Life on the edge. *Discover*, 12 (March), 76–78.
Discusses why people with diabetes may be living on the brink of metabolic disaster.

Videos

Homeostasis: Coping with Change. 1992. Films for the Humanities & Sciences, Princeton, N.J.
A ten-minute color video that introduces the concept of homeostasis. The program includes an example of internal conditions being balanced.

Search for Solutions: Adaptation. 1981. Karol Media, Wilkes-Barre, Pa.
A 19-minute color video that illustrates feedback as a form of adaptation. Includes segments on a marathon swimmer and vital signs during surgery.

MOST **FEATURES** OF ORGANISMS ARE DUE TO INHERITANCE.

INHERITANCE

WHY WOULD YOU WANT TO KNOW ABOUT YOUR GENETIC MAKEUP?

nitial Inquiry

WHY ARE WE THE WAY WE ARE?

Setting

You make plenty of decisions every day. Some decisions are more difficult than others. When you are dealing with genetics, it's especially hard to decide when you can foresee the consequences. Sooner or later, you will have to make decisions that involve reproduction and genetics.

The individuals who enter the Genetic Counseling Center (Figure 5.1) want to find out enough to make informed decisions. This knowledge will increase greatly their confidence in dealing with decisions about their families.

The Genetic Counseling Center Video

You'll begin this unit by watching a video segment on a genetic counseling center. As you watch, focus on the concerns of the people at the center. Why are they seeking help? What questions do they have? How can a counselor trained in the field of genetics help them? What do they actually learn?

Figure 5.1

Learning that you have a genetic disorder can affect decisions you make in your life.

Record your thoughts and questions about the video in your *Log*. For instance, what problems can you identify? What information is missing that would allow you to understand each situation more completely?

Then copy the ethics grid from Figure 5.2 into your *Log*. Use this grid to record what you think should be the goals, rights, and duties of the individuals in the video. For example, what are the goals of each individual or couple in seeking genetic counseling? What rights do they have to know genetic information about themselves or their children? What duties do they have, and to whom, with regard to genetic testing? What are the duties, rights, and goals of the genetic counselor?

	Goals	Rights	Duties
John and Susan Clarke			
Maria Stevens			
Tanya and James Weston			
Genetics Counselor			

Figure 5.2

Make an ethics grid like this one in your Log *to record your opinions on the goals, rights, and duties of the individuals in the video.*

Brainstorming

Discuss the video scenarios with some of your classmates. Consider the viewpoints of both the patients and the counselors. How would you respond if you had to make the decisions that the individuals in the video faced?

Discuss the following questions in your group. Then record your thoughts in your *Log*.

1. How might you use information from prenatal testing in your life?

2. How would your life be different if you suffered from sickle-cell anemia? What activities would you avoid?

3. How would you decide whether or not to take the Huntington's test if you knew that you were at risk? Take a vote by secret ballot in your class. What percentage of the class would seek the Huntington's test? How does the class response compare to your decision?

4. Suppose it were possible to cure Huntington's disease, Down syndrome, or sickle-cell anemia? How would this possibility affect your decision to use genetic counseling before starting a family?

5. How could it benefit a family group of several generations (Figure 5.3) to visit a genetic counseling center?

AT THE GENETIC COUNSELING CENTER

Susan Clarke is the aunt of a teenager child who has Down syndrome. She and her husband, John, plan to have a baby and are visiting a genetic counseling center to learn what their risk might be of having a child with Down syndrome. They want to investigate the types of services that the Center can provide to them. They are meeting with Phyllis Watson, a counselor at the center.

Susan: *Ms. Watson, you know that my sister's child Joey has Down syndrome. If there is a chance that our child will have Down syndrome, we prefer to know that before the child is born. Can we take a test to find that out?*

Ms. Watson: *Yes, there are ways to test for Down syndrome in a fetus. In fact, the Down syndrome test was one of the first prenatal genetic tests to be developed. In this test, a laboratory technician inspects the chromosomes in the developing fetus to determine whether they show any abnormalities.*

Chromosomes

Figure 5.3

People at the Genetic Counseling Center want to learn more about how inheritance works.

You have 23 pairs of chromosomes in the nucleus of every one of your cells. You received one of the chromosomes of each pair from your father's sperm and one from your mother's egg. Chromosomes are the structures that carry genetic information from one generation to the next. They determine nearly all of your characteristics. If you have children someday, you will contribute to them one half of their genetic information. All organisms that reproduce contain chromosomes or a comparable genetic material. Genetics is the study of the traits carried by chromosomes and how these traits are expressed in an individual.

Chromosomes are made of long strands of the chemical, DNA (deoxyribonucleic acid). There is a tremendous amount of information in a single chromosome. This is because specific positions on the DNA molecule make up genes. Each gene is a code to determine or help determine some characteristic. An example of a characteristic determined by one gene on a chromosome is the simple trait, widow's peak—whether your front hairline comes to a point or not. Most chromosomes contain thousands of genes which, all totaled, determine the organism's total makeup. This gives an individual, such as a human, thousands of genetic traits.

Down syndrome (Figure 5.4 on page 286) is a genetic disorder caused by an extra chromosome in chromosome pair No. 21. This disease can be detected through observ-

Inheritance

Genetic Counseling Center

Facts About Genetic Counseling

What Is Genetic Counseling?

Genetic counseling involves one or more appropriately trained people helping an individual or family to:

- Understand disorders in terms of medical facts, diagnoses, and management;

- Comprehend how heredity contributes to the disorder;

- Understand the choices for dealing with the chance of recurrence;

- Choose a course of action that seems appropriate;

- Make the best possible adjustment to the disorder.

Is Genetic Counseling for You?

Anyone who has questions or concerns about diseases or traits in his or her family might consider genetic counseling. This includes:

- Women who are pregnant or planning to be pregnant after the age of 34;

- Couples who already have a child with a disorder;

- Families with a history of birth defects or mental or developmental retardation;

- Couples who have had excessive exposure to toxic chemicals, drugs, or alcohol;

- Couples who are close blood relatives and who plan to have children;

- Women who have had two or more miscarriages.

ing an individual's actual chromosomes in a karyotype. A karyotype is an arrangement of all of the chromosomes in a cell and can be made by staining the DNA of the individual's cell nucleus. To make a karyotype, a technician photographs the chromosomes from a single cell and cuts out the pictures of the individual chromosomes. The chromosomes are then identified by number according to size and banding patterns and arranged in order. The result is a vivid picture of all of the individual's chromosomes, which can be used to study their genetic makeup. 🐞

Figure 5.4

A teenager with Down syndrome.

Making and Analyzing Karyotypes

Down syndrome is named for the British physician Dr. John Langdon Haydon Down, who first described it in 1866. It is called a syndrome because there are multiple effects seen with this disorder. Some of these effects include mental retardation, short stature, and distinct facial characteristics.

In this Inquiry, you'll examine the genetic basis for Down syndrome, study karyotypes, and make a karyotype.

MATERIALS

- Prepared karyotypes (Figures 5.5, 5.6, and 5.7)
- A photo of the chromosomes from a single human cell
- A blank karyotype page
- Scissors, transparent tape

Procedure

1. Work in groups of three or four students. Carefully examine the karyotypes in Figures 5.5, 5.6, and 5.7. Notice the arrangement and labeling of each chromosome pair. Look for similarities and differences between the chromosome pairs; look especially at the chromosomes shapes, sizes, and banding patterns.

2. Compare your list with those of the other groups.

3. Now make a new karyotype. Cut out the chromosomes in the photo that your teacher provides.

4. Match pairs of chromosomes and line them up on the blank karyotype form using Figures 5.5, 5.6, and 5.7 as models.

Guided Inquiries

Figure 5.5

Karyotype for Susan Clarke's nephew, who has Down syndrome.

Figure 5.6

Normal human male karyotype.

Figure 5.7

Normal human female karyotype.

5. When you think that you have correctly identified all of the chromosomes, tape them onto the blank karyotype sheet. Place the sheet in your *Log*.

Interpretations: Respond to the following in your *Log*:

1. How is Joey's karyotype (Figure 5.5) different from the normal male karyotype (Figure 5.6)?

2. How are the karyotypes in Figures 5.6 and 5.7 alike? How are they different?

3. What did you notice when you compared the chromosome pairs?

4. Which karyotype (Figures 5.5, 5.6 or 5.7) is more like the one you made? Explain. Would you predict that the individual whose karyotype you made has Down syndrome?

5. What is the sex of the individual whose karyotype you made? How do you know?

Applications: Respond to the following in your *Log*:

1. Explain why karyotyping is useful.

2. Do you know someone who has Down syndrome? If you do, describe some of the special challenges this person faces in adapting to society. If you don't, do some research on Down syndrome to learn about some of these challenges. Record your thoughts in your *Log*.

Genetic
Counseling
Center

Facts About Down Syndrome

What Is The Nature of the Genetic Disorder?

- The affected individual has three (instead of two) No. 21 chromosomes.

- Nondisjunction, the failure of chromosomes to separate properly during egg and sperm formation, is a cause of the disorder. It occurs most frequently in egg cells; only 5 percent of all Down syndrome cases are due to nondisjunction in sperm.

- The same genetic disorder can occur if a large piece of chromosome No. 21 is transferred to another chromosome (usually No. 14) by a process known as translocation.

How common Is Down Syndrome?

- One in 800 to 1,000 children born to women in their teens and twenties has Down syndrome.

- The frequency of occurrence increases as the age of the mother increases (as shown in the graph).

What Are the Physical Symptoms of Down Syndrome?

- Short, stocky body with a short, thick neck and short fingers

- Enlarged tongue and lips, which cause speech difficulty

- Mild to severe mental retardation

- Almond-shaped eyes

- Susceptibility to multiple infections

- Abnormal internal organs, especially the heart and kidneys

Detecting Genetic Disorders before Birth

Medical doctors can detect some genetic disorders, including Down syndrome, in fetuses before birth. Two of the procedures used to inspect fetal cells for prenatal testing, amniocentesis and chorionic villus sampling, are described in Figure 5.8. In both tests, cells from the developing fetus are removed and examined without harming the fetus (though in rare cases, the procedures have a slight risk of miscarriage).

Amniocentesis (Figure 5.8A) is performed between the fourteenth and sixteenth weeks of pregnancy. A needle is inserted into the placenta to collect amniotic fluid for chemical analyses and fetal cells to detect chromosomal abnormalities (the cells are naturally shed by the fetus during growth). These cells are grown in culture for two to three weeks, treated with colchicine to stop cell division at the point when the chromosomes are condensed, treated with a salt solution, placed on a microscope slide, and squashed to free the chromosomes. The chromosomes are photographed, cut from the photograph, and arranged (as you did in Guided Inquiry 5.1) to produce a karyotype.

Chorionic villi sampling (Figure 5.8B) provides prenatal testing as early as the eighth or ninth week of pregnancy with less disturbance to the fetus. A small piece of chorion, an embryonic membrane, is removed using a small tube. Because the cells of the chorion are dividing rapidly, there are many dividing cells available for karyotyping. Thus, it takes only one day to prepare the karyotype. 🌐

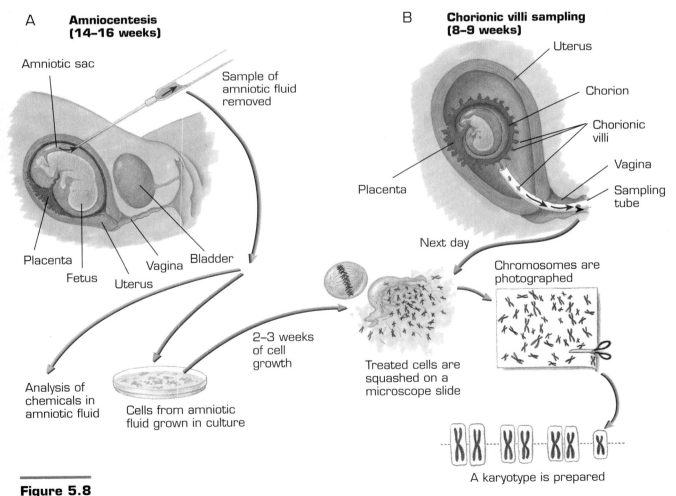

Figure 5.8

Amniocentesis and chorionic villi sampling are used for prenatal diagnoses of genetic conditions.

Chromosomes Have Bands

As you saw in the karyotypes in Guided Inquiry 5.1, chromosomes have bands. You see the bands because of the way they absorb various stains.

Think of the DNA from one chromosome as a piece of thread about 6 centimeters long. Now imagine that you have to fold up the thread to fit into a cell's nucleus, an area so small that you need a microscope to see it. You can't fold the thread randomly; you have to be precise. The DNA strand forms a series of loops through several levels of folding (Figure 5.9).

Technicians stain chromosome samples to examine them. Some areas of DNA become more densely stained than others, forming bands. Chromosome bands can be quite prominent (Figure 5.10).

Banding patterns on chromosomes can help scientists to identify specific chromosomes by comparing them with chromosomes of a known karyotype. If bands are missing or if the pattern of the bands is rearranged, abnormalities in the chromosomes can be identified more easily. Scientists can use this information to diagnose some genetic disorders. 🌍

Chromosomes and Sex Determination

Each type of living organism has a specific number of chromosomes in each of its body's cells. For example, most humans have 46 chromosomes. The common fruit fly, on the other hand, has only eight chromosomes. A human cell that has 46 chromosomes is said to be in the diploid state.

BIOthoughts

The total number of chromosomes in a body cell is not related to the organism's size or complexity. Some insects have hundreds of chromosomes, whereas humans have 46.

Figure 5.9

Folding of DNA in chromosomes.

DNA molecule (double helix)

DNA coils around protein cluster

Proteins and DNA molecule coil to form fiber

Fiber coils to form chromosome

When you examined the karyotypes in Guided Inquiry 5.1, you probably noticed that the chromosomes occurred in pairs. Humans have 23 pairs of chromosomes. A human cell that has 23 chromosomes, one from each pair, is said to be in the haploid state. Twenty-two of these 23 pairs of chromosomes can be identified by a number. The chromosomes in each of these 22 pairs look like each other. These 44 chromosomes are called autosomes. If you examine the pairs of autosomes in Figures 5.5, 5.6, and 5.7, you will notice that the chromosomes in each pair are the same size and shape and have the same banding pattern. Each pair of chromosomes is called a homologous pair, and each chromosome in the pair is called a homolog.

Sex Chromosomes

If you look very closely at the karyotypes in Figures 5.5, 5.6, and 5.7, you will notice that one of the pairs is composed of two chromosomes that are very different in size, shape, and banding pattern. This chromosome pair is not assigned a number. Instead, each of the chromosomes in this pair is identified by a letter. These are called the X and Y sex chromosomes. It is these chromosomes that determine the sex of an individual. The Y chromosome is responsible for genetic male traits. Human males have one X chromosome and one Y chromosome. Human females have two X chromosomes.

Refer to the karyotype that you made in Guided Inquiry 5.1. What was the sex of that individual?

Why Chromosomes Are in Pairs

Humans have pairs of chromosomes because humans reproduce sexually as pairs. Each parent contributes a copy of one chromosome from each pair to the offspring. So an individual has two sets of chromosomes: one from the father, the other from the mother.

The 23 chromosomes that each parent contributes to an offspring are carried in the parents' sex cells, or gametes. The father's sperm and the mother's egg are gametes (Figure 5.11). These gametes contribute their chromosomes to the offspring when the sperm combines with an egg to form a zygote, or fertilized egg.

Sex Determination

A single human sperm carries either an X or a Y chromosome. Human eggs normally contain one X chromosome from the XX pair. If an egg with its X chromosome is fertilized by an X-carrying sperm, the offspring is XX, a female. If the egg is fertilized with a Y-carrying sperm, the offspring is XY, a male. Which parent determines the sex of a child (Figure 5.12 on page 292)?

Figure 5.10

Chromosome banding is especially easy to see in these giant chromosomes from Drosophila melanogaster, *a fruit fly.*

Figure 5.11

A human sperm fertilizing an ovum.

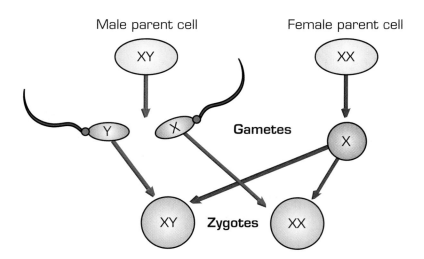

Gamete Formation

How do sperm and eggs end up with only one set of chromosomes? Cells that form sperm and eggs are specialized. They go through a type of cell division called meiosis, which reduces the chromosome number to half. At the time of fertilization the chromosome number is restored to the diploid state. (In humans, that's 46 chromosomes.) Once a human zygote is formed, a different type of cell division is necessary for continued growth of the individual. This division replicates the genetic material of the zygote over and over again as more and more cells are formed. This process is called mitosis. 🌎

Guided Inquiry 5.2

Modeling Mitosis

How do cells divide and produce more cells? How do multicellular organisms grow in size? Each cell plays a role in passing genetic information to the next generation. In this Inquiry, you will model the process of mitosis, an important part of cell division.

MATERIALS

- Four long strips of paper of the same size, two in one color and two in another
- String
- Scissors
- Paper clips or tape

- Four short strips of paper of the same size, two in one color and two in another, using the same colors as for the long strips

Procedure

1. Use two long strips and two short strips of paper to represent four chromosomes. Let's say you have two green strips, one long and one short, and two blue strips, one long and one short. Place the strips on your desk or table so that the two long strips form a pair and the two short strips form a pair. Your cell model should resemble the one in Figure 5.13.

2. Make a single circle around the strips with your string. This string represents the cell membrane of a simplified cell with two pairs of chromosomes.

3. Separate the chromosomes in the cell. Match up each chromosome with another of the same size and color. Tape or paper clip strips of the same size and color together. Each new pair of strips represents a replicated chromosome midway through the cell division process. Taped together, each chromosome strand is called a chromatid. At this stage in the division process, chromosomes are densely coiled and quite visible.

4. Separate the chromosomes that you replicated by removing the tape or paper clips and moving one strip of each pair to an opposite side of the cell. Enclose these replicated chromosomes in string to form two daughter cells. Each daughter cell must be identical to the parent cell. Not only must it contain the same number of chromosomes, but the chromosomes must have the same color and size as those in the parent cell.

5. Record in your *Log* each step of the process that you used to form two identical daughter cells from the original parent cell. Use drawings and text notations to describe the process.

   ◆ Identify the number of chromosomes in the cell at each stage of the division process. Remember, each bundle that you taped or clipped together is still only one chromosome even though it is composed of two chromatids.

   ◆ Identify whether the chromosomes at each stage are replicated.

   ◆ Count the total number of paper strips at each stage of the process. Divide this number by the haploid number (2), the number of types of chromosomes in the original cell. This will give you the *n* number, which represents the total amount of genetic material in each cell.

Figure 5.13

Your cell model should look like this as you start Guided Inquiry 5.2.

Interpretations: Respond to the following in your *Log*:

1. What do the different colors of the chromosomes represent?

2. How many different types of chromosomes does this cell have?

3. Suppose the daughter cells underwent a division cycle (Steps 1 through 4). What would the daughter cells of this second division look like?

4. Define mitosis on the basis of the procedure you followed in this Inquiry.

Applications: Respond to the following in your *Log*:

1. The cells of mice and elephants are about the same size. What is different about cell division for these two organisms that explains the difference in their sizes?

2. What is the difference between cell growth and cell duplication? In which does mitosis play a role?

Mitosis in the Cell Division Cycle

For a daughter cell to keep the same number and types of chromosomes as its parent cell, the genetic material in the cell must be duplicated before the cell divides. In Guided Inquiry 5.2, you modeled mitosis. In this kind of division, the chromosomes are replicated to produce identical cells in each generation that follows.

Figure 5.14

The cell cycle in a eukaryote cell.

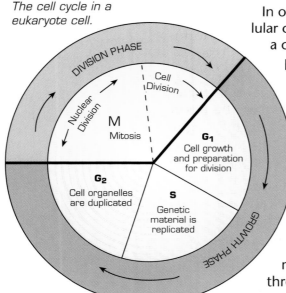

The Cell Cycle

In order for cell division to occur, the cytoplasm and other cellular components must also divide. A living cell passes through a cycle of events that alternates between a long growth phase and a relatively shorter dividing phase (Figure 5.14). The genetic material condenses and separates into daughter cells during mitosis, when nuclear and cell division takes place. G_1 is a resting phase of sorts as the cell grows and prepares for division. During the S phase, the genetic material is replicated. Cellular organelles are duplicated during the G_2 phase.

Producing Identical Cells

Mitosis is a continuous process that has several visually definable phases (Figure 5.15 and Figure 5.16 on page 296). When a body cell is not undergoing mitosis, the chromosomes appear as a tangled mass of threads in the nucleus (Figures 5.15A and 5.16A).

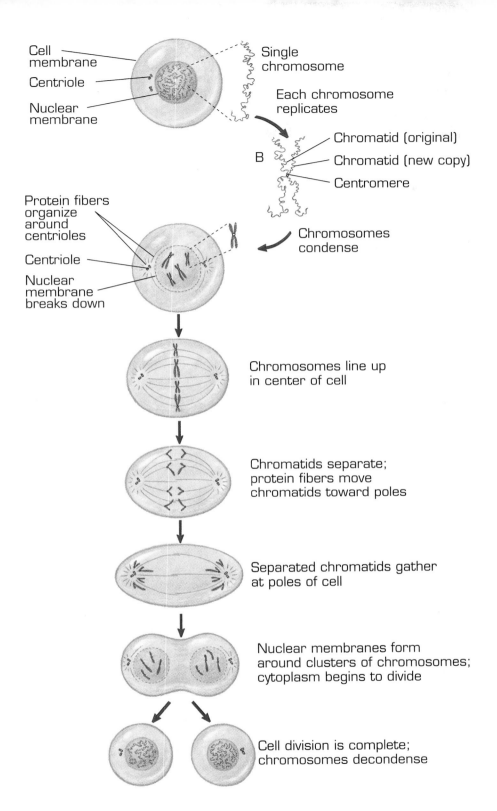

Cell membrane

Centriole

Nuclear membrane

Single chromosome

Each chromosome replicates

Chromatid (original)

Chromatid (new copy)

Centromere

B

Chromosomes condense

Protein fibers organize around centrioles

Centriole

Nuclear membrane breaks down

Chromosomes line up in center of cell

Chromatids separate; protein fibers move chromatids toward poles

Separated chromatids gather at poles of cell

Nuclear membranes form around clusters of chromosomes; cytoplasm begins to divide

Cell division is complete; chromosomes decondense

Figure 5.15

Mitosis in animal cells.

Figure 5.16

Mitosis in plant cells.

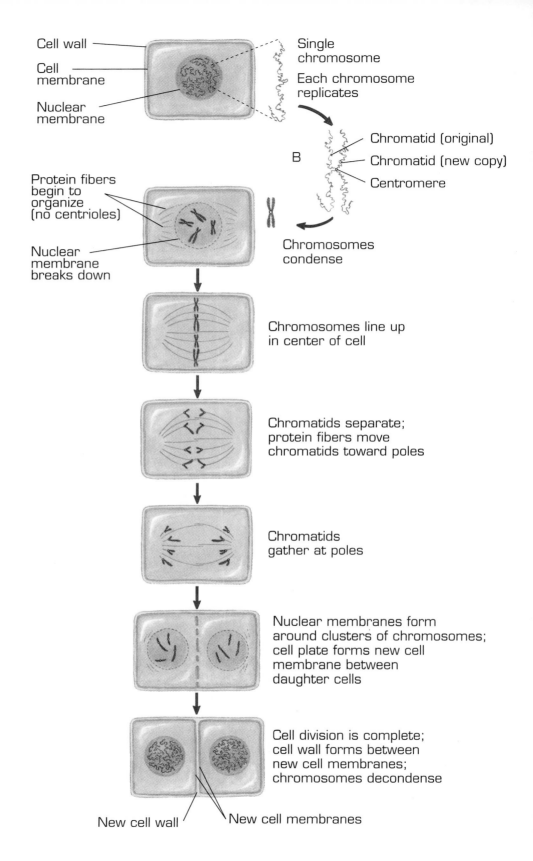

Cell wall

Cell membrane

Nuclear membrane

Single chromosome

Each chromosome replicates

B

Chromatid (original)

Chromatid (new copy)

Centromere

Chromosomes condense

Protein fibers begin to organize (no centrioles)

Nuclear membrane breaks down

Chromosomes line up in center of cell

Chromatids separate; protein fibers move chromatids toward poles

Chromatids gather at poles

Nuclear membranes form around clusters of chromosomes; cell plate forms new cell membrane between daughter cells

Cell division is complete; cell wall forms between new cell membranes; chromosomes decondense

New cell wall

New cell membranes

As mitosis begins, each chromosome makes an identical copy of itself. This copy remains attached to the original chromosome at a central region called the centromere. At this point, each chromosome is made up of two chromatids (Figures 5.15B and 5.16B).

Each chromosome becomes visually shorter and thicker as it folds multiple times on itself (Figures 5.15C and 5.16C). These chromosomes next move toward the center of the cell (Figures 5.15D and 5.16D) and then split apart at the centromeres. Protein threads that are attached at the centromeres pull each chromatid to the opposite sides of the cell (Figures 5.15E and 5.16E).

Each side of the cell now has the diploid (2n) number of chromosomes, exactly like the original cell (Figures 5.15F and 5.16F). Nuclear membranes form around each of these clusters of chromosomes, thereby completing nuclear division (Figures 5.15G and 5.16G). Division of cytoplasm and cellular organelles and reformation of the plasma membrane around the two new cells complete the cell division cycle (Figure 5.15H and 5.16H). In plants and microorganisms that have a cell wall, formation of cell walls around the new cells is the final step in the division cycle (Figure 5.16H).

Cells that are produced through mitosis contain exactly the same genetic information as the parent cells. For multicelled organisms, mitosis occurs as a zygote develops into an embryo. It also occurs as body cells grow and replace themselves.

Asexual Reproduction

For some organisms, mitosis is a type of asexual reproduction. In single-celled organisms the process produces entirely new organisms. It is called asexual because it does not involve the fusion of parent gametes to form a zygote.

Although most larger organisms reproduce sexually, some organisms (such as flatworms, protists, bacteria, Hydra and most plants) can reproduce by budding or in ways which do not require contributions from two parents. We call this asexual reproduction. Some organisms can either reproduce sexually or asexually, depending on the environmental conditions. During asexual reproduction, the organism replicates cells (just like in mitosis) that may separate from the parent organism to become free living individuals or that may remain attached to the original as part of a colony. Production of these cells involved mitotic nuclear divisions. Each of these new cells is identical genetically to the original, single parent cell or organism.

Since no exchange of gametes occurs, no routine source of genetic variability is present and the offspring are clones of the original organism. Advantages of this type of reproduction include saving energy by not having to produce gametes, maintain a reproductive system, or be fertilized by a mate. And, not needing a mate means that organisms can reproduce even if they are the last individual alive. 🦠

BIOoccupation

Patsy Livingston: Laboratory Technician, Orchid Cloning

Humans have, for centuries, used controlled breeding to produce domestic animals and plants that have desired characteristics.

Orchids, for example, are highly prized flowering plants. Have you ever thought about where these beautiful flowers come from? Patsy Livingston and the rest of the staff at Carter & Holmes, an orchid-breeding company, know all about orchids.

Breeding Orchids

In a process quite different from standard breeding, Ms. Livingston clones new orchid plants from existing ones. To make a clone, a lab technician removes an actively growing tip from inside of an orchid bud and places it in a nutrient solution for a few days before planting it on sterile agar gel, a growth medium. The agar allows the plant pieces to produce more cells, which eventually become stems, roots, leaves, and flowers. Over 10,000 orchid plants can be grown from a single piece of orchid tissue!

Because the rain forests where many orchids grow are threatened, breeders provide a commercial source of existing and new varieties. According to Gene Crocker, manager of Carter & Holmes, the current focus in orchid growing is to cultivate and make crosses from orchids that were collected as long ago as the 1800s.

What a Technician Does

Staff members at Carter & Holmes do a variety of jobs. Laboratory technicians like Patsy Livingston clone and cross-breed plants. She learned to do this through on-the-job train-

ing after high school. The technicians keep an exact record of each orchid's breeding history, which requires attention to detail. They also must code labels accurately. Technicians must be very patient; orchids normally do not produce their first flowers until the plants are six to seven years old.

If you are interested in working for a company like Carter & Holmes, consider volunteering or working part-time while you are in school. Or get involved with growing orchids or other plants as a hobby. Several of the company's employees began their careers as high school students working part-time and during the summer.

Modeling Meiosis

Gametes (sperm and egg cells) are formed though the process of meiosis. How is this cell division process different from mitosis? In this Inquiry, you will explore some important differences between meiosis and mitosis.

MATERIALS

- Four long strips of paper of the same size, two in one color and two in another
- String
- Scissors
- Paper clips or tape

- Four short strips of paper of the same size, two in one color and two in another, using the same colors as for the long strips

Procedure

1. Use strips of paper to represent four chromosomes (two long strips of each color, two short strips of each color), as you did in Step 1 of Guided Inquiry 5.2. Place the strips on your desk or table so that the two long strips form a pair and the two short strips form a pair.

2. Make a single circle around the strips with your string, which represents the cell membrane. Draw a picture of this cell in your *Log*. Leave space on the side for additional columns of information.

3. Match each chromosome with the other one of the same color and size. Tape or paper clip the centers together.

4. Paper clip together all four of the long chromosomes (both colors). Paper clip together all four of the short chromosomes (both colors).

5. Separate the homologous chromosomes by moving them, still in pairs, to opposite sides of the cell. This time don't remove the paper clips joining the chromatids. For example, both of the long chromosomes of one color will move together to one side of the cell, and both of the long chromosomes of the other color will move together to the other side of the cell.

6. Use string to make a new cell membrane around each of the two new cells formed. (Because you didn't remove the paper clips, each of these chromosomes will be paired.) Draw a picture in your *Log* of each of these cells.

7. Next, remove the tape or paper clips from the double-stranded chromosome in each cell. Take these chromosomes through a second division cycle, moving the chromosomes to the sides of the cells and reforming the cell membrane. But this time, don't duplicate the chromosomes. Use string to make a new cell membrane around each of the four new cells formed. Draw pictures of each of these cells in your *Log*.

8. Record in your *Log* each step of the process that you used to form four daughter cells (Figure 5.17).

◆ Identify the number of chromosomes in each cell at each stage of the division process.

◆ Identify whether the chromosomes at each stage are duplicated.

◆ Identify the chromosome at each stage as either paired or not paired.

◆ Count the total number of paper strips at each stage of the process. Divide this number by two, the number of types of chromosomes in the original cell. This will give you the n number, which represents the total amount of genetic material in each cell.

Interpretations: Respond to the following in your *Log*:

1. How many different types of chromosomes does each of your final four cells have? How many different types of chromosomes were in the original cell?

2. Compare your final four cells, using the models on your desk and your *Log* drawings, with those made by at least three other

Figure 5.17

Students modeling mitosis.

Inheritance

students or groups of students in your class, and explain why the final products might be different.

3. Define meiosis on the basis of what you learned in this Inquiry.

Applications: Respond to the following in your *Log*:

1. What is the role of meiosis in the life cycle of a sexually reproducing organism?

2. One form of Down syndrome is known as trisomy 21 because affected individuals have three No. 21 chromosomes in their body cells. How many No. 21 chromosomes should the cells have? How many should the gametes have? When the cells of a person with trisomy 21 undergo meiosis, how many No. 21 chromosomes will their gametes contain?

The Process of Meiosis

All cells duplicate their genetic material before dividing. However, eggs and sperm must contain half the number of chromosomes (and half the total amount of genetic material) as the original cell. That's because the egg and sperm will join, producing a cell that should have the same number of chromosomes and the same amount of DNA as the original cell.

Meiosis is a division process in which diploid cells produce haploid cells. In humans, this is the division process that produces gametes (eggs and sperm). As with mitosis, meiosis is a continuous process that has several visually definable phases, as in Figure 5.18 on page 302.

As meiotic cell division begins, each chromosome makes an identical copy of itself, which remains attached to the original chromosome at the centromere. At this point, each chromosome is made up of two chromatids. Each chromosome becomes visually shorter and thicker as it folds multiple times upon itself. Up to this point, meiosis and mitosis are identical.

Meiosis Versus Mitosis

The crucial difference between meiosis and mitosis occurs at the point when the chromosomes line up in the center and then are pulled to opposite sides of the cell. In meiosis, pairs of homologous chromosomes (that is, chromosomes that have the same structure) move to opposite sides of the cell. As in mitosis, each side of the cell now has the same amount of genetic material as the original cell. At this stage in the division process, the homologous chromosomes remain paired.

In meiosis, the nuclear membranes do not reform after this first stage. Instead, a second division cycle begins. It is in this second division cycle that the homologous chromosomes split at their centromere regions and are pulled to opposite sides of the new cells. This second division cycle of meiosis is identical to mitotic division except that it is not preceded by duplication of the genetic material. Thus each of the four new cells that are formed

MEIOSIS I

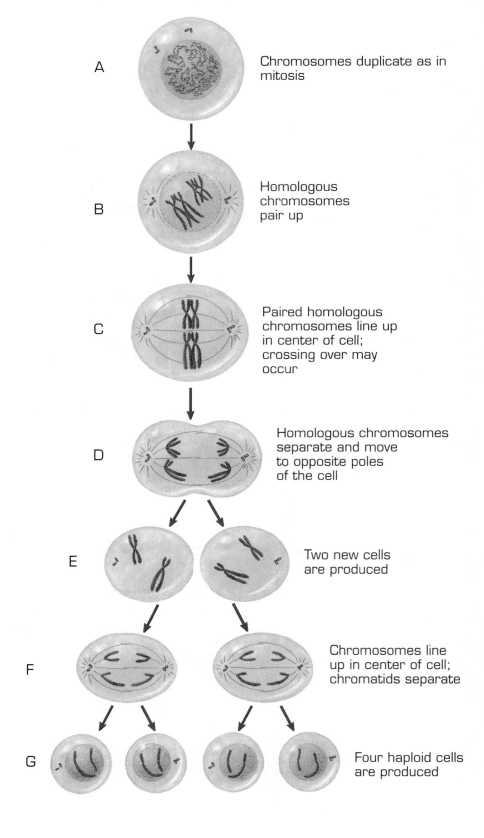

A   Chromosomes duplicate as in mitosis

B   Homologous chromosomes pair up

C   Paired homologous chromosomes line up in center of cell; crossing over may occur

D   Homologous chromosomes separate and move to opposite poles of the cell

E   Two new cells are produced

MEIOSIS II

F   Chromosomes line up in center of cell; chromatids separate

G   Four haploid cells are produced

Figure 5.18

Meiosis produces haploid cells from diploid cells. Exchange of segments between homologous chromosomes has occurred in step C.

by the end of meiosis contains only half the number of chromosomes as are in the original cell. The products of the meiotic division of a single diploid cell are four haploid cells.

Another important difference between mitosis and meiosis is that in meiosis, cells undergo a process of recombination, or crossing over. When all four chromatids of a chromosome pair are together, large pieces of chromosomes may exchange with their counterparts on the opposite chromosome. In this process of crossing over, or recombination, maternal and paternal chromosomes become mixed.

Consequences of Abnormal Mitosis and Meiosis

The processes in our bodies are not infallible. Sometimes, something goes wrong. Abnormal events in mitosis or meiosis can result in cells having the wrong number of chromosomes. Down syndrome is most commonly caused when one set of duplicated chromosomes doesn't separate during meiosis, producing a gamete cell with an extra No. 21 chromosome. The failure of chromosomes to separate is called nondisjunction (see Figure 5.19 on page 304). 🌐

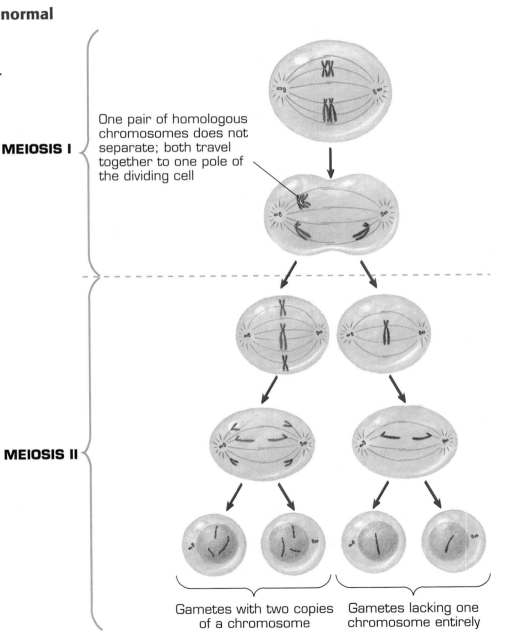

MEIOSIS I

One pair of homologous chromosomes does not separate; both travel together to one pole of the dividing cell

MEIOSIS II

Gametes with two copies of a chromosome

Gametes lacking one chromosome entirely

Figure 5.19

Nondisjunction occurs when chromosomes fail to separate during the first or second division in meiosis.

Reproduction and Development

The only cells that are formed by meiosis in humans are gametes, the eggs produced by the mother and sperm produced by the father. Fertilization, or conception, is a complex process that brings the genetic material of two parents together. The zygote, the cell formed by the union of the parents' gametes, must develop from an unspecialized single cell into a specialized unicell or a multicellular individual with tissues, organs, and organ systems. There are many opportunities for something to go wrong during these processes.

Male Gamete Production and the Male Reproductive System

Sperm cells are produced and stored in the testes (see Figures 5.20 and 5.21). They are ejaculated through the vas deferens and urethra and out through the penis (Figure 5.21). The mixture of fluids that is produced to lubricate, nourish, and protect the sperm is called semen.

Hormonal Controls

Hormones are chemicals that the body releases into the bloodstream to control the functions of organisms. Hormones control the development of both male and female gametes as well as the development of the zygote and its environment in the uterus.

Male Sex Hormones

In males, the pituitary gland at the base of the brain secretes two hormones that act on the testes. One hormone, luteinizing hormone (LH), stimulates androgen production. Androgens are steroid hormones. One example of an androgen is testosterone. Androgen hormones are responsible for the development of male primary sex characteristics, for example,

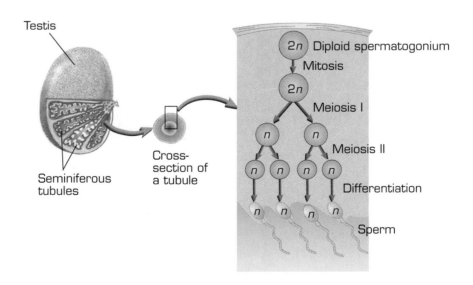

Figure 5.20

Sperm formation in the human male.

Figure 5.21

Kidney

Ureter

Seminal
vesicles

Urinary bladder

Prostate gland
Urethra

Vas deferens
Epididymis
Scrotum
Testes
Penis

*The human male
reproductive system.*

penis development and sperm production. Androgens also cause a young man's beard, chest, and body hair to grow and his voice to deepen. These are secondary sex characteristics.

Another hormone that is produced by the pituitary gland, follicle-stimulating hormone (FSH), increases sperm production. A third hormone, gonadotropin-releasing hormone (GnRH), regulates both FSH and LH and is produced in the brain. When androgen levels rise above a normal level, production of GnRH stops, which turns off production of LH and FSH. This regulation is called feedback inhibition. It is another way in which the body maintains homeostasis.

Female Gamete Production and the Female Reproductive System

Eggs are produced in the ovaries, a pair of small organs in the human female body (Figures 5.22 and 5.23 on page 306). Females are born with all of the egg-producing cells they will ever have. These cells start meiosis before a female is born, but they do not complete the process until after an egg is fertilized.

At approximately 28-day intervals throughout a female's reproductive years, one or more eggs mature and are released in the process of ovulation (Figure 5.23). Following ovulation, an egg enters the oviduct leading to the uterus. Fertilization usually occurs in the upper end of the oviduct. The fertilized egg, the zygote, continues its journey to embed itself in the wall of the uterus.

Figure 5.22

The human female reproductive system.

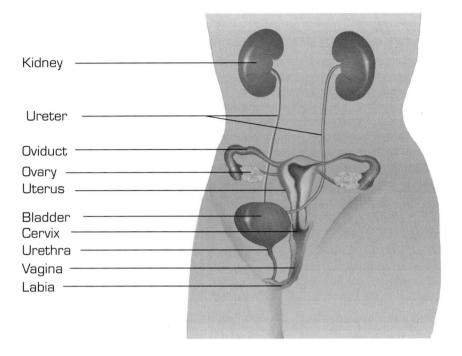

Kidney

Ureter

Oviduct
Ovary
Uterus

Bladder
Cervix
Urethra
Vagina
Labia

Female Sex Hormones

In females, the pituitary gland produces LH and FSH and the brain produces GnRH. These hormones, along with estrogen and progesterone, two female hormones, regulate the menstrual cycle and prepare the uterine lining for pregnancy (Figure 5.24 on page 308).

FSH stimulates the growth of the ovarian follicle during the first half of the menstrual cycle. This usually lasts about 14 days. Just before ovulation, there is a surge of LH. During ovulation, the follicle ruptures to become a temporary endocrine gland, called the corpus luteum, which secretes estrogen and progesterone. These hormones prepare the uterus

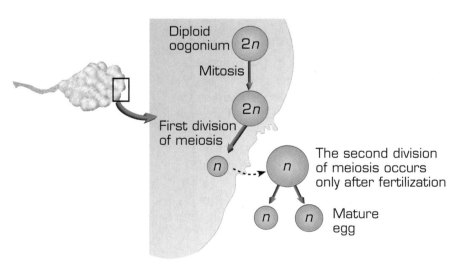

Diploid oogonium $2n$

Mitosis

$2n$

First division of meiosis

n ⤍ n The second division of meiosis occurs only after fertilization

n n Mature egg

Figure 5.23

The first division of meiosis occurs within an ovary. The second division occurs after the egg is fertilized.

for incubating the fertilized egg. They also stop the brain from producing more GnRH, which stops production of LH and FSH. Consequently, no new egg-producing cells develop in the ovary.

Menstruation

In the two weeks before ovulation, the lining of the uterus develops a dense network of blood vessels in preparation for connection to a zygote. If the egg is not fertilized, pregnancy does not occur. The egg disintegrates, and the corpus luteum stops producing hormones. Because there is no embryo to be incubated, the thickened lining of the uterus is not needed, and it disintegrates. The blood and dead tissue is then expelled. This process is called menstruation (Figure 5.24 on page 308).

Pregnancy

If an egg is penetrated by a sperm, pregnancy occurs and the corpus luteum continues to produce progesterone and estrogen. The embryo itself also produces a protein hormone. Pregnancy tests are designed to detect this hormone. As the zygote develops into a fetus, the placenta develops in the uterus. The placenta is a temporary organ that allows nutrients to pass from the mother to the fetus. Eventually the placenta takes over for the corpus luteum to synthesize estrogen and progesterone.

BIOthoughts

Sperm can live for several days in a female vagina, making it possible for a female to become pregnant from sexual intercourse that occurred days before she ovulated.

Birth Control Pills

Birth control pills contain a combination of synthetic estrogen and progesterone. The pills maintain a high level of these hormones so that the brain does not produce FSH and LH. When FSH and LH levels are low, ovarian follicles do not mature. When a woman stops taking birth control pills for several days at the end of each month (or takes pills that do not contain hormones), their estrogen and progesterone levels drop and menstruation occurs.

What Do Chromosomes Do?

Chromosomes contain all of the information that guides the cell in its development throughout its life. During pregnancy, a single-celled zygote develops into a multicellular embryo. Many cells that contain the same genetic information must now become different types of cells. This process is called cellular differentiation, and it requires a genetic program. You might say that the program signals the genes that make up the chromosomes.

Zygote Development and Differentiation

Differentiation begins soon after fertilization. The single-cell zygote divides into two cells, then four, eight, and more by the process of mitosis. Initially the cells get smaller and smaller, but each new cell has the same genetic composition as the original zygote.

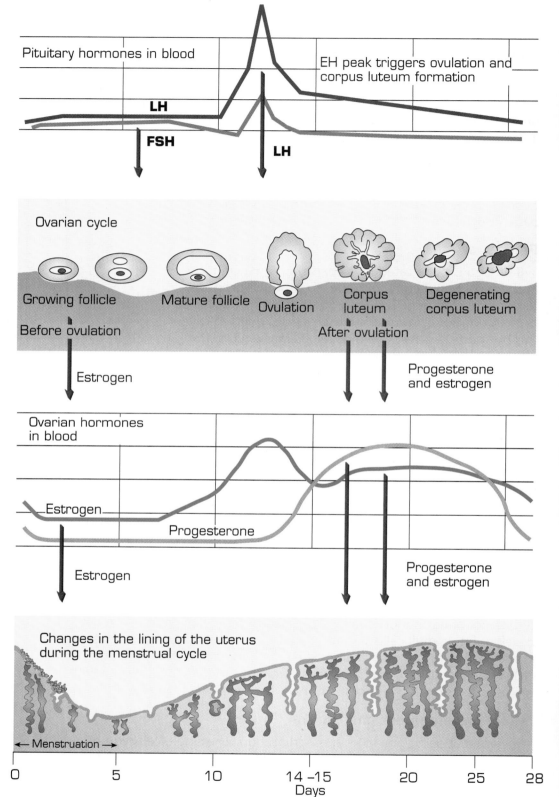

Figure 5.24

Feedback inhibition of hormones in human females.

Pituitary hormones in blood

EH peak triggers ovulation and corpus luteum formation

LH

FSH

LH

Ovarian cycle

Growing follicle

Mature follicle

Ovulation

Corpus luteum

Degenerating corpus luteum

Before ovulation

After ovulation

Estrogen

Progesterone and estrogen

Ovarian hormones in blood

Estrogen

Progesterone

Estrogen

Progesterone and estrogen

Changes in the lining of the uterus during the menstrual cycle

← Menstruation →

0   5   10   14 –15   20   25   28

Days

This process of cleavage forms a compact ball of genetically identical cells (Figure 5.25). As the developing embryo continues to grow, the cells rearrange to form a multilayered sphere. Individual cells and groups of cells migrate as cells begin to differentiate to assume specialized functions. When they divide, these cells can produce new cells like themselves. Once a cell line is differentiated, the cells cannot form other types of cells. 🌐

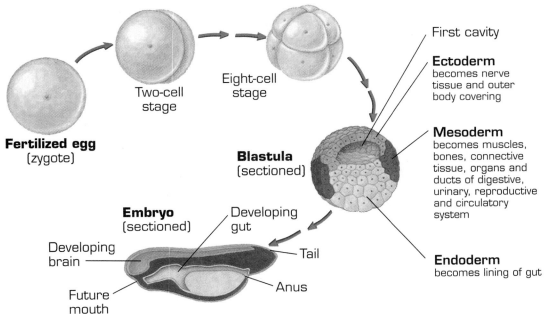

Fertilized egg (zygote)

Two-cell stage

Eight-cell stage

Blastula (sectioned)

First cavity

Ectoderm
becomes nerve tissue and outer body covering

Mesoderm
becomes muscles, bones, connective tissue, organs and ducts of digestive, urinary, reproductive and circulatory system

Endoderm
becomes lining of gut

Embryo (sectioned)

Developing brain

Future mouth

Developing gut

Tail

Anus

Figure 5.25

Cell layers in a tadpole zygote differentiate to form different tissues.

Back at the Genetic Counseling Center

Maria Stevens is talking to Phyllis Watson, the genetic counselor.

Maria: *My husband and I are concerned because my family has a history of Huntington's disease. My mother, my grandfather, an uncle, and a cousin all died from the disease. It was just terrible for the family. We saw family members die slowly over 10 to 20 years. They degenerated mentally and physically. What are the chances that I will get Huntington's disease? Can I have children? If so, what are the chances that they will get the disease?*

Ms. Watson: *Fortunately, we can now test for the presence of the gene that causes Huntington's disease. The physical symptoms of Huntington's disease may not become evident until the affected individual reaches middle age. Without the test, couples might have children without knowing whether they were passing the disease on to them.*

Genes and Alleles

Since chromosomes are paired, each gene carried on one chromosome has its pair on the other chromosome. That means that you have at least two genes for every trait. Sometimes these genes for the same trait are exactly alike. Sometimes genes occur in different forms, each form producing a different effect. These two versions of the same gene are called alleles. Alleles can be identical or different. If one allele is normal and one is mutated, they are referred to as the normal allele and the mutated allele.

For example, there are two different alleles for Huntington's disease, one that causes physical symptoms of the disease and one that does not. An individual who develops Huntington's disease has at least one mutant allele that causes it.

Figure 5.26

Symbols used in pedigree analysis.

□ Male

○ Female

○—□ Mating between individuals

Parents (top row) and children (bottom row)

○ or □ Affected individuals

? or ? Questionable whether individual was affected

⊘ or ⊘ Deceased individuals

Maria Stevens

Figure 5.27

In Maria Steven's family, her mother, her grandfather, an uncle, and a cousin died from Huntington's disease.

Genetic
Counseling
Center

Facts About Huntington's Disease

What Is The Nature of the Genetic Disorder?

- The disease is caused by a single dominant gene on chromosome No. 4.

- The gene has an excessive number of repeats of a three-nucleotide sequence (CGG).

How Common Is Huntington's Disease?

- The dominant gene appears in four to seven out of every 100,000 people in North Europe.

- About 25,000 individuals in the United States are affected.

What Are the Physical Symptoms of Huntington's Disease?

- It affects the nervous system and muscles of the body.

- Symptoms develop between the ages of 35 and 45 years.

- Physical symptoms appear first and consist of involuntary movements such as jerking, twisting, and spasms of the face muscles, tongue, neck, arms, and legs. These symptoms become progressively worse with time.

- Mental syptoms include irritability, poor judgement, loss of memory, and carelessness.

- Loss of brain cells gradually leads to the person becoming totally dependent on others.

How Can Huntington's Disease Be Treated?

- There is no treatment for this disease.

An individual who has two identical alleles for a specific trait is said to be homozygous for that trait. An individual who has at least two different alleles for a specific trait is said to be heterozygous for that trait.

What happens when an individual is heterozygous, that is, has two different alleles for a trait? Which allele winds up directing the expression of the trait? This can be a difficult question that can have many different answers depending on the specific gene. For some genes, however, the answer is easier: One allele clearly has a greater effect than the other. The allele that has the greater effect is said to be dominant. The allele that has the lesser effect is said to be recessive.

Determining Dominance and Recessiveness

How do you know which alleles are dominant and which are recessive? Can a family pedigree provide clues for simple traits? In this Inquiry, you will investigate several family case histories to learn which allele for a specific trait is more likely to be expressed when it is present in the heterozygous condition.

Part A: Widow's Peak

Widow's peak is a condition in which the hairline comes to a point in front. Have you ever seen *The Munsters* in reruns on TV? Except for Herman Munster, everyone in the family has widow's peak. What kind of inheritance pattern does widow's peak have?

Figure 5.28

This pedigree shows that five family members (solid squares and circles) in three generations have widow's peak.

Procedure

Examine the pedigree in Figure 5.28. It shows three generations of a family. Refer back to Figure 5.26 to review the symbols that are used in making family pedigrees.

Interpretations: Respond to the following in your *Log*:

1. What do you notice about the parents of those who have widow's peak compared to the parents of those who do not have widow's peak?

2. Does any family member with widow's peak have a parent who does not have widow's peak? Propose a hypothesis that explains this.

3. From whom did the aunt and uncle in the second generation get the allele for widow's peak? What is your evidence?

4. What evidence is there that having widow's peak requires a contribution from only one parent? How can this be explained?

5. Decide how many widow's peak alleles an individual needs to have the condition. How does this pedigree support your answer?

6. Record in your *Log* the evidence from this pedigree that widow's peak is caused by a dominant allele.

7. Define *dominant allele*.

Part B: Sickle-Cell Anemia

People who suffer from sickle-cell anemia have an abnormally high number of red blood cells that are sickle shaped. These cells cannot carry oxygen like normal, disk-shaped red blood cells can. Carriers of sickle-cell anemia are said to have sickle-cell trait. This is because their red blood cells are still abnormal and they can be affected under some conditions. James and Tanya Weston are married. Members of both of their families are afflicted with sickle-cell anemia. They are planning their own family and want to know what the chances are that their children will have sickle-cell anemia. What can they learn about this trait from their family pedigree?

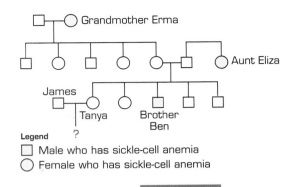

Procedure

Examine the pedigree for Tanya and James Weston's family in Figure 5.29.

Figure 5.29

The pedigree for a family that carries the gene for sickle-cell anemia.

Interpretations: Respond to the following in your *Log*:

1. Does anyone in this family who has sickle-cell anemia have parents who do not? Are there cases in which neither parent of an affected individual has this disorder? Propose a hypothesis to explain how this can happen.

2. Which of Brother Ben's parents gave him the sickle-cell allele(s)? What evidence does the pedigree provide to support your answer?

3. Will it be possible for James and Tanya's children to inherit sickle-cell allele(s)? How do you know?

4. Can an individual with only one sickle-cell allele have the disease? Was the same true for widow's peak? What is the difference?

5. How do you know whether sickle-cell anemia is caused by a recessive allele?

6. From your study of this pedigree, define the criteria for a recessive allele.

Part C: Hemophilia

Individuals who have the disease of hemophilia suffer from excessive bleeding. The blood of hemophiliacs lacks a protein that is essential for blood to clot. The most famous example of a family afflicted by hemophilia is the family of Queen Victoria. Because marriages between members of the various royal families of Europe were common at the time, the disease became widely spread among these families. Since relatives have a greater chance of carrying the same recessive allele, when they marry, they have an increased chance of having an affected child. In such families, there is a greater chance of a child getting two mutant alleles. In this part of the Inquiry, you will determine what kind of inheritance pattern this genetic disease has. Keep in mind that a carrier is someone whose genetic material includes a gene for a particular trait, though that trait does not show up in that individual.

Procedure

Examine the pedigree for Queen Victoria's family in Figure 5.30. Locate the individuals who had hemophilia. Locate the carriers. How many people in this pedigree are familiar to you from history classes?

Interpretations: Respond to the following in your *Log*:

1. What do you notice about the sex of the individuals in this family who had hemophilia?
2. What do you notice about the sex of the individuals in this family who were carriers of hemophilia?
3. What evidence do you have that an individual must have two alleles for hemophilia to have the disease?
4. Is hemophilia caused by a recessive allele? How do you know this?
5. Form a hypothesis to predict the chromosome pair on which the gene for hemophilia might be located. Do some research to find the answer.

Applications: Respond to the following in your *Log*:

1. Identify the number of students in your class who have a widow's peak. Convert this number to a percentage of total students in the class. Record this information in your *Log* for possible use in a future Inquiry.

Figure 5.30

Pedigree for hemophilia in Queen Victoria's family.

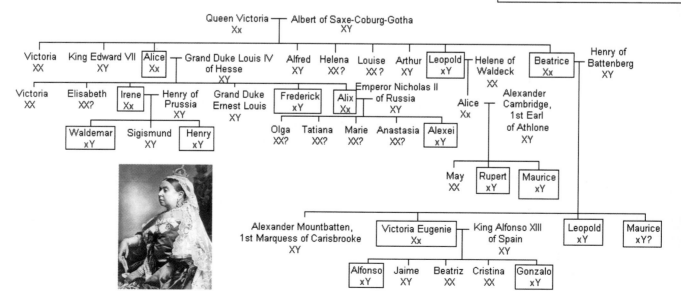

314

Inheritance

2. Summarize the different ways in which widow's peak, sickle-cell anemia, and hemophilia are inherited.

Some Facts about Inherited Traits

We can identify traits through a genotype, a kind of shorthand code. A genotype usually has two letters, one for each gene of a specific trait. Typically, a capital letter represents a dominant allele and a lowercase letter represents a recessive allele.

Widow's Peak

The gene that causes widow's peak is dominant. This means that if a person has one allele for widow's peak and one for a straight hairline, the widow's peak will be expressed. Straight hairline, therefore, is a recessive allele. A person who has widow's peak, as illustrated in Figure 5.31, can have the alleles WW or Ww, and the result is the same. Only someone with the genotype ww will have a straight hairline.

Sickle-cell Anemia

Sickle-cell anemia is common among people of African and Mediterranean descent. People who have this disorder often die young before they have children. An individual who has two alleles for the sickle-cells, one allele from each parent, will have sickle-cell anemia. An individual who has one allele for sickle cells and one for normal cells also will be affected, but not as severely.

Malaria is a very common disease in the regions of the world where the incidence of sickle-cell anemia is high. An individual who has one sickle-cell allele is able to withstand malaria infections better than someone who does not have the allele. So what is the biological relationship between malaria and the sickle-cell genes? The malaria parasite destroys normal red blood cells but cannot survive in sickle cells. So in malaria regions, it can be advantageous to have some sickle cells (Figure 5.32). The incidence of sickle-cell anemia will diminish in situations where there is little advantage to being heterozygous, as in the United States.

Figure 5.31

Do you know anyone who has widow's peak?

Figure 5.32

In areas where malaria is common, the gene for sickle-cell anemia provides some protection against malaria.

Hemophilia

Hemophilia is a sex-linked trait; that is, it is carried on the X chromosome. It is also a recessive trait. X-linked genes are not matched by homologous genes on the Y chromosome. Since females have two X chromosomes, both must contain the recessive allele for hemophilia in order for a female to be a hemophiliac. Since a male has only one X chromosome, it takes only one recessive allele to produce a male hemophiliac. Therefore more males than females tend to have this disease.

Before there was a treatment for hemophilia, few afflicted individuals survived into adulthood. Now hemophiliacs can receive injections of the protein that their bodies lack. The protein extract, which is prepared from blood donated by many individuals, has allowed many hemophiliacs to live more normal lives. But this life-saving injection has also proved to be deadly; in the past, before blood was screened for the human immunodeficiency virus (HIV), many hemophiliacs received extract prepared from blood that was contaminated with this virus. HIV is believed to be responsible for acquired immune deficiency syndrome (AIDS). As many as 50 percent of the hemophiliacs in the United States are infected with HIV. All donated blood is now tested for the presence of HIV to prevent future blood-borne infections. The use of protein extract produced using genetic engineering will eventually eliminate this problem for hemophiliacs. 🌍

Gregor Mendel: The Father of Genetics

In the mid-1800s, Gregor Johann Mendel (Figure 5.33), an Austrian monk working in what is now Brno, in the Czech Republic, made a startling discovery. He was studying the inheritance patterns of the common pea plant in his monastery garden. Mendel studied seven traits of the pea plants. Each trait that he selected had two alternative ways in which it was expressed. For example, pea seeds could be either round or wrinkled and either yellow or green. The plants themselves could be tall or dwarf. Because each of these traits was expressed in two forms, Mendel visualized that they were controlled by discrete factors that occurred in pairs. Though he did not have these names for them at the time, Mendel had discovered genes and alleles.

Mendel's Crosses

Mendel worked with true-breeding plants, or plants that displayed the same traits in every generation (Figure 5.34). He also cross-bred plants that had alternative traits, such as round-seeded plants and wrinkled-seeded plants. He then examined the first generation of offspring, called the F_1 generation. All of the offspring in the F_1 generation showed only one of the two alternative traits. In the described example, the cross-breeding of true-breeding round-seeded plants and true-breeding wrinkled-seeded plants produced F_1 plants that all had round seeds (Figure 5.35). Mendel called this trait dominant. The trait that did not show up in the appearance of these F_1 offspring was called recessive. In this example, the wrinkled-seed

Figure 5.33

Gregor Johann Mendel.

Inheritance

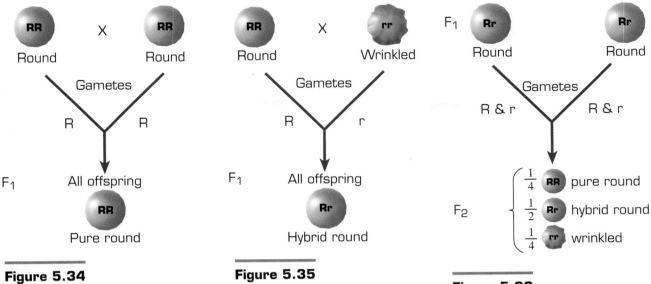

Figure 5.34

All of the offspring of true-breeding round-seeded pea plants have round seeds.

Figure 5.35

True-breeding round-seeded plants are cross-bred with true-breeding wrinkled-seeded plants.

Figure 5.36

A cross of two pea plants, each of which is a hybrid for pea shape.

trait is the recessive trait. When Mendel bred two of the offspring, the alternative trait, wrinkled seeds, would show up again in one-fourth the F_2, or second, generation (Figure 5.36 above) seeds.

Each time he made a genetic cross, Mendel counted the number of off-spring that displayed each of the alternative traits. Mendel observed that when plants from the F_1 generation were cross-bred to produce an F_2 generation, the proportion of plants that displayed the recessive trait was always approximately the same.

Both of the parent plants in Figure 5.36 have round peas since this is the dominant trait. But each parent is a hybrid plant. The offspring of these parent plants display both types of pea shapes: round and wrinkled. In a given sample, three-fourths of the offspring have round peas. Only one-fourth of the offspring have wrinkled peas. These results indicate that the round expression is dominant and the wrinkled expression is recessive. 🐾

Frank and Ernest

Copyright (c) 1991 by Thaves. Reprinted with permission.

Back at the Genetic Counseling Center

The counselor, Phyllis Watson, is explaining the inheritance patterns for Huntington's disease to Maria Steven.

Ms. Watson: *The inheritance pattern for Huntington's disease is easy to describe. The gene for Huntington's disease is carried on the No. 4 chromosome. It is a dominant trait, so an individual who has only one allele for the trait will have the disease. Your mother and grandfather each had at least one allele for Huntington's disease. Family members who remain unaffected past middle age most likely don't have the allele that causes Huntington's disease.*

Let's use the abbreviation H for the allele that specifies Huntington's disease and h for the normal allele. In your family the allele for Huntington's disease (H) was passed from your grandfather to his son and daughter. They also each received from their mother one allele that did not specify the disease (h).

Most likely, the family members who had Huntington's disease had a genotype of Hh. Individuals with the Hh genotype inevitably developed Huntington's disease. Having the disease is their phenotype, which means their appearance or other apparent characteristics. A phenotype might describe a person's body style or hair color. It might also describe a genetic condition, such as Huntington's disease.

So why didn't your uncles have only mild cases of Huntington's disease if they had alleles specifying each expression of the trait? As Mendel discovered, one gene tends to exert dominance over the other gene, the recessive gene. The allele for Huntington's disease is dominant and expresses itself fully, even when it is paired with the allele for the unafflicted condition.

We can use this information about your family to calculate the probability that you will develop the disease.

Guided Inquiry 5.5

The Chances of Inheriting a Single Trait

If you are heterozygous for a trait such as Huntington's disease, what is the likelihood of passing on the trait to your children? You will explore the likelihood that Mrs. Stevens' grandmother and grandfather passed on the Huntington's disease trait. Assume that the grandfather is heterozygous for Huntington's disease and that the grandmother does not have Huntington's disease. What would be the grandmother's genotype?

MATERIALS

- 2 Coins
- Paper
- Tape
- Pen

Procedure

1. Work with a partner. Use the two sides of a coin to represent the two alleles for Huntington's disease. On the coin representing the grandfather, tape a small piece of paper with the letter *H* on one side and tape a piece of paper with the letter *h* on the other side. On the other coin representing the grandmother, tape small pieces of paper with the letter *h* on both sides.

2. In your *Log*, make a table like the one in Figure 5.37 but including 40 rows.

Your Coin Toss	Partner's Coin Toss	Combined Coin Tosses	
Allele from the grandfather	Allele from the grandmother	Genotype of offspring	Phenotype of offspring
H	h	Hh	Huntington's disease

Figure 5.37

Sample data table for Guided Inquiry 5.5.

3. Flip the coin to determine which allele the grandfather might contribute to his offspring. Now your partner will toss the other coin to determine which allele the grandmother might contribute. Record the result of the coin tosses in your table. Write the genotype of that offspring; then write the phenotype, using Figure 5.37 as an example.

4. Repeat the tosses for a total of 40 trials. Count the number of times you produce each genotype and phenotype, and record the numbers in your *Log*.

Interpretations: Respond to the following in your *Log*:

1. Describe your results in terms of genotype ratio. Judging from your coin tosses, what is the likelihood (expressed as a percentage) that each offspring will have the genotype Hh? What is the likelihood for the genotype hh?

2. Why isn't it possible for this couple to have offspring with the genotype HH?

3. Describe your results in terms of phenotype ratio. What is the likelihood that each offspring will have Huntington's disease?

319

Unit 5

Applications: Respond to the following in your *Log*:

1. Suppose Maria Steven's grandfather was homozygous dominant for the trait (that is, he was HH). What would be the likelihood for each offspring of eventually developing Huntington's disease?

2. Suppose both the grandfather and the grandmother were heterozygous for the trait (that is, they were Hh). Is it certain that their offspring would develop the disease? Explain.

The Punnett Square

When an Hh individual produces gametes, he or she can contribute either H or h. In Mendel's law of segregation of alleles, he hypothesized the existence of "factors" that segregated independent of each other during the formation of gametes (sperm or eggs). In the case of Huntington's disease, whether the egg carrying H or the one carrying h is fertilized by a sperm carrying H or one carrying h is purely a matter of chance. Mendel's "factors" were the genetic units that we now know as alleles.

In meiosis, pairs of chromosomes split so that the alleles from each parent are distributed and assort independently into the gametes. This independent assortment ensures a random mix of the parents' chromosomes in the gametes and, ultimately, in the offspring. Therefore each offspring is not an exact copy of either parent, but rather contains a mix of characteristics inherited from one or the other parent.

The activity in Guided Inquiry 5.5 should have demonstrated that each allele from either parent has an equal chance of winding up in an offspring. After tossing the coin just a few times, you might not have gotten each allele 50 percent of the time. But the more times you flip the coin, the more closely the ratio will approximate 50/50. Genetic counselors apply probability in this way to predict the chance that a particular trait will show up in a family.

You can graphically represent genetic crosses using a Punnett square. As the Punnett square in Figure 5.38 shows, the offspring of Mrs. Stevens' grandparents had a 50 percent chance of receiving the Huntington's gene. Which of these genotypes did Maria Steven's mother have?

	Grandfather's gametes	
	H	**h**
h	Hh afflicted individual	hh unafflicted individual
h	Hh afflicted individual	hh unafflicted individual

Grandmother's gametes

Figure 5.38

This Punnett square shows the genetic probabilities that the offspring of Mrs. Steven's grandparents have Huntington's disease.

Finding the Gene for Huntington's Disease

In the late summer of 1968, Marilyn Wexler's daughters learned that Marilyn had just been diagnosed with Huntington's disease. This inherited disease attacks regions deep within the brain. Death from Huntington's disease usually takes years and is often caused by malnutrition or choking. Early on, Marilyn showed symptoms of depression, irritability, and difficulty relating to others. Her daughter Nancy (Figure 5.39) watched her mother's progressive slide toward death over the next 10 years. Marilyn developed short-term memory loss and progressively worse twitching of her body. She died in 1978, bedridden and skeletal. Nancy knew that she herself had a 50/50 chance of inheriting the dominant gene and dying of Huntington's disease like her mother.

Figure 5.39

Nancy Wexler holding Venezuelan boy who has the Huntington's disease allele.

Nancy and her father took action even before Marilyn's death. Their family created the Hereditary Disease Foundation, which brought scientists together for discussions about tracking down the renegade gene that causes Huntington's disease (Figure 5.40). Nancy not only was the organizer of the foundation, but also became a field researcher in 1979. She started a long-term study of an isolated population along the shores of Lake Maracaibo in Venezuela. Inbreeding and large families were common in this population. For example, one woman had 18 children, and one man with Huntington's disease fathered 34 children. In this population, the Huntington's gene is concentrated as nowhere else in the world. Nancy and her colleagues returned year after year to collect blood samples and to construct a large pedigree of the devastated population.

In 1981, Dr. James Gusellas, using a combination of classical genetics and modern molecular biology techniques, identified the locations of the gene for Huntington's disease in the samples from Wexler's Venezuelan study. He found it on the upper part of chromosome No. 4. This discovery permitted the first genetic screen for the Huntington's gene with 96 percent reliability.

Over the next 10 to 15 years, scientists closed in on the Huntington's disease gene, using the ever-growing array of molecular techniques. In 1992, the gene was located. By 1996, scientists had identified much of the structure of the gene and were investigating how this gene functions and how it causes Huntington's disease.

Nancy Wexler and her father chose not to be passive victims of a terrible genetic disease. Thanks to their efforts and those of many scientists, Huntington's disease is one of the genetic disorders for which genes have been identified. The bright hope for the future is that this horrible killer will one day have a treatment and maybe even a cure. Nancy Wexler's choice of action made a difference. 🌎

Figure 5.40

These brothers have Huntington's disease, which has affected their nervous and muscular systems.

Exceptions to Mendel's Ideas

Not all genetic traits are inherited in the ways that Mendel predicted. That is, alleles on homologous chromosomes do not always move independently during mitosis and meiosis.

Nondominance

As it turns out, many genes are not simply dominant or recessive. What Mendel found to clearly determine shape and color in peas is more the exception than the rule. Most genes do have an effect on expression and interact with other genes. This is the case with sickle-cell anemia. The genotype Ss for the sickle-cell anemia trait is expressed differently than genotype SS (normal blood cells) or ss (sickle cells). Individuals with Ss are less severly affected.

Another example of nondominance occurs in flower color. In primroses, the W gene (for white petal color) and R gene (for red petal color) are neither dominant nor recessive even though they are on the same position of the homologous chromosomes. A flower that has genotype WW is white; a flower that has genotype RR is red. But genotype WR produces a pink flower (see Figure 5.41). In this case, the genotype letter designation could just as well be lowercase because both alleles are expressed.

Figure 5.41

The pink flower phenotype in these primroses is produced by two nondominant alleles.

Linked Genes

Mendel worked with only seven traits of the garden pea plant. His results seemed to demonstrate that these traits were controlled by genes on separate chromosomes. But each chromosome contains many genes. One of the most common exceptions to Mendel's laws is the case of linked genes. Genes that occur in close proximity to each other on the same chromosome are linked. Linked genes generally do not assort independently during gamete formation.

Sex-Linked Genes

The genes carried on the X and Y sex chromosomes are called sex-linked genes. These genes have a pattern of inheritance and expression that differs from that of genes on the other chromosomes. Both hemophilia (Figure 5.30) and color blindness are sex-linked recessive traits. Any male whose X chromosome carries the affected gene will display these traits. Females are afflicted only if both of their X chromosomes carry the affected gene. Therefore both of these conditions occur almost exclusively in sons and rarely in daughters of affected mothers. If a mother is heterozygous, her sons have a 50/50 chance of being affected.

Multiple Alleles

So far, you have examined traits that are controlled by two alternative alleles. However, genetics is not that simple. For many traits, there are three or more alternative forms of the gene. A good example is found in human blood types. There are three alternative forms of the gene for blood type: A, B, and O.

Blood type is determined by two alleles on the homologous No. 9 chromosomes. The four phenotypes for human blood type are A, B, AB, and O. These

PHENOTYPE (BLOOD TYPE)	GENOTYPE	ANTIGENS	ANTIBODIES
A	$I^A I^A$ or $I^A I^O$	A	anti-B
B	$I^B I^B$ or $I^B I^O$	B	anti-A
AB	$I^A I^B$	AB	—
O	$I^O I^O$	—	anti-A anti-B

Figure 5.42

Genotypes for the major blood types in humans

letters typically are written as superscripts beside the letter *I*, which stand for immunoglobin proteins that control blood type. These blood proteins determine the way in which different blood types react with each other. Blood types need to be matched prior to a transfusion to avoid clumping of cells due to antigen-antibody reactions. Figure 5.42 above shows the different genotype possibilities for each phenotype for blood group.

Polygenic Inheritance

Some traits are clearly influenced by heredity but vary from one extreme to the other. These usually are the result of polygenic inheritance, which involves genes at more than one chromosome location. Body stature, eye color, hair color, and skin color are good examples of traits that are affected by more than one gene. The expression of the trait results from the cumulative effects of all of the genes. In humans, skin color is controlled by four genes. When eight dominant alleles, *AABBCCDD*, are present, skin color is very dark. When eight recessive alleles are present, the skin is very light. The distribution of skin colors in human populations is shown in Figure 5.43.

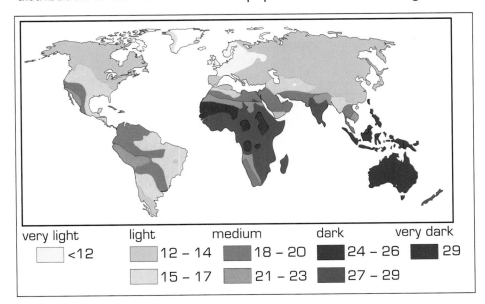

very light | light | medium | dark | very dark
<12 | 12 – 14 | 18 – 20 | 24 – 26 | 29
 | 15 – 17 | 21 – 23 | 27 – 29 |

Figure 5.43

This map shows the geographic distribution for categories of skin color on a standard scale of skin darkness.

BIOoccupation

Frank Dukepoo: Genetics Researcher

Dr. Frank Dukepoo is a geneticist, biology professor, and educator from the southwestern United States. He is very proud of his Native American roots. "Among my Hopi people, I go by Pumatuhye Tsi Dukpuh," he says. (*Pumatuhye,* pronounced pu-mat-uh-ye, means "the first little plants that come up in the soil.") He was the first member of his tribe to earn a Ph.D.

Dr. Dukepoo's genetics research focused on albinism in his tribe. Albinism is an inherited metabolic condition that affects the melanin level in the body. Melanin is the pigment that determines skin color. The bodies of albino individuals cannot make melanin, so their skin is absolutely white. Dr. Dukepoo constructed the first family pedigrees to study the inheritance patterns of the albino gene among the Hopi.

Another of Dr. Dukepoo's interests is encouraging academic success among Native Americans. He is the founder of the National Native American Honor Society, an organization that rewards outstanding professional, intellectual, academic, and personal achievement among Native American students. Membership in the Society is open to any Native American

Frank Dukepoo

student from fourth grade to graduate and professional school who has earned a 4.0 GPA during any semester of his or her academic career. The Society's philosophy "incorporates ancient traditions, customs, and values from a number of tribes," according to Dr. Dukepoo. Members perform community service and write stories of their personal success or academic achievement. Dr. Dukepoo wants the students to see how much they will accomplish "if they believe in themselves, set high goals, work hard, and have an unfaltering faith in the Great Spirit."

Back at the Genetic Counseling Center

Genetic counselor Phyllis Watson invites Tanya and James Weston into her office.

Ms. Watson: *Why have you come to the Genetic Center?*

Tanya: *We both have family histories of sickle-cell anemia. My brother Ben died from the disease when he was a teenager. We would like to have a child but are worried about whether we would pass on the disease. We need advice.*

Ms. Watson: *To effectively help you, I need to know more about your*
continued *family background and medical histories. First, though, let's*
discuss some basic information about sickle-cell anemia.

Facts About Sickle-Cell Anemia

Genetic Counseling Center

What Is The Nature of the Genetic Disorder?

- The gene for sickle-cell anemia is recessive.

- Afflicted individuals have two alleles for sickle-shaped cells and often die before reaching maturity.

- People who have only one allele for sickle-shaped cells can lead normal lives.

- A parent with one sickle-cell allele can pass it on to his or her children.

- When each parent has one sickle-cell allele, the two can have a child who is afflicted with sickle-cell anemia.

How Common Is Sickle-Cell Anemia?

- One out of every 400 to 600 African-American children in the United States has sickle-cell anemia.

- The sickle-cell gene is frequent in individuals of African, Arabian, Greek, Maltese, Sicilian, Sardinian, Turkish, and South African ancestry (as shown in the map below).

What Are the Physical Symptoms of Sickle-Cell Anemia?

- Sickle-shaped blood cells can clog small blood vessels and limit the amount of oxygen supplied to the body's tissues.

- Afflicted individuals can be pale, tired, and short of breath. They can experience joint pain, recurrent infection, jaundice, and enlargement of the heart and liver. They can have lung, kidney, and spleen damage.

- Individuals who carry one allele for sickle-shaped cells may experience problems at high altitudes or during surgical anesthesia, when oxygen pressure in the blood is diminished.

How Can Sickle-Cell Anemia Be Treated?

- There is no cure for sickle-cell anemia.

- Drugs can relieve some symptoms, such as joint pain.

Gene Frequency (%)
- 0 - 3
- 3 - 6
- 6 - 9
- 9 - 12
- 12 - 15
- > 15

Geographic distribution of the allele for sickle-cell hemoglobin

A   B

Figure 5.44

Photomicrographs of sickle cells (A) and normal red blood cells (B).

Genotypes and Phenotypes of Sickle-Cell Anemia

How can you discover whether a person carries the gene for sickle-cell anemia? You could make a family pedigree, as you did in Guided Inquiry 5.4. A more accurate way is to examine a sample of the person's blood (Figure 5.44). Under atmospheric oxygen conditions, the red blood cells of a person who has one sickle-cell allele usually appear normal. A simple laboratory test removes oxygen from a sample of blood by putting it in a vacuum. As the oxygen level is lowered, the blood cells from an individual who carries the mutant gene become rigid and sickle-shaped. Usually, only about 1 percent of the red blood cells of a person with sickle-cell trait (Ss) are sickled, compared to up to 50 percent of the blood cells of a person with sickle-cell anemia (ss).

When blood cells become sickled under low oxygen conditions, vessels in capillary beds of tissues and organs become clogged, and circulation of the blood through the body is slowed. The more slowly the blood moves, the less oxygen is delivered to tissues. Normal red blood cells get stuck in the clogs that the sickled cells form. People with sickle-cell anemia (ss) have enough sickled blood cells that symptoms can occur even under normal oxygen conditions. Sickled cells are also more readily destroyed by the liver. 🌍

Back at the Genetic Counseling Center

A lab technician takes blood samples from Tanya and James Weston. The samples are tested in a vacuum, and some of the cells from each of them are sickled. What do you conclude?

Tanya: *Ms. Watson, why do cells become sickled? What actually causes the cells to change shape?*

Ms. Watson: *If you want to know the answer to that, you will need to know how the genetic instructions within cells affect how they function.*

Guided Inquiry 5.6

DNA Extraction

This Inquiry provides you with a basic procedure for extracting DNA and the explanation of what each action in the procedure accomplishes. After you master this extraction method with the suggested tissues, check with your teacher about DNA extractions from other tissues.

MATERIALS

- DNA source
- Blender or food processor for grinding cells
- Latex gloves
- Extraction solution (0.9 g NaCl/100 mL water)
- Gentle liquid laundry detergent
- 2 molar salt solution (11.7 grams of noniodized table salt, add distilled water up to 100 milliliters)
- Ice-cold 100% alcohol
- 2 test tubes and 1 stopper
- Wooden stir rod or a glass stir rod scored on one end

Procedure

1. Chill the extraction solution on ice.

2. Mix the DNA source with the chilled extraction solution in a food processor or blender. Homogenize the tissue (see Figure 5.45 on page 328).

3. Transfer the pureed tissue into a test tube. Add a few drops of detergent.

4. To the slurry in the test tube, add twice the volume of the 2 molar salt solution. Stopper the tube, and shake it vigorously for at least two minutes.

5. Allow the contents of the tube to chill on ice for at least 15 minutes. After chilling, remove the upper portion of the liquid containing the DNA into a chilled test tube or beaker.

Effect

1. Usually, a buffer solution (salt and EDTA or $NaHCO_3$) is needed to maintain an appropriate environment for the cells and the extracted DNA. A plain salt solution can be used for soft animal tissues. See your teacher for special instructions for plants, microorganisms, or other animal tissues.

2. Homogenization breaks cells and membranes to release DNA.

3. This helps to break down cell membranes and alter the structure of proteins.

4. The salt solution alters the structure of some of the cell proteins, causing them to denature and fall toward the bottom of the tube. The DNA is released into the salt solution.

5. Two layers will form. Cell particulate matter, including the altered proteins, falls to the bottom of the tube. DNA remains in the upper liquid layer. This segregates the DNA-containing liquid for further purification.

(continued on page 328)

PROCEDURE

1. Chill extraction solution

2. Mix DNA source with extraction solution; puree

3. Transfer tissue to test tube; add a few drops of detergent

4. Add twice the volume of salt solution; stopper tube and shake vigorously

5. Chill tube 15 minutes; transfer upper portion of liquid to a chilled beaker

6. Add cold alcohol; spool DNA on a wooden or glass rod

EFFECTS

2. Tissues and membranes are broken down

3. Membranes are broken down; proteins are altered
- Protein
- Altered protein

4. DNA is released; proteins are altered and they precipitate

5. Proteins and cell particulates precipitate; DNA remains in solution

6. DNA spools onto rod when it is brought up into alcohol
- Ethanol
- Salt solution

Figure 5.45

How DNA is extracted from cells.

Procedure (continued)

6. Slowly add two volumes of ice-cold alcohol to the liquid containing the DNA. Stir gently with a wooden or glass rod to spool the whitish DNA fibers. Do this by extending the rod through both layers, stirring with an upward motion to bring the DNA out of the suspension and up into the ethanol. You can store the spooled DNA in a vial of fresh alcohol at 4°C.

Effect (continued)

6. DNA is soluble in the salt solution but insoluble in ice-cold alcohol. As you stir, the rod picks up the white DNA strands. If the DNA has been damaged (as from excessive heat or homogenizing), it may precipitate rather than spool. Animal DNA (testes or thymus) is easiest to spool. Some plants tend to precipitate.

Interpretations: Respond to the following in your Log:

1. Describe in detail your observations of the DNA extraction procedure and the appearance of the DNA.

2. Why does isolated DNA appear to be stringy?

3. How would you revise this procedure to extract DNA from other organisms? What other cell structure(s) might need to be broken or removed to free the DNA?

4. On the basis of your knowledge of cell membrane composition, how do the chemical components act to disrupt cell membranes?

Applications: Respond to the following in your *Log*:

1. What uses could be made of extracted DNA?

2. Which cells of an organism, such as a human, have the greatest DNA-to-cytoplasm ratio? Why?

3. Find out whether there are any laboratories that extract and use DNA in your community. If it is practical, call or visit one such laboratory to learn about what it does.

DNA Is the Chemical Basis of Life

All living organisms on earth contain DNA and RNA. The chromosomes in the nucleus of your cells are composed of DNA, which provides information. This information can be thought of as the language of heredity. DNA is a large molecule. Its real name is deoxyribonucleic acid. If you unwind the DNA in all of the chromosomes in a single cell's nucleus and arrange the pieces end to end, you will find that you have approximately 2 meters of DNA. Your body contains approximately 10^{14} cells. How much DNA do you have in your body?

The size and complexity of an organism is not always proportional to the amount of DNA in the cell's nucleus. The single-celled organism *Amoeba dubia* has almost 20 times more DNA than is found in a single human cell.

DNA is a type of molecule known as a nucleic acid. It is made up of four types of nucleotides. Each nucleotide consists of a five-carbon sugar (deoxyribose), a phosphate group (PO_4), and one of the following nitrogenous bases:

Adenine (A)

Guanine (G)

Cytosine (C)

Thymine (T)

These nucleotides link together to form long strands. The DNA molecule consists of two strands of nucleotides bonded together and twisted into a helix (Figure 5.46 on page 330). When making DNA, the nucleotide base

Figure 5.46

A DNA molecule.

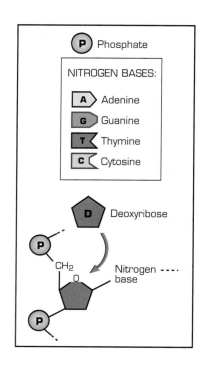

adenine (A) must always be paired with Thymine (T). Guanine (G) must always be paired with Cytosine (C). These pairings are called base pairs.

DNA must duplicate itself each time a cell divides. To initiate division, the individual strands of the DNA double-stranded helix must unwind. New DNA strands are formed by using each of the original strands as templates or models (Figure 5.47).

What Does DNA Do?

Chromosomes are made up of genes, and genes are made of DNA. The English alphabet contains 26 letters, from which we can make millions of letter sequences or words of different lengths, and each word has a specific meaning. Similarly, the DNA alphabet contains four letters for the four nucleotide bases: adenine, cytosine, guanine, and thymine. This DNA "sentence" carries information as a code that specifies how proteins will be assembled in the cell.

RNA Transcription

Protein synthesis occurs in the cytoplasm, but the DNA that codes for these proteins is located in the nucleus. Moving DNA back and forth from the nucleus to the cytoplasm may damage a cell's main information source.

For this reason, DNA is transcribed (or copied) into a different language, the language of ribonucleic acid (RNA). RNA is similar in structure to DNA, but it has a ribose sugar rather than a deoxyribose sugar. Ribose retains the

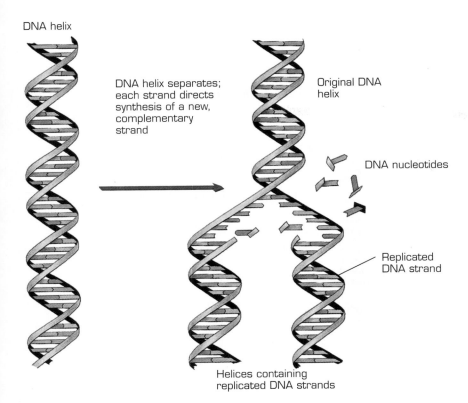

DNA helix

DNA helix separates; each strand directs synthesis of a new, complementary strand

Original DNA helix

DNA nucleotides

Replicated DNA strand

Helices containing replicated DNA strands

Figure 5.47

Replication of DNA.

oxygen atom that is missing in the deoxyribose of DNA. The nitrogenous bases that are found in RNA are adenine (A), guanine (G), cytosine (C), and uracil (U). You might think of DNA and RNA as being sentences in English and Spanish that say the same thing differently.

RNA is made from DNA by following the same rules used in DNA replication (Figure 5.48 on page 332). In making RNA, the nucleotide adenine (A) must always be paired with uracil (U). Guanine (G) must always be paired with cytosine (C). These pairings are called base pairs. Thus DNA serves as a template, or pattern, for forming a complementary RNA strand. The DNA template provides the information for the RNA. So, for example, if the DNA sequence is TCAGAC, the RNA sequence produced is AGUCUG. This process of making RNA from a DNA template is called transcription. 🌐

Guided Inquiry 5.7

Building Models of DNA and RNA

Chromosomes are composed of long molecules of DNA. Each gene is just a small section of the DNA molecule. How are DNA and RNA molecules constructed in the cell? In this Inquiry, you will build models of DNA and RNA molecules.

Figure 5.48

RNA transcription.

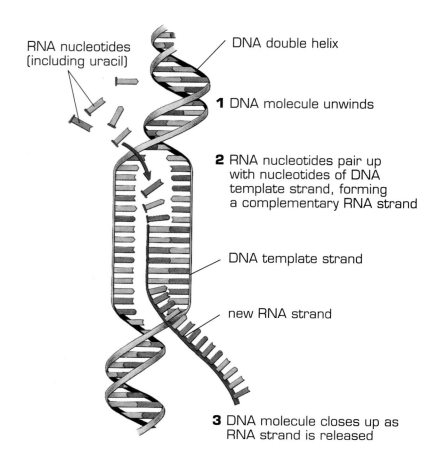

RNA nucleotides (including uracil)

DNA double helix

1 DNA molecule unwinds

2 RNA nucleotides pair up with nucleotides of DNA template strand, forming a complementary RNA strand

DNA template strand

new RNA strand

3 DNA molecule closes up as RNA strand is released

Part A: Making a DNA Model

MATERIALS

- Copper wire
- Ruler
- Wire cutters or scissors
- Cardboard tubes (from paper towels) or other cylinders

- Colored gumdrops (four different colors) or modeling clay (or use a model kit)
- Round toothpicks
- Tape or paper tags

SAFETY NOTE

- Keep toothpicks and wires away from your face and eyes as well as those of others.

Procedure

1. Cut two 50-centimeter lengths of copper wire. Shape both wires into a loose coil by wrapping them around a cylinder (such as the cardboard tube from a roll of paper towels). These will form the backbone of the molecule. Remove the wires from the cylinder.

2. Assign one color to represent each of the following nucleotide bases: adenine (A), thymine (T), guanine (G), and cytosine (C).

Create the first single strand of DNA by threading gumdrops onto one of the lengths of copper wire in the following sequence:

DNA base sequence: G G T G T A A A T T G A G G A C T T C T T T T T

Space the gumdrops approximately 1 centimeter apart.

3. Insert two toothpicks into each A and each T (to represent the two hydrogen bonds that connect these bases). Insert three toothpicks into each G and each C (to correspond to the three hydrogen bonds that link these bases).

4. Attach a paper tag or piece of tape to the G end of this single DNA strand. Label it *DNA Template.*

5. Using this first strand as a guide, thread the complementary bases onto the other 50-centimeter length of copper wire. Attach the two strands using the toothpicks. This is now a model of a double-stranded DNA molecule (Figure 5.49).

Part B: Making RNA

MATERIALS

- Model of DNA created in Part A
- Copper wire
- Ruler
- Wire cutters or scissors
- Tape or paper tags
- Cardboard tubes (from paper towels) or other cylinders
- Colored gumdrops (five different colors) or modeling clay (or use a model kit)

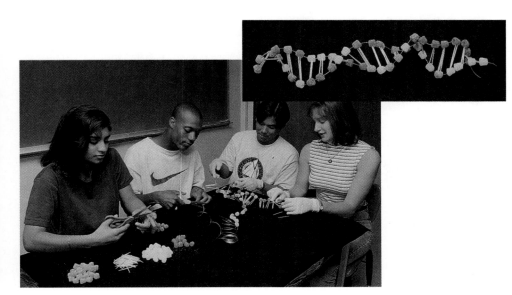

Figure 5.49

These students worked together to assemble the model of a DNA molecule.

Procedure

1. Cut one 50-centimeter length of copper wire. Shape the wire into a loose coil by wrapping it around a cylinder (such as the cardboard tube inside a roll of paper towels), as you did to make the DNA strand in Part A. This will be the strand on which the RNA model is formed.

2. Use the DNA model that you created in Part A as a template for making the RNA model. Separate the two strands of your DNA model by removing the toothpicks from the second strand that you created. Retain the toothpicks in the strand that you labeled as the DNA template.

3. Using your DNA template strand as a guide, thread the complementary bases onto the new wire. Use the same colors used to create your original DNA model. Assign a new color to represent uracil, which is unique to RNA and pairs with adenine.

4. Thread the gumdrops onto the wire.

5. Label the C end of the RNA model *mRNA*. Your completed model should look like the one in Figure 5.50.

Figure 5.50

An RNA molecule is synthesized on a DNA template. Complementary nucleotides are added one at a time.

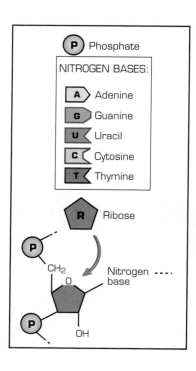

Interpretations: Respond to the following in your *Log*:

1. Starting from the tagged end, list the letters (A, C, G, T) for the nucleotide bases that make up your DNA template strand.

2. Starting from the tagged end, list the bases (U, G, C, A) that make up the RNA strand.

3. What must happen to a double-stranded DNA molecule before it can make mRNA?

4. How is the structure of mRNA different from that of DNA?

Applications: Respond to the following in your *Log*:

1. Hypothesize the type of mechanism that would be needed for this DNA to replicate itself exactly, as it must in preparation for the process of mitosis. How could you check your hypothesis?

2. What would be the result if RNA synthesis started from the untagged end of your DNA molecule? How might this affect the next steps in protein production?

The Genetic Code and Protein Synthesis

The information in RNA is read as groups of nucleotides, called codons. Each RNA codon is composed of three nucleotide bases. The genetic code chart (Figure 5.51 on page 336) allows you to match RNA codons with their specific amino acids.

How many different combinations of three nucleotides can be made? You can use a formula for computing combinations. In this case, you will consider four possible items (bases), taken three at a time. The number of combinations of 4 nucleotide bases taken 3 at a time = 4^3 = 64.

Thus our cells can make 64 different triplet sequences from four bases. However, code sequences have meaning only when we know what they stand for. Coded sequences in cell RNA provide the information for making proteins.

A protein is a large molecule made up of chains of amino acids. Proteins are the building blocks of cells, and many proteins act as enzymes controlling cellular functions. Each triplet sequence in RNA specifies a particular amino acid. There are 20 different amino acids and 64 code words, so some amino acids are specified by more than one code word. No single code word, however, specifies more than one amino acid. What would happen if it did?

The genetic code is written in messenger RNA, which is one of three main types of RNA in cells. The different types of RNA are named for their function or location in the cell. Messenger RNA (mRNA) is made from DNA strands in the nucleus and then carries the message out of the nucleus to the ribosomes, where proteins are synthesized. The ribosomes are themselves made up of proteins and RNA molecules called ribosomal RNA (rRNA).

FIRST BASE	SECOND BASE				THIRD BASE
	U	C	A	G	
U	phenylalanine	serine	tyrosine	cysteine	U
U	phenylalanine	serine	tyrosine	cysteine	C
U	leucine	serine	stop	stop	A
U	leucine	serine	stop	tryptophan	G
C	leucine	proline	histidine	arginine	U
C	leucine	proline	histidine	arginine	C
C	leucine	proline	glutamine	arginine	A
C	leucine	proline	glutamine	arginine	G
A	isoleucine	threonine	asparagine	serine	U
A	isoleucine	threonine	asparagine	serine	C
A	isoleucine	threonine	lysine	arginine	A
A	(start) methionine	threonine	lysine	arginine	G
G	valine	alanine	aspartate	glycine	U
G	valine	alanine	aspartate	glycine	C
G	valine	alanine	glutamate	glycine	A
G	valine	alanine	glutamate	glycine	G

Figure 5.51

The genetic code. The codon AUG signals the start of a protein.

A third type of RNA, transfer RNA (tRNA), transports amino acids to the ribosomes to be added to the protein coded for by the mRNA strand. The making of proteins from a mRNA message is termed translation. This process is described in Figure 5.52.

Each triplet codon designates a specific amino acid. For example, in Figure 5.51, UCC (a codon composed of one uracil and two cytosine

1 After being transcribed from DNA, mRNA leaves the nucleus

2 tRNA transports amino acids to ribosomes

3 Ribosomes coordinate binding of tRNA molecules to mRNA codons. As this occurs, amino acids on tRNA molecules are linked together

4 As adjacent amino acids bond together, the protein chain grows

5 After a tRNA links its amino acid to the protein it leaves the ribosome and binds to another amino acid

Figure 5.52

Proteins are synthesized on ribosomes from RNA codons. This process is called translation.

bases) codes for the amino acid serine. UGG codes for the amino acid tryptophan. Several amino acids are specified by more than one codon. Three codons, UGA, UAA, and UAG, do not code for any amino acids. When these codons are reached in the mRNA during translation, the process stops and the protein is completed. They signal the end of the information for a protein, like a period at the end of a sentence.

To use the chart in Figure 5.51 on page 336, locate the letter symbol for the first base in the codon in the leftmost column. Then choose the middle column that corresponds to the symbol for the second base of the codon. Finally, identify the specific amino acid by locating the row in the right column that corresponds to the symbol for the last base of the codon. 🌑

Back at the Genetic Counseling Center

Phyllis Watson continues the meeting with Tanya and James Weston.

Tanya: *So what does all of this have to do with sickle-cell anemia? I thought that the disease affected blood cells. Why are you telling us about protein?*

Ms. Watson: *Red blood cells contain molecules of an essential protein called hemoglobin. Hemoglobin carries oxygen in the blood. It also gives red blood cells their color. When the structure of hemoglobin is changed, its ability to carry oxygen is reduced. A change in the protein's shape causes the red blood cells to become sickled, to look like crescents; hence the name for the disease, sickle-cell anemia. These sickled cells tend to clump together, impeding blood flow. Let's see what happens at the molecular level.*

Figure 5.53

*Amino acid sequences
for normal and sickle-cell
hemoglobin.*

Normal ß hemoglobin: (Protein 1)	VAL 1	HIS 2	LEU 3	THR 4	PRO 5	GLU 6	GLU 7	LYS 8
Sickle-cell ß hemoglobin: (Mutated protein)	VAL 1	HIS 2	LEU 3	THR 4	PRO 5	VAL 6	GLU 7	LYS 8

Sickle-Cell Hemoglobin

Hemoglobin is a complex protein molecule. Sickle-cell anemia is caused by a mutation in the DNA sequence that codes for hemoglobin. Sickle-cell hemoglobin differs from normal hemoglobin by a single amino acid change in the protein, a valine instead of a glutamate (Figure 5.53 above). This change occurs when a single nucleotide base, adenine, is substituted for a thymine.

How can a change at the molecular level change what happens at the cellular level? Substituting valine for glutamate causes hemoglobin molecules, whether they are normal or sickled, to stick together to form long chains that deform the red blood cell. As cells sickle and clog capillaries, areas of the body become even more starved for oxygen. When this happens, red blood cells unload their oxygen, and more sickling occurs. The blood test for sickle-cell anemia requires cells to be put under low oxygen concentration. The change in shape of sickle-cells in low oxygen environment is illustrated in Figure 5.54. 🌐

Figure 5.54

*When sickle-cell hemo-
globin molecules stick
together, they deform
the red blood cells.
Deformation is greatest
when oxygen levels are
lowest.*

Individual sickle-cell hemoglobin molecules

Fiber of sickle-cell hemoglobin molecules

Fibers

In lungs

In tissues and capillary beds

100%   50%   0%

Decreasing oxygen saturation

Back at the Genetic Counseling Center

James: *If this disease is caused by a mutated allele, do Tanya and I have this allele? If we have a child, could that child inherit the allele? Would our child have sickle-cell anemia or just carry the allele without being affected by it, like Tanya and me?*

Ms. Watson: *We already know that both you and your wife are heterozygous for the sickle-cell trait. This means that each of you carries one allele for normal hemoglobin and one allele for sickle-cell hemoglobin.*

During gamete formation, you have a 50/50 chance that any one sperm or egg will carry the allele for normal hemoglobin (S) or the allele for sickle-cell hemoglobin (s). Therefore there's a 25 percent chance that any child you produce will have sickle-cell anemia and a 50 percent chance that the child will have sickle cell-trait. There is only a 25 percent chance that your child will not carry the sickle-cell hemoglobin allele at all (see Figure 5.55).

	S	s
S	SS	Ss
s	Ss	ss

Expected frequency in children:

1/4	SS	(normal blood)
1/2	Ss	(sickle-cell carriers)
1/4	ss	(has sickle-cell disease)

Figure 5.55

Calculation of the chances of offspring having sickle cell anemia.

What Would You Do?

Suppose you were in Tanya and James Weston's position. How would what you have learned about sickle-cell anemia and your own genotype affect your decisions? Consider the following questions that Tanya and James might ask the counselor:

- Can you determine before the baby is born whether the baby has sickle-cell anemia?

- If we have a child who is heterozygous, what are the chances that he or she will mate with another heterozygous person?

- Will I get the disease if I have a transfusion from someone with sickle-cell anemia?

- Why can't sickle-cell anemia be cured with a transfusion, totally replacing a person's blood supply with normal red blood cells?

- Can sickle-cell anemia be cured?

- How many people have sickle-cell anemia?

- Is sickle-cell anemia contagious?

- Does having sickle-cell disease alter the way a person looks or acts?

- How would having sickle-cell anemia affect my lifestyle?

Record your thoughts in your *Log*.

Self-Check 1

By the time you have completed all or most of the Guided Inquiries in this unit, you should understand how heredity works. You know about chromosomes and genes, which cause expressions of traits. You can predict what will happen in simple cases of inheritance, and you understand how inheritance works at a molecular level and how genetics can influence your life. Check your knowledge and skills by responding to the following questions and topics in your *Log*. Begin by assigning questions among your group. Work on your questions as homework. Check and discuss all answers with your group. Revise your answers accordingly, and write your final answers in your *Log*.

1. Describe the cause and effects of Down syndrome.

2. What are some uses of a karyotype?

3. Distinguish between mitosis and meiosis with respect to how chromosomes move and the number and types of chromosomes in the final daughter cells.

4. Describe the functions of meiosis and mitosis in the life of an organism.

5. Give examples of how inheritance plays a major role in defining the characteristics of offspring.

6. What is the difference between a trait and an expression of a trait?

7. How can you recognize patterns of inheritance if you know quite a bit about a family's history going back two or more generations?

8. What are dominant and recessive expressions of a trait, and how do you recognize them?

9. Predict the genotypes and phenotypes resulting from a cross between a homozygous individual and a heterozygous individual. Predict the same for a cross between two heterozygous individuals.

10. Which sex chromosomes are possessed by normal human males? By normal human females?

11. How are alleles segregated during meiosis? Explain the independent assortment of alleles in terms of the number of chromosomes in a cell during meiosis.

12. How is chromosome number in a species maintained?

13. What is DNA and what does it do?

Conference

For the Conference, you will present your best work from the Guided Inquiries as an abstract. Remember that an abstract is a written document that briefly summarizes the results of an experiment and suggests what new research needs to be done on the topic.

Procedure

1. Have your teacher explain the evaluation criteria for the abstract.

2. Work in pairs. Select the Guided Inquiry in this unit from which you feel you learned the most. Identify what is important about what you learned.

3. With your partner, prepare a written abstract that contains:
   a. the title of the Guided Inquiry,
   b. the particular question or hypothesis you were investigating,
   c. the procedure you followed,
   d. what you learned from the Guided Inquiry,
   e. what more you need to know,
   f. which of the Extended Inquiries that follow that would help you find out what you need to know, and
   g. A research plan for your new Inquiry.

4. Organize your abstract carefully so that it is very concise. One page is best.

5. When the draft of your abstract is complete, form groups of six or eight that represent three or four different abstracts. Each pair will then present its abstract to this group. The other members of the group will critique the abstract.

6. Discuss with your partner how you can improve your own abstract. For homework, revise your abstract with your partner for submission to the teacher the next day.

Probabilities of Multiple Traits

How can you estimate the probability of inheriting more than one trait? For example, if you are heterozygous for widow's peak, you are genotype Ww. Half of your gametes will have a W gene, and half will have a w. Therefore you have a 50 percent chance of passing on a W or a w to each of your offspring.

MATERIALS

- One penny
- One nickel

Procedure

1. Work with a partner. Flip a penny. Note that the outcome is either heads or tails. What is the possibility of each?

2. Flip a nickel. What is the possibility of each outcome?

3. Flip a penny and a nickel at the same time. These are two independent events. This means that the outcome of one is not affected by the outcome of the other. How many total possible outcomes are there? Check your answer in Step 4.

4. Hypothesize the probability of getting each of these outcomes: two heads, a penny head and a nickel tail, a penny tail and a nickel head, and two tails.

5. In your *Log*, make a data table like the one in Figure 5.56 on page 344. Allow for 40 rows and enough room to write your data for the result of each trial.

6. Take turns flipping the penny and nickel together 40 times. Record each outcome in the tally row.

7. Total the number of each of the four different outcomes, and determine the probabilities.

Interpretations: Respond to the following in your *Log*:

1. What, in round numbers, seems to be the probability of each of the following events occurring: HH, H(penny)T(nickel), T(penny)H(nickel), TT?

2. What would be the results after 100 flips of the coins?

3. If the probability of getting a head from flipping a penny is one-half, what would need to be done mathematically to predict the probability of heads from both a penny and a nickel when both are flipped at the same time?

Toss Number	Possible Outcomes			
	HH	H(penny)T(nickel)	H(nickel)T(penny)	TT
1				
2				
3				
(leave 40 rows, one for each set of coin tosses)				
Total Number of Each Outcome				
Percent of 40 Outcomes				

Figure 5.56

Sample data table for Extended Inquiry 5.1.

4. How would you determine the outcome HHH from flipping a penny, a nickel, and a dime at the same time? What about the outcome HHHH from adding a quarter?

Applications: Respond to the following in your *Log*:

1. Summarize the mathematical rule that is used to determine the number of possible outcomes for more than one independent event.

2. What is the probability of getting snake eyes (two ones) or boxcars (two sixes) when two dice are rolled?

Extended Inquiry 5.2

Protein Production and Mutations

Other than meiotic recombination of chromosomes and the genes they carry, mutation is the largest source of variation responsible for evolution. How can small changes in the DNA result in significant changes in expression?

The DNA model that you made in Guided Inquiry 5.7 describes a portion of a gene. In this inquiry you will use the models that you made to understand the nature of the DNA mutation that causes sickle-cell anemia. In this case, substitution of a single nucleotide, adenine, in place of a thymine causes a drastic change in the protein that is made from the mRNA, and the altered protein causes sickle-cell anemia.

Part A: Making Protein

MATERIALS

- Your DNA template and RNA strands from Guided Inquiry 5.7
- Markers (water soluble)
- Index cards or heavy paper, cut to approximately 5 × 2 centimeter
- Tape

Procedure

1. Separate the RNA strand from the DNA template. Retain the toothpicks in the DNA strand. Put the DNA template aside.

2. Starting from the tagged end of the RNA molecule, synthesize a protein. Use the information in Figure 5.51 on page 336 to match each three-nucleotide codon with the amino acid it codes. Write the names of these amino acids on the card labels.

3. Attach the card labels, in order, with tape. This is the protein that was coded for by the mRNA and, ultimately, by the original DNA template. Label this strand *Protein 1*.

Interpretations: Respond to the following in your *Log*:

1. Using your mRNA chain as the reference, record the names of the amino acids and their RNA codons.

2. Does any codon ever code for more than one type of amino acid? Why is this important?

3. There are 64 codons but only 20 amino acids. Why?

4. Observe what is coded for by the codons UGA, UAA, UAG, and AUG. These are the codons that signal the start and end of each protein. Why are they important?

Part B: DNA Mutations

MATERIALS

- Your DNA template and RNA strands from Guided Inquiry 5.7
- Gumdrops
- Copper wire
- Ruler
- Wire cutter
- Cylinder
- Index cards or heavy paper, cut to approximately 5 × 2 centimeters
- Markers (water soluble)
- Tape

Procedure

1. Select your original DNA template strand.

2. Counting from the tagged (G) end of the DNA strand, identify the seventeenth nucleotide. It should be a thymine. Remove this nucleotide, and replace it with a gumdrop that represents adenine. Label this DNA strand *Mutated DNA*.

3. Cut 10 centimeters of copper wire. Shape it into a loose coil by wrapping it around a cylinder, as in Guided Inquiry 5.7.

4. Make a new RNA strand. Place your DNA template strand down on the table. Observe the bases (gumdrops) that are present on this strand, and place a line of complementary colored gumdrops adjacent to each DNA base. Use the same color gumdrops as you used in making RNA (in Guided Inquiry 5.7) to represent the nucleotide bases A, C, U, and G.

5. Thread the RNA bases onto the coiled copper wire. Space them to match the spacing on the DNA strand.

6. Use the toothpicks (representing hydrogen bonds) already attached to the DNA template to attach the two strands. Be sure that each base is attached with the proper number of hydrogen bonds (two between each A-U pair and three between each G-C pair).

7. Label the C end of the new RNA strand *New mRNA*.

8. Make your new protein (as in Part A). Label it *New Protein*.

Interpretations: Respond to the following in your *Log*:

1. Record the amino acids for the new protein.

2. Does it look like the first protein you made? What is different?

3. What do you think the consequences might be when the amino acids are changed in a protein that has a specific metabolic function?

Applications: Respond to the following in your *Log*:

1. Although some mutations occur as DNA is replicated, many are caused by agents in the environment. Some common environmental agents are ultraviolet radiation from the sun, dangerous chemicals, and human-made sources of radiation. What are some common sources of possible mutations in your community? What can you do to avoid them?

2. Hypothesize the general effects of changing one or more amino acids in a protein. Why should this affect how the protein functions in your body?

   The first protein that you made in Extended Inquiry 5.2 described a portion of the amino acid sequence for normal hemoglobin. The new protein that you made when you changed a single nucleotide base on the original DNA strand was sickle-cell hemoglobin. The amino acid sequences for normal and sickle-cell hemoglobin were listed in Figure 5.53. Do the proteins that you synthesized in Extended Inquiry 5.2 match these?

Observing Human Development

In this Inquiry you will view the development of a human fetus from a zygote.

MATERIALS

- *The Miracle of Life* video
- Paper and drawing supplies
- A computer (optional)

Procedure

1. As a class or in a small group, watch the video *The Miracle of Life,* and record in your *Log* insights or new information.

2. Discuss your questions and observations in your group or the entire class.

3. As a group, organize your thoughts and notes from the video under the following headings:

   ◆ Male and Female Anatomy (Gamete Production)

   ◆ Fertilization of the Egg (Conception and Contraception)

   ◆ Embryological Development (Mother and Child)

4. Create a set of questions under each heading in preparation for writing a pamphlet on one of the topics. The purpose of the pamphlet is to share what you know with others who have not had an opportunity to see the video.

   a. Choose one of the three topics. Do additional research to answer the questions you listed for that topic.

   b. Organize your information into an informative brochure that might be available at a doctor's office or genetic counseling center. If possible, produce your pamphlet using a computer.

   c. Add some illustrations.

DNA Fingerprinting

Dr. Grimm walks into the genetic counseling center waiting room and asks, "Detective Findum, how can I help you?" The detective replies, "Dr. Grimm, I have a very complicated criminal case, and we have a lot of evidence from the scene. We're not sure which of two individuals was involved. The forensics lab says that DNA fingerprinting would give us some answers. Could you run the samples for us and then testify in court as an expert witness?"

In this activity, you can play the role of Dr. Grimm. Your group will learn to make and analyze DNA fingerprints and see how they are used to identify individuals.

MATERIALS

- DNA fingerprinting kit

Procedure

Follow the procedures in the DNA fingerprinting kit.

Interpretations: Respond to the following in your *Log*:

1. Describe in your own words how DNA fingerprinting works.
2. Describe how DNA fingerprinting can be used to identify an individual who was at the scene of a crime.

Applications: Respond to the following in your *Log*:

Develop a presentation that explains to jurors how DNA fingerprinting works. Then assume that you have found the culprit in the scenario, and prepare a possible presentation to the jury that explains your findings.

DNA Fingerprinting

The term DNA fingerprinting is an obvious reference to an earlier method for identifying individuals. Whereas traditional fingerprinting relies on the pattern of ridges on an individual's fingers, which is a phenotypic trait, DNA fingerprinting is based directly on an individual's genotype. The DNA for every individual is unique. Only identical twins have identical DNA. Properly conducted DNA fingerprinting can provide positive identification of an individual.

Use of DNA fingerprinting has revolutionized fields such as forensic medicine, paternity testing, and criminal investigations that rely on accurate identification of individuals. Only a very small sample of an individual's DNA, such as blood at the scene of a crime, skin cells under the fingernails of an assault victim, sperm from a rape victim, or any other body cells, is needed to prepare a DNA fingerprint.

Many scientists are actively involved in DNA research.

HindIII

Cut
```
- A ─│─ A - G - C - T - T -
- T - T - C - G - A ─│─ A -
```
Cut

BamHI

Cut
```
- G ─│─ G - A - T - C - C -
- C - C - T - A - G ─│─ G -
```
Cut

EcoRI

Cut
```
- G ─│─ A - A - T - T - C -
- C - T - T - A - A ─│─ G -
```
Cut

Figure 5.57

The restriction enzymes HindIII, EcoRI, and BamHI each cut DNA at only these specific sequences.

Restriction Enzymes

DNA fingerprinting became possible only after scientists developed tools to cut DNA into smaller pieces, to render it more manageable for analysis and manipulations.

Scientists use a collection of tools known as restriction enzymes for cutting up DNA in specific ways. Restriction enzymes are naturally produced in various bacteria. Their probable function is to destroy the DNA of invading organisms, thereby protecting the bacterial cells. Each restriction enzyme recognizes a specific sequence of four-to-eight nucleotides and cuts a DNA molecule only in the locations where that sequence occurs. For example, the restriction enzyme *EcoRI* recognizes the sequence GAATTC and then cuts the DNA between the bases G and A. Figure 5.57 shows the DNA cutting sites for three restriction enzymes.

Preparing a DNA Fingerprint

Because of differences in each individual's DNA sequence, a restriction site in an individual's DNA can be lost or gained. This leads to differences in length of some restriction fragments, referred to as restriction fragment polymorphisms (RFLPs). Following digestion with restriction enzymes, DNA is loaded into a gel and subjected to an electric current. The DNA fragments separate by size. The pattern produced by these fragments in the gel is visualized using a procedure known as Southern blotting. The DNA fingerprint is the unique pattern of DNA fragments that are formed in the Southern blot procedure (Figure 5.58).

Extended Inquiry 5.5

Modeling Genetic Engineering

In this activity, you will model the technique for using a restriction enzyme to cut human DNA and then insert that DNA into the DNA of a bacterium. The restriction enzyme that you will use, *HindIII*, recognizes the DNA nucleotide base sequence shown in Figure 5.57.

Figure 5.58

Comparison of the bands in this DNA fingerprint positively identified a murder suspect.

MATERIALS

- DNA strand paper models
- Scissors
- Tape

Procedure

1. Ask your teacher for two paper strips representing pieces of DNA. The shaded segment represents DNA from a human chromosome. The white piece of DNA represents bacterial DNA. Tape the nucleotide strands together to form the linear human DNA and a circular ring of bacterial DNA.

2. Use a pair of scissors to cut both the human and the bacterial DNA as they would be cut by the restriction enzyme *Hind*III.

3. Insert the human DNA into the bacterial DNA, and tape the fragments together.

Interpretations: Respond to the following in your *Log*:

How are restriction enzymes used in genetic engineering?

Applications: Respond to the following in your *Log*:

Design a plan to insert a second piece of human DNA into the ring of bacterial DNA. Include use of one of the restriction enzymes whose DNA cutting sites are shown in Figure 5.57.

a. Which of these restriction enzymes would you use? Why?

b. What would be the required characteristic of the human DNA sequence that you planned to insert using this restriction enzyme?

c. Create an appropriate human DNA sequence to insert into the bacterial DNA.

Recombinant DNA Technology and Genetic Engineering

The purpose of genetic engineering is to manipulate the genetic material of a cell so that it produces a molecule that it would not naturally produce and that it may neither use nor need. Doing this requires recombinant DNA technology, which is the process of cutting and recombining DNA molecules in order to isolate DNA fragments and to generate large numbers of them.

Genetic engineers insert fragments of foreign DNA into the DNA of rapidly growing bacterial cells. As the bacterial cells grow, they produce their own DNA as well as the foreign DNA.

The bacterium *Escherichia coli* (*E. coli*) is most often used as the host because it has been studied and used for decades as a model system to understand the genetics and biochemistry of organisms. The *E. coli* chromosome is approximately 3,400,000 nucleotides long. However, *E. coli* and other bacteria may contain smaller (3,000 to 5,000 nucleotides) circular pieces of DNA that are outside of the main chromosome. These extra-chromosomal circles of DNA are called plasmids. Foreign DNA is typically inserted into bacterial plasmids.

Recombinant DNA

To create a recombinant DNA molecule, a scientist first cuts the DNA from an organism, such as a human, using a restriction enzyme. Next, a bacterial plasmid is cut with the same restriction enzyme. The cut pieces of human and plasmid DNA are joined together to form a circle containing a plasmid DNA molecule and the human DNA. This process is described in Figure 5.59.

Figure 5.59

Genetic engineering begins by using a restriction enzyme to cut a fragment of foreign DNA that is then is inserted into a bacterial plasmid.

The recombinant DNA plasmids are put into *E. coli* cells by a process called transformation. The transformed bacteria, carrying the recombinant plasmids, are then grown on culture plates. Each bacterial cell forms a separate colony. A marker trait, usually resistance to a specific antibiotic, is used to identify those colonies carrying the recombinant plasmid. Each of the transformed bacterial cells contains hundreds of copies of the identical recombinant plasmid.

Some plasmids can be engineered to produce the gene product coded for by the foreign DNA. Products currently produced in this way include human insulin, which is used to treat human diabetes, and bovine somatotropin, a hormone that induces cows to produce milk. Other useful products of genetic engineering are being developed. 🌐

The Human Genome Project

The most ambitious planned experiment in the history of biological science, the Human Genome Project, began in 1988. A genome is the genetic material that defines a specific organism. The ultimate goal of the Human Genome Project is to determine the nucleotide sequence for the DNA of all human chromosomes.

To understand the magnitude of this undertaking, imagine identifying each letter in a full-length novel. The DNA of the haploid human genome consists of approximately 3,000,000,000 (3×10^9) nucleotides, comprising some 100,000 genes. If you think of each nucleotide as a letter in a book, and each page in the book contained 5,000 letters, then it would take a book of 600,000 pages to list the nucleotide sequence for the human genome.

The Human Genome Project is creating genetic maps that detail locations on chromosomes for many human traits (Figure 5.60). These maps will have many benefits, particularly for human health. Identifying genes for diseases, such as those examined in this unit, should lead to improved therapies.

In addition to providing human health benefits, knowledge gained from the Human Genome Project will help scientists answer many questions such as: Who were our ancestors? How does a fertilized egg know when to develop? How do individuals within a species differ from each other?

Think of some other questions that you would ask an expert on genetics of the Human Genome Project. Consider questions about health care, development of new organisms or technologies, and education and ethical concerns.

Use your questions to gather information from your family, friends, teachers, and others. Record your questions, ideas, and answers in your *Log*. 🌐

Figure 5.60

Locations of these and other genes on human chromosomes have been identified.

Researching Chromosomal Disorders

Procedure

1. Investigate at a library or on the World Wide Web the following chromosomal disorders. In your *Log*, make a chart describing the chromosomes that are affected. Record the symptoms of the disorder.

   ◆ Cri du chat ("cry of the cat") syndrome

   ◆ Chronic myelocytic leukemia (CML)

2. Some genetic problems are caused by having an abnormal number of chromosomes. Do some library or Internet research on the disorders listed below. In your *Log*, make a chart describing the way in which the chromosome number for each of the following disorders has changed. Indicate whether the abnormality involves the sex chromosomes or the autosomes. Record the symptoms of each disorder:

   ◆ Edwards' syndrome

   ◆ Patau's syndrome

   ◆ Turner's syndrome

   ◆ Klinefelter's syndrome

   ◆ XYY syndrome

This malformed hand is a characteristic of Patau syndrome.

Determining Environmental Effects on Fetal Development

Conduct a literature search of one or more of the following factors for its possible impact on conception and fetal development.

◆ Accutane
◆ Alcohol
◆ Sexually transmitted diseases
◆ Nutrition
◆ Physical fitness
◆ Controlled drugs
◆ Illegal drugs
◆ Viral infections
◆ Bacterial infections
◆ Age (males and females separately)
◆ Rh factor
◆ Stress
◆ Teratogens
◆ Radiation
◆ Excessive exposure to ultraviolet light (sunlight)

Consider using the following as a sources of information.

◆ A local public, university, or school library
◆ A local newspaper
◆ Computer databases such as ERIC, BIOSIS, or AGRICOLA
◆ The Internet, by using a web browser
◆ Experts in your community
◆ Organizations in your community devoted to your topic (such as Alcoholics Anonymous, support groups or national groups supporting research)
◆ Federal agencies, such as the National Institutes of Health (NIH)

Prepare a report. Your report should contain the following sections:

◆ Title
◆ Your research question(s)
◆ Your data and data sources
◆ Your interpretations
◆ Your recommendations for ways to avoid negative impacts on conception and fetal development

What Should Kate Do?

Kate will soon graduate from college with a degree in chemical engineering. She has a bright future and is excited about creating environmentally safe products. She has interviewed with her first prospective employer, one of the chemical industry's giants, ChemCompany. The interviewers ask her to take a genetic screening test. Eager to work for the company, she agrees.

After several weeks of waiting, she is told "We can't use you. You have a gene that has been linked to a type of liver cancer that results from exposure to workplace chemicals."

Using an ethics grid based on Figure 5.2 (page 283), decide what Kate should do. Consider the goals, rights, and duties of Kate, ChemCompany, Kate's insurance company, and society. Record your thoughts in your *Log*.

Then, acting as Kate, write a letter to the president of ChemCompany, Dr. Natasha Kidder, explaining your decision, your point of view, and your evidence. Alternately, acting as Dr. Kidder, write a letter to Kate explaining ChemCompany's position.

Self-Check 2

Check your knowledge and skills by responding to the following in your *Log*. Begin this self-check by dividing the questions among students in your small group. Do your questions as homework. Then discuss your answers to all the questions with your group. Your teacher will guide you if you have difficulty. After the groups have discussed all the responses, revise your answers in your *Log*.

1. Describe in operational terms the roles of the chromosome, gene, alleles, base pair complementary, and genetic code in protein expression.

2. Explain simply how DNA can be extracted from a cell.

3. Explain the chemical differences between DNA and RNA.

4. Explain how protein is made.

5. Explain the different roles of DNA and RNA.

6. Give examples of how modern DNA technology can influence your life.

7. Why was learning the genetic code such an important discovery?

8. Explain the procedure of genetic engineering in simple terms.

9. Summarize the scientific and societal benefits and concerns that have arisen about the use of genetic engineering.

10. Explain the purpose of the Human Genome Project.

11. Explain the role of genetic counselors and when people might want to seek their advice.

12. Explain one way in which DNA technology might be used in a criminal investigation.

Congress

The Human Genome Project may provide many benefits, but it has been the source of much controversy. What medical advances will result from this research? Who has the right to know your genome? What are acceptable uses of this knowledge? Might we find the key to immortality in the pages of a genetic sourcebook? Will we be able to recreate an individual? What will scientists, policymakers, and others in the future do with this information? Will accidents occur that may create monster organisms to plague the earth?

Setting

If the Human Genome Project is to continue, the U.S. Congress must appropriate continued funding. This will require legislative support from voters. What position should Congress take? Congress is seeking informed opinion on the matter. Since you have just finished a unit on inheritance, your class has been asked by your community to prepare a position paper that will be forwarded to Congress. Your paper will represent you and your community at the Capitol!

Procedure

1. You will need to try to represent a wide cross-section of your community. To do this, you need to anticipate the possible interests of groups such as those listed below. Choose one of these groups that you would like to represent. (Not all groups need to be chosen.)

 ◆ A scientific society
 ◆ A civil liberties group
 ◆ An association of physicians
 ◆ A local group of clergy
 ◆ Insurance company executives

- ◆ Law enforcement agencies
- ◆ Members of the armed forces
- ◆ Local educators
- ◆ A children's advocate group
- ◆ Members of a taxpayer's association
- ◆ Other groups that you think might need to be represented

2. Form committees of students who have chosen the same group to represent.

3. Study the issues and evidence, thinking about the interests of this group.

4. Decide on a committee position. Will you be in favor of continued funding for the Human Genome Project, against additional funding, or neutral?

5. List the arguments that support your position, and decide which arguments your group will present. Use scientific evidence for your assertions whenever possible; use everything you have learned from this unit. Other groups may disagree with your position. Anticipate their arguments so that you can effectively counter them. Summarize your position in your *Log*.

6. Choose one member of your committee to present your arguments to the class for feedback. The proceedings of these presentations from each committee will be transcribed and sent to Congress on behalf of your community.

7. Make each presentation in about one to three minutes. Then take a vote in your class for or against continued support of the Human Genome Project.

Homework

Having heard the pros and cons presented by the class about the merits of the Human Genome Project, you are now in a position to take a personal and individual position on this issue. You may have even changed your own mind. Write your position down in no more than one page in your *Log*. Be sure to give reasons supporting your views. Your teacher may wish to review your entry.

AUTOMOBILE INSURANCE: A PROPOSAL TO YOUR COMMUNITY

Automobile insurance rates have for some time been based on variables representing the driver's risk group. For example, the accident and citation rate for the age group 15 to 18 is relatively high. So insurance coverage for your age group is the most expensive of all. For people between 18 and 25, the rates are a little lower—and even lower yet if they are married. Males have higher rates in almost all of these categories. The lowest rate is for individuals (of both genders) who are 55 and over. However, some states are now considering much higher rates for people over 70. The insurance companies believe that groups with the greatest risk for accidents should pay the highest rates.

Now that society has the technology to keep accurate medical records and map individual genomes, suppose that your insurance company has proposed to your community that all insured people supply the information in the following list.

1. Your age, gender, marital status, and driving record, as before.

2. Your complete medical history, particularly for any conditions that might impair your judgment, reaction time, or alertness. For example, have you ever been diagnosed and treated for hyperactivity, attention deficit disorder, neurosis, psychosis, schizophrenia, heart problems, diabetes, vision correction, glaucoma, dyslexia, asthma, AIDS, or epilepsy?

3. Your entire genome map, with indication of illnesses in your family history such as Huntington's disease, sickle-cell anemia, hemophilia, alcoholism, obesity, or mental illness.

The more of the conditions you have and the higher the relative weights assigned to their seriousness, the higher your auto insurance rates will be. These variables will also be used to determine life insurance rates.

For this Forum, assume that the insurance company's proposal is before the Town Council. Members of your class will be assigned (or will self-assign) to the following roles:

◆ Five to nine Town Council members, depending upon number available in class (An odd number is needed so a decision by voting can be made.)

◆ Expert witnesses, including

■ One member from insurance company lobby

■ CEO of a large insurance auto company

■ One geneticist with expertise on the Human Genome Project

■ One physician

■ Two members from a human rights organization

■ One attorney with expertise in human rights

■ One attorney with expertise in insurance litigation

■ The president of the local AAA

■ Two members of a community consumer group

■ One economist

■ One professor of philosophy with expertise in ethics

■ Other experts or citizens with specific concerns that you may wish to add if enough students are available in your class

The major issue to be resolved is whether the insurance company has the right to have the requested information. There are legal, moral, ethical, economic, and practical considerations.

Each of the experts will have the opportunity to make a one-minute statement to convince the Town Council of his or her point of view. The Council members can ask each speaker brief questions. They will then confer among themselves and make a decision before the end of the class period to either accept or reject the insurance company's proposal.

Summarize in your *Log* the advantages and disadvantages of this proposal. Explain why your Town Council made the decision that it did.

Summary of Major Concepts

1. Heredity is responsible for most of what organisms are. In sexually reproducing organisms, one-half of an individual's inherited traits comes from each parent, dictating the range of possible physical and mental structures.

2. Nondisjunction during mitosis or meiosis can result in an abnormal number of chromosomes in the cells produced by these division processes. Offspring that are produced by fusion of one or more of these abnormal gametes may have severe genetic defects.

3. A chromosome is one of many strands of DNA in the nucleus of a cell that is responsible for heredity. Chromosomes tend to occur in pairs, called homologs. Each homolog has one gene for the same trait. Therefore most organisms have two genes for each trait in the nucleus. These are called alleles.

4. Mitosis is the division of a cell nucleus before the cell divides; it is a normal part of tissue growth. Cells resulting from mitosis are identical and have the same number of chromosomes as the original cell.

5. Meiosis is the division of a cell before it forms a gamete. Each gamete contains only one homologous chromosome. Then when fertilization occurs, the normal number of chromosomes is established.

6. A gene is one specific section of DNA on a chromosome responsible for a trait. Together, two homologous chromosomes carry at least two genes for every trait. Sometimes, only one of these genes is expressed, or dominant, sometimes recessive, and sometimes incomplete or a blending.

7. Dominant expressions of a trait can sometimes be recognized over recessive traits in a family pedigree. If a dominant and a recessive expression of a trait both show up frequently in a family, the dominant expression is the one that tends not to skip generations.

8. Normal male humans have one X chromosome and one Y chromosome. Normal females have two X chromosomes.

9. During meiosis, homologous chromosomes segregate into different gametes, only one of each pair of genes for a trait being taken into the gamete.

10. During meiosis, homologous chromosomes segregate to one or the other gamete. They move independently of other segregating chromosome pairs.

11. The technology now exists to break DNA strands and insert new DNA pieces into existing DNA, thus making new DNA. The possible outcomes of DNA technology are now almost unlimited.

12. New DNA technology has raised many ethical issues about who has the right to manipulate the natural genome of individuals.

13. Since the exact DNA makeup of individuals is very specific, DNA marker technology makes it possible to identify the DNA of an individual with almost complete certainty.

Suggestions for Further Exploration

Bloom, M. 1995. *Understanding Sickle Cell Disease.* University Press of Mississippi, Jackson, MS.

A guide to "understanding a debilitating genetic disease that affects tens of thousands who are of African ancestry."

Farrell, M.H.J. 1994. Growing up *Down*: Two Down syndrome friends discuss their condition. *People Weekly,* 42(16), 117–120.

Highlights two friends, ages 23 and 19, who wrote a book together about growing up with Down syndrome.

Harris, A. 1995. *Cystic fibrosis: the facts.* Oxford University Press, New York.

Facts about cystic fibrosis in children; contains illustrations and an index.

Lowenstein, J.M. 1992. Whose genome is it, anyway? *Discover,* 13(5), 28–31.

Information about the Human Genome Project and the DNA that was chosen to be studied.

Lowenstein, J.M. 1992. Genetic surprises. *Discover,* 13(12), 82–88.

A discussion of why large sections of the genetic material do not have any apparent purpose.

Müller-Hill, B. 1993. The shadow of genetic injustice. *Nature,* 362, 491–492.

The author is concerned about the possible societal effects of the discoveries emerging from the Human Genome Project.

Reich, W.T., Ed. 1995. *Encyclopedia of Bioethics.* Macmillan, New York.

Over 2,950 pages of information about bioethics issues.

Revkin, A. 1993. Hunting down Huntington's. *Discover,* 14(12), 98–108.

Tells the personal and professional story of Dr. Wexler's work in finding the cause of this disease.

Sutherland, et. al. 1991. Hereditary unstable DNA: A new explanation for some old genetic questions? *The Lancet,* 338:289–291.

A discussion of the abnormal number of CCG sequences that characterize the DNA of individuals who have Fragile X syndrome.

BOTH HEREDITY AND ENVIRONMENT AFFECT PEOPLE.

SIX

BEHAVIOR AND THE NERVOUS SYSTEM

HOW CAN

PEOPLE CHANGE

THEIR BEHAVIOR?

How can chemicals alter our behavior?

THE DAVID GARABEDIAN CASE

Setting

In the early 1980s, David Garabedian was convicted of committing a murder. His actions were unusual because he did not have a history of violent behavior. In defending him, Garabedian's lawyer claimed that his client had been exposed to toxic chemicals (insecticides) and that this exposure affected Garabedian's behavior.

Was this a legitimate defense? What level of responsibility must people take for their own actions, regardless of the circumstances in which these actions occur?

The David Garabedian Video

You'll begin this unit by watching a short video about the case of David Garabedian. As you watch the video, look for possible explanations of Garabedian's behavior. Try to determine what may have caused him to become aggressive. Jot down your observations in your *Log*.

Brainstorming

Share your observations with others in a small group discussion. Brainstorm the following questions, and record your ideas in your *Log*.

- ◆ What is a drug? Does the insecticide in the Garabedian case fit your definition of a drug? If so, how?

- ◆ Garabedian may have ignored the warnings regarding the use of the insecticide. How would this have any bearing on whether he is responsible for his behavior?

- ◆ Are we as individuals responsible for our behavior even when drugs modify that behavior? What if the intoxication occurs accidentally rather than deliberately?

- ◆ Should people be held responsible if the effects of the drugs that they take are unpredictable? For example, if intoxication from a particular drug were rare, would the person who took the drug still be responsible?

- ◆ Most victims of insecticide poisoning do not have the aggressive responses described in the video. How does this information affect the case?

- ◆ According to his family, Garabedian had never acted aggressively in the past. How does this information affect the case?

What Is Behavior?

Behavior can be described as the external physiology (functioning) of an organism. It is any observable activity that is initiated by the organism's internal mechanisms (for example, hormones or nerve impulses). All animals, not just humans, exhibit behavior. The ways in which animals move, eat, migrate, and communicate are all examples of behavior.

The study of behavior is really a comparison of how behaviors vary among individuals within a single population or across species. A behavioral scientist might suggest that no behavior can be permanently identified as normal. Normal only describes a condition or behavior that is exhibited by a greater proportion of organisms within the population. The definition of normal, even within a single population, has a range and changes continually as environmental, societal, and cultural conditions change.

Behaviors that are considered normal (or accepted) in one human culture may be considered absolutely abnormal and unacceptable in another culture. Consider the practice of eating without utensils. Eating with one's fingers might be considered normal in some regions of northern Africa but might be offensive in Sweden. Travel guides are full of hints to travelers, warning them about behaviors that are offensive to individuals in other cultures. 🌍

How Can a Brain Injury Affect Personality?

In 1848, railroad crew foreman Phineas Gage had a dramatic accident. Before the accident, he had been a healthy, capable employee with a bright future. Then one day he was checking an explosive charge with a tamping rod–a piece of steel about four feet long and one inch in diameter with a sharp point at one end. He was standing directly over the charge when it suddenly exploded. The rod was propelled upward into Gage's cheek and out through the top of his head, passing through his brain.

Amazingly, Gage lived! He even said that he had felt no pain during the accident. After a few months of rest, Gage seemed physically as healthy as before. His behavior, however, was very much changed. He seemed to be an entirely different person, impatient and easily angered. He was verbally abusive and aggressive, and he trusted no one. Eventually, his wife left him.

The company refused to let him return to his old job, which infuriated Gage. Miserable and unproductive, he lived for 12 more years. Since his death, Gage has been declared a medical marvel. His skull, with a large hole in the top, and the tamping rod that pierced it are now on display in a museum near Boston.

More than 100 years after the death of Phineas Gage, scientists examined his skull to determine which parts of his brain were damaged.

Respond to the following questions in your *Log*:

1. If one of your friends had an accident that affected his or her personality, how do you think you would react?

2. How might physical changes to the brain alter personality?

3. On the basis of this case, what would you say is the connection between a person's brain and his or her behavior?

The Blind Walk

How do we perform complex actions that apparently require no thinking? You can listen to a conversation and eat at the same time. Even driving a car can become automatic. However, although you might not be aware of it, brain coordination is involved in your behavior. What happens when one of the senses used in an action is impaired? In this Inquiry, you will investigate the relationship between the senses (in particular, vision) and the performance of an automatic behavior (in this case, walking). You will find out what happens when your brain can no longer rely on visual signals to coordinate an activity that you seldom think about consciously (Figure 6.1).

MATERIALS

- Graph paper (either 5 squares to the centimeter or 10 squares to the inch)
- Paper towels
- Tape
- Goggles
- Long hallway or open area

Procedure

1. Work in groups of three. Together construct a hypothesis that states how being blindfolded might affect your ability to walk a specified path.

2. Draw six grids on your graph paper. Each grid should contain 30 squares on any side. Label each grid with a different trial number (1 through 6). Mark an X in each grid to indicate the starting point of the path. (The location of the starting point should be about five squares from the left and 15 squares down from the top.) Figure 6.2 on page 370 shows a sample grid.

Figure 6.1

What senses might this person be using to navigate while wearing a blindfold?

Start at X:

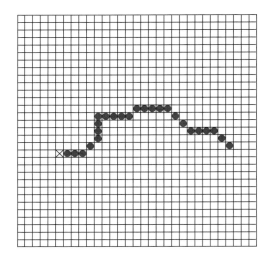

Figure 6.2

Sample grid used to record the path walked. Each mark indicates one step.

3. Tape a paper towel securely over the goggles to create a blindfold.

4. Find a long hallway or an open area such as an outdoor walkway. One person puts on the blindfold goggles and closes his or her eyes in preparation for making six blind walk trials. Another person will record the results on the grids, drawing the path walked. The third person reads the directions aloud for each trial and watches for potential hazards.

5. Each student should perform each of the following six trials:

   Trial 1: Keep your hands down at your sides. Walk forward 25 steps taking normal steps.

   Trial 2: Keep your hands down at your sides. Walk forward 25 steps taking very long steps.

   Trial 3: Hold your arms out in front of you keeping them even with your shoulders. Walk forward 25 steps.

   Trial 4: Hold your arms straight out from your sides keeping them even with your shoulders. Walk forward 25 steps.

   Trial 5: Hold your arms straight out at your sides again. Let your partner spin you 10 times in a clockwise direction. Stop momentarily. Then walk forward 25 steps.

   Trial 6: Hold your arms straight out at your sides again. Let your partner spin you 10 times in a counterclockwise direction. Stop momentarily. Then walk forward 25 steps.

6. Reverse roles and repeat the six trials.

Interpretations: Respond to the following in your *Log*:

1. Explain how being blindfolded influenced the behavior of walking.
2. How does arm position influence your ability to walk in a straight line?
3. How does the size of the step taken relate to your ability to walk straight while blindfolded?
4. What new effects did spinning introduce?
5. Did the direction of the spin make a difference? How?
6. How do you think sight, balance, and walking are related?

Applications: Respond to the following in your *Log*:

1. Have you ever closed your eyes on a roller coaster at an amusement park? How did closing your eyes change your perceptions?
2. List the following senses in order of their importance to you for walking: hearing, sight, touch, smell, and taste. Explain your order.
3. Describe what it would be like to carry out a typical day's activities without the benefit of vision.

BIOthoughts

Sometimes when people lose the use of one or more of their senses, the other senses seem to become keener. The physiological mechanism for this change is not adequately understood. But it is believed that we rarely take advantage of the full potential of our senses.

For example, it is not unusual to find a sight-impaired person walking confidently through a shopping mall. How do people accomplish this? Consider how they might use their other senses to navigate from one end of a mall to the other. Which of their other senses would be used? What would be some examples of important sensory input from the environment? How would this input be processed by the nervous system to navigate through the mall?

BIOprediction

How Do Magnetic Fields Affect Animal Behavior?

Humans and other animals use a variety of senses to help them move around. Birds, for example, use visual cues to help them locate positions on the ground. But what if everything below them looks the same? What if the birds are flying long distances over water, for example? Birds use their perception of the earth's magnetic fields to help them navigate, especially during annual migrations, when visual cues might not be sufficient.

The earth naturally produces magnetic fields. But so do some human inventions. For example, major power lines, which transfer electricity from its source in power plants to where it is used, produce magnetic fields.

Dr. Sidney Gauthreaux studies the effects of magnetic fields on bird migrations. Dr. Gauthreaux is particularly interested in finding out how electrical power lines affect magnetic fields in the atmosphere and how these altered magnetic fields affect birds' abilities to navigate. He uses radar to track the movement of flocks of birds as they migrate through the eastern United States. Radar allows him to study bird migrations at night, when they are most likely to occur, and through clouds.

Answer the following questions in your *Log*:

1. What do you think could happen to migrating birds if the magnetic field from power lines affected them?

2. How do you think Dr. Gauthreaux could find out whether this possible effect is actually occurring?

3. Under what conditions—sunny or overcast—do you think birds would rely on magnetic fields instead of visual cues? Why?

Dr. Sidney Gauthreaux monitors bird migrations on a radar screen.

These radar screens show the arrival of birds at a resting site (A and B) and night departure (C).

Human Physiology and Behavior

Two body systems coordinate to control human physiology and behavior. The nervous system sends high-speed electrical signals to specific parts of the body through specialized cells called neurons. The endocrine system provides a slower means of communication, sending chemical messages, often through the bloodstream. These two systems together provide the major means of communication within the human body.

The Human Nervous System

The human nervous system (Figure 6.3) is composed of neurons and other cells that support and nourish the neurons. Sensory cells sense stimuli from the environment and from within the body. Neurons convey electrical messages about these stimuli to the brain and the spinal cord and from these organs out to the body where an action takes place.

The brain and the spinal cord make up the central nervous system. The neurons that receive stimuli and carry messages to and from skeletal muscles and internal organs form the peripheral nervous system.

The specialized cell called a neuron has three major structures (Figure 6.4 on page 374). The cell body contains the nucleus and most of the organelles and cytoplasm. Dendrites receive sensory information from sensory cells and other neurons and carry signals toward the cell body. The axon is an elongated structure that extends from the cell body. It carries an electrical signal to other neurons or a site in the body where an action takes place. The axon portion of a neuron can be very long—up to 1 meter in length.

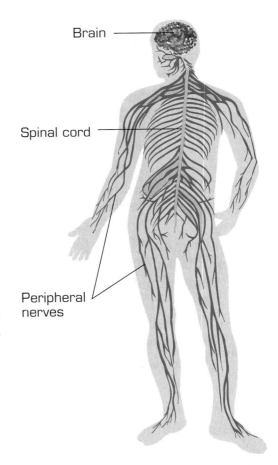

Brain

Spinal cord

Peripheral nerves

Figure 6.3

The major components of the human nervous system.

Figure 6.4

The structure of a human neuron. Electrical signals are transferred to a neuron through its dendrites and carried in the axon towards other body cells. The myelin sheath insulates and protects the axon.

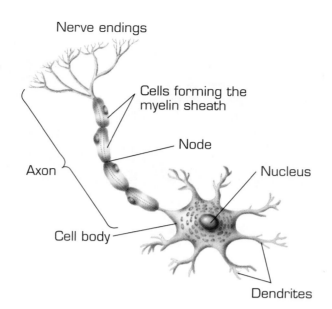

Nerve endings

Cells forming the myelin sheath

Node

Nucleus

Axon

Cell body

Dendrites

The Sense of Vision

You use different senses as you walk, but your sense of sight is particularly important. You are probably not aware that you use your eyes to keep your balance. Without vision, though, you would have trouble standing still. Doctors can use the body's reliance on vision to test damage to the nervous system. The test is called the Romberg sign. During this test, the patient stands straight with arms down at the sides and eyes closed. Even people with intact nervous systems tend to weave back and forth a little. But a person whose nervous system is damaged will not be able to stand and will fall over.

The human eye (Figure 6.5) is a fluid-filled sphere composed of three major layers of tissues. The outermost layer of the eye is the sclera. This layer, made up of fibrous connective tissue, protects the eye. The front portion of the sclera is transparent. This section, the cornea, permits light to enter the eye. The middle layer of the eye, the choroid, contains blood vessels. The front of this layer, the iris (the colored part of the eye), is made up of a ring of smooth muscles. The iris contracts and relaxes involuntarily in response to the amount of light coming through the cornea. This changes the size of the pupil, the hole in the center of the iris. Thus the iris regulates the amount of light that passes through the lens to focus on the retina, the innermost layer of the eye.

Vitreous humor

Muscle

Lens

Pupil

Retina

Cornea

Choroid

Iris

Sclera

Aqueous humor

Muscles

Optic nerve

Figure 6.5

Anatomy of the human eye.

Light images are translated to sensory signals to the brain by light receptor cells on the retina. These specialized light receptor cells are called rods and cones, named for their shapes (Figure 6.6). Rods are very sensitive to light and thus help us to see in dim light. Rods do not detect color, so dim light images appear to be black and white. Cones can detect colors, but they need more light to be functional. Cones operate in daylight to provide color vision. Electrical impulses, produced when light is absorbed by the rods and cones, are transferred to the neurons of the retina and then to the brain through the optic nerve.

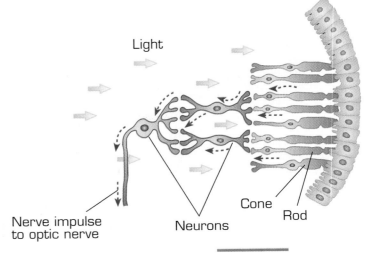

Figure 6.6

Layers of the human retina. Light passes through several layers of cells in the retina before being absorbed by the rods and cones.

Hearing and Balance

Although vision is important in maintaining balance, it is not the sole contributor. In fact, your sense of balance (also called equilibrium) comes mainly from the inner ear. In humans and many other animals, the sensory receptors for balance are located within the ear, along with the sensory receptors for hearing.

The human ear (Figure 6.7) contains three distinct areas: the outer ear, the middle ear, and the inner ear. The outer ear consists of the fleshy pinnae (what you think of as your ear) and the auditory canal. These structures collect sound and funnel them toward the sensory organs in the middle ear and the inner ear. Sound vibrations are transmitted to the middle ear through a membrane, the eardrum, which is the barrier between the outer and middle ear. Sound vibrations through the eardrum cause three small bones–commonly known as the hammer, the anvil, and the stirrup–to move. These bones trans-fer the sound vibrations to the cochlea, the sensory organ for hearing, which is located in the inner ear. The cochlea detects sound and relays information to the brain.

You are able to maintain balance as you move because of another organ in the inner ear, the semi-circular canals. Specialized cells within these canals detect movements of your head and relay this information to the brain. 🐾

Figure 6.7

Ears enable humans to hear and to maintain balance.

Figure 6.8

Does your medicine cabinet at home look like this? Do you and your family know the ingredients in each medicine and how they affect your body?

Over-the-Counter Drugs

What do you think of when you hear the words *drug abuse*? You probably think of popping pills, smoking dope, drinking alcohol, or something even worse. But there's another type of drug abuse. This is the abuse of over-the-counter drugs, and it goes on daily in many households in America.

Over-the-counter medications—that is, the drugs that people buy at the pharmacy without prescriptions—can be helpful when they are taken as indicated and used in moderation. But they can be dangerous, and they are often overused. Some doctors say that half of the ailments for which people take medication are either imagined or misperceived. The human nervous system is both delicate and complex. Many over-the-counter (OTC) drugs—especially sleeping pills, diet pills, and cold medications—are designed to affect some part of this delicate, complex system (Figure 6.8).

In this Inquiry, you will investigate the nature of some OTC drugs. You will also explore the extent of their use. Your data source for this Inquiry will be your home medicine cabinet.

MATERIALS

- Medicine cabinet at home
- Pharmaceutical reference books such as *The Physician's Desk Reference*

Procedure

1. In your *Log,* make a data table like the one in Figure 6.9.

Figure 6.9

Sample data table for Guided Inquiry 6.2.

Name	Active Ingredients	Mode of Action

2. Check your medicine cabinet at home. Read the labels on the bottles and any information sheets that are enclosed in the packaging. Identify any over-the-counter drugs that you believe affect the nervous system. (*Hint:* Read about the side effects. Remember that the nervous system includes the brain, the spinal cord, and all of the nerves throughout the body.) List those drugs in the data table in your *Log.*

3. For each drug that you list, write the active ingredients and the mode of action (how the chemicals in the drug will affect the body). You may need to consult a pharmaceutical reference book such as *The Physician's Desk Reference* or *The Pill Book*.

Interpretations: Respond to the following in your *Log*:

1. Write a paragraph summarizing your findings.

2. What are the some of the inactive ingredients in the drugs you studied? What is the purpose of inactive ingredients?

3. What might be the long-term effects of the excessive use of any of the drugs you listed in your data table?

4. Which of the drugs that you examined seemed safest? Explain why you think that drug seems safe.

Applications: Respond to the following in your *Log*:

Research some ways in which individuals may inadvertently misuse OTC medications. (Use the library, the Internet, or personal interviews.) Consider how advertising and other features of our society might influence this misuse. Compile your findings in your *Log*.

What Is a Drug?

Depending on how you define the word, almost anything can be a drug. The federal government classifies drugs in two categories: over-the-counter and prescription. According to the government, prescription drugs must be effective. In other words, they must help to cure a specific disease or relieve a specific symptom. The drug must be prescribed by a medical professional, someone who is qualified (by education and experience) to keep track of the drug's desirable and undesirable effects.

Over-the-counter drugs must be both safe and effective. To be sold without a prescription, a drug is not supposed to be dangerous to use. Of course, it must still be taken according to the instructions printed on the packaging; otherwise, it may cause a person to become ill or even to die.

Many OTC drugs have undesirable effects on the nervous system, and people should understand the side effects before they take the drug. For example, cold medicines often contain antihistamines, a group of drugs that block receptors for the chemical histamine on cells in the nose. The cold medication blocks these receptors in the nose, decreasing mucus production and swelling of the nasal passages. As a result, the person feels better. So the medication is effective. Unfortunately, the parts of the brain that keep people alert also have histamine receptors. These receptors also are affected by the antihistamines, and the person becomes drowsy and less alert. If you read the instructions that come with these medicines, you will see that you are not supposed to drive or operate heavy machinery while taking this drug. Many people ignore these warnings, however, and are hurt—or hurt others—because they are not as alert as they should be.

As we mentioned, OTC drugs must be effective, just as prescription drugs must be. Drug companies must submit studies showing that a particular medication is more effective than a placebo, an inert substance that looks like the drug but has no measurable effect on the body. Take a look at drug advertisements in magazines, or read the package inserts. You will notice that some percentage of the people taking the placebo reported that they were cured. 🌐

Guided Inquiry 6.3

The Limits of Learning

Think of a simple, routine task that you do repeatedly. Over time, you have probably gotten better or faster at the task. Can you continue to get better or faster, or are there limits to the improvement? How does learning relate to improved performance? In this Inquiry, you will assemble some simple jigsaw puzzles as a way of exploring these topics (Figure 6.10).

MATERIALS

- A simple puzzle, such as a 6–12 piece jigsaw
- A clock that displays seconds
- Graph paper

Procedure

1. Working alone, assemble the simple jigsaw puzzle as quickly as you can. Let your partner keep time and record the data in your *Log*. Repeat for a total of 10 times.

2. Switch roles, and let your partner work the puzzle while you record the time for each trial.

3. Working in pairs, construct hypotheses for how fast you can complete a jigsaw puzzle working alone and working with your partner.

Figure 6.10

Does putting together a jigsaw puzzle involve learning?

4. Working with your partner this time, assemble the puzzle. Record the time data in your *Log*. Repeat for a total of 10 times.

5. Construct a graph that illustrates the relationship between the time needed to finish the puzzle and the trial sequence. Display all of your data for the puzzle on one sheet of graph paper. Each graph will have three graph lines, one for each individual performance and one for the team effort. Make *trial number* the independent variable and *time taken to complete the puzzle* the dependent variable.

Interpretations: Respond to the following in your *Log*:

1. Evaluate your hypotheses (Step 3 of the procedure) on the basis of the data you collected.

2. What evidence of learning did you find?

3. How did the learning change over trials? How do you know?

4. What individual differences in performance patterns between partners did you see?

5. How was performance changed when you worked together? What may have caused these changes?

6. What does memory have to do with the results?

7. How did your speed change as you worked the puzzle?

8. Make a summary statement about learning or experience and performance in simple, routine tasks. Be sure to refer to both independent and dependent variables in your statement.

Applications: Respond to the following in your *Log*:

1. Compare the results on this experiment to experiences you have had with other tasks you've done repeatedly. How are the learning and performance patterns similar?

2. What are some occupations in your community that require workers to repeat a task many times? How long does it take to learn the task? Do workers get faster as they repeat the task again and again? What variables influence the time taken?

Genotypes and Behavior: Is There a Connection?

In Guided Inquiry 6.3, you observed that practice can improve your skill and speed with a routine task such as assembling a puzzle. We can refer to this improvement as learning, which is a specific behavior. You probably found in the Inquiry that practice did not continue to improve skill or speed over time. That's because there is a limit to the improvement, or at least to the rate of improvement, for most tasks. What determines that limit?

You know from Unit 5 that your genotype determines much of what you are. It is easy to observe how genotypes affect physical features of phenotype, such as hair color or blood type. But genotype is not the only determinant of other phenotypic characteristics, such as height, weight, or the tendency to acquire a particular disease. A malnourished child from a family of tall individuals, for example, may never attain his or her genetic potential for height. History reveals that populations suffering from famines or food shortages during wars often produce shorter or slighter people, even in families of tall or large people. Similarly, an individual from a family that has a history of diabetes may be able to prevent the disease, or at least delay its onset, by following a careful diet and exercise regime.

Natural Selection and Behavior

Behavior is a phenotypic trait that is determined by an organism's genotype and the influences of its environment. An organism's behavior can affect its chances of survival. In fact, much of the study of animal behavior focuses on actions that affect an animal's chances for survival. As is true for other phenotypic traits, any behavior that allows an individual to survive long enough to reproduce may also be exhibited by that individual's offspring.

When Charles Darwin traveled to the Galapagos Islands, he observed a remarkable diversity of finches. Darwin hypothesized that the finches had diverged from a single type but became differentiated when they were geographically isolated on the many islands. After long periods of isolation, some of these new forms of finches became so different that they could not interbreed. In this way, new species originated. Since different food sources were available on each island, each type of finch evolved beaks and behaviors adapted to their local food sources (Figure 6.11). The shapes of their beaks and the accompanying food-gathering behavior identify the many species of Galapagos finches.

As this example shows, the change in a behavior—in this case, a way of gathering food—can contribute to evolution and to the development of a new species. In this case, environment was the impetus for a shift in

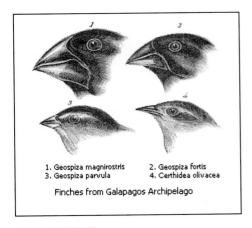

1. Geospiza magnirostris   2. Geospiza fortis
3. Geospiza parvula   4. Certhidea olivacea

Finches from Galapagos Archipelago

Figure 6.11

*These different species of Galapagos Islands finches have differently shaped beaks,
which are specialized for gathering different foods.*

behavior. We say that the environment exerted a selective pressure on
the population of finches. This is the basic principle of Charles Darwin's
theory that explained how evolution might occur because of natural
selection.

Relative Fitness

Does the success of the food-gathering behavior of the Galapagos
Islands finches prove that they were the fittest birds in all environments?
For each type of organism on earth, can we identify behavior that makes
that organism superior to all others on the earth? Specifically, is there any
ideal human behavior for all environments? The answer to all of these
questions is no.

Relative fitness is the actual fitness of a certain genotype, in comparison to
the most fit genotype. But the fitness of a behavior is like most other phenotypic traits: It is directly affected by the environment in which an organism
lives. What determines fitness in one environment or society may not be so in
another. This is also true for humans.

You may recall the example of sickle-cell trait from Unit 5. Individuals
who are heterozygous for sickle-cell anemia enjoy some measure of protection from malaria. Therefore they have a relatively better chance of survival
than do individuals who have no alleles for the sickle-cell trait. But this is an
advantage only if they live where malaria occurs. A single sickle-cell allele
would not be an advantage to someone in the United States.

Likewise, the ability to learn is a phenotypic trait. It is determined to some
extent by genetics, but environment influences the expression of its potential. Some environments may nourish its potential, and others may not. 🌍

Improving Your Memory

As the self-help books in Figure 6.12 show, many people attempt to improve their memories. What strategies work? What are the ideal conditions for remembering information or experiences? Think of some different ways that you have tried to memorize facts for a test. You may have tried to study a list of facts, such as history dates or math theorems, by reading them over and over again. In this Inquiry, you will try a different method: Your teacher will tell an outrageous story as you learn a set of facts; in recalling the facts, you will draw on your recollection of the story.

By participating in this memory-learning process, you are actively working with your brain. The results will amaze you. Frequently, when you "learn" or memorize things for a test, you keep the information in your mind for only a short period of time. When you engage more parts of the brain, you can retain the information much longer.

MATERIALS

- Handout, "List of Brain Structures and Functions"

Procedure

1. Listen to your teacher tell the story, which will be accompanied by visual descriptions and movement.

2. After telling the entire story once, your teacher will go back to the original starting place in the room. From there, your teacher will move around the room again asking you to tell the parts of the story that correspond with each location.

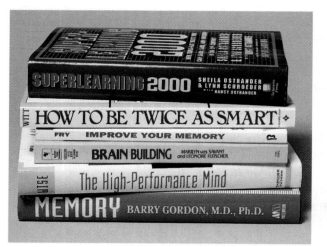

3. Work with a partner. Tell the story to your partner, and let your partner tell the story to you.

4. Review the handout "List of Brain Structures and Functions," which contains information that correlates with the story. Draw scenes from the story next to the brain parts to which they correspond.

Figure 6.12

People can work to improve memory and their ability to access information.

5. As homework, rethink the story in your mind. Use the second handout, "Memory Tagging Story for Brain Physiology and Function," as a guide. Tell the story aloud, and go through the motions. Teach the story to an adult or to a brother or sister.

Interpretations: Respond to the following in your *Log*:

1. How did learning the outrageous story help you to remember the parts of the brain and their functions?

2. Offer a hypothesis that explains the effects of the story.

3. How could you use these principles to memorize other lists of information?

Applications: Respond to the following in your *Log*:

1. Suppose you met a person whose name you really needed to remember. What devices could you use to remember this person's name?

2. A phone number (with area code) is really a string of 10 digits. In listing phone numbers, however, we always put a break after the three-digit area code and between the first three and last four digits of the local phone number. How is this helpful in remembering the phone number?

How We Recall Information from Memory

Much of your behavior is based on your memory of circumstances and your ability to recall those memories. For example, when you were younger, you probably touched something hot and burned your hand. You stored the memory of that experience in your brain. The next time you found yourself in that situation, you probably remembered (consciously or not) not to touch the hot surface that had burned you before.

The human brain tends to remember information best under the following conditions:

◆ When strong emotions such as love, joy, or sorrow are involved. Do you remember the first boy or girl you ever had a crush on?

◆ When more than one sense is involved and sensory associations are especially vivid. Do specific smells or songs remind you of significant places or times in your life? Do you remember better if you experience with a combination of sight, smell, touch, or hearing?

◆ When outstanding or unique qualities are involved. Do you remember the names of unique people you have met or special experiences you have had?

◆ When the associations that are made with the memory are intense. Humans tend to remember things that are colorful, exaggerated, and absurd.

- When the memory is of personal importance. Suppose that someone you are attracted to gives you his or her telephone number. You will not be likely to forget it.

- When the memory is vital to survival. Suppose you are extremely sensitive to poison oak and poison ivy. On a wilderness hike, your guide shows you what these plants look like. You will not be likely to forget.

- When what the person is trying to remember is repeated. You have probably used this method before. Think of the combination lock on your school locker. If you use it several times a day, you probably won't forget the combination. But if you use it only once every two weeks, you will probably have to write the combination down somewhere and look at it each time you need to open your locker. 🌎

BIOthoughts

Sometimes people can do amazing things with their minds. For example, have you ever known anyone who can:

- describe to someone much later (and to the smallest detail) everything some person was wearing after only an initial glance?

- take an entire car engine apart and replace each part in its original place without even making a sketch or making notes of where the parts belong?

- recite accurately and with the most vivid details the entire plot and dialog of a lengthy movie several days after having seen the movie?

- share with you an amazingly detailed, play-by-play account of an entire ball game?

- meet over a dozen new persons in rapid succession and later repeat to each of them their correct names?

- remember an exact and lengthy entry sequence needed to enter a secret chamber in a computer adventure game?

How can people accomplish these feats? What mental aids could they be using? Are there any common elements in their mental processing? What explanations do you have based upon what you have learned in this unit thus far?

BI🌐occupation

Douglas Wong: Biology Teacher

Meet Douglas Wong, a veteran high school biology teacher in San Jose, California. Although Mr. Wong has taught many science courses, his regular assignments have been sophomore biology and senior physiology. An outgoing and energetic person, he is also active outside the classroom. He serves as advisor to his school chapter of the National Honor Society, head class advisor, and coach for the Academic Decathlon. In return, his students have honored him many times with the school yearbook dedication. In 1996, he was selected by University of California, Irvine, students as one of the 10 California teachers honored for their contributions as role models.

"This is my 29th year teaching, and I could retire in one more year," he says. "But I don't want to. I love my job. I am healthy. My students are the greatest. I really want to help them suc-

ceed in life. Many students at our school are ethnic minorities facing economic struggles. I think I am making a big difference in their lives. I try to motivate them to go on to college and realize their potential. At this point, I also want to help new teachers grow."

And help he does. Mr. Wong regularly takes student teachers into his classroom. He has been a California Teacher Mentor and has worked with the Biology Teacher Assessment Project at Stanford University. He also publishes in professional journals and presents papers at science teacher meetings. He serves as a consulting teacher at Santa Clara University.

Mr. Wong grew up in San Francisco with Cantonese as his primary language. His first exposure to English was in kindergarten. He holds a degree in biology from San Francisco State University and a master's degree in education from the University of San Francisco.

What does Mr. Wong do in his spare time? "I like to go where there are interesting things to see," he says. "I enjoy my summers off to travel. I like collecting insects, especially unusual butterflies." Mr. Wong shares his personal insect collection with his students as they work on their insect collection assignments in biology class.

How do you prepare for a teaching career like Mr. Wong's? "Take all the science courses you can in high school. Yes, you will need chemistry and physics, too. Don't forget about math. It's a good idea to take math classes through calculus. Then earn your undergraduate degree in biology or biology education, take courses in curriculum and learning, and finish up by practice teaching in biology for your state teacher certification."

Measuring and Comparing Reaction Rates

How quickly can you react to sensory stimuli? Does everyone have the same reaction times? Will you react more quickly to a stimulus that is visual, tactile (by touch), or auditory (by hearing)? In this Inquiry, you will explore the answers to these questions. You will test the reaction rates of three major sensory pathways to the brain: visual, auditory, and tactile.

MATERIALS

- A meter stick
- Blindfold goggles from Guided Inquiry 6.1
- Graph paper
- Markers or colored pencils in three colors

SAFETY NOTE

- Take care when dropping the meter stick. (Place a book on the floor directly under the meter stick to cushion its fall.)
- Take care that you don't get splinters from grabbing the meter stick.

Procedure

1. Work with a partner. In your *Log,* draw a data table like the one in Figure 6.13.

Trial Number	Visual		Auditory		Tactile	
	You	Partner	You	Partner	You	Partner
1						
2						
3						
4						
5						
Average Distances						
Calculated Time						
Class Average Distances						
Class Average Calculated Time						

Figure 6.13

Sample data table for Guided Inquiry 6.5

2. Study Figures 6.14 and 6.15, which show how to hold and release the meter stick in conducting this Inquiry.

3. Construct a hypothesis that predicts which of the three stimuli (visual, auditory, and tactile) will allow you to grab the stick fastest and which slowest. Record your prediction in your *Log.*

Figure 6.14

The subject places his or her thumb and first finger at the 0-centimeter mark. When the experimenter gives the signal, the subject tries to grab the stick quickly.

Figure 6.15

The experimenter holds the meter stick at approximately the 30-centimeter mark so that the subject can grab the stick when the signal is given.

4. Take turns with your partner testing the visual stimulus variable as follows:

   a. One person holds the meter stick at approximately the 30-centimeter mark. The partner stands ready with arm extended, with the top of the thumb and forefinger aligned with the 0-centimeter mark of the meter stick.

   b. The person holding the meter stick releases it, and the partner grabs it as quickly as possible between the thumb and forefinger.

   c. Read the value to the nearest 0.5 centimeter from the top of the thumb and forefinger to the bottom of the meter stick. Record this value in the data table.

   d. Repeat for a total of five trials, recording each value in the data table.

5. Take turns with your partner testing the auditory stimulus variable as follows:

   a. Begin as you did for the visual stimulus variable, except this time the partner wears blindfold goggles.

   b. The person holding the meter stick says "Go" as he or she releases the stick, and the partner grabs the stick as quickly as possible.

c. Read the value along the meter stick, and record it in the data table.

d. Repeat for a total of five trials, recording each value in the data table.

6. Take turns with your partner testing the tactile stimulus variable as follows:

a. Begin as you did for the auditory stimulus variable.

b. The person holding the meter stick releases it as before with the partner trying to grab it as quickly as possible. However, instead of signaling the release by saying "Go," the person touches the partner's hand to signal the release of the meter stick.

c. Read the value along the meter stick, and record it in the data table.

d. Repeat for a total of five trials, recording each value in the data table.

7. For each type of stimulus, calculate the average for the five trials. Compute your reaction time. Where you grab the meter stick depends on at least two variables: 1) your individual reaction time and 2) the effect of gravity on the meter stick. To adjust for the effect of gravity, use the graph in Figure 6.16. Find your calculated average distance in centimeters on the horizontal axis on the graph. Look straight up from that point to where it meets the curve. Then look straight across from that point to the vertical axis and read your reaction time in milliseconds. Record this value in your data table.

Figure 6.16

Use this graph to determine your reaction times in Guided Inquiry 6.5.

Interpretations: Respond to the following in your *Log*:

1. How do your findings support your hypothesis?

2. To which sensory stimulus were you able to react most quickly?

3. To which stimulus did you react most slowly?

4. Compare your average times and your partner's average times to the class averages. Are there differences?

5. Prepare a bar graph. Group the stimulus conditions together on a single graph; but use different colors to identify the average times for you, your partner, and the class.

6. After studying your bar graph, evaluate your hypothesis again.

7. Write a brief paragraph that explains what your bar graph shows and relates how the class data compares to the data that you collected.

8. Propose a hypothesis based on your data that explains the differences in reaction time among the three stimuli.

9. For Step 6 in the procedure, the tactile stimulus, what is there in the procedure that might affect reaction time differently than in the other trials?

Applications: Respond to the following in your *Log*:

1. Think of some ways in which the body prepares itself for action (sometimes called flight-or-fight responses). Which of these responses did you feel during the Inquiry?

2. Design an experiment to test whether female reaction rates are faster than male reaction rates. How many subjects would you need? What would your testing procedure be? How many trials would you need? What is your hypothesis?

3. Optional: Design an experiment to further test the hypothesis that you described in item 8 of Interpretations.

4. Optional: The equation for the curve that converts distance on the meter stick to milliseconds of reaction time is based on acceleration due to gravity. This formula is

$$d = 0.5at^2$$

where d is the distance traveled, a is the acceleration due to gravity (9.8 meters per second squared, a constant), and t is the time in seconds.

Solve this equation for t. Enter the values for gravity (a) and distance (d) in your new equation, and calculate t for several values of d to check the conversion curve. Did it agree? Explain your results. If you want a simplified equation, use

$$t = 0.45 \sqrt{d}$$

where d is in meters and t is in seconds.

Reflexes and Nonreflex Reactions

If someone taps just below your knee, the foot of that leg will kick out slightly. The reaction happens unintentionally; any other reaction may indicate a physical problem. This simple reflex is sometimes referred to as "hard-wired": Even if you want to stop or modify the reflex, you cannot do so. It can occur without your being aware of it—when you are asleep, for example.

2 Upper leg muscle is also stretched; receptor detects the stretch

4 Signal is transmitted to motor neuron within spinal cord

3 Sensory neuron carries signal to spinal cord

Muscle

Kneecap

Tendon

5 Motor neuron carries signal back to muscle

1 Mallet tap stretches tendon

6 Skeletal muscle contracts

7 Leg moves

Figure 6.17

The human knee-jerk reflex involves primarily two neurons: one to carry the sensory signal to the spinal cord and the other to carry the signal that causes the muscle to move.

What are some other examples of reflexes? If you see a flash of light out of the corner of your eye, you will probably move both eyes automatically to look in the direction of the light. Both eyes move even though only one eye saw the flash. You may even turn your head or raise a hand. All of these actions are reflexes.

Reflexes and other reactions to environmental stimuli are coordinated throughout the nervous system. A tap just below the knee stretches the tendon, which attaches the kneecap to the leg bone. The knee-jerk reflex travels from the tendon through the spinal cord. The two main functions of the spinal cord are to initiate reflexes in response to environmental stimuli and to carry information to and from the brain. The knee-jerk reflex (Figure 6.17) primarily involves two neurons: one to carry the sensory signal to the spinal cord and another to send the signal back to the muscle, causing the knee to jerk. Doctors can test a patient's knee-jerk reflex to determine the health of that person's nervous system.

Some behaviors that we call reflexes are not really reflexes at all. Suppose that you and a friend are driving along a busy highway and a child darts out in front of you. You hit the brake (Figure 6.18), and your friend cries, "Good reflexes!" Unlike the hard-wired behavior described above, however, your reaction was really an example of quick decision making by your brain. What really happened? Your visual system saw the child. Part of your brain processed the information, along with stored past experiences. Another part of the brain decided what to do about it. ("Better hit the brake.") A third part of the brain translated "hit the brake" into a specific motion and sent the signals to the spinal cord to move the

Figure 6.18

How quickly could you react in this situation?

Behavior and the Nervous System

correct muscles. Finally, neurons in the spinal cord caused your muscles to contract. Information had to be passed from cell to cell and from place to place. The time that this process takes is called the reaction time. 🌎

The Human Muscle and Skeletal Systems

A skeleton supports an organism, protects it, and facilitates movement. The reflex actions described in the previous reading ultimately cause bones to move by the action of their attached muscles. Movement depends on the connections between the nervous system, the skeletal system, and the muscle system. This is the case for all animals, including humans—even those with external skeletons, such as insects.

The Muscle System

The human body has three kinds of muscle tissue: skeletal muscle, cardiac muscle, and smooth muscle. Cardiac muscle is the tissue that makes up the walls of the heart. In fact, this type of muscle is found only in the heart. Smooth muscle is found in the walls of arteries and many internal organs, including the bladder and the intestines. This reading is concerned mainly with skeletal muscle tissue, which is the only kind of muscle that connects to bones and is responsible for movement. Figure 6.19 illustrates the system of skeletal muscles in the human body.

Skeletal muscle consists of bundles of muscle cells called fibers. Each fiber is itself a bundle of filament strands. If you look at muscle tissue through a microscope, you will see a pattern of light and dark bands on the filament strands. (Because of these alternating bands, skeletal muscle is also called striated muscle.) A single repeat of these alternating bands is called a sarcomere (Figure 6.20). For the purpose of explaining the mechanism of muscle contraction, a sarcomere is the basic unit of skeletal muscle.

Figure 6.19

The human muscle system.

Muscle cell filament · Sarcomere

Actin (thin filaments)

Myosin (thick filaments)

A Extended muscle

B Contracted muscle

Figure 6.20

Arrangements of actin and myosin in a filament strand of a muscle fiber (cell) during (A) muscle extension and (B) muscle contraction.

Some filaments in the sarcomere are thick, and some are thin. When muscle is stimulated by a motor neuron, molecules of myosin (a type of protein) on thick filaments attach to molecules of actin (another type of protein) on thin filaments. This causes the thin filament to bend and pull in toward the center of the sarcomere. The thick and thin filaments actually slide past each other, shortening the distance of the sarcomere. When the myosin molecule releases the actin molecule, the filament straightens out. This process, which can occur several times per second, is known as a muscle contraction.

The Skeletal System

To generate movement, muscle contractions must occur against a supportive structure. That's where the skeletal system (Figure 6.21) comes in. The pattern of muscle movement involves contraction and relaxation. Muscle tissue cannot push or expand. For this reason, muscles must work in antagonistic pairs, pulling in opposite directions.

Bone is a mineralized form of connective tissue. There are many types of connective tissue in the human body, but the purpose of all connective tissue is the same: to support and hold together other kinds of body tissue. If you looked at hard bone tissue through a microscope, you would see a network of circular layers of mineral surrounding open spaces. Each open space contains blood vessels and nerves. The insides of some large bones are spongy rather than hard. Blood cells are produced in this soft bone tissue, which is called marrow. 🌀

Figure 6.21

The human skeletal system.

Guided Inquiry 6.6

Arthropod Responses to Environmental Stimuli

Often, when humans respond to conditions in their environments, they modify their surroundings to make them more suitable. Most organisms, such as arthropods (which includes brine shrimp and pill bugs, a type of isopod), cannot respond to environmental stimuli by modifying their surroundings. How, then, would brine shrimp and isopods respond to stimuli such as light, temperature, and degree of acidity or alkalinity (pH)? This Inquiry explores how.

You can choose to study the responses of brine shrimp, pill bugs, or both (if time permits). Before you begin this Inquiry, predict in your *Log* how the brine shrimp and isopods will respond to these stimuli (light, temperature, and pH levels in the water). How do you think brine shrimp and pill bugs will respond to each of the stimuli? In what kinds of environments would you expect to find each of these organisms?

Part A: Brine Shrimp Experiment

MATERIALS

- Brine shrimp culture
- A syringe
- Three 1-meter lengths of clear plastic tubing
- Six small corks or stoppers to fit into the ends of the tubing
- Transparent tape
- Nine screw clamps
- Fourteen 10 × 25 centimeter rectangles of screening
- Cold and hot water
- Two small zipper-type plastic bags
- Ice
- A thermometer (nontoxic)
- A dropper bottle of 0.1 M HCl
- A dropper bottle of 0.1 M NaOH
- Dark cloth
- Safety goggles
- A meter stick

Procedure

Work in a small group. Together, decide how you will share the work.

1. Stir the brine shrimp culture carefully to distribute the culture evenly. Use a syringe to fill each of the three 1-meter lengths of plastic tubing to within 2 centimeters of the end of the tube. As each tube is filled, plug the ends with the small corks provided.

2. Place the tubes on your table and straighten them. Use tape to fasten them to the table to hold them in a straight position. Loosely place the screw clamps around the tubes at the 25-, 50-, and 75-centimeter positions. Do not tighten them at this time.

3. For tube 1, place a stack of eight rectangles of screening over the tube, covering the section up to the first clamp. Place four rectangles of screening over the next section of the tube, covering it from 25 centimeters to 50 centimeters. Place two rectangles of screening over the next section, leaving the last section uncovered. Try not to leave gaps between sections. See Figure 6.22a on page 394.

4. For tube 2, place a cold pack (made from a zipper-type plastic bag, ice, and water) over the first section and a hot pack (made from a zipper-type plastic bag and water at about 40°C) over the last section. See Figure 6.22b on page 394. Cover the entire tube with dark cloth.

SAFETY NOTE

- Wear your goggles.
- Wash your hands after cleaning up your lab stations.

Figure 6.22

Setup for Part A procedure of Guided Inquiry 6.6.

5. For tube 3, uncork one end and gently place one drop of 0.1 M HCl into the tube. Working in the same way, place one drop of 0.1 M NaOH into the other end. See Figure 6.22c. Cover the entire tube with dark cloth.

6. Make a prediction about the direction in the tubes in which the brine shrimp will tend to move.

7. After 20 minutes, uncover each tube, and quickly tighten the clamps at their positions. Observe each section carefully, and try to count the brine shrimp in each section. Record your results in your *Log*.

8. Evaluate your prediction.

Part B: Pill Bug Experiment

MATERIALS

- Six 50-centimeter sections of approximately 3-centimeter-diameter hard plastic tubing
- Three 1-centimeter sections of clear plastic tubing to use as connector sleeves
- Paper toweling
- Fifteen pill bugs
- Cold and hot water

- Fourteen 10 × 25 centimeter rectangles of screening
- Six corks to fit into the ends of the plastic tubing
- Two small zipper-type plastic bags
- Ice
- A thermometer (nontoxic)
- Two lengths of dark cloth

Procedure

Work in a small group. Together, decide how you will share the work.

1. Prepare tube 1 as follows: Place two or three strips of moistened paper toweling inside each of two 50-centimeter plastic tubes. Connect a plastic sleeve over the end of one of these tubes. Then place five pill bugs in the sleeve area, and connect the two sections, being careful not to squash any of the pill bugs between the sections (Figure 6.23). Place corks in the ends of the tube.

2. Cover the first 25 centimeters of tube 1 with eight sections of screening. Cover the next 25 centimeters of the tube with four layers of screening. Cover the length from 50 to 75 centimeters with two layers of screening. Leave the final section uncovered.

3. Prepare the two halves of tube 2 with moistened paper toweling as you did for tube 1. Place five pill bugs in the sleeve area and connect the two sections, as you did for tube 1. Cork the ends of the tube.

4. Place a cold pack (made from a zipper-type plastic bag, ice, and water) over one end of the tube and a hot pack (with 40°C water) over the other end. Cover the entire tube with dark cloth.

5. Prepare tube 3 as follows: Insert moistened paper toweling in one tube half and dry paper toweling in the other half. Place five pill bugs in the sleeve area and connect the two sections as you did for tubes 1 and 2. Cover the entire tube with dark cloth.

6. Make a prediction about where the pill bugs will move in the tubes.

7. After 20 minutes, uncover the tubes and observe each section carefully. Count the number of pill bugs in each section. Record your results in your *Log*.

8. Evaluate your prediction.

9. Return the pill bugs as directed by your teacher, clean your lab station, and wash your hands.

Figure 6.23

Setup for Part B procedure of Guided Inquiry 6.6.

Interpretations: Respond to the following in your *Log*:

1. Obtain the data from other groups that experimented with the same organism that you studied. Summarize the data for the class totals.

2. Obtain the data from teams that experimented with the other organism, and total the class data. Record your data in your *Log*.

3. Construct histograms to represent your data graphically. Compare your results to the class average results.

4. Write a summary of your findings in your *Log*. Consider your initial predictions, and compare these to your actual results. Why were the tubes covered during the experiment? What difficulties did you have in obtaining data?

Applications: Respond to the following in your *Log*:

1. Think about the animal responses that you observed in this experiment. How do you think these responses help the organisms to survive in their natural habitats?

2. What other types of environmental changes, besides those tested in this experiment, might elicit similar responses? Explain the basis for your answer.

3. Design an experiment to test responses of larger organisms to environmental change.

4. How have humans modified their environment to make it more suitable to their needs?

5. Recall your past visits to a zoo. Most zoo organisms are vertebrates with well-developed sensory and response systems. What are the primary sources of stimuli to zoo organisms? What generalizations can you make about patterns in their responses to these stimuli?

Nerves and Sensitivity

Your behavior is the result of the electrical and chemical activity of nerve cells. Even though your nervous system is extremely complex, only a thin layer of naked skin stands between it and a harsh environment. Constantly battered by extremes of heat, cold, scrapes, dry conditions, chemical assaults, and wear and tear, your skin can nevertheless communicate almost instantly with your brain, which prompts you to respond. Your responses may even enable you to survive.

Touch Receptors

Your nervous system sends more than one type of information about the body to your brain. If you closed your eyes and held out your hand, for example, you might ask yourself whether your fingers are aimed up, down, or straight out. Sensors in your muscles and tendons send information to the spinal cord and brain to let you know the location and position of all

Frank and Ernest

your body parts. This awareness is called proprioception. Together, all of the body parts that contribute such information make up the somatosensory system. The prefix *somato-* means "body."

The body senses touch in distinct ways. Different receptors sense pain, cold, warmth, light touch, movement of hairs on the skin, vibration, and deep pressure. The first three types—pain, cold, and warmth—take one pathway to the brain; the others take a different path. This is why a doctor might test pain (perhaps with a pinprick) and vibration (with a tuning fork) in the same area of skin. Because these sensations take different routes to the brain, these tests may determine where a problem has occurred.

Receptor Locators in the Brain

During the early 1900s, some researchers tried to determine which part of the brain was responsible for touch and joint position information. From studying injuries to the brain, doctors had a pretty good idea of the general area where skin sensation information is relayed. Dr. Wilder Penfield went one step further. Some of his patients suffered from epilepsy, a nervous system disorder characterized by seizures. Dr. Penfield wanted to remove the part of the brain that causes seizures. But he did not want to remove any other parts. So he mapped the general brain location for the origin of the seizures by stimulating specific brain areas with mild electrical impulses and observing the patient's response. Then he opened the patient's skull and electrically stimulated different parts of the brain near the origin of the seizure. This did not hurt the patient because there are no pain, temperature, or touch receptors in the brain.

For more than 50 years, Penfield and his team gathered data from patients. They used this information to develop a map of the body space on the surface of the brain (Figure 6.24 on page 398). This map, called a homunculus, is more or less the same for everyone. It shows the comparative amounts of brain area that are allocated to sensory and motor input from various regions of the body. The allocation of brain area is approximately proportional to the input to the body.

Parts of the Brain

The human brain (Figure 6.25 on page 398) consists of several distinct regions, each with a specialized function. The cerebrum, at the front of the brain, controls responses to sensory stimuli (taste, sight, smell, hearing, and touch). It also controls personality and behavior.

Figure 6.24

This map of the brain shows the comparative amounts of brain area that are allocated to sensory and motor input from various body areas.

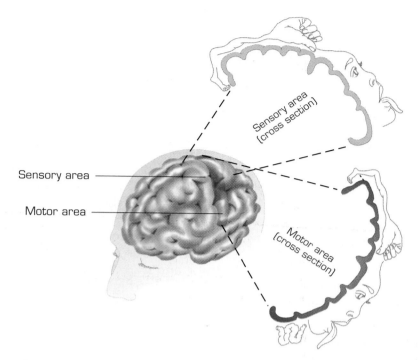

Sensory area

Motor area

Sensory area
(cross section)

Motor area
(cross section)

In most people, the left side of the cerebrum controls language and analytical abilities (reading, math, and logic), and the right side controls spatial abilities and certain artistic abilities. The cerebellum controls movement of muscles attached to bones; this part of the brain is, therefore, necessary for such activities as walking and running. The medulla controls unconscious, automatic actions, including breathing and heart rates.

Cerebrum:
Frontal lobe
• Social behavior
• Reasoning & planning
• Taste & smell
• Speech
• Voluntary movement

Parietal lobe
• Sensory input processing
• Taste

Occipital lobe
• Vision

Cerebral hemispheres

Temporal lobe
• Auditory
• Memory processing

Thalamus
• Emotion
• Relay station for all senses except olfactory recognition, memory

Cerebellum
• Muscle coordination
• Homeostasis
• Balance

Midbrain
• Auditory and visual reflexes
• Fluidity of movement

Medulla
• Involuntary muscle control
• Sleep/wakefulness

Spinal cord
• Body/brain communication
• Reflex arcs

Figure 6.25

Anatomy of the human brain.

Observing Animal Behavior

Have you ever wondered why animals in nature behave the way they do? How do their behaviors relate to their survival needs? What do animals do most of their time? In this Inquiry, you will make a brief but systematic study of the natural behavior of one or more individuals in an animal population.

You may choose any kind of animal to study. However, it would be most appropriate to choose an animal in its natural environment. Insects, spiders, squirrels, raccoons, birds, fish, rabbits, deer, lizards, slugs, snails, mice, and frogs are all appropriate. Pets and domesticated animals are less appropriate because it is sometimes difficult to determine which behaviors are natural to them. In urban areas, you should be able to observe animals in a natural environment in parks, backyards, alleys, and so on.

MATERIALS

- *Log*

Procedure

1. Select an organism (nonpoisonous) and a site for the study. If possible, focus on an individual animal rather than a group.

2. Develop a proposal for your study, and write it in your *Log.* Your proposal should mention or include the following items:
   - the animal chosen
   - the proposed site for observation
   - your time schedule
   - a hypothesis about the expected behavior of the animal chosen and a suggestion about how this relates to the animal's survival needs

   Allow approximately one hour of continuous observation or an equivalent amount of time spread out over several visits to the observation site.

3. Share your proposal with your teacher, and get suggestions for improving it. Get your teacher's approval of your final proposal before proceeding.

4. Carry out your study, and collect data according to your plan.

5. Organize and display your data so that others can easily interpret it. Consider grouping your data by specific kinds of behavior, such as feeding, mating, sleeping, and defending territory.

SAFETY NOTE

- Do not startle or crowd animals or get so near that they may strike out.

Interpretations: Respond to the following in your *Log*:

1. What were the patterns in the animal's behavior?
2. What did you learn from this study that you did not know before?
3. What did you observe that was particularly interesting?
4. How was your hypothesis about the animal's behavior supported?
5. What hypothesis would you construct if you were to do this study again?
6. What were any effects of the animal being aware of your presence?

Applications: Respond to the following in your *Log*:

1. Conduct some additional research (from reference books, CD-ROM sources, or the Internet) on the animal you observed. To what extent did your observations appear to be typical of this organism?
2. What is the interaction of this organism with the rest of the community?
3. What other organism would you choose if you were to repeat this study? Why?
4. What recommendations do you have for someone who is just beginning a study of this organism?
5. How could you have made your study completely unobtrusive (so that the animal was not in any way responding to your presence)?

Frank and Ernest

BI🌐occupation

Joe Baxter: Pest Control Specialist

Knowledge of animal behavior is required for many professions. Joe Baxter uses his knowledge of insect behavior to control them. Joe Baxter is a pest control specialist. You might call him a "bug man," but his job is much more sophisticated than that. He uses integrated pest management. "This involves using fewer chemicals than before–mechanical traps and glue boards as well as public education," says Baxter. "Most environmental groups are not trying to eliminate pest control businesses, but they're trying to encourage them to educate the public and use fewer chemicals."

Baxter works with restaurants, houses, nursing homes, warehouses, and large apartment complexes. In his seventh year of pest control, Baxter now owns his own business. He also works very hard. "The pest control business is extremely competitive," says Baxter.

Baxter's worst enemy, however, is not the competition. It is the German cockroach. There are over 100 species of cockroaches, and they can easily overpopulate an area in less than 30 days. Baxter usually needs three to four months to get them under control.

"One common misconception that the public has about this profession is that we exterminate pests. We are not in the killing business. We are in the controlling business," Baxter says.

How can you prepare for an occupation in the pest control business? You should take biology and chemistry in high school, then earn a two-year college degree in pest management. After completing your exams, you need about a month of on-the-job training. Once you pass the state tests, you will be officially certified by the U.S. Department of Agriculture, which oversees the profession. You can obtain additional certification for specific insects and other pests, such as rodents and snakes. "Specialists and technicians work on their own with no direct supervision, and people entrust us with keys to their homes. Pest control specialists also need to know how to budget their time," Baxter explains. Clearly, Joe Baxter is more than just a "bug man."

Self-Check 1

By the time you have completed the Guided Inquiries in this unit, you should have some understanding of how the environment and heredity influence behavior. This self-check is designed to help you find out how much you understand about the concepts and skills presented in this unit. Working in small groups, distribute the questions among members of your group. Work on your questions as homework. After everyone has answered the assigned questions, get together as a group to review all of your responses. Modify answers as necessary. Each member of your group is responsible for understanding the final responses to all questions.

Write complete responses to the following statements or questions. If you have difficulty, discuss your responses with a classmate or your teacher.

1. Give a definition of behavior.

2. Give at least two examples of the interaction or dependency between our senses.

3. Explain the consequences of the overuse of some over-the-counter drugs.

4. What factors are responsible for the time limits needed to accomplish repeated tasks?

5. Draw a "learning curve" and explain its three parts.

6. List some conditions under which learning may be enhanced.

7. List some conditions under which learning may be limited.

8. Provide evidence that there is variation in human response to stimuli.

9. Give examples of how humans depend on sight for many simple tasks that also involve the sense of touch.

10. Describe how the muscular and skeletal systems work together.

11. Give examples of how your sense of touch varies according to the stimulus.

12. Give some examples of strategies that you can use to memorize important information.

13. What factors are most responsible for the behavior of an animal in its natural setting?

14. What suggestions would you have for someone who is going to study animal behavior?

15. Give an explanation of how muscles contract.

16. List the major parts of the brain and their specific functions.

From the Guided Inquiry activities in this unit, you should have some knowledge of how organisms use behavioral adaptations to survive. You need to reflect and share briefly with your conference group what you've discovered. It is now time to create and present an abstract. Here are a few broad questions, at least one of which should be addressed in your abstract:

◆ Why do animals exhibit behavior?

◆ What general patterns of behavior do you see?

◆ How is behavior an adaptation for survival?

◆ How does behavior differ among different animals?

◆ What did you learn about behavior that you found really interesting?

Preparing the Abstract

Work in groups of two students. From which Guided Inquiry did you think you learned the most? What was the most important thing you learned? Prepare in your *Log* no more than a two-page abstract that includes:

◆ The title of the Guided Inquiry

◆ The particular question or hypothesis you were investigating

◆ The procedures you followed

◆ What you learned from the Inquiry about animal behavior

◆ What else do you need to know

◆ Which of the Extended Inquiries in this unit would help you find out what you need to know

Presenting your Abstract

Get together with the authors of four or five other abstracts, a total of eight or ten other students. Present your abstract with your partner to this larger group and ask for their suggestions. How does your abstract make some contribution to the class's knowledge of behavior? How can you improve it?

Revising your Abstract

You and your partner should now talk about the changes you want to make. For homework, revise your abstract.

The Extended Inquiries that follow might address some of the questions you raised. You may develop your own Inquiries to answer other questions. You might find answers to some of the questions later in the year in your study of biology, but some may not be answered in your lifetime. This is typical of scientific research.

By now, you have probably discovered specific topics in behavior that interest you. These topics may not have been covered in the unit. Here's your chance to learn more about them. You will be the investigator. It will be up to you and your partner or group members to find answers to your own questions.

Select one or more of the following Extended Inquiries, or design your own. Ask your teacher to approve your selection. Check with classmates to see what they're investigating. Your research topics may complement theirs. If so, you might want to collaborate. Keep in mind that you are personally responsible for your specific part of the research. You will present your results in a poster session during the Congress at the end of this unit.

Extended Inquiry 6.1

Human Behavior in a Shopping Mall

A shopping mall is usually full of people exhibiting many different types of behavior (Figure 6.26). That's why the mall is a perfect place to study behavior. You can also see how different environments and conditions influence behavior.

You may already have some ideas for your study of human behavior in the mall. Here are some other suggestions for your observations:

◆ Why do different areas in the mall play different types of music?

◆ What type of lighting does the mall use, and how do you think it affects behavior?

◆ Can you find patterns of behavior among shoppers? What categories of behavior can you develop on the basis of these patterns?

Figure 6.26   *Shoppers at a mall.*

- Is there a "normal" mall behavior that can be generalized to all people?
- What strategies do merchants use to encourage people to come into their shops and also stay?
- Do people spend more time in some shops than in others? What factors explain why this happens?
- Are the shops in the mall arranged in a pattern? How do you think the pattern affects behavior?
- Compare different malls. Is there a difference in the types of shops that are located at different malls? How are the architectural styles different? Do the shopping malls in your area exhibit any hierarchy? Are some malls more expensive? Are some malls designed for practical shoppers?
- What does the mall environment give people that a shopping plaza, shopping strip, or downtown area does not?
- Is the display window a critical element in attracting shoppers? Why or why not? Give some examples of how merchants display stock.
- Do clerks who are paid on commission behave differently from clerks who receive an hourly wage?
- What patterns do you find among people who rest on mall benches? Consider how close together or far away from each other they sit. Do people use the benches more (or for longer periods) at specific times of the day?

Procedure

1. Formulate (or choose) a mall research question that interests you.
2. Design a study that will investigate the question you have chosen. Write a procedure for your study. Design a form that you can use for collecting data.
3. Head for the mall. Here are some guidelines to consider.
   - If you plan to ask people to respond to a survey, it's a good idea to check with the mall authorities beforehand; you might need permission.
   - Be discreet and courteous. Dress like a professional. You might be surprised at how well people respond to polite, well-dressed students.
   - Carry a clipboard with a form on it for each person you interview.
   - Don't be obtrusive. This is a passive, observational study, not an experiment. You should not interact with, interfere with, or even be noticed by those you observe (unless you are asking

people to respond to a survey). If your subjects react to you or are aware that you are observing them, you will not be observing their natural, normal behavior.

4. Review your plan. If it seems to be working, continue gathering data. If it doesn't seem to be working, try to figure out why. Ask your teacher for help if you need it.

5. Once you have finished gathering data at the mall, begin your report. It should contain the following four sections:

   a. *Introduction:* Include a one-paragraph abstract that tells your reader what you studied, why, and how you planned to study it.

   b. *Procedure:* Explain how you set up the study and how you collected your data.

   c. *Results:* Provide an analysis of your data. You may include figures and tables that present the results of surveys, notetaking, frequency tallies, graphs, or anything else that you did while researching your topic.

   d. *Discussion and Conclusions:* Provide your own inferences and interpretations that are not classified as results. Discuss any errors that might have affected your data. Explain what you could do to correct these errors in future studies. Finally, compare your study to other research, and make conclusions.

Extended Inquiry 6.2

Awareness of Our Surroundings

As you know by now, the ways in which an organism senses its environment depend to some extent on its phenotypic characteristics. What senses does the organism use, and how does it use them effectively (Figure 6.27)? How do the organism's senses enhance its chances of survival? Are there any limits to the sensing ability of humans? You will explore these questions in this Extended Inquiry.

The activities in this Inquiry are arranged in stations around the room, and you can perform them in any order. Work with a partner. If one station is occupied, move on to another one.

Figure 6.27

How do snakes sense with their tongues?

Station A: Temperature Awareness

MATERIALS

- Three buckets of water
- A thermometer (nontoxic)
- Hot water and ice chips

Procedure

1. Before you begin this activity, measure the temperature of the water in each bucket. The water in one bucket should be about 37°C to 40°C. And there should be a difference of at least 10°C from one bucket to the next. If not, adjust the temperature by adding hot water or ice chips. Record the temperatures in your *Log*.

2. Predict what you will sense when you put one hand in the bucket of water that has the lowest temperature at the same time that you put your other hand in the bucket of water that has the highest temperature.

3. Predict what you will sense when you remove both hands and place them simultaneously into the middle bucket.

4. Try these activities, and explain the results.

Station B: Taste

Are taste receptors located in specific areas of the tongue, or do all areas of the tongue have a variety of taste receptors? At this station, you will find four different liquids: sweet, sour, salty, and bitter. Your partner will apply each solution to specific areas of your tongue and make a record of where you experience specific taste.

SAFETY NOTE

- Do not reuse any cotton swabs. If you need to repeat any procedure, dispose of the original swab and use a new one. If you forget and double-dip, inform your teacher immediately.

MATERIALS

- Cotton swabs
- Dilute solutions of sodium chloride ("salt"), sucrose ("sweet"), acetic acid ("sour"), and quinine sulfate ("bitter")
- Latex gloves

Procedure

1. For this activity you will work with a partner as shown in Figure 6.28. Make a diagram in your *Log* like the one in Figure 6.29.

2. Dry off your tongue as much as possible. (Air-drying should be sufficient.)

3. Let your partner immerse a cotton swab in one of the solutions and touch your dry tongue with it in the areas indicated in Figure 6.29. (Your partner should use a fresh cotton swab for each solution and touch one area at a time.)

4. Identify where on your tongue you detected the taste of the solution. Record the location of these taste sensations on the diagram in your *Log.* Keep your mouth open and your tongue extended while you prepare for the next solution.

5. Repeat this process for each of the four solutions.

6. Reverse roles and repeat so that your partner can identify the location of taste receptors on his or her tongue.

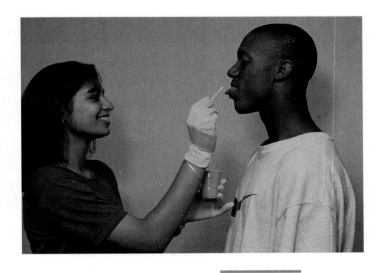

Figure 6.28

Where can sensory areas for salt, sweet, sour, and bitter be detected on the tongue?

Station C: Taste and Smell

Is there a relationship between taste and smell? Do you detect foods such as chocolate, cola, apples, and oranges by taste or smell? In this activity, you will do a blind test to identify foods by taste, both with and without being able to smell the foods as you taste them. You will find three different food samples cut into pieces of about the same size in opaque containers. Do not look at the food before you begin this activity because its appearance may influence your assessment of taste.

Figure 6.29

Taste receptor areas on a typical human tongue. Draw four tongues in your Log *to record on each the locations for each type of taste receptor.*

Areas to test

Figure 6.30

Can you identify a food by its smell?

MATERIALS

- Three containers with food samples
- Cotton swabs with cotton ends clipped off
- A trash can
- Paper cups
- Water

- Students with known food allergies should check with the teacher before doing this activity.

Procedure

1. Work with a partner as shown in Figure 6.30. Make a prediction about how the senses of taste and smell are related. Write your prediction in your *Log*.

2. Create in your *Log* a data table to record the results of this activity.

3. Close your eyes. Your partner will use a toothpick to give you one piece of food at a time. Taste the food, but don't eat it. Once you have identified the food sample, spit it into a trash container and rinse your mouth with water. Your partner will record information about your identification of the food in the data table. Continue until you have tried each sample.

4. Close your eyes and hold your nose. Your partner will give you samples of the same foods in a different sequence. Identify each food sample, and record the data. Make a note of how easy or difficult it was to identify the food this time.

5. Reverse roles with your partner and repeat.

6. Evaluate your earlier prediction. Write a statement in your *Log*.

Station D: Visual Acuity

Using its lens, a normal, healthy eye can focus an image on the inside back of the eye (on the retina). Some lenses can't do their job though. The lenses themselves may be the problem, or the shape of the eye may prevent the lens from focusing properly. As a result, the person may be either nearsighted or farsighted.

In this activity, you will use a Snellen Eye Chart to determine how well the lenses in your eyes can focus. This chart contains a series of rows of letters. Each row is smaller than the row above it. To the side of each row is a number expressed as a fraction, such as 20/200. The upper number indicates how many feet you stand from the chart to read the letters. The lower number indicates how many feet from the chart a person with normal vision can stand and still read the letters. If you can read only the 20/200 line at 20 feet, then 20/200 is your visual acuity. That means that you have to stand only 20 feet away to read letters that a person with normal vision could read at 200 feet. A reading of 20/20 means that you see at 20 feet what a person with normal vision sees at 20 feet.

MATERIALS

- A Snellen Eye Chart posted on the wall
- A yardstick or measuring tape
- Masking tape

Procedure

1. Work with a partner. Measure a distance of 20 feet from the eye chart. Mark the distance on the floor with a small piece of masking tape.

2. Stand at the tape marker and face the chart.

3. Cover one eye with your hand, as shown in Figure 6.31. (Do not close the eye that you cover because that can change your open eye's ability to see.) Your partner should stand by the chart and check for errors. Read the rows of letters from top to bottom. If your partner tells you that you have made an error, repeat the entire line. Your visual acuity is the number of the lowest line that you can read with no errors.

In many states, people cannot get a driver's license unless their vision can be corrected to 20/40. Would you have to correct your vision with glasses or contact lenses to get your license? A person whose vision cannot be corrected to 20/200 or better is considered legally blind. Do you know anyone who has 20/200 vision without correction?

Figure 6.31

How good is your eyesight?

411

4. Repeat this procedure for the other eye.

5. Repeat the procedure with both eyes uncovered.

6. Record your vision fraction for your left eye, right eye, and both eyes.

7. Reverse roles with your partner and repeat.

Tying Your Shoelaces

MATERIALS

- Shoes with laces
- Thick gloves

Much of human behavior is a coordinated response to the stimulation of two or more senses at the same time. What senses do you use to tie your shoelaces? Take a moment to untie and then retie one of your shoes.

◆ Try it with your eyes closed.

◆ Try it with thick gloves on.

◆ Try it with your eyes closed and thick gloves on (as in Figure 6.32).

Interpretations: Respond to the following in your *Log*:

1. Which trial was most difficult? Why?

2. Which senses do you rely on the most when you tie your shoes?

3. Which senses did you rely on most when you first learned to tie your shoes?

4. Have the senses on which you relied changed? If so, why did this happen?

Figure 6.32

Tying your shoes can be difficult when your movements are restricted by heavy clothing.

Independent Research

Choose a topic to research. Several topics are listed below; you may choose one of these or one of your own. Be sure you have your teacher's approval before you begin your research. In conducting your research, try electronic resources as well as your school and public libraries. Use a web browser to locate some likely sources.

Guidelines for Research Reports

Once you have researched your topic and gathered data, it is time to begin writing your report. Your report should include the following five sections:

1. A one-paragraph abstract that tells your reader what you are studying and how you will study it.

2. An explanation of your procedures that tells how you collected data. Include copies of any data collection instruments such as surveys or checklists of behavior.

3. A summary of your data from completed surveys, notes, frequency tallies, graphs, or anything else that you did while researching your topic.

4. Conclusions, inferences, and interpretations of your research, including a discussion of possible errors that might have affected your data and an explanation of what you might do to correct these errors in future studies.

5. A list of the articles, books, and other resources that you used to research your topic and support your conclusion.

If you are working in a group, divide the project tasks so that everyone contributes equally to the end product. Remember that you are all responsible for this project and you might be asked to make a progress report at any time. You will have some time in class to work on your project, but you should also plan to meet with your group outside of class.

Suggested Research Topics

1. Focus on case studies of behavior or behavior modification programs that involve addiction, antidepressants, behavior-altering drugs, stress and stress management, or group altruism.

2. Investigate how behavioral control reflects the demands and restrictions of society.

3. Monitor human effects on plant behavior (for example, the effects of street lights, pollution, housing developments, greenhouses and nurseries).

4. Develop a profile of people's behaviors in exercise clubs, in fast-food restaurants, or at sporting events.

5. Observe the relationship between flowers and insects.

6. Conduct a case study of an individual who is physically and/or mentally challenged (for example, someone who is hearing-impaired or has had a stroke).

7. Design an advertisement to sell your brand of irradiated food or milk from cows that have been fed a drug to make them produce more milk.

8. Conduct an experiment to determine the effects of nicotine on fish or *Daphnia,* a specific kind of small freshwater crustacean. Ask your teacher to help you set up this experiment.

9. Read about how dogs see color, whether they see the world as humans do or in black and white. You might begin with the article "Canine Color Vision" by D. K. Vaughan in *AKC Gazette,* May 1991, pp. 52–58.

10. Read at least one chapter from one of the following books, and prepare a report on the disorders of the brain cells or behavioral disorders that the author describes.

    Toscanini's Fumble (Harol L. Klawans)

    The Brain Has a Mind of Its Own (Richard M. Restak)

    The Man Who Mistook His Wife for a Hat (Oliver W. Sacks)

Possible Sources of Information

- ◆ A local public, university, or school library
- ◆ A local newspaper
- ◆ Computer databases such as ERIC, BIOSIS, or AGRICOLA
- ◆ The Internet, by using a web browser
- ◆ Experts

Self-Check 2

ow that you have completed some Extended Inquiries, you should have some additional understanding about the relationship between environment, genetics, and behavior. This self-check is designed to help you find out how well you understand the fundamental concepts of this unit.

Form groups of four students. Each group member should select and answer two or three of the following questions. (Make sure that no two people choose the same questions to answer.) As resources, use the work that you did on the Guided Inquiries and Extended Inquiries, your notes in your *Log*, and books in the classroom or library. You might want to work in advance on some answers as homework.

When all members of your group have reasonable answers to their selected questions, assemble as a group to have each member share her or his answers with the entire group. Discuss and evaluate the completeness of each answer, and modify it as necessary. Everyone in the group should eventually have a complete set of answers to all questions. Then everyone in the group will be ready for the Forum and the Unit Exam.

1. As a system becomes more complex, it becomes more difficult to understand and predict behavior. Discuss this statement and give an example.

2. Discuss evidence for this statement: "Animals are creatures of habit."

3. Describe how important our senses are in functioning during a day.

4. Give an example of a behavior that has potential risks for the physical and mental well-being of an individual. Describe how that behavior can be modified and/or controlled.

5. To what extent is eyesight helpful in performing manipulative tasks?

6. What is behavior, and why do organisms exhibit behavior?

7. Describe how behavior can be influenced by advertising. How can people avoid being victims of this control?

8. Give an example of a human behavior that is not learned. How does this compare with behaviors that are learned?

9. Describe the interrelationships of learning, memory, and behavior. How does this explanation apply to other animals besides humans?

10. Describe a plan to study the behavior of an organism.

11. How can certain behaviors be selected for over several generations?

12. How can some behaviors be completely out of the control of an individual?

THE USE OF MOOD-ALTERING DRUGS

Behavior-altering medications have been used for decades. Many such drugs have been used to treat severe behavior disorders such as schizophrenia. The use of these medications is considered legitimate if it follows a physician's diagnosis, the drug is obtained through a pharmacy by prescription, and the physician monitors the drug's use. In recent years, behavior-altering medications have been prescribed to treat milder behavior disorders such as hypertension, hyperactivity, inattention, sleeplessness, and restlessness.

Some medications are prescribed to alter mood. For example, people can take prescription medications to help them relax if they are worried or nervous. They may be able to take medications to help them become more attentive when they need to focus better. It is important to note that these examples describe the use of medication not to treat disorders but to alter moods.

Mood-altering medications are not illegal. For the most part, they are not expensive, and they are not narcotics. They are not likely to establish a black market and, therefore, lead to drug-related crime. Taken in the recommended doses, they are not particularly harmful to the user or to others who come in contact with the user. Currently, there is little evidence that they are habit forming, although this seems to be an open question. So what's the problem?

Some people think that mild mood-altering medications should be available over the counter, just like remedies for arthritis, headaches, colds, and coughs. After all, isn't everyone who can buy these medications capable of using them according to the directions on their containers and not abusing them? Why can't mood-altering medications be classified the same as aspirin and cough syrup?

You probably concluded from your studies in this unit that there is a fine line between over-the-counter medications and drugs that can lead to problems. Some people will argue that tobacco and alcoholic beverages are drugs, and their sales are more controlled than over-the-counter medications. It is clear from studies of human behavior that tobacco and alcohol products can be addicting and abused. Should these factors affect the availability of mood-altering drugs?

Your class will participate in a Congress to discuss whether mood-altering drugs should be available as over-the-counter drugs. At some point during this Congress, the class will form a recommendation on this issue. The Congress will consist of three parts. All parts will be completed in the same class period.

Procedure

Work in a small group. Some of the groups will develop arguments in favor of a proposal to allow mood-altering drugs to be sold over the counter. The other groups will develop arguments against the proposal. Spend about 20 minutes developing your position statement. Draw on your work in the Guided Inquiries and Extended Inquiries in this unit as well as other sources. Make sure that you document your sources. Each group member should focus on a different argument statement; however, all group members should help each other strengthen their statements. Prepare to deliver one brief, coherent group statement about the proposal. The statement might begin "Our reasons for supporting (or opposing) this proposal are. . . ."

When the class convenes for the Congress, a representative from each group will clearly state the group's position, taking no more than two minutes to complete the statement. As others speak, try to keep an open mind on the issue, and take notes. This will help you to make an informed decision later. If necessary, the representative may call on other group members for additional information.

As the final stage of the Congress, vote on the proposal. Each student may cast a vote. You may vote for or against the proposal, regardless of your group's position. Let the most convincing, most scientifically based statements influence your final decision.

Summary

For homework, write a brief summary in your *Log* of what transpired at the Congress. Try to capture the main arguments for and against the proposal. Summarize why you cast the vote that you did.

In this Forum, your class will role play the experiences of a 16-year-old, John Smith, as he goes through the juvenile justice system. Neither this person nor the setting described is real, but the experiences are drawn from real files of juvenile justice crimes. This role play provides an opportunity to further examine the question of a person's responsibility for actions committed while under the influence of chemical toxins.

The Case of John Smith

John Smith is a high school student. Until the past year, he had reasonably good grades and a decent attitude toward school. He didn't have many friends, but the friends he had were important to him.

Last year, things changed. The work in tenth grade seemed harder than in years past. His biology teacher was particularly demanding. John had to work hard to keep up in class, but he was handling it. His good friend, Jason, was an important part of his success. He and Jason met almost every day after school to do homework and to hang around. But then, in the middle of the semester, Jason moved. John didn't know what to do with himself after school. His grades began to drop.

One Friday, some boys who he knew only slightly invited him to a party. John jumped at the chance to have some fun. That evening they picked him up at his house and drove to the party.

The party was wilder than he had expected. People were drinking alcohol, and some were using illegal drugs. John didn't want to be rejected by this new group of potential friends, so he had a few drinks. But he was careful not to drink too much. By the time the party started to wind down, many of the kids were either drunk or high on drugs. John felt okay, so he offered to drive his new friends home.

The ride home was going well until a dog raced out in front of the car. When John swerved to avoid the dog, he lost control of the car

Behavior and the Nervous System

and it rolled down an embankment. One of boys in the back seat was thrown from the car. He died while the others were frantically waving down passing vehicles to call for help. John was distraught at the thought that he had caused someone else's death.

But the nightmare worsened. Police and emergency medical technicians arriving at the accident scene first tended to the boys' medical needs, then questioned them about what happened. The police asked John to take a Breathalyzer test to determine if he was intoxicated. John was astounded when that test and a blood test taken later at the police station showed that his blood alcohol level was just over the legal limit. He could hardly look at his parents when they arrived at the police station.

John was charged with *vehicular manslaughter* and *driving under the influence of alcohol.* His parents hired a lawyer to defend him. The lawyer said that, since John had never been in trouble before and was only 16, the manslaughter charges would probably be dropped. But the district attorney wanted to try John as an adult since the accident resulted in a death.

At the first hearing, the judge looked at the evidence in the case and decided that John would be tried as a juvenile. After consultation with his attorney, John admitted his guilt in the accident. His lawyer asked the court to put John on probation.

Procedure

You will play the roles of various people involved in John's case. John is to appear in juvenile court to receive a sentence for his actions.

1. Determine who will play the following roles:
   - John Smith
   - John's parents, who will work with and pay for his lawyer and try to support John emotionally
   - John's lawyer, who will handle the legal aspects of the case
   - The district court judge, who will decide whether John receives probation or a corrections facility sentence and who will determine the length of the sentence
   - The Department of Juvenile Justice counselor, who will make recommendations to the judge
   - The social worker in the corrections facility, who will work with John if he is sent to the facility
   - Members of the parole board, who will determine the restrictions to be placed on John if he is granted parole
   - John's schoolmates, community members, and teachers, who will react to John's problems and will influence his life in the future

2. Use the following background information to help individuals assigned to each role to make decisions:

- The district court judge has recently presided over three hearings that involved teenagers who were driving while intoxicated. He is tired of seeing kids kill themselves and others on the roads.
- The maximum sentence under the juvenile justice system is in John's case 12 to 36 months in the juvenile corrections institution.
- If sent to the institution, John could be eligible for parole in 12 months.
- John's chance at parole would depend entirely on his behavior, but if he were institutionalized, he would encounter many threats to his self-control. Once in the institution, his rights would be sharply curtailed. He would have to obey staff members promptly and politely. He could not get into a fight—even if someone else started it.
- If John is put on probation, the restrictions decided upon would probably be in effect until John was 21 years old. His probation conditions could include:
  - release into the community without restrictions,
  - release under supervision of a Department of Social Services caseworker,
  - a curfew,
  - a requirement that he sign an agreement that he won't be present in places where alcohol is being served or imbibed,
  - a requirement that he not associate with anyone who has ever broken the law.
- John will lose his driver's license, until he is 21 years old. Even then, he will have a very difficult time getting insurance—and it will be very expensive.

3. Enact the day in court when John is sentenced. You may include a separate meeting of the parole board to discuss the conditions of probation should the judge rule for probation rather than institutionalization. In making your decisions about what should happen to John, consider the following:
   - Was he within his conscious control?
   - Was he responsible even though he didn't feel like he was drunk?
   - Who else might have been at fault?

4. After the role play, discuss the impact that this single incident will have on John's life. You may invite a juvenile justice worker from the local community to help your discussions.

5. In your *Log*, reflect upon how a chemical change in your body can influence behavior and impact your life.

Summary of Major Concepts

1. Behavior is the interaction of genetics and the environment resulting in a physiological response.

2. Many of the ways in which we use our senses depend on other senses.

3. Some over-the-counter drugs can be overused or even abused.

4. There is wide variation in human responses to environmental stimuli.

5. Although humans can practice routine tasks to improve their performance, there are physiological and neurological limits of learning.

6. Behaviors that allow organisms to survive in a competitive environment are likely to be passed down from generation to generation.

7. The skeletal system provides a rigid framework on which muscles can contract.

8. When muscles contract, an organism is able to move parts of its body.

9. Muscles are able to contract when layers of muscle protein are electrically stimulated, causing some filaments to shorten and pull against other filaments.

10. People can apply strategies to help them memorize and learn information.

11. As a system becomes more complex, understanding and predicting behavior become more diffcult.

12. Behavior occurs at distinctly different levels of complexity.

13. Behavior can be modified and/or controlled.

14. Behavior can be studied systematically to give insights into why organisms behave the way they do.

15. The science of behavior is currently under much investigation. There is much we do not know about behavior.

Suggestions For Further Exploration

Barrett, S. L. 1992. *It's All in Your Head: A Guide to Understanding Your Brain and Boosting Your Brain Power.* Free Spirit, Minneapolis.

This book, written for teenagers, discusses the brain and how a person learns and remembers. It is accompanied by a teacher's guide.

Center for Substance Abuse Prevention. 1994. *Tips for Teens About Hallucinogens.* Rockville, MD.

Produced by the federal government, this six-page brochure discusses the behavioral and physiological effects of hallucinogenic drugs on teenagers.

Dobkin, B.H. 1992. The absentminded professor. *Discover*, 13(10), 111–115.

For years, a professor showed temporary erratic, dangerous, or antisocial behavior. He would have no memory of his actions afterwards. This article describes his symptoms and the work on a treatment for him.

Dobkin, B.H. 1993. Netting the butterfly. *Discover*, 14(9), 40–44.

A skull-fracture patient who had lost most of his memory and cognitive powers was getting worse months later. Removing excess fluid that had built up restored some of his mental abilities.

Kerstitch, A. "Primates" of the sea. *Discover*, 13(2), 34–37.

Octopuses are considered the most intelligent invertebrates. Not only is an octopus a fast learner, but it remembers what it learns.

Kinoshita, J. 1992. Dreams of a rat. *Discover*, 13(7), 34–42.

Scientists at Rockefeller University are using rats to study dreams. Their research finds that humans may use dreams to combine new experiences with their existing memory.

Manning, A., and Dawkins, M.S. 1992. *An Introduction to Animal Behavior*, 4th ed. Cambridge University Press, New York.

This college-level introductory book on animal behavior includes information on classic animal behavior research. Topics that are covered include the development of behavior, motivation and decision-making, learning and memory, and social organization.

U.S. Food and Drug Administration and the Nonprescription Drug Manufacturers Association. 1997. *Nonprescription medicines: What's Right For You?*

This free pamphlet of helpful tips on using nonprescription medicines safely can be obtained by writing to: Dept 59, Consumer Information Center, Pueblo, Colorado, 81009.

Seachrist, L. 1995. Mimicking the brain: using computers to investigate neurological disorders. *Science News*, 148(4), 62–63.

This article discusses computer models that are being used to study phantom limb pain, Alzheimer's disease, and migraine headaches.

Shreeve, J. 1995. The brain that misplaced its body. *Discover*, 16(5), 82–91.

This article discusses a neuroscientist's view of why a woman could not perceive her paralysis on one entire side until she had cold water poured in her ear.

Simon, G I. and H.M. Silverman. 1990. *The Pill Book*. 4th edition. Bantam Books, NY.

An exhaustive identification and use guide for prescription and nonprescription drugs that are normally taken in pill form. Contains colored photos of many common pills.

Sutherland, M. 1993. *Advertising and the Mind of the Consumer: What Works, What Doesn't, and Why.* Allen & Unwin, St. Leonards, NSW, Australia.

This 246-page book discusses marketing techniques used by advertisers to effect consumer behavior. It includes sections on 15-second commercials, influencing people, and seasonal ads.

How did we get all of the diversity of life on earth?

SEVEN

BIODIVERSITY

Why is biodiversity important?

nitial Inquiry

What can we do to preserve biodiversity on the earth?

THREATS TO BIODIVERSITY

Setting

Life on earth is composed of millions of types of organisms, each having a unique role in the functioning of the earth's ecosystems. The organisms constituting this biological diversity, or biodiversity, compete and interact among themselves to use the energy they need. As humans, we depend upon the diverse organisms of the earth to supply the oxygen in the air that we breathe, to purify the water that we drink, and to provide the food that we eat.

Biodiversity is extremely important for many other reasons. Diversity and variation together provide organisms with the genetic tools to make changes in their future generations. This allows survival and adaptation to changes in the earth's environmental conditions. Genetic diversity gives humans access to the DNA that may lead to new breakthroughs in medicine, agriculture, and genetic engineering. This knowledge, if used wisely, should improve life on earth for humans.

But, biodiversity on earth is being threatened. This concerns people from all walks of life. Let's briefly investigate this problem.

The Video

View the Unit 7 video. Consider the issues raised in the video in the context of what you have learned about biology and the functioning of organisms in previous units. As you watch the video, create a list of questions to discuss with your classmates. Include the following in your list of questions:

◆ How might the structural complexity of a rain forest enhance biodiversity?

◆ How would the biodiversity of a clear cut area compare to that of a forested area? Why?

◆ How can we compensate for the loss of biodiversity in nature? Is the "frozen zoo and garden" an adequate substitute?

◆ How did the video increase your appreciation of the need to maintain and respect diversity among humans?

Brainstorming

As a class, list the additional questions that you created on a blackboard or overhead. Assemble into small groups. Each group will discuss one of the above questions and at least one of the additional questions created by others in the class. Your teacher may help in assigning questions. Create group answers to the assigned questions. Write your best answers in your *Log*. Your teacher may ask you to share some of your responses with the entire class.

As you share your group's answers with the class, try to come to a class consensus on answers to the following more general questions about biodiversity. Record your answers to these questions in your *Log* and refer back to them as you work through this unit.

◆ What is biodiversity?

◆ Why is biodiversity so important to all organisms?

◆ How is biodiversity being threatened, and who is responsible for this?

◆ Who is concerned about loss of biodiversity?

◆ How can biodiversity become lost forever?

◆ What is being proposed to preserve biodiversity?

◆ What should be done to preserve biodiversity? What should you do?

Visualizing Five Billion Years

In this Inquiry, you will prepare a timeline that illustrates the major events on the earth over the last 4.6 billion years. This timeline will focus on the relationship between the short duration of life on the earth and the enormous stretches of time before life forms developed.

You will revisit the earth's timeline in several Inquiries as you work though this unit. In other Guided Inquiries, you will add to and expand the timeline to include events in more recent history. But first, let's practice by preparing a timeline of the events in your own life.

MATERIALS

- Adding machine tape
- Brightly colored yarn
- Nontoxic, water color type markers or colored pencils
- The biodiversity outline

- Paper or 3 × 5 inch cards for illustrations and annotations
- Resource materials: old biology textbooks, newspapers, magazines, and other pictures and articles

Part A: Personal Timelines
Procedure

1. List some major events of your life.
2. Draw a horizontal line across two facing pages in your *Log*. Place the major events of your life on that line in chronological order. Figure 7.1 gives you a sample personal timeline.
3. A few volunteers could share their timelines with the class.

Part B: Earth's Timeline
Procedure

1. As a class, measure and cut a strip of adding machine tape 2 meters long. Mark it in intervals of one billion years (40 centimeters = 1 billion years). Post this tape on the wall of your classroom. Label the display as in Figure 7.2.
2. Form groups of four students.
3. Your teacher will assign events to each group.
4. Distribute the event assignments among the students in your group. Research your assigned event; then annotate and illustrate the events on a card. Use classroom resource books for help with

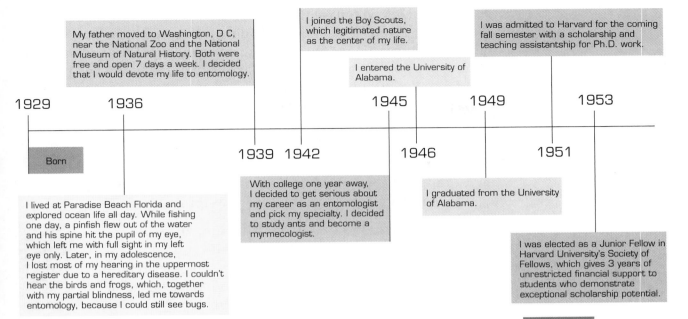

1929

1936

My father moved to Washington, D.C., near the National Zoo and the National Museum of Natural History. Both were free and open 7 days a week. I decided that I would devote my life to entomology.

I joined the Boy Scouts, which legitimated nature as the center of my life.

I entered the University of Alabama.

I was admitted to Harvard for the coming fall semester with a scholarship and teaching assistantship for Ph.D. work.

1945   1949   1953

Born

1939 1942   1946   1951

I lived at Paradise Beach Florida and explored ocean life all day. While fishing one day, a pinfish flew out of the water and his spine hit the pupil of my eye, which left me with full sight in my left eye only. Later, in my adolescence, I lost most of my hearing in the uppermost register due to a hereditary disease. I couldn't hear the birds and frogs, which, together with my partial blindness, led me towards entomology, because I could still see bugs.

With college one year away, I decided to get serious about my career as an entomologist and pick my specialty. I decided to study ants and become a myrmecologist.

I graduated from the University of Alabama.

I was elected as a Junior Fellow in Harvard University's Society of Fellows, which gives 3 years of unrestricted financial support to students who demonstrate exceptional scholarship potential.

Figure 7.1

A personal timeline for Dr. E.O. Wilson. The information was obtained from his autobiography, Naturalist.

unfamiliar words and concepts. Be creative. Magazine photos, articles, poems, and drawings are all useful. Your goal is to make others in your class really understand the event.

5. Once you have illustrated and annotated all the events, return the event cards to your teacher. Your teacher will redistribute the cards to other student groups.

6. Read and show your new event cards to the class. Estimate approximately where each card belongs on the timeline. After the class predicts a date, your teacher or the group that made the card will announce the correct date.

7. Place each card in its correct place on the timeline; connect it to the line with yarn if you run out of room. The group that illustrated each event should lead a class discussion of the event. The timeline now presents an outline of five billion years.

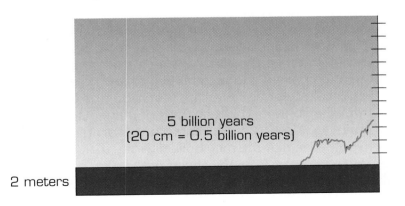

5 billion years
(20 cm = 0.5 billion years)

2 meters

Figure 7.2

The five-billion-year timeline for Guided Inquiry 7.1.

8. Your teacher will place the biodiversity graph cutout on the timeline (see Figure 7.2). This added dimension shows the origin of life on the earth and its changing diversity over time. Adding the cutout also adds a vertical, or *Y,* axis, which represents the number of families of organisms that are alive at each point in time.

Interpretations: Respond to the following in your *Log:*

1. What general trends over time do you see?
2. What do the dips in the biodiversity graph represent?
3. Compare the length of time life has existed on the earth to the length of time since the earth was formed.

Applications: Respond to the following in your *Log:*

Select one event on this timeline for further study throughout this unit. Consult encyclopedias, biology reference books, newspapers, the Internet, and magazines for additional information. Make notes in your *Log.* Add condensed information on your selected event to the class timeline.

What Is Biodiversity?

Biodiversity means the total variety of life on the earth and the interrelationships of these life forms. It centers on living organisms, which we call the biota. It includes all levels of biological organization, from genes and chromosomes to complete ecosystems. As a citizen of the earth, you are a part of the world's biodiversity. Each of us relates to nearly every other form of life on the earth either directly or indirectly. We have been shaped by interactions with other life: Our skin and immune systems protect against parasites; our digestive systems let us use food; our senses find prey or warn of danger. What other interactions can you think of? As a result of human interaction with the biotic environment, we are rapidly changing our world—and ourselves.

What Is the Origin of Our Present Biodiversity?

Today we recognize that all life comes from preexisting life. But there was a beginning. Figure 7.3 shows how the early earth might have looked before the beginnings of life. Scientists believe life on the earth is a product of the earth itself. When the earth was new, the chemical elements that were present combined and recombined to form complex molecules called macromolecules. About 3.8 billion years ago, the earliest forms of life formed from the continued interactions of these macromolecules. These early prokaryotic cells are the genetic ancestors of life on the earth.

Scientists hypothesize that the metabolic diversity that we see in modern prokaryotes resulted in part from the effects of the early earth's environment on the metabolic needs of the organisms. For example, on the early

Figure 7.3

Environmental conditions on the prebiotic earth.

earth, volcanoes erupted frequently, and ultraviolet light at the earth's surface was extremely intense. The atmosphere at that time consisted mostly of water vapor (H_2O), carbon monoxide (CO), carbon dioxide (CO_2), nitrogen (N_2), methane (CH_4), and ammonia (NH_3). These conditions would not support life on earth as we know it today.

Starting from 3.5 billion years ago, photosynthesis produced oxygen that changed the earth's atmosphere. Over the next 2 billion years, simple organisms evolved to form more complex organisms. According to one hypothesis, single, free-living cells became internal (*endo*) components of other, larger cells. Ultimately, the cells evolved to form a cooperative relationship called endosymbiosis (see Figure 7.4). This process produced the first eukaryotic

Figure 7.4

Endosymbiosis is one hypothesized model for the formation of eukaryotic cells.

A — Ancestral prokaryotic host cell — Genetic material

B — Cell membrane — Cell membrane folds in to form nuclear membrane, endoplasmic reticulum, and Golgi apparatus

C — Heterotrophic bacterium — Photosynthetic bacterium — Primitive eukaryotic cell — Bacteria enter cell and become symbionts

D — Chloroplast — Mitochondrion — Nucleus — Golgi apparatus — Present day eukaryotic cell — Endoplasmic reticulum organisms, single cells that contained internal, membrane-bound organelles. The organisms that we know today developed from these complex origins.

Early organisms developed characteristics that enhanced biodiversity. The ability to reproduce sexually (see page 292 in Unit 5) allowed exchange of genetic information and the creation of new genotypes. As blue-green algae made oxygen available in the earth's atmosphere, the first animals appeared, their metabolism fueled by plant matter and oxygen. The number of species and major groups of organisms increased rapidly. About 1.4 billion years ago, multicellular, nucleated organisms that used oxygen and reproduced sexually evolved. Figure 7.5 lists major biological events in the history of the earth.

Figure 7.5

Biological events in the history of the earth.

Era	Period	Epoch	Representative Biological Events	Millions of Years Ago
Cenozoic	Quaternary	Recent	Human civilizations Glaciers	0.01
		Pleistocene	Increase in herbaceous plants	2.5
	Tertiary	Pliocene	First humans	
		Miocene	Diversification of mammals and angiosperms	
		Oligocene	First apes	
		Eocene	Increase in mammal diversity and angiosperm dominance	
		Paleocene	Age of mammals	65
Mesozoic	Cretaceous		First angiosperms Gymnosperms decline Dinosaur extinction Radiation of insects	136
	Jurassic		Gymnosperms dominant Last of the seed ferns Dinosaurs abundant First birds	190
	Triassic		Gymnosperms dominate land flora First mammals First dinosaurs	225
Paleozoic	Permian		Decline of lycopsids, sphenopsids and seed ferns	280
	Carboniferous		Coal forests dominated by lycopsids and sphenopsids, later by ferns and gymnosperms Amphibians dominant First reptiles Radiation of insects	345
	Devonian		Expansion of plants First liverworts Age of fishes First amphibians	395
	Silurian		Invasion of land by plants Invasion of land by arthropods	430
	Ordovician		Abundant marine algae First vertebrates	500
	Cambrian		Primitive marine algae (green and blue-green algae) Marine invertebrates abundant	570
Precambrian			First life forms on earth	

Figure 7.6

Marine invertebrates from the Cambrian period.

Figure 7.7

Land plants from the Devonian period.

Early Plants and Animals

Life in the oceans (Figure 7.6) was very diverse by the Middle Cambrian period (530 million years ago). Animals were eating animals, and protective skeletal features were common in living things. Nearly all modern groups of invertebrate animals existed by this time, but vertebrates were just beginning to evolve. Fish were the first vertebrates. Early land plants (Figure 7.7) were common by the Late Silurian period (420 million years ago), and diverse land plants were common by the Middle Devonian period (380 million years ago), including

◆ the first trees,

◆ ferns,

◆ lycopods, including the club mosses, and

◆ horsetails (*Equisetum*).

Figure 7.8

Mesozoic era birds and mammals.

Life on land became more diverse as new life forms evolved. Animals moved onto land in the form of arthropods and amphibians. Seed plants and reptiles appeared and diversified in the Late Paleozoic era and dominated the earth in the Mesozoic era. During the Mesozoic era, birds, mammals, and flowering plants developed (Figure 7.8). Flowering plants and insects evolved together, each dependent on the other, during the Cretaceous period. Most of the diversification of birds, mammals, and flowering plants occurred in the Cenozoic era. Figure 7.9 on page 434 shows the great increase in the number of types of organisms on the earth. The web of interrelationships between the diverse types of life in the world today has been woven through deep time. 🌎

Figure 7.9

World biodiversity: the number of families of living organisms through geological time. The lightning bolts indicate periods of mass extinctions.

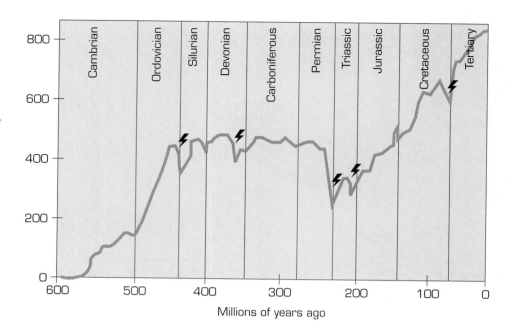

Guided Inquiry 7.2

Who Else Goes to School?

How many different kinds of living things can you find if you look around outdoors? How long does it take to find them? In your search for different organisms, such as those in Figure 7.10, focus on the subtle differences between them. Notice, for example, the differences between two birds of the same size.

MATERIALS

- A pencil
- A student-generated data table

Procedure

1. Find a place outdoors where you can make a brief visual inspection, looking for organisms.

2. Observe this area carefully for five minutes, making mental notes of the organisms that you see.

3. In small groups, predict how many different kinds of organisms you will find around your school. Develop a data table that will show the locations as well as the differences you will find in the organisms. Your teacher will help you construct the table.

Figure 7.10

Organisms such as this beetle, these dandelions, and this caterpillar may be found in your schoolyard.

4. Taking your *Log* to record data, return to the outdoor area for about 20 minutes. Make a note on your data table of each different kind of organism that you observe and its location. Turn over rocks or other objects to see what is under them, but return everything to its original position. Look in the parking lot, in puddles, in cracks in curbs, in walls and eaves of the building, around lights, and anywhere else you might find living things. Get close to what you are observing, as in Figure 7.11.

5. At the end of 20 minutes, report your findings to your group. Everyone in the group should now have access to the same data.

6. What organisms did you expect to find that weren't there? Return to the outside area for another 5 to 10 minutes, and look for those organisms. Complete your data table.

Figure 7.11

Students surveying their schoolyard.

Interpretations: Respond to the following in your *Log:*

1. How many organisms did you find?
2. How did your prediction compare to what you found?
3. Categorize the types of organisms that you found (insects, birds, plants, etc.). Select one type of organism. Describe how the organisms of this type differ from each other.
4. What organisms do you know exist in your community that were not found in this study? Write a hypothesis that explains why you didn't observe them.
5. What was most surprising about the amount of diversity you found? Explain.

Applications: Respond to the following in your *Log:*

1. How did you decide whether or not to count humans as one of the organisms in your study?
2. What limited your observations?
3. What could you do to find some of the "missing" living things?
4. Complete this statement: "To me, biodiversity is. . . ."

Why Should We Care About the Diversity of Life on the Earth?

Because humans depend on other life forms, the less we disturb the web of life, the better we live. To preserve that web, we need to understand the diversity of life on the earth and the interrelationships between the organisms that live here. Unfortunately, human activities are destroying vast numbers of species. Many scientists believe that we should try to survey, sample, and understand the biological diversity in the world. Perhaps we will find unique new foods, medicines, fibers, beauty, and lessons that will benefit our own lives. We are surveying, collecting, and studying the diversity of life on the earth as never before.

Classification

The science of classifying organisms is taxonomy, and scientists who do the classifying are taxonomists. Think of taxonomy as a model to help organize the incredible diversity of life. Of course, scientists do not have complete knowledge of the natural world, so they build the taxonomic model with the information that they do have. Like all models, taxonomy will evolve and adapt as we learn more about the natural world.

When scientists build a taxonomic model, they look for characteristics that are most constant—characteristics that define an organism. Some of the characteristics that they use are:

- ◆ structure,
- ◆ function,
- ◆ biochemistry,
- ◆ behavior,
- ◆ nutritional needs,
- ◆ embryonic development,
- ◆ genetic system,
- ◆ cellular and molecular makeup,
- ◆ evolutionary history,
- ◆ ecological interactions, and
- ◆ DNA and RNA sequences.

The currently accepted taxonomic model helps us to categorize and better understand the biodiversity on the earth. This taxonomic model is composed of groups of various sizes. Each group in the model is subdivided into smaller groups, down to a particular type of organism. This model is a hierarchy with the largest group at the top. The largest groupings are kingdoms. Some organisms in each kingdom and their evolutionary relationships are shown in Figure 7.12 on page 438. Each kingdom is divided into phyla (called divisions in the plant kingdom). Each phylum is divided into classes. Each class is divided into orders, each order into families, each family into genera, and each genus into species. For example, human beings are classified as follows:

Kingdom:	Animalia
Phylum:	Chordata
Class:	Mammalia
Order:	Primates
Family:	Hominidae
Genus:	*Homo*
Species:	*sapiens*

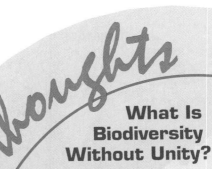

What Is Biodiversity Without Unity?

In spite of their diversity, the organisms of the earth all share certain characteristics. This unity supports the concept that we are all descended from a common ancestor. Shared characteristics of life on the earth include the following:

- ● a body structure based on cells,
- ● use of ATP (adenosine triphosphate) as the primary energy storage molecule,
- ● glycolysis in cellular respiration, and
- ● many common biochemical processes in cells.
- ● DNA and RNA

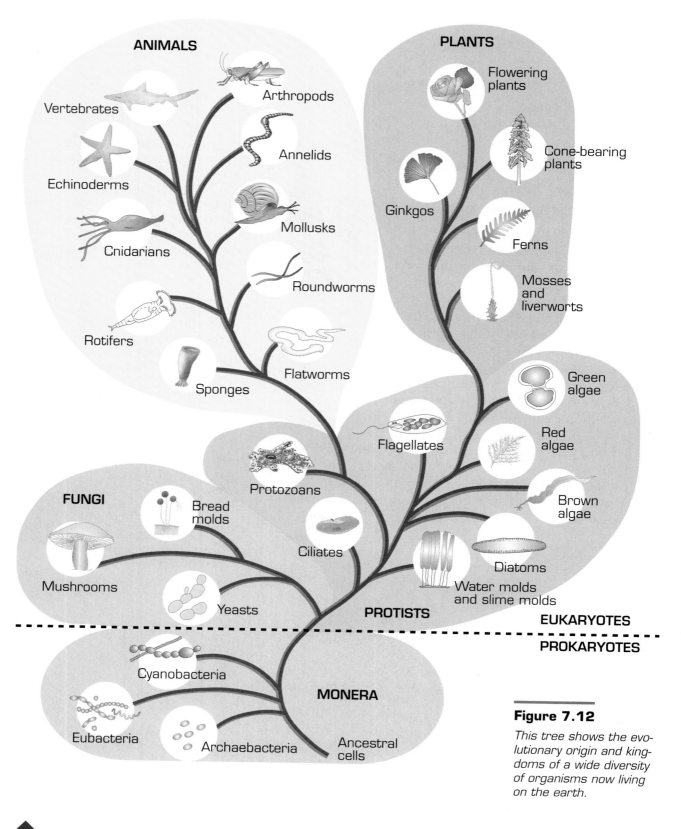

ANIMALS

Arthropods

Vertebrates

Annelids

Echinoderms

Mollusks

Cnidarians

Roundworms

Rotifers

Flatworms

Sponges

PLANTS

Flowering plants

Cone-bearing plants

Ginkgos

Ferns

Mosses and liverworts

Flagellates

Green algae

Red algae

Protozoans

Brown algae

FUNGI

Bread molds

Ciliates

Diatoms

Mushrooms

Yeasts

Water molds and slime molds

PROTISTS

EUKARYOTES

PROKARYOTES

Cyanobacteria

MONERA

Eubacteria

Archaebacteria

Ancestral cells

Figure 7.12

This tree shows the evolutionary origin and kingdoms of a wide diversity of organisms now living on the earth.

Each identified organism on the earth has both a genus name and a species name. The genus and species names together form the scientific name of a species. Figure 7.13 caption gives the genus and species for the domestic cat and dog. Note that the genus name is always capitalized and the species name is usually not capitalized. Both names are always underlined or italicized.

 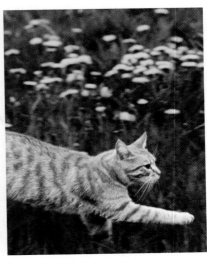

What Is a Species?

In its least complicated definition, a species is a particular type of organism. Members of the same species share certain genotype and phenotype characteristics; this means that they have genes, an evolutionary history, and some visible traits in common. Most important, members of the same species are able to interbreed with each other to produce offspring that can reproduce.

Figure 7.13

Canis familiaris *and* Felis domesticus *are the scientific names for the familiar domesticated dog and cat.*

For example, all domesticated dogs belong to the species *Canis familiaris*. Each breed of dog, such as the German shepherd in Figure 7.13, belongs to this one species. If this German shepherd were mated to another breed of *Canis familiaris*, fertile offspring would normally result. This is evidence that these dogs are the same species. What would happen if you could mate a dog and a cat: Would the mating result in fertile offspring?

Identifying distinct species can be more complicated than it seems. Early efforts at taxonomy fell into two categories. Some taxonomists, such as Carolus Linnaeus in the 17th century, saw every species as a distinct type. His Systema Natura formed the basis of the taxonomic system that we use today. Others denied the existence of species at all. They claimed that there were only individuals in nature and that any classification into groups was artificial.

How to Identify Distinct Species

Modern biologists define species as identifiable populations of organisms that can interbreed and have a common genetic and evolutionary heritage. They define a species according to individuals' genetic similarities, not only by the way humans see them. After all, why must groups of organisms be completely different in size or color to be recognized as distinct species?

The differences between one species and another are not necessarily complex. For example, two species of green lacewings, a type of insect, live in the same place in New York. The only difference between them is one gene. This gene causes one species to fly in the spring and the other to fly in the fall. They are morphologically identical, as you can see in Figure 7.14 on page 440. However, because they cannot interbreed in nature due to the difference in their life cycles, they are different species. Would you have

Figure 7.14

Each of these green lacewings is a distinct species though they seem phenotypically identical.

identified them as separate species? Conversely, Figure 7.15 shows examples of phenotypically different individuals that represent a single species.

Speciation

Speciation is the formation of new species. New species can form by many mechanisms, some quite rapid. For example, the volcanic Hawaiian islands contain hundreds of species of crickets. When a volcano erupts, lava flowing to the sea can split a population of crickets in half for several decades until the vegetation recovers. During this time, the cricket mating calls on either side of the flow can become so different that when contact resumes, the two populations no longer respond to each other's mating calls. Because they don't respond, they don't mate with each other. In this way, two separate, noninterbreeding populations are formed. But are they different species? Over a short period of time, the genetic differences are quite small, and the crickets could mate and produce healthy offspring if they responded to each other's calls. Would you identify them as unique species?

Zookeepers have crossed lions and tigers, two separate species (Figure 7.16), and produced fertile offspring. However, such matings do not occur in nature. Since these organisms do not share a common gene pool in nature, they must be considered distinct species. They no longer exchange genes, and each species moves along its own evolutionary path.

In many biological species, when populations are separated by space and time, a range of differences gradually develops. Eventually, the differences can become so great that individuals from the separated populations will not mate, even when they are placed in contact. At what point can we say that a population has changed enough from its original type to be called a new species?

Figure 7.15

Each of these populations is one species. Can you find evidence of variation within the species?

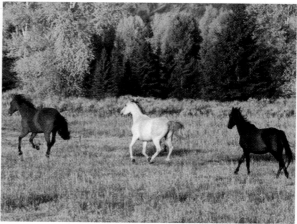

Biodiversity

The complexity of nature presents some problems in defining species on the basis of reproduction alone. For example, many bacteria reproduce asexually and produce exact genetic clones of themselves. No one would treat every clone as a distinct species. How can we define species among organisms that do not reproduce sexually?

Furthermore, some different species may be able to exchange genes. If you look at a field guide to trees in the United States, you will see many species of oaks. If you have ever tried to identify individual oaks, you know that there are distinct species and in-between forms. These in-between trees demonstrate that hybridization, the exchange of genes between different species, is possible for some organisms.

Figure 7.16

This tiglion is an offspring resulting from a cross between a lion and a tiger.

How Many Kingdoms?

How do biologists construct the largest taxonomic grouping, the kingdom? Biologists ask a number of questions to create the groupings:

◆ Is the organism a simple cell (prokaryotic) or a more complex cell (eukaryotic)?

◆ Is it a producer or a consumer?

◆ Does it reproduce sexually or asexually?

In addition, biologists consider:

◆ the biochemical aspects of the organism,

◆ how it develops from a fertilized egg,

◆ its cellular makeup and structure,

◆ its DNA sequences, and

◆ its evolutionary relationships.

The Five-Kingdom Taxonomic System

When Carolus Linneaus developed his taxonomic scheme, he divided all of life into two kingdoms. Each species was a member of either the plant kingdom or the animal kingdom. Today most scientists use the five-kingdom system (Figure 7.17 on page 442).

When Linneaus developed his taxonomy, every organism he described was assigned to either the plant or the animal kingdom. This system of organization persisted for more than 100 years. As improved methods for observing and studying organisms became available, differences among organisms within each of these kingdoms became apparent.

The currently accepted classification model divides all life on earth into five kingdoms. Organisms within the kingdom Monera are distinguished by lack of internal membrane-bound organelles. This is the only currently defined prokaryotic kingdom. The kingdom Fungi is composed of organisms that were earlier classified as plants but that lacked chlorophyll and had chitin rather than cellulose cell walls. The remainder of the eukaryotes

Figure 7.17

The five-kingdom taxonomic system.

KINGDOM	DISTINGUISHING CHARACTERISTICS	EXAMPLES
Monera	Prokaryotic organisms	Bacteria, blue-green algae
Protista	Unicellular eukaryotes	*Amoeba*, eukaryotic algae
Fungi	Develop from spores Multicellular heterotrophs that feed by absorption	Mushrooms, molds
Plantae	Multicellular autotrophs Develop from a blastula in an embryonic stage	All green plants, ferns, mosses
Animalia	Multicellular heterotrophs Feed by ingestion Develop from a blastula in an embryonic stage	Humans

are now classified within the kingdom Protista. This kingdom contains organisms of diverse lifestyles, reproductive methods, and morphology. It includes mostly simple, mostly unicellular organisms that have characteristics of animals, fungi, or plants.

Taxonomic Quandaries

Even at the level of kingdoms, scientists debate the groupings. As you have seen, defining a species is difficult. Grouping organisms into kingdoms is equally difficult. For example, recent research indicates that a group of organisms that might normally be placed in Monera are different from all other species in the kingdom. Their wall structure is different, and their plasma membranes and a ribosome protein are like those in eukaryotes. But these organisms are clearly not eukaryotes. Where should they be placed?

Some taxonomic schemes solve this problem by dividing Monera into two kingdoms. They place these unusual organisms in the new kingdom Archaebacteria. The other, more "typical" monera are placed in the kingdom Eubacteria. This adjustment of an earlier taxonomic model does not mean that the previous system was wrong. Rather, it shows that science is dynamic. As scientists learn more about organisms and their relationships and as technology improves, scientists develop new models to include this new information. 🐾

How do scientists decide in which kingdom to place a species? This question comes up every time a new species is discovered or a new method of looking at organisms is developed.

Read the following descriptions of a slime mold and two recently discovered bacteria, and then determine their classifications. To which kingdoms would you assign them on the basis of the following characteristics? Record your responses in your *Log*.

Slime Molds

Cellular slime molds begin their life cycle as individual cells that look very much like other single-celled organisms. As individual cells, they ingest bacteria and other organic particles. When the food supply is exhausted, slime mold cells gather together to produce a large mass. These cells then move and reproduce as a single organism. In which kingdom would you place the cellular slime molds?

Bacteria

Two new bacteria have recently been discovered. They are prokaryotic cells, but they contain the same types of chlorophyll as do green plants and algae. In addition, these bacteria are more like the chloroplasts of eukaryotic cells than they are like eubacteria. In which kingdom would you place these organisms?

Microbe Diversity in Standing Water

When you look at a community of organisms, you get a general impression of the biodiversity in the community. But are your impressions accurate? How can you decide how diverse a community really is?

In this activity, you will learn one method for quantifying biodiversity. You will calculate a number that you can use to compare the biodiversity of different ecosystems or communities. The calculation is called the Simpson Diversity Index.

You can use any collection of organisms or objects to learn how to calculate biodiversity. The procedure that follows uses the technique on a community of organisms in standing water.

MATERIALS

- A dissecting microscope
- Small sampling containers, such as baby food jars

- A compound microscope
- Deep-well microscope slides
- Pipettes

Note:

In this Inquiry, you will perform a series of sequential calculations. The best, least confusing way to do this is to set up a table like the one in Figure 7.18 in your *Log* or on a computer spreadsheet.

Figure 7.18

Copy this table into your Log, *or create a computer spreadsheet. Complete it as you go through Guided Inquiry 7.3.*

Type of Organism	Number of Individuals of Each Type	Proportion of Each Type of Organism	Square of the Proportion of Each Type of Organism

Procedure

1. On the day of this Inquiry, bring to class a small sample from natural standing water. Use a small container such as a baby food jar. Everyone in the class should try to find a different source. You might sample a pond, a marsh, or a horse or cattle watering trough; take water trapped in a rain gutter or in a tree hole; or sample puddles along a remote road or any other natural pool of standing water. The longer the water has been standing undisturbed, the better.

2. Place a few drops of water from your sample onto a deep-well microscope slide. See how many different organisms you can find under low (100×) power of a compound microscope or under a dissecting microscope.

3. Scan the water sample quickly to get an idea of the number and types of organisms in it. Decide whether the sample is very diverse, moderately diverse, or not at all diverse. Record your impression in your *Log*.

4. Sketch each different organism quickly, and give it a name or number. Count the number of each type of organism that you see. Record the names and numbers in your *Log*. (You don't need to use scientific names.)

5. Add the numbers of each type of organism to determine the total number of organisms.

6. Calculate the proportion of each kind of organism in the total sample. For example, you would calculate the proportion of green algae as:

$$\frac{\text{Number of green algae counted}}{\text{Total number of all types of organisms}}$$

Record the proportion of each type of organism in your sample in your *Log*. All the proportions added together should equal 1. If they do not, recheck your calculations.

7. Calculate the square of each proportion. Record these numbers in your *Log*.

8. Add all of the squares of the proportions. Record this number in your *Log*.

9. Subtract the number that you calculated in Step 8 from the number 1. This number is the Simpson Diversity Index value of your pond sample.

10. Compare your Simpson Diversity Index value with others in the class. Record these values and a description of the source of each water sample on the blackboard. Brainstorm reasons why the diversity index calculations differ for the different samples.

Interpretations: Respond to the following in your *Log*:

1. How many different types of living things did you find in a few drops of water?

2. How many different types of organisms did the other student groups find?

3. Which water sources had the greatest number of organisms?

4. Which water sources had the greatest diversity?

Applications: Respond to the following in your *Log*:

1. Some of the water samples from your community probably had much more life than others had. Why do you think that this happens?

2. What ecosystems near your community might be more or less diverse than those you studied? Why?

3. Why is maintaining microbial diversity important?

4. Repeat the procedure to calculate the diversity of organisms in the compost columns and piles that you established in Guided Inquiry 1.2. If you continued to maintain your compost, assess the diversity of organisms in it now. Or use the organisms that you collected and preserved for Guided Inquiry 2.7 on page 128.

Pond Water Organisms Described

You can find representatives of each of the kingdoms in a pond water sample. The following examples show the types of life that you are likely to encounter in natural standing water. Use the examples to help you organize what you see in your own water sample. Depending on the source of your sample, you may find representatives of each group. Or you may find only a few different types of organisms in one or two of the following groups.

Bacteria

Bacteria (Figure 7.19) are prokaryotic organisms, and the species are tremendously diverse in their metabolism, though they may look alike. They tend to be very small, often less than 1 micrometer in length. You can't easily see bacteria using the low-power objective of a compound microscope, and you can't see them at all if you use a dissecting microscope. Figure 7.19 shows some examples of how bacteria look under high power of a compound microscope and under much higher magnification, as they are more efficiently viewed.

Figure 7.19

Bacterial waste in water.

Cyanobacteria

The proper taxonomic name for these organisms is cyanobacteria (*cyano* means "blue-green"). But these organisms (Figure 7.20) are sometimes called blue-green algae, even though they are very different from all the other algae. Cyanobacteria are prokaryotic; they lack membrane-bound organelles. They are placed in the kingdom Monera, in the evolutionary lineage of the Eubacteria.

Cyanobacteria can be much larger than other bacteria. The largest have cells that are about 100 micrometers in diameter! But most are 1 to 10 micrometers in diameter. You can easily see most cyanobacteria using low- or medium-power magnification on a compound microscope. Each cyanobacterium is an independent round, rod-shaped, or cylindrical cell. Sometimes, these single cells form chains or clusters.

You can identify cyanobacteria by their blue-green color and by their absence of visible internal cellular structures.

Figure 7.20

Nostoc *is a cyanobacterium that forms long chains of cells within a dense polysaccharide sheath.*

Figure 7.22

An Amoeba *engulfing a food particle.*

Figure 7.23

Cilia move food particles into Stentor *and move the unattached end of the cell through the water.*

Figure 7.21

The thousands of cilia covering Paramecium *help it to move and to take in food.*

Protozoa

These one-celled organisms (Figures 7.21, 7.22, and 7.23) are members of the kingdom Protista. You can usually find them in watery environments. There are several different groups of protozoa, separated by the ways they move and eat. All are heterotrophs; that is, they feed on algae and organic debris. Some have tiny hairlike projections, called cilia, to help them move rapidly through the water. Because they are colorless, you can sometimes see the colored algae they have ingested.

Algae

The term *algae* refers to an amazingly diverse collection of single-celled and multicellular eukaryotes in the kingdom Protista. They are grouped together because they seem to have similar living requirements. However, you won't find the term *algae* in any taxonomy. It is a remnant of older taxonomic systems, when these organisms were placed in the kingdom Plantae because they all have chlorophyll and can photosynthesize. As often happens, scientists changed the kingdom assignment of these organisms as they discovered more about them.

To identify algae (Figure 7.24 on page 448), look for green, greenish-yellow, or golden-brown single cells, colonies, and filaments. They are usually larger than cyanobacteria cells but smaller than protozoa. Some have beautiful symmetry; some are elongated strands. Many are multicellular, and they all have pigments for photosynthesis.

Fungi

The fungi that you find in pond water usually look like gray or transparent filaments. You may also see fungal spores, their sexual or asexual reproductive structures (Figure 7.25). These organisms are members of the kingdom Fungi, which also includes mushrooms and molds. All fungi are eukaryotic heterotrophs; they get food energy by absorbing organic nutrients from other organisms.

Figure 7.25

A water mold (Achlya) with spores.

Invertebrates

Invertebrates make up about 95 percent of the animal species. They are members of the kingdom Animalia, but are very different from most of the animals that you know. Invertebrates do not have the backbone (vertebrae) that you find in familiar animals, including humans, so they tend to be small unless they live in water, which helps to support their bodies. Some invertebrates support their bodies with external structures called exoskeletons.

Representatives of several invertebrate animal phyla can be found in pond water. Figures 7.26 through 7.29 show some examples. *Hydra* (Figure 7.26) is a freshwater relative of marine jellyfishes. Rotifers (Figure 7.27) are tiny multicellular animals that are found mostly in fresh water. You can often see their internal organs and the food they have ingested when you look at them under a microscope.

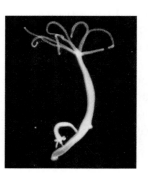

Figure 7.26

Hydra are small, transparent, tube-shaped organisms with tentacles. This Hydra *is forming a bud, which will produce an identical organism.*

Figure 7.27

The cilia on this rotifer move water to bring food into its mouth.

Figure 7.28

A freshwater nematode. These transparent, often curly worms have bodies that taper at both ends. Many wiggle under the microscope light.

They use cilia to bring food into their mouths. Nematodes (Figure 7.28) are roundworms, one of the most numerous types of invertebrates. They live in many environments, including fresh and salt water, damp soil, and even human body fluids. Crustaceans are a diverse group of organisms that are united by a common body form. Crabs, lobsters, and microscopic zooplankton are all crustaceans. They are all hard-bodied organisms with many legs. Sometimes they have antennae, and they frequently have eyes, a mouth, and a tail. They use specialized feeding appendages to gather algae for food. In microscopic crustaceans, such as the *Daphnia* in Figure 7.29, you can often see the food inside their intestinal tract. Insects are another major group of invertebrates that occur in surprising number and diversity in many habitats. Many insects live in water in their early stages of development, like the mosquito larvae in Figure 7.30. You can usually find

Figure 7.29

Daphnia is a common microscopic crustacean in fresh water.

Figure 7.30

Mosquito larvae amass in standing water.

mosquito larvae in warm, stagnant (unmoving) water. These elongated organisms have many legs, eyes, a head, and a mouth, but they are not transparent. In your water sample, you might also find the eggs or egg cases of nematodes, crustaceans, or insects, though you probably won't recognize them.

Plants

Though you might not find entire plants in your pond water sample, they are very much a part of the aquatic ecosystem, and you can see parts of them if you know what to look for. You might find pollen grains (Figure 7.31), which contain the male gametes of plants. Or you could find spores, which can be products of asexual or sexual reproduction. Both pollen and spores are very resistant to degradation once they sink to the bottom of a lake. Scientists analyze these collections of pollen and spores to learn about the plants that surround the lake. By looking deeper into the sediments at the bottoms of lakes, scientists can determine what the surrounding vegetation was like hundreds, even thousands, of years ago. 🌍

Figure 7.31

Pollen grains, such as this pine pollen, are often found in water samples. The two air-filled chambers on each pollen grain aid in wind dispersal.

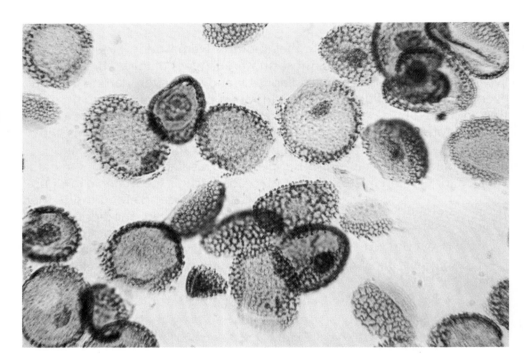

BIOccupation

David Dilcher: Natural Historian

"What was the first flower in the world?" "When did it appear?" "What factors were involved in its appearance?" These are the questions that drive Dr. David Dilcher's research as a natural historian for the Florida Museum of Natural History and a member of the National Academy of Science.

From the time he was four years old, Dilcher was curious about the world around him. He used to go out for walks in the woods and look at the plants and animals there. To be able to spend his life doing something that he liked, Dilcher went to college to study natural history, botany, geology, and biology. He became very interested in the interactions of plants and animals. As he says, "It turns out that plants and animals coevolved. These beautiful flowers evolved with fragrances and nectars that enticed insects to them. The insects would then carry the pollen away and help the plants cross-pollinate."

When asked about his job, Dilcher says, "The most important thing I do in my job is to ask questions." He travels all over the world studying the fossils of the first flowering plants. Recently, at a clay pit in southern Minnesota, he saw fossil plants that were over 100 million years old. He has also found ocean snail fossils on a mountaintop in Costa Rica.

Dilcher loves his job. He divides it into three parts: discovery, working with people, and sharing. He enjoys discovering new fossil material and new plant/animal associations and explaining how plants live in their environments today. Working with his colleagues in the museum and his students at the University of Florida keeps Dilcher motivated. Finally, Dilcher welcomes sharing his discoveries with his colleagues, students, and fellow scientists around the world.

The hardest part of his job, says Dilcher, is maintaining the discipline to record his discoveries and write about them. "Collecting the fossils is so much fun, but sitting down and writing details about the find in my field notebook is not as much fun." He knows, however, that a good scientist must do these things so that other scientists can learn from his work.

"Go out in the woods!" is Dilcher's advice to high school students who want to study natural history. They should develop a broad interest in all areas of science and the humanities. He also suggests that students volunteer for summer conservation camps, help with nature trails, or serve as nature guides for youth groups. He says, "Go do it now!"

Would You Have Stocked Nile Perch in Lake Victoria?

Note: Before you start reading this BioIssue, get a map of Africa. Locate Lake Victoria in Africa.

How can you know what the results will be when you add an exotic organism to an established ecosystem? In 1957, scientists were asked to find a way to increase the amount of food in the region of Africa around Lake Victoria. They concluded that a good way to do this would be to stock the lake with a species of fish, the Nile perch. The Nile perch was exotic, a species new to this lake. The decision seemed quite reasonable because the Nile perch is large and fairly easy to catch. However, some people expressed concern about introducing a large carnivorous fish weighing more than 90 pounds into a lake where most fish grew to less than 1 pound.

When you located Lake Victoria on a map, you should have noticed that it is a very large lake, approximately the size of Switzerland. Introducing the perch dramatically and rapidly changed this massive body of water. Here are some results of the fish stocking:

- The Nile perch became well established in Lake Victoria.

- People had difficulty preserving the very large perch for later consumption.

- Many native fishes in the lake disappeared. Many of these fish had been found only in Lake Victoria and so became extinct.

- People discovered that the Nile perch is extremely oily and has to be smoked to preserve it, rather than sun dried. Smoking food, obviously, requires a fuel source. Cutting wood to smoke the fish has deforested massive areas around the lake. Smoked food has also been implicated as a cause of cancer.

- The extinct fish can never be replaced.

The decision to stock the lake was well-intentioned, but it resulted in serious problems. Many people believe that the Nile perch is so well established in the lake now that it would be impossible to eliminate.

Before you judge decisions that were made decades ago, imagine that you lived near the lake in 1960, a few years after the fish were first stocked. The fish that you used to catch in the lake are disappearing. You now catch very large perch. Getting wood to smoke the perch is costly and time-consuming. You know that cutting wood on the islands off the coast of Africa has led to deforestation of these islands. Unfortunately, food is often scarce, and the Nile perch provides your only reliable source of protein.

Record your thoughts in your *Log.*

- Would you continue to catch, smoke, and eat the Nile perch if you lived near the lake?

- How can you support your decision?

- How do you balance your decision to damage your own environment against the need to feed yourself and your family? Do you have any alternatives?

The number of fish species in Lake Victoria decreased dramatically after Nile perch was stocked in the lake.

Variation

What is variation? How does variation help to drive evolutionary change? What is the difference between diversity and variation? In this Inquiry, you will investigate genetic variation within one species. You will use a system called multistage classification. You will see that variation is a factor in natural selection leading to evolutionary change.

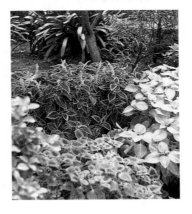

The different colors and patterns on the leaves of these Coleus plants show variation within a species.

MATERIALS

- Meter sticks
- String or metric tapes
- Scissors
- Six-hole punched index card, one per student

Procedure

1. Collect data about some of your own characteristics. First, determine whether you express the dominant or recessive gene for each of the six traits listed below.

2. Get an index card with six holes punched along one side. Each hole will represent an observable characteristic. Place the card with holes to the right. Write a label to the left of each hole in the order shown below indicating your expression of the trait. If you express the dominant allele for the trait, leave the hole intact. If you express the recessive allele, cut a notch out of the circle to make an open U for that trait. Figure 7.32 shows a sample card.

Figure 7.32

A completed sorting card for six human traits.

3. Write your name on your card, and give it to your teacher. Your teacher will arrange the cards so that the holes are aligned, place a straightened paper clip through one hole, and shake the cards. The cards that fall out will be those of students who express the recessive gene for that particular characteristic. Your teacher will repeat this selection simulation for each trait. In your *Log,* make a table like the one in Figure 7.33, and record the number of students in each of the expression categories. Then determine the percentages of these expressions for your class.

Figure 7.33

Sample data table for sorting six human traits in a biology class.

Expression	Number	Percent	Expression	Number	Percent
Unattached earlobes			Attached earlobes		
Left thumb over right thumb			Right thumb over left thumb		
Mid-digital hair present			Mid-digital hair absent		
Tongue roller			Not tongue roller		
Dimples present			Dimples absent		
Widow's peak on forehead			Straight hairline on forehead		

4. The expressions of the six human traits above are discrete. This means that you have one or the other expression. There is no gradation in between. But many traits have continuous expressions, with many possible values. Arm span is an example of a trait with continuous expressions (see Figure 7.34). With a partner, measure your arm span from fingertip of one hand to fingertip of the other hand. Stand erect, and hold your arms straight out to the side at shoulder height with your fingers extended. Your partner will measure the distance between the tips of the longest fingers. Repeat the process, measuring your partner's arm span. Record the lengths in a table on the chalkboard or overhead projector and in a data table in your *Log.*

5. Construct a table in your *Log* showing the range of arm spans for your classmates. Use the data to graph results, using Figure 7.35 and Figure 7.36 as models. Notice that the data in Figures 7.35 and 7.36 are grouped by ranges to bring order to the information illustrated in the graph. If the data were graphed by individuals' values, the graph would be almost flat and would not have a normal curve, with the greatest number of individuals grouped in the middle and the fewest at the limits of the range.

Figure 7.34

The people in this photo have arm spans that vary from 152 to 211 centimeters. Can you think of advantages of a long arm span? Can you think of advantages of a short arm span?

6. Calculate the average arm span for the class.

Student Arm Span (cm)	Number of Students
136–140	1
141–145	2
146–150	0
151–155	4
156–160	5
161–165	8
166–170	5
171–175	5
176–180	3
181–186	1

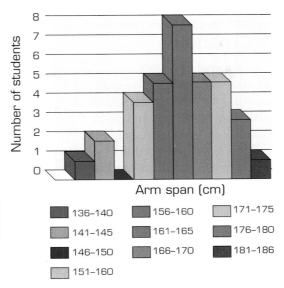

Figure 7.36

A graph of arm span versus number of students.

Figure 7.35

Arm span sample data

Interpretations: Respond to the following in your *Log:*

1. List reasons for variation in arm span. Is your class representative of the school as a whole? Look up data on average arm span for people your age. Is your class representative of your age group in the United States? Is your class representative of your age group in the world?

2. Consult a field guide for information on the wing span of one or more bird species. Do you find the same amount of variation in these organisms as in humans?

Applications: Respond to the following in your *Log:*

1. Some physical features are basically the same in every human. Everyone has two eyes and one nose, for example. What are some of the physical features that can be different in some people? Think of features such as hair color, height, and pulse rate. What features or measurements do you think would show the most variation?

2. (Optional) Choose a measurement that would vary in humans, such as change in pulse rate in response to exercise or another variable measurement. Develop and record in your *Log* a scenario that would favor selection in the population.

Figure 7.37

Charles Darwin.

Figure 7.38

From 1831 to 1837, Charles Darwin explored the diversity of life from the survey ship the H.M.S. Beagle.

Charles Darwin's Contributions to Our Understanding of Evolution

Biological evolution accounts for the changes that led to the diversity of life that we find on the earth today. Charles Darwin (Figure 7.37) dramatically altered our understanding of how the diversity of life came to be when he published his book *On the Origin of Species by Means of Natural Selection* on November 24, 1859.

Darwin's book contains two very important contributions. First, he presented evidence that existing species evolved from other, ancestral species. In doing so, he refuted the view that species were created in their present forms. Second, he proposed a mechanism by which this evolutionary change took place. This mechanism is known as natural selection.

Darwin's Experiences

Darwin's understanding of the process of evolution came about in much the same way as any scientist—or you, in this course—learns about a new subject. It began with his passionate interest in nature when he was a boy in England. Darwin pursued this passion throughout his schooling at Cambridge University. His life was changed forever at age 22 when he traveled around the world on a sailing ship, the H.M.S. *Beagle* (Figure 7.38). This voyage exposed the young Darwin to diverse communities of organisms, many of them unlike any he had known in England yet all uniquely suited for their particular environments. He collected and cataloged thousands of plant and animal specimens, especially from the coast of South America and the near islands. These collections and his notebooks from his journey formed the basis of Darwin's understanding of evolutionary processes.

Darwin was fortunate to live in a time when many exciting discoveries about the natural world were being made. He combined information from geologists, other biologists, and even an economist with his own observations of nature to better understand evolutionary processes. Some of the most significant influences on Darwin's thinking are described below.

Geological Studies

The systematic study of fossils, which are the remains of once-living organisms preserved in stone, began in the late 18th and early 19th centuries. As geologists explored successively older layers of rock, they found distinct communities of fossils in each layer (Figure 7.39). Many of the fossil organisms were different from any living organisms and thus provided the first evidence that extinctions occur. These geological studies also documented the very slow speed at which landforms, such as mountains and valleys, are made. Darwin was influenced by these geological findings to consider that changes in living organisms could occur gradually over long periods of time.

Jean Baptiste Lamarck and the Beginnings of a Description of Biological Evolution

The possibility that life forms had evolved along with the observed geological changes on the earth was a much-discussed topic among naturalists by the end of the 18th century. One of these scientists, the French museum curator Jean Baptiste Lamarck, recognized that organisms evolved from very simple to very complex forms. Lamarck believed that evolution was driven by environmental pressures: As organisms evolved, they became better adapted to their environments.

Some aspects of Lamarck's theory were not accurate, at least not as he expressed them nearly 200 years ago. Lamarck hypothesized that organisms

Figure 7.39

This vertical section through sedimentary rock in Capitol Reef National Park in Utah shows several layers, or strata, of fossils.

could inherit characteristics that their ancestors had acquired in response to environmental pressures. For example, he proposed that a giraffe's long neck evolved because its ancestors stretched their necks to greater and greater heights to eat tree leaves. We know now that acquired characteristics such as a stretched neck are not inherited by future generations. (see Figure 7.40).

Lamarck formed his hypotheses without the benefit of any knowledge of genetics. Gregor Mendel, whom you studied in Unit 5 (page 316), made his discoveries about genetics in the 1860s, long after Lamarck died in 1829. Mendel's work was not noticed by scientists until the early 1900s. Therefore Lamarck could not use Mendel's proofs of the existence of heritable factors to support his theories describing the mechanism of evolution. Though Lamarck's theory that acquired characteristics are inherited was wrong, his conclusion that environment influences evolution was basically correct.

Thomas Malthus: The Influence of Economics

As you learned in Unit 3, one of the environmental pressures that affects population size is the availability of food and other essential resources. Darwin was very much influenced by Thomas Malthus's essays on the natural laws of population growth (see page 165). Malthus contended that humans produced far more offspring than could be supported by available supplies of food and other resources. Therefore, he said, human populations would always be controlled by starvation and disease. Darwin extended Malthus's arguments to nonhumans as he developed natural selection as a hypothesis for the mechanism of evolutionary changes. 🌎

Natural Selection

In any environment, some individuals are more likely to survive than others, and some will produce more offspring. When a successful individual produces offspring, those offspring will also have the genes that caused success. In this way, particular genes that give an individual an advantage in a certain environment will eventually predominate in the population in that environment. This mechanism of evolution is called natural selection.

Sometimes, genetic changes in one species can influence the evolution of another species. Different species in the same geographical area may have strong effects on each other. Think of predator and

Figure 7.40

The extremely stretched neck of the Asian tribeswoman will not be inherited by her offspring.

prey relationships, for example. Changes that help a prey species to avoid an attack can lead by natural selection to changes in the predators to bypass these defenses. Changes in the predators lead to new defenses in the prey, and so on. This readjusting of capabilities has been termed coevolution. The organisms do not consciously choose certain behaviors or physical features to improve their chances of catching their prey or of escaping from a predator. Organisms that have genes for certain traits that are helpful will tend to survive and reproduce better than others. These genes will then naturally predominate in future generations.

You can also see coevolution in hosts and their parasites and other disease-causing organisms and in plants and their animal pollinators and consumers. Some plants have evolved chemical defenses to protect themselves against insects. Humans have been able to use some of these substances for medicines and other uses. For example, the nicotine in tobacco plants is a particularly toxic defense against insects. Humans use it as an insecticide. 🌍

Coevolution of Plants and Insects: The Yucca Flower and the Yucca Moth

Many plants depend on insects or other animals to deliver the pollen that promotes the development of seeds. Pollination is the transfer of pollen from the male reproductive parts of a flower where it is produced to the female reproductive parts where it will fertilize an egg cell.

Almost all relationships between pollinators and plants involve some mutual morphological and behavioral adaptations. The effects of such relationships, in which the interaction of two or more species influences their adaptations, is termed coevolution. Some plants and insects are so adapted to each other as to be completely interdependent. Such is the case for the relationship between the *Yucca* plant and the yucca moth.

All species in the genus, *Yucca*, are dependent upon the yucca moth for pollination. These moths emerge from the soil during the time of year when *Yucca* plants are in flower. The moths live for only a few days. The female moth gathers pollen from one *Yucca* flower and carries it to a flower on another *Yucca* plant. The moth lays her eggs and leaves the harvested pollen in the second flower. When the eggs hatch, the moth larvae eat some of the seeds that have developed in the fertilized flower. As the *Yucca* fruit ripen, the larvae fall to the ground, where they develop into adult moths.

In this cycle of coevolution, the *Yucca* plant has a pollinator, and the yucca moth has a place to protect and nourish its offspring. Through coevolution, the Yucca plant and the yucca moth have become completely dependent upon each other for their existence.

How Many Species Are Found in the World?

Although humans have been studying the diversity of life for many centuries, we have identified probably no more than 10 percent of the species on the earth. We have identified more than 1,500,000 species, but as many as 30 to 50 million species—or even more—may exist on the earth.

Why is there such great uncertainty about the number of species? Some groups of organisms are better known than others. Few bird species remain unknown to science anywhere on the earth, for example. A number of large animal species have been discovered in the past century. These include the world's largest primate, the mountain gorilla of central Africa; the world's largest reptile, the komodo dragon of Indonesia; and a 10-foot-long shark named megamouth near Hawaii. But the number of large animal species that are still undiscovered is probably small. On the other hand, we have barely begun to explore the diversity of the microscopic organisms of the earth. The 1,500,000 named species include relatively

The komodo dragon is the largest living reptile.

few bacteria, nematodes, mites, protozoa, or parasites, although we suspect that enormous numbers of such creatures exist. In one extreme example, a survey of species of insects determined that nearly half of the insects contained unique species of prokaryotic parasites of the genus *Spiroplasma.* There may be one million species in this genus alone!

Expeditions to Explore Biodiversity

Some of the world's most biologically diverse regions are also the most poorly explored. We can assume that the 126 species of fish identified from the Great Lakes are most of the species present in that system. We can be equally certain that the 1,500 species identified from the Amazon River system is only a small portion of the actual number. Scientists long assumed that the ocean floor at 1,000 meters or deeper was a biological desert. It is always dark and cold, and it contains no food except for organic matter that sinks from the surface. It is also subject to enormous pressure. How could any living organisms exist under those conditions? But they do. Ocean bottom samples collected off the New Jersey coast contained many species of worms, crustaceans, mollusks, and other unique creatures. Biologist J. Frederick Grapple estimated that tens of millions of species live on the deep ocean floor. That is as many species as we expect to find in the tropical rain forest!

Treetops are another relatively unexplored habitat. Biologist Terry Erin hauled insect foggers high into the canopy of a single species of tree in Panama. He identified more than 1,100 species of beetles alone among the collection of insects that fell from the treetops.

Perhaps 160 of these beetle species were unique to that species of tree. He used this species count to predict the number of other organisms in the beetle's class that might live in that single species of tree. He calculated that, since beetles comprise roughly 40 percent of all known species in their class, Insecta (order Coleoptera), 400 total species might be living in this one tree species. He then estimated that an additional 200 species would be found in the lower parts of the tree and among leaves on the ground. The number of species of tropical trees is estimated at more than 50,000. Therefore, he estimated that there may be 30 million tropical arthropods. This is obviously a guess, but Dr. Erin's uncertain numbers highlight how little we know about what species exist.

Respond to the following in your *Log:*

- Is it important to know how many species there are on the earth?

- We may lose millions of species in the next few decades without even knowing that they existed. Does this matter?

- Where would you search for new species in your area?

- How has biodiversity changed in your area as humans and their associated organisms have replaced the natural communities?

Discoveries of New Organisms by Western Scientists in the 19th and 20th Centuries

In 1812, Cuvier said, in essence, that there were no large animals left on the earth unknown to science. Since then, numerous large species have been found, including the following:

1819	Tapir
1820	Celebes ape
1821	Siamang (Sumatra), largest gibbon on earth
1835	Gelada baboon (East Africa), largest baboon on earth
1840–1900	Pygmy hippo (West Africa)
1847	Lowland gorilla (West Africa)
1865	Pere David deer (China)
1869	Giant panda (China)
1869	Lesser kudu (African antelope)
1882	Grevy's zebra (Africa)
1882	Przewalski's horse (Asiatic wild horse)
1898	Brown bear (Kamchatka, Manchuria, Sakhelin Islands)—the largest carnivore on the earth, 10 feet tall, 1,600 pounds
1900	White rhinoceros, a new subspecies of the second largest land animal on earth, 6 feet high, 15 feet long, >2 tons, was discovered on Upper Nile, 2,000 miles north of its previous known range
1901	Mountain gorilla (East Africa), largest primate on earth
1900+	Okapi (Central Africa), forest giraffe
1904	Meinertzhagen's forest hog (Kenya), largest pig on earth, 4 feet high, 8 feet long
1912	Komodo dragon (Malay Archipelago), largest lizard on earth, 12 feet long
1918	Freshwater dolphin, new genus (China), 8 feet long
1925	Pygmy chimpanzee (Africa)
1937	Wild oxen (Cambodia)
1976	Megamouth (Pacific Ocean), one of largest shark species known, in its own new family

Additional Discoveries

1900s	Eleven of 80 known species of cetaceans (whales and porpoises), most recent in 1991: at least one undescribed species sighted in eastern Pacific
1930s	Coelacanth (Indian Ocean), 6-foot-long fish well known in fossil record, disappeared 70 million years ago, a living fossil
1970s	A new class of prokaryotes, the Mollicutes. One genus, *Spiroplasma*, is believed by one expert to contain more than 1 million species
1983	New animal phylum, Loricifera, from ocean floor
1980s	Deep ocean found to be perhaps as diverse as tropical rain forest: one patch at a depth of 4 kilometers, the size of a living room, yielded 798 species, 460 new
1980s	Recent surveys of tropical forest insects suggest 10 million to 30 million species
1990s	Studies in Norway found 4,000 to 5,000 species of bacteria in 1 gram of beech forest soil

The extinction rate of vertebrates is now one species every nine months.

461

Timeline Revisited: Let's Blow Up Time

In the long history of the earth, how have volcanic activity and other drastic changes to the environment strongly influenced living conditions? How have these changes contributed to the extinction of some kinds of organisms, especially mass extinctions, in which a large number of different types of organisms disappeared? The actual causes of these extinctions are active topics for scientific investigations. For example, some scientists have deduced that extinction of the dinosaurs was caused by climatic changes resulting from a large meteorite striking the earth.

In this Inquiry you will explore the major mass extinctions (Figure 7.41), including which organisms were affected and what scientific evidence exists to determine the reasons for these extinctions. Some scientists believe that present life forms may be entering the sixth great decline in biodiversity, this time due to the impact of human activities.

MATERIALS

- Adding machine tape
- Brightly colored yarn
- Index cards
- Colored construction paper or poster paper

- The biodiversity graph transparency
- An overhead projector

Procedure

1. Review with your classmates the following list of events in an evolutionary time continuum:

   ◆ 500 million years ago: first vertebrates (jawless fish)
   ◆ 430 million years ago: first land plants

Figure 7.41

This biodiversity timeline shows the 5 major extinctions. Each resulted in a decrease in biodiversity.

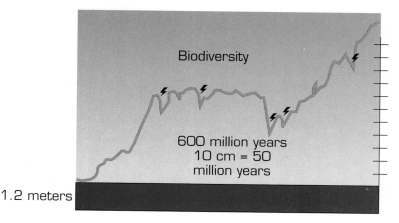

Biodiversity

600 million years
10 cm = 50
million years

1.2 meters

- 370 million years ago: first trees
- 355 million years ago: first amphibians
- 345 million years ago: first reptile
- 225 million years ago: early dinosaurs
- 210 million years ago: early mammals
- 200 million years ago: breakup of Pangaea starts
- 147 million years ago: first birds
- 125 million years ago: first flowering plants
- 60 million years ago: first primates
- 15 million years ago: first hominids
- 0.2 million years ago: *Homo sapiens*

This fossilized brachiopod lived about 400 million years ago.

2. Your teacher will provide one index card for each of these events. Form one group for each event. In your group, research your event and prepare a brief description of it. Annotate and illustrate your event card so that it explains the event.

3. Place your event card on the adding machine tape timeline provided by your teacher. Briefly describe the event to your classmates.

4. As a class, agree on a symbol or word to represent mass extinction. Place this symbol on five index cards. Place these cards on the timeline at the times for the following major extinctions:

- 440 million years ago: extinction of two-thirds of the trilobite families (common marine arthropods)

- 365 million years ago: extinction of many very common species

- 245 million years ago: largest extinction ever known. Some scientists estimate that as many as 90 percent of all species disappeared, including trilobites, many reptiles, and amphibians.

- 210 million years ago: early dinosaurs replaced early reptiles and amphibians

- 66 million years ago: extinction of dinosaurs and many marine invertebrates

What would your life be like if all the organisms in the kingdoms Monera, Protista, and Fungi became extinct?

5. Form five groups. Each group will take one extinction card from the timeline and research this extinction event. Illustrate and annotate your extinction card to describe this event. Then return the card to the timeline. In a classroom discussion, briefly describe this extinction event to your classmates.

6. As a class, discuss the probable effects of these major extinction events on other organisms and their ecosystems. Refer to the event cards that you placed on the timeline in Step 3 to see which organisms existed on the earth at the time of each extinction.

Interpretations: Respond to the following in your *Log:*

1. What trends do you see developing in any one section of the timeline?

2. What is the significance of the history of mass extinctions as you see it on this timeline?

3. What changes do you see in the frequency of extinctions through time? Discuss some possible explanations for your observations.

Applications: Respond to the following:

1. Add to your timeline through the remainder of this year. Bring in articles and pictures from newspapers, magazines, or other sources that illustrate or discuss some event on the class timeline. Post entire articles below the timeline for your classmates to read, or prepare a brief summary of the article on an index card.

2. Choose one event on the timeline for independent library research. Write up your research, and post it on the class timeline. Present your research to the class in a brief oral report.

3. Find an event that is not yet included on the timeline, and research it. Describe this event to the class in a brief presentation.

Kathleen Futrell: Zoo Owner

When the children's photographer bought the baby lion to use as a prop in his pictures, it was cute and cuddly. Within a few months, though, he wanted to get rid of the rapidly growing cub. This little lion became the first inhabitant of what is now a zoological farm with over 400 animals ranging from domestic pigs to tigers to peccaries. The owner of Waccatee Zoological Farm is Kathleen Futrell. She has a four-year college degree in biology education and a great love of animals. As Futrell puts it, "You have to have a definite interest in animals and in animal welfare—not just the fun part, but the cleaning up behind the animal, its nutrition and medical care."

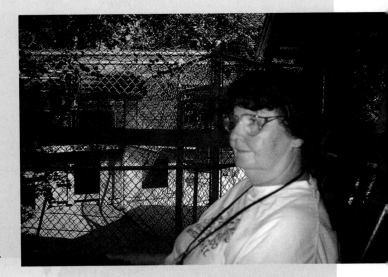

Futrell's natural love of animals was supplemented by her biology coursework in college, but even that didn't prepare her to care for exotic animals such as camels and gibbons. She researches the specific nutritional and health needs of each species. To provide the best nutrition for her animals, Futrell customizes their diets, though she also uses commercial foods. Animal feed companies provide such specialized items as monkey biscuits and camel food. For expert help in the care and nurturing of her zoo animals, Futrell has several veterinarians on call. She has even taken some of her animals to a university veterinary school for medical diagnoses.

As a licensed zoo, Waccatee Zoological Farm undergoes regular and unannounced inspections by the U.S. Department of Agriculture. Futrell must stay informed about rules regarding her animals and their care. Also, since the zoo is open every day of the year, she and her staff must prepare for the safety of the people who visit and of the animals being visited.

Futrell's farm is home for the farm animals, hoofstock (zebras and other animals with hooves), primates, reptiles, and exotic cats that inhabit her zoo. It also provides temporary sanctuary for nesting migratory birds. Located in South Carolina on the Intracoastal Waterway, Waccatee Zoological Farm was the site of 363 cattle egret nests, 87 little blue heron nests, and 25 anhinga nests when it was surveyed in May 1994.

The employees of the zoo include local high school students and adults who have expressed a strong interest in the animals. Futrell recommends that high school students who are interested in working with animals get experience as apprentices or volunteers with animal handlers.

Timeline Revisited: The Last 12,000 Years

Can you name a few significant events that have occurred in the last 12,000 years? You have already enlarged one section of the timeline to see the changes. What would you find if you took a closer look at the last 12,000 years?

In this Inquiry you will investigate extinctions since the waning of the last ice age. Some organisms that became extinct in the last 12,000 years are shown in Figures 7.42, 7.43, and 7.44.

MATERIALS

- Adding machine tape
- An outline of the graph
- List of extinction events
- 3" × 5" cards

Procedure

1. Familiarize yourself with the following extinction data:

KNOWN ANIMAL EXTINCTIONS SINCE 1600

VERTEBRATES	NUMBER OF SPECIES	INVERTEBRATES	NUMBER OF SPECIES
Mammalia	60	Cnidaria	1
Aves	122	Mollusca	191
Reptilia	23	Insecta	59
Amphibia	2	Crustacea	4
Pisces	29		
Total vertebrates	236	Total invertebrates	255
Total Animal Extinction		491	

2. Your teacher will assign an extinction event to you.
3. Research your assigned event. Annotate and illustrate this event on a card. Place your card in the appropriate location on the timeline.
4. As a class, discuss these extinction events. How do you know whether the number of extinction events is accurate? Is it possible to be accurate without knowing about every species on the earth?

Figure 7.42

The common dodo
(Raphus cucullatus),
which became extinct
by 1670.

Figure 7.43

The wooly mammoth
(Mammonteus primigenius).

Figure 7.44

Stellar's Sea Cow
(Hydrodamalis gigas).

Interpretations: Respond to the following in your *Log:*

1. What is the relationship between human population growth and extinction of species?

2. How does this relationship compare with previous extinctions that you observed on the other timelines? How do the time frames compare?

3. Refer to the timeline that you prepared in Guided Inquiry 7.5 for the 500,000-million-year interval. How might your timeline look during the next million years?

4. Will another major extinction event occur? How is this event likely to affect the human population?

Applications: Respond to the following in your *Log:*

1. Find some important milestones in the development of human culture. Put these dates on the timeline.

2. How can you explain the extinction of 73 percent of North American large mammal genera about 10,000 years ago? How significant is it that this extinction coincided with the presence of humans in North America? What other factors may have affected animal survival at that time?

3. Explore other, more localized extinctions, such as the disappearance of bird and mammal species as humans colonized many islands.

BIOprediction

Can This Population Be Sustained?

Much of the world's population depends on rice as its main food source. Highly populated countries such as India rely on a productive rice harvest each year to sustain its population. Drastic reductions in the rice harvest can cause mass starvation. Consider the following information about rice crops in India today:

- At one time, Indian farmers grew over 30,000 strains of rice.

- New strains of rice can produce greater yields of high-quality rice.

- More farmers are planting these new strains of rice.

- By the year 2005, more than three-quarters of Indian rice fields may contain only 10 varieties of rice.

- Many of the new strains of rice have low resistance to disease.

- In 1970, a virus suddenly appeared that spread rapidly from rice field to rice field, destroying rice crops all across India. The International Rice Council studied 6,273 varieties of rice and found only one that was resistant to this virus. This variety was crossbred with the new rice varieties, and resulting strains of rice were planted. The spread of the virus was checked.

Rice fields such as these feed the Indian population.

Record your responses to the following in your *Log*:

1. How has a reduction in the biodiversity of the rice crop placed annual harvests at risk?

2. Evaluate the level of risk to the rice crop in India if the rice crop contains only 10 species by the year 2005.

3. What would you do if you were a farmer in India today? How would you decide which rice variety to plant? What would the advantages and disadvantages be?

4. What recommendations could you make for planting rice in India?

5. What would happen if many strains of rice became extinct?

6. Is there a lesson about the value of biodiversity here that applies to other species?

Self-Check 1

You have spent the last couple of weeks investigating the diversity of life on the earth. Divide the questions below among your group and work on your questions as homework. Then discuss each question with your group until you reach agreement on all questions. Each member of the group will be responsible for understanding the answers to all questions. If you are not confident of your responses, check with a classmate or ask your teacher.

1. Distinguish between biological diversity and biological variation.

2. Identify the first life forms that appeared on the earth. When did they appear?

3. Why and when did oxygen become a major part of the earth's atmosphere?

4. List four reasons why you need to know about diversity of life on the earth.

5. Describe four well-documented geological events that serve as reference points in the biological history of our planet.

6. List the criteria for a species. Why can genetic change in individuals in a population produce a new species?

7. Give several reasons for creating a taxonomy of living things.

8. Describe a plausible scenario for natural selection.

9. Describe conditions under which coevolution can occur.

10. Give two different definitions of the evolution of life.

11. What is incorrect about a video scene in which humans fight off marauding dinosaurs?

12. How is variation beneficial to the survival of a species?

As a class, you have constructed three different timelines. For this Conference, the class will select one segment of a timeline and research it in detail.

First, review your Log notes from the Guided Inquiries. Then, choose any time period. Modern history (the last 2,000 years or so) is one possibility, but don't limit your choice to this time period.

After you choose a time period, construct a new timeline and hang it on the wall or bulletin board close to the previously constructed timelines. Connect your new timeline to one or more previously constructed timelines with string to indicate the time period you chose.

Research a small segment of the new timeline, individually or in small groups. Create event cards or other visual displays, and present your information to the class. Then put the information on the timeline. As you research, you should explore in detail changes in biodiversity during this segment of the earth's history.

As a class, discuss your findings in the context of the Guided Inquiries that you have completed. What do you now know about biodiversity? What questions did your investigations lead you to ask?

Next, design individual inquiries or small group inquiries that will give you more information about biodiversity.

Become an . . . ologist!

You have made a brief survey of your local environment to determine the number of different kinds of organisms. You probably missed a few species because you did not notice distinguishing characteristics that separated species. Scientists have the same problem when they try to count the species in an exotic habitat. They ask experts to identify particular groups such as beetles, millipedes, flowering plants, or trees. In this activity, you will become the expert.

Choose a group of organisms that you find around your school or home. Here are some possible groups or subgroups to consider:

"OLOGIST"	GROUP	EXAMPLES OF SUBGROUPS
Botanist	Flowering plants	herbs, trees, grasses
Zoologist	Animals	mammals, birds, reptiles
Entomologist	Insects	aphids, beetles, flies, bugs
Dendrologist	Trees	conifers, deciduous trees
Mycologist	Fungi	mushrooms, shelf fungi, pathogens
Ornithologist	Birds	waterfowl, songbirds
Microbiologist	Bacteria	free-living (in the environment) or pathogenic (in other organisms)
Phycologist	Algae	red algae, green algae, diatoms, brown algae

You will need classification keys to these groups. You can find field guides at most bookstores and libraries. Local libraries usually have a variety of books for identifying organisms.

You might wish to physically collect and mount your collection if you are sure that this is legal (woodland wildflowers and other organisms are often protected) and that you will not harm the ecosystem. Otherwise, you should identify them in the field. You can write a description or draw pictures of your specimens. You can photograph or videotape them. You might read more about the natural history of each organism that you identify. Your records could make an interesting display for the Congress. You might also use your findings at the Community Council during the Forum.

At the Congress, you will:

◆ present a list of the different species found in your area,
◆ tell what you learned about identifying organisms,
◆ relate problems that you encountered, and
◆ explain your new insights into determining the biodiversity in your local area.

What else might you include?

Alien Invaders

Warning: Exotics are invading your city! You know from the BioIssue on page 452 that an exotic species introduced into a new area can have dramatic impacts on biodiversity. Japanese honeysuckle, for example, is an introduced plant that grows in dense mats, smothering plants around it. Where trees are removed, enough sunlight penetrates to allow Japanese honeysuckle to grow rampant. It threatens some already endangered woodland wildflowers. The Japanese honeysuckle easily eliminates the native low-growing plants and can prevent reforestation by shading saplings too much as they grow.

Find out what invasive exotic animals or plants you have in your area. You might even find some around your schoolyard or home. Invasive exotic plants include Japanese honeysuckle (Figure 7.45), multiflora rose, Canada

Figure 7.45

Japanese honeysuckle can cover other plants, ultimately killing them by limiting photosynthesis.

thistle, and spotted knapweed. The English sparrow and the starling are both exotic birds. These birds compete aggressively with native species for food and nesting sites. Call the local agricultural extension office, the local forestry office, or representatives of local bird or garden clubs, and ask about introduced species that are problems in your area.

You may find that an exotic plant species grows around your home or school. If so, compare that site with a similar site where you don't find the species. How do these sites compare? Supplement your data with library research.

If you can't do your own study of locally introduced exotic species, research an invasive organism in your area. Include natural history information about the organism's life cycle and the history of its intro-duction. Explain how to identify it. Does this organism pose a threat to local diversity? Does it displace or eliminate native species? Does it have any value to humans or other wildlife? Is it being dealt with effectively? Explain.

Extended Inquiry 7.3

Diversity Case Studies

Consider the following questions:

What has happened to the many species of prairie grasses that once dominated the heartland of the United States? Why are fire ants becom-ing a problem throughout the southeastern United States? Why should we be concerned about tropical habitat destruction? Why should we protect endangered species? This Inquiry will give you some important insights to aid you in answering these questions.

Procedure

1. Divide into four groups, one for each case study. Each group is responsible for reading and presenting one case study to the class.

2. You have approximately 15 minutes to read your case study and answer the Interpretation questions on page 479 in your *Log*.

3. Each group will then describe the threat to biodiversity with which it has become familiar.

Case Study 1:   The Disappearance of the Prairie

The tallgrass prairie (Figure 7.46 on page 474) once covered 240 mil-lion acres of North America. This biologically diverse ecosystem devel-oped almost 10,000 years ago. As the last of the four glacial episodes ended and the last great ice sheet withdrew to the north, the North American plains had a very cool climate. The climate of the ice ages favored the development of a spruce forest, whose remnants are found

Figure 7.46

A tall grass prairie.

in the north and high mountain areas. As the glacier withdrew, the climate of the prairie changed, allowing plant species to advance from all directions. Species could now mix and develop a complex and diverse community.

Grasses dominated the new plant community. The four dominant grass species in the tallgrass prairie were big and little bluestem, Indian grass, and switch grass. Scientists estimate that the tallgrass prairie harbored over 25 species of grasses with 600 species of wildflowers. The thick, rich humus that accumulated as the grasses decomposed over 10,000 years made the soil very rich. Each type of soil in the prairie developed its own characteristic natural vegetation. A diverse base of about 3,500 species of plants, trees, shrubs, fungi, and algae supported nearly 700 kinds of fishes, amphibians, reptiles, birds, and mammals and 25,000 varieties of insects.

Prairies developed in arid or semiarid regions and were subject to periodic drought. Fire was another physical component of the prairie. Any particular patch of prairie burned naturally about once every five years. Tremendous fires, started by lightning, burned for weeks up to 200 miles wide, with flames reaching 25 feet into the sky and fed by the southern winds. Fires were a part of keeping this diverse community healthy. The above-ground portion of prairie vegetation is only one-third of the total biomass of the community. The remaining two-thirds of the prairie biomass forms a thick root mat below the surface of the soil. This was the critical part of the prairie community. The fires recycled nutrients to the root mat and helped to remove woody invaders.

Prairie streams generally flowed year-round, fed by the underground root mass. The root mass also acted like a sponge, soaking up the rainfall and slowly releasing it throughout the year. In 1806, Zebulon Pike reported many springs along the Arkansas river near Kendall in western Kansas.

In the 1880s, the prairies began to change forever. When settlers first came out of the eastern forests, they were daunted by the prairie environment. Because their wooden plows could not cut through the thick root mats of the prairie, they introduced the steel sodbuster plow. With the help of this plow, the settlers discovered the rich soil below the prairie grasses and wildflowers and used the soil to grow a limited number of agricultural grasses. Thus an energy intensive, annual, agricultural community replaced the natural prairie community. Only 0.5 percent of the original tallgrass prairie community remains. When the root mass of the prairie is disturbed, it is very difficult to reestablish the prairie community.

In the 1930s, the fragile nature of this new agricultural community became apparent. By then, even in the rainiest years, streams like the Arkansas River west of Great Bend, Kansas, no longer flowed above ground. Between 1930 and 1937, the prairies received 65 percent less annual precipitation than normal. This prolonged period of drought overcame the artificially supported community and caused many crop failures. A 64,750-square-kilometer area of the prairie states became known as the Dust Bowl. Wind from the west swept across the exposed soils, causing dust storms of unbelievable magnitude. The dust was carried so far that it even discolored the Atlantic Ocean several hundred miles off the east coast of the United States.

Case Study 2: Fire Ants

In 1942, a teenage boy named Edward Wilson noticed some strange-looking red ants near his home in Alabama. They were swarming around a foot-high mound. When disturbed, they attacked together with vicious stings. This was the first documented sighting of an ant species that has spread throughout the southern states in just a few years in spite of a massive federal program to stop it (Figure 7.47). The

Figure 7.47

Fire ant mounds in a field in Georgia.

fire ant was accidentally introduced from its native habitat on the western border of Brazil. These ants have an unusually large reproductive potential. A mature queen can lay over 5,000 eggs per day, and a single colony may contain over half a million ants. Fire ants eat almost anything the colony can overpower, from insects to small mammals.

Recently, these ants have changed their territorial behavior. Before 1980, fire ant colonies had strong territorial dispositions, and this limited the number of colonies that could occupy a given area. Now the fire ants have formed populations of "super-colonies." These super-colonies consist of many separate ant colonies living close together in an apparently cooperative arrangement. This has resulted in as many as 500 to 600 mounds or colonies per acre. These super-colonies expand at a rate of several hundred square feet per year.

A recent study showed that when fire ant super-colonies move into a new area, the population of other ant species drops by 70 percent and the number of insects, ticks, and mites drops by 40 percent. Spraying powerful ant killers where these ants were advancing was not effective in the long term. Spraying also killed native species that were one of the primary barriers to fire ants. Once the poison was washed away, fire ants, adapted for rapid recolonization, invaded and established themselves more quickly than the native ant species could.

Releasing predators or parasites that prey on fire ants is the latest idea for controlling fire ants biologically.

Case Study 3: Threats to Tropical Hot Spots

Unique tropical habitats are being destroyed at an alarming rate. Biologists realize that there simply is not enough time to learn about the species that live in these unique habitats before the habitats are completely destroyed. Destructive agricultural practices, cattle raising, mining, harvesting timber, pollution, and dam building all threaten these areas as countries try to make short-term profits in a global economy.

International organizations are working to identify biological hot spots as they develop priorities for preserving and studying these areas. Hot spots are tropical or semitropical areas where biodiversity is very high; an estimated 14 percent of the world's plant species exist in only 0.02 percent of its total land surface! One hot spot includes 23,200 plant species, of which 80 percent are found only in that unique location. The world map in Figure 7.48 shows the locations of 18 hot spots.

The threats to biodiversity in these places are varied. The native forests of western Ecuador, for example, where the human population increased from 45,000 to about 300,000 in only 40 years, are being converted to palm oil plantations. On the southwestern Ivory Coast, local

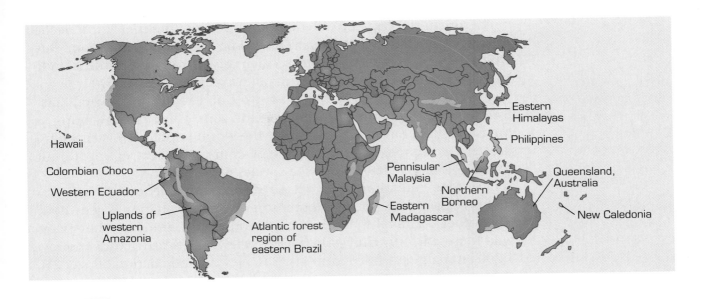

Figure 7.48

These eighteen "hot spots" were identified by Norman Meyers as areas of the world where biodiversity is most threatened.

government regulations protect the forest, but illegal logging and gold prospecting are problems. On the island of Madagascar, the forest has been reduced to one-third of its original size through slash-and-burn agricultural practices. The forests on the lower slopes of the Himalayas have been reduced to two-thirds of their original area because of unrestricted logging and conversion to farmland. The Philippines, a thickly populated country consisting of thousands of islands, has lost most of its original forest through logging followed by farming. As funding becomes available, the international conservation community hopes to work with local governments to find effective long-term ways to protect the remaining forests.

Case Study 4: Threats to the Genetic Diversity of Endangered Species

When a species is threatened by declining numbers, there is still hope for its survival. Populations can grow when they are protected in the wild, and high-tech methods are available for careful breeding in captivity. Breeders can now freeze eggs and sperm, use artificial insemination, or transfer the embryos of endangered species into nonendangered relatives. However, the loss of genetic diversity that these populations experience in their brush with extinction presents a grave threat that is harder to remedy.

The Guam rail (Figure 7.49), a ground-nesting, flightless bird, needed no defenses against predators on its Pacific island home of Guam. But when the brown tree snake was accidentally introduced to the island, the rail population declined within a few years from about 40,000 to just over 200. Fortunately, biologists were able to capture several rails for breeding before the population fell to zero. There are now hundreds of Guam rails in captivity, but the world population is entirely descended from just 16 individuals. Of course, this sets an upper limit to the amount of diversity in the species' gene pool.

Over time, mutations will increase the amount of genetic diversity, but that process is slow. The only other source of new variation is gene flow from other Guam rails, but there are no other rails. Similarly, the Asiatic wild horse, the only truly wild horse species on the earth, consists of over 1,200 animals descended from just 13; the world population of over 250 red wolves is descended from 13 animals; and the 300 to 400 black-footed ferrets in the world are descended from only nine ferrets.

Isn't it enough that endangered species survive at all? Why should we care about the loss of genetic variation?

There are two reasons. First, generations of breeding among close relatives can lead to reduced vigor, survival rates, and fertility. These genetic disorders are called inbreeding depression. In addition, the long-term survival of each species may depend on its ability to respond to challenges from environmental change or new diseases. This ability requires genetic variation on which natural selection can act. We have seen that a genetically homogeneous strain of rice, or of any other organism, might do quite well under one set of conditions, but it may prove extremely vulnerable if conditions change. To face this threat, zoos worldwide have formed regional and international organizations to coordinate breeding programs for literally hundreds of species in

captivity: endangered primates, cats, antelope, birds, snakes, turtles, and the like. Their goal is to preserve not only the species but also the genetic diversity that the species needs before it can be reintroduced successfully into the wild.

Figure 7.49

Predation by the brown tree snake completely eliminated all natural populations of the Guam rail.

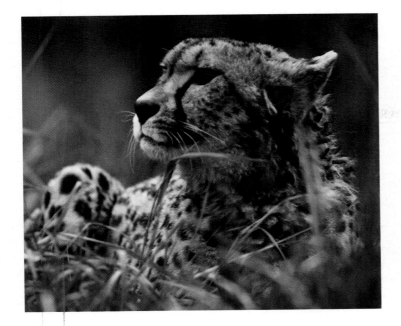

The gene pool of cheetahs is so dangerously reduced that the viability of the species is threatened.

Interpretations: Respond to the following in your *Log:*

1. In what way was biodiversity disrupted in your case study?

2. What were the immediate effects of this disruption?

3. What might be the long-range effects?

4. What are possible solutions to this problem?

5. What more do you need to know before you can suggest reasonable solutions to the problem?

Applications: Respond to the following in your *Log:*

Investigate another situation that threatens biodiversity. Identify the species involved, the nature of the threat, and the potential impact on the rest of the biotic community. This can be a local concern. Prepare a short essay about this situation. In the essay, suggest what can be done to improve the situation.

Extended Inquiry 7.4

What's New at the Zoo?

Many zoos are deeply involved in conservation activities, especially for endangered species. Because some people have accused zoos of contributing to the problem by removing animals from their native habitats, many zoos make a special effort to establish breeding programs so that they no longer need to take animals from the wild and, in some

Many zoos engage in captive breeding programs to maintain and increase populations of threatened and endangered species.

cases, can even restock species in the wild. Investigate this controversial issue more thoroughly. Find out whether zoos have been successful in reintroducing zoo-bred species into the wild. If so, how did they do it?

How do zoos keep the gene pool as diverse as possible? Conduct a survey to find out about zoo programs that address the issue of biodiversity. Visit a local zoo for additional resources. Contact nationally known zoos such as the Cincinnati Zoo, the St. Louis Zoo, the San Diego Zoo, the Bronx Zoo in New York, and the National Zoo in Washington, D.C. Public libraries, scientific journals, and special publications also provide resources.

Extended Inquiry 7.5

Protection and Restoration of Biodiversity

Find patches of vegetation near your home or on your school grounds that vary in size, perhaps garden areas in a lawn or concrete area. Identify at least two areas that differ significantly in size. Sit for 20 minutes beside each island of vegetation, and record in your *Log* each different kind of organism that you see and how many times you see it. You do not have to identify the organism by name; you can just describe it. You may include organisms that are flying through your area as well as those that live there. Calculate the Simpson Diversity Index of each patch size. Look at Guided Inquiry 7.3, to review the procedure for calculating this index. How is the location of a habitat related to its biodiversity? Why or why not? Is preservation of small patches of habitat areas enough to solve the problem of loss of biodiversity?

Self-Check 2

ivide the questions below among your group, and work on your questions as homework. Then discuss each question with your group, until you reach agreement on all questions. Each member of the group will be responsible for understanding the answers to all questions.

1. Evaluate the statement "All living things are the products of the origin and evolution of life on the earth."

2. Give reasons why the earth's environmental changes allowed multicellular plants, flowering plants, insects, and reptiles to evolve. When did this happen?

3. Give several examples of organisms in each of the five kingdoms. Discuss the possibility that a sixth kingdom may soon be defined.

4. Explain the role of distinguishing characteristics in classifying organisms in a taxonomy.

5. Give four examples of resources from the diversity of life that make human existence easier, healthier, safer, or more pleasant.

6. State when each of the following groups of organisms first appeared on the earth: blue-green algae and bacteria, invertebrate animals, vertebrates, land plants, amphibians and reptiles, dinosaurs, mammals, birds, flowering plants, primates, hominids, and humans.

7. Explain why extinction is a natural result of evolutionary change, and list five causes of extinction.

8. Discuss natural selection as a mechanism for evolution.

9. Explain how humans have accelerated extinction beyond its expected natural rate. Give examples of the cost of this extinction both to future humans and to other organisms on the earth.

10. Describe three ways that we know that life forms on earth have changed through time.

11. Explain why preserving biodiversity is important.

Congress

In a poll of 1,200 randomly selected adults in the United States (*Science News*, Vol. 143, June 26, 1993), 73 percent were unfamiliar with the notion of the loss of biological diversity. Moreover, very few people connected the destruction of habitat with the loss of species. Most blamed pollution and the misuse of natural resources as the major threats to biodiversity.

Your task is to help inform the public about biodiversity. What is biodiversity? Why is it important? What threats to biodiversity are now present? What can be done to protect and restore biodiversity?

Refer to the work you did in the Extended Inquiries. You must select a means of communicating this information to your community. It must be presented in a fashion that is informative and entertaining. (People don't learn when they are bored.)

You will work in groups and use one of the following approaches to educate the public. You are also welcome to design another way to accomplish this task.

1. **Billboard:** Draw a scale model of a large billboard advertisement similar to those you see along highways.

2. **Radio talk show:** Produce a radio talk show, perhaps a call-in show, that addresses the issues. Present the show on a public radio station in your area or over the school intercom to other biology classes. You may be able to use a classroom phone or a cellular phone for students to call in questions to you in the front office.

3. Public access TV program: Produce a video that can be shown on public access TV or/and to various citizens of your community. Consider showing it to various civic groups such as the Rotary Club, Optimists, Chamber of Commerce, PTA, Boy Scouts, and Girl Scouts. You might wish to produce an educational video for elementary school children in your area. Consider your audience when you are creating your video. A video that is intended for elementary school children will be very different from one aimed at adults.

4. Newspaper or newsletter: Create a newspaper or newsletter that presents the issues to the public in an interesting, attractive manner. (Many large newspapers make sample layouts for producing mock papers available to schools.) Distribute your newspaper or newsletter to a substantial number of citizens of your community.

SHOULD YOU SUPPORT ZOOS IN YOUR COMMUNITY?

Almost every person has been delighted by visits to zoos. They are almost an American institution. Zoos are very popular with the public largely because many of the animals seem to have interesting behavior and even their own personalities. As much as we all enjoy a visit to the zoo, are zoos good to have? There may be several sides to this question. Are there advantages that are not obvious to the casual observer? Are there any disadvantages? Should your community continue to support zoos?

Some Possible Advantages of Having Zoos

1. Zoos are fun for children.

2. Zoos can be useful for teaching biology.

3. Visiting zoos provides a relaxing family activity.

4. Zoos provide a protective habitat for endangered species.

Some Possible Disadvantages of Having Zoos

1. Some people believe it is inhumane to keep wild animals in captivity.

2. Zoos are an unnatural animal habitat. Animals get bored in zoos, sometimes do not reproduce, and die early in some cases.

3. Zoos cost a lot of money to maintain.

4. Zoo animals sometimes exhibit abnormal behavior.

5. Zoo animals may be dangerous to people.

Procedure

Form small groups. Each group should think about and research one of the advantages or disadvantages listed on page 484. In addition, each group should think of an additional advantage or disadvantage. If you choose an advantage from the list, for example, you should think of another advantage. Each group will then have two statements to evaluate, one from the list and another that is original.

Brainstorm, research, and discuss each of the two statements with your group. Develop two different statements as arguments. Each argument should begin "We should continue to support zoos because . . ." or "We should not continue to support zoos because. . . ." Each argument should be convincing and supported with data.

Community Council Meeting

The class should create a Community Council setting. The Council will be seated in the front of the classroom. One member of each group will become a representative on the Community Council. Two members of each group should present the group arguments to the Council. They should try to be very persuasive. The Council will then vote on whether your community should continue to support zoos or not.

As each council member votes, she or he should explain the reasoning behind the vote. If there is an even number on the Council and the vote ends in a tie, the entire class, including your biology teacher, should vote to break the tie.

Homework

Reflect on the arguments that were presented. Record in your *Log* why you think the Council voted as it did. Also, record your personal reaction to the vote, and explain the basis for your reaction.

Summary of Major Concepts

1. Biological diversity is the total variety of life on the earth, from genes to ecosystems.

2. All living things are the products of the first life forms on the earth. All organisms, therefore, share certain characteristics.

3. The first life forms appeared on the earth about 3.5 billion years ago. They were prokaryotic cells similar to present-day bacteria.

4. Oxygen became a major part of the earth's atmosphere when cyanobacteria started producing it as a by-product of photosynthesis. This available oxygen allowed heterotrophic organisms to evolve.

5. Study of the biodiversity of the earth is important because biodiversity contributes to making human existence easier, healthier, safer, and more pleasant.

6. Major geological events have led to mass extinctions.

7. A species is a particular type of organism, a group of individuals that interbreed in nature and that have a common genetic and evolutionary history. New species arise when a population is isolated and changes to a point at which it can no longer interbreed with members of the original population.

8. Biological variation is the genetic difference in a characteristic within a species.

9. Taxonomy helps to organize our knowledge of living things.

10. An organism's distinguishing characteristics are used to assign it to a taxonomy, that is, a particular kingdom, phylum (or division), class, order, family, genus, and species.

11. The five kingdoms of life are Monera, Protista, Fungi, Plantae, and Animalia.

12. The Simpson Diversity Index is one way to measure biological diversity.

13. Some individuals in a population are more likely to survive and reproduce than others. They pass on their genes to their offspring. This process of natural selection results in evolution.

14. Coevolution can occur when two organisms have life cycles that depend on each other.

15. Evolution is all the changes that have transformed and diversified life on the earth.

16. Different groups of organisms first appeared on the earth at different times.

17. Extinction is a natural result of evolutionary change.

18. Dinosaurs were extinct about 60 million years before humans appeared on the earth.

19. Humans have accelerated extinction beyond its expected natural rate by selective predation and by changing the environment.

Suggestions For Further Exploration

1993. *Endangered Wildlife of the World*. Marshall Cavendish, New York.

This 11-volume encyclopedia describes various endangered or threatened species around the world, covering their habitat, their behavior, and efforts to protect them.

Burton, J.A., Ed. 1991. *The Atlas of Endangered Species*. Macmillan, New York.

This atlas looks at endangered species of the world through geographical regions. It includes a section on conservation in action and a list of conservation organizations.

Burton, R., Ed. *Nature's Last Strongholds*. 1991. New York, Oxford University Press.

An authoritative guide to habitats and protected areas in nearly every country on the earth, with beautiful photographs and extended discussions. It was developed in association with the International Union for the Conservation of Nature.

Facklam, M. 1990. *And Then There Was One: The Mysteries of Extinction*. Sierra Club Books, San Francisco.

This book examines the many reasons for the extinction and near-extinction of animal species. It discusses how some near-extinctions have been reversed through special breeding programs and legislation to save endangered species.

Franklin, D. 1991. The shape of life. *Discover*, 12(10), 10–15.

This article highlights the work of Dr. Mimi Koehl, who specializes in biomechanics. She uses a combination of science research and art to study the natural forms found in life.

Kraus, S.D., and Mallory, K. 1993. *The Search for the Right Whale*. Crown Publishers, New York.

This book follows a team of New England Aquarium scientists as they study migrating North Atlantic right whales and speculates about the future survival of this endangered species.

Martinelli, J., Ed. 1994. *Going Native: Biodiversity in Our Own Backyards*. Brooklyn Botanic Garden, Brooklyn, N.Y.

In this guide, natural landscapers describe how to combine wildflowers and other native species in plantings that provide a refuge for the plants and animals that are disappearing from the land. It includes easy-to-follow garden plans for every major region of the United States.

Morell, V. 1993. Golden window on a lost world. *Discover*, 14(8), 44–52.

Thirty-million-year-old fossils of the residents of a forest were discovered in Caribbean amber. These are being used to study evolutionary biology.

Pringle, L.P. 1992. *Antarctica: Our Last Unspoiled Continent*. Simon & Schuster Books for Young Readers, New York.

This 56-page book surveys the plant and animal life, impact on global ecology, history, and politics of the white continent.

Shipman, P. 1988. An evolutionary tale: What does it take to be a meat eater? *Discover*, 9(9), 39–44.

Humans consume much more meat than other primates do. This article discusses the reasons for humans evolving into carnivores.

Wilson, E.O. 1994. *Naturalist*. Island Press, Washington, D.C.

This autobiography of one of the world's foremost naturalists, Edward O. Wilson, traces his life from a "childhood spent exploring the Gulf Coast of Alabama . . . to life as a tenured professor at Harvard." The book illustrates that a child's curiosity about nature can become a lifelong career.

Wilson, E.O. and Peter, F.M., Eds. 1988. *Biodiversity*. National Academy Press, Washington, D.C.

A collection of essays presented at the National Forum on BioDiversity held in 1986. It offers a view of the complex biological diversity found in the world and lists concerns about mass extinctions of plant and animal species.

How can we improve all life in our global environment?

EIGHT

THE
BIOSPHERE

nitial Inquiry

How can we make earth's resources available to us for the indefinite future?

WHAT IS THE IMPACT OF HUMANS ON THE EARTH?

Welcome to "The Biosphere," the last unit of BIOLOGY: A COMMUNITY CONTEXT. The purpose of this unit is to pull together many of the concepts from earlier units in this text and extend them to a global level. Much of what you learned earlier was in the context of your local community. However, the concepts of biology apply almost everywhere. This unit will let you find out how what you learned about the biology in your community applies to the entire world.

The biosphere is the part of the earth in which all of its organisms live: the surface, water, and atmosphere. The biosphere belongs to all the earth's organisms. We are all part of a global community.

The Video

The setting of this opening video is our entire world. It emphasizes the impact of humans on other organisms. Watch the video, and try to see the connections between organisms. Focus on questions such as the following:

◆ Can we humans learn to coexist with other organisms?

◆ Is it possible to protect, perhaps even improve, the environment?

◆ What can we do better?

◆ What can you as an individual do to make a difference?

Brainstorming

After watching the video, you should have some questions of your own. Discuss them as a class, and record important responses in your *Log*. The following are a few possible questions:

◆ What major issues does the video present?

◆ What human activities are destructive to the biosphere?

◆ What human activities are constructive to the biosphere?

◆ What examples are shown of important connections between organisms?

◆ What are some ways to improve the quality of the biosphere?

Perspective and Scale

Sometimes it is useful to step back and take a look at our environmental issues in a new way. In trying to solve a local dilemma, we can fail to see the larger biological questions. One way to see the larger issues more clearly is to put on "biological glasses."

Imagine a new kind of spectacles with three different views, as shown in Figure 8.1. You can call them BioSpecs. The three views that make up these BioSpecs are:

1. an understanding of the resources needed to sustain life,

2. a grasp of the processes needed to sustain life, and

3. a sense of scale.

You already know quite a bit about the resources that organisms and populations need to sustain life. These may include the soil or growth medium, atmosphere, water, an energy source, and other organisms.

You also know something about the processes that are necessary to sustain life. You have learned about cycles. You've seen resources moving through an organism, a population, a community, an ecosystem, and an entire biosphere. These processes include the water cycle, carbon cycle, nutrient ion cycles, biochemical cycles, ways in which an organism uses energy, the process of nutrition (ingestion to digestion to excretion), reproduction, locomotion, coordination, maintenance, growth, and development.

Now you need to add a sense of scale to your BioSpecs. Scale will help you to see the cumulative effect of both an organism's and a population's impact on an ecosystem. When you look at an individual organism, scale will tell you something about the time period of one generation, how much living space the organism needs, and what resources it requires. When you look at an entire population, scale helps you to consider the size of an individual organism, its population, the area over which the population is spread, and the concept of time. 🌍

Figure 8.1

BioSpecs.

— Scale
— Processes
— Resources

Guided Inquiries

Guided Inquiry 8.1

A Study of Local Human Impact

Human activity has been a major force in changing our environment. Figure 8.2 shows you examples of how human activity has affected local communities. How has human activity changed your local environment? Has it hurt your community? How has it changed from the times of explorers such as John C. Fremont in 1844? In this Inquiry, you will examine human impact in your community.

MATERIALS

- A thermometer
- Pencils
- A metric ruler
- A spoon or trowel
- An outdoor area near school selected by your teacher

Procedure

1. Read "Diary of an Explorer" by John C. Fremont. Then, in a small group, discuss your impressions of the explorer's diary. Write your impressions in your *Log*.

Figure 8.2

How is each of these an example of human impact?

The Biosphere

Diary of an Explorer

The following is an excerpt from the 1844 journal of John Charles Fremont, explorer:

March 27, 1844

Today we traveled steadily and rapidly up the valley—for, with our wild animals, any other gait was impossible—and making about 5 miles per hour. . . .

About one o'clock we came again among innumerable flowers; and a few miles farther, fields of the beautiful blue-flowering lupine, which seems to love the neighborhood of water, indicated that we were approaching a stream. We here found this beautiful shrub in thickets, some of them being twelve feet in height. Occasionally three or four plants were clustered together, forming a grand bouquet about ninety feet in circumference and ten feet high. The whole summit was covered with spikes of flowers, the perfume of which is very sweet and grateful. A lover of natural beauty can imagine with what pleasure we rode among these flowering groves, which filled the air with a light and delicate fragrance.

We continued our road for about half a mile, interspersed through an open grove of live oaks, which in form were the most symmetrical and beautiful we had yet seen in this country. The ends of their branches rested on the ground, formimg somewhat more than a half-sphere of very full and regular figure, with leaves apparently smaller than usual. The California poppy, of a rich orange color, was numerous today. Elk and several bands of antelope made their appearance.

Figure 8.3

This large valley takes up much of the center of California.

Figure 8.4

Once rich in grasses that supported a diverse population of animals, the San Joaquin Valley is now used almost entirely for farming to support Homo sapiens.

2. The valley that John C. Fremont described is the fertile San Joaquin Valley in California (Figures 8.3 and 8.4). Find the San Joaquin (pronounced "wah-keen") Valley on a map of California. How do you suppose it has changed since Fremont described it many years ago? Record your thoughts in your *Log*.

3. Create a data table in your *Log* that you will use to describe the physical features of the outdoor area your teacher has selected. Consider the following variables:

   Air temperature

   Amount of sun

   Soil: (type [sand, loam, clay, topsoil, etc.], depth, moisture, color, compactness)

   Wind (calm, light breeze, windy, strong wind)

4. Journey to the outside area identified by your teacher as a place to observe human impact.

5. At the site, complete your data table for the physical features. Also, describe the following if applicable: asphalt or concrete

under your feet; the materials used in the surrounding buildings, fences, and walls; the sounds of cars, trucks, and air
conditioners.

6. Create another data table to list all the organisms that you see.
Use common names if you know them, or make up names.

7. Visualize what your study area might have looked like at the
time of John C. Fremont. In your *Log,* describe the contour
(curve) of the land's surface and the way it appears to have
been altered. Visualize the plants and animals that might have
been found where you are standing. Describe what might have
been the soil temperature, the amount of sun, and the intensity
of the wind. Speculate on what happened to the plants and
animals that lived here before our time. Explain whether
human activity had a significant impact on the organisms
living here then.

8. Back in the classroom, discuss in small groups how the habitat
that you observed was affected by humans in the past 100 years.
Identify some of the ways in which human activity has affected
the physical features. How do the physical factors now affect the
living things that you found in this habitat?

9. Categorize the different kinds of organisms that you found in
the habitat. Determine the total number of different species that
you identified at the site.

10. Evaluate the reliability of your data. Discuss with your group why
you might have missed some important observations. Consider
season, time of day, or other variables that could account for limited observations at this time. Record some of these reasons.

Interpretations: Respond to the following in your *Log:*

1. How close to the actual number of species do you
think you found? How do you explain this?

2. How many different types of organisms did you find in this
habitat compared to what might have been there when John C.
Fremont was exploring the San Joaquin Valley?

3. What are some of the factors that may have changed the number
of species that are now present?

4. What human activities may have altered or influenced the physical features that you observed?

5. How have humans directly or indirectly affected the biodiversity
in this habitat?

6. How are the problems that you encountered in collecting data similar to the problems that scientists have in trying to determine the number of species in a particular environment?

Applications: Respond to the following in your *Log:*

1. How far do the human influences that you observed reach beyond your schoolyard?
2. In what ways are human activities threatening biodiversity in your community?
3. In what ways are human activities likely to be threatening biodiversity outside your community?
4. Make a list of some significant worldwide human impacts.
5. How desirable is it to try to minimize human influences on the environment? What steps can be taken to do this?

The Earth Summit

Only one head of state attended the 1970 Stockholm Conference on the Human Environment. The 1992 Earth Summit (Figure 8.5), a conference with a similar focus, attracted 115 heads of state. By that measure alone, the human environment has become a vital global issue.

The Stockholm Conference led to the creation of the U.N. Environment Program. At the Earth Summit, one proposal was to convene the U.N. Conference on Environment and Development (UNCED) to judge the success of the U.N. Environment Program. UNCED led to the creation of yet another program, the U.N. Commission on Sustainable Development. Sustainable development means that we should preserve our earth's

Figure 8.5

The 1992 Earth Summit.

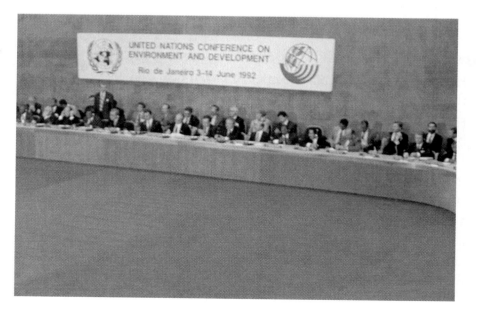

The Biosphere

resources for the future, using them only at a rate that allows them be replenished. Many people now realize that:

◆ environmental degradation is closely related to poverty,

◆ meaningful environmental protection for the planet requires economic development for the poor countries of the world, and

◆ development should be sustainable both economically and environmentally.

How much progress on the quality of the human environment do you think will be noted at the next Earth Summit? Since the 1992 Summit, international agreements have been established on rights in Antarctica, fishing and whaling rights, and rights to minerals on the sea floor. What agreements should we make about development of other planets in our solar system? What right do we have to develop, or even explore, the planets? 🌎

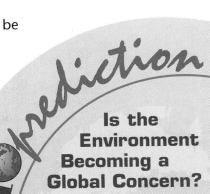

BioPrediction

Is the Environment Becoming a Global Concern?

Do you see any trend in participation by nations in global environmental conferences such as UNCED? What do you think will be the trend over the next 20 years? Respond in your *Log.*

A 40th Century View of Today's Human Niche

An archeologist is a scientist who studies human civilizations of the past. One thing an archeologist might study is a population's ecological niche. The term *ecological niche,* as you probably remember, describes a population's role in an ecosystem. It includes everything that a population removes and returns to the biosphere. To determine a population's ecological niche, archeologists look at how an ancient civilization interacted with other organisms and with the environment. They ask what species the civilization used for food and how the population interacted with other species. A species' niche distinguishes it from all other species. Archeologists get clues about a population's niche from the remains it leaves behind. How might future archeologists interpret current U.S. society from its remains? (Figure 8.6 on page 499).

In this Inquiry, you will be part of a team of archeologists in the year A.D. 4000, approximately 2,000 years in the future. (This could be much the same as looking back to the first century A.D. from today.) You have uncovered what appear to be the remains of an ancient city in what once was the United States of America. You estimate that the ruin dates back to approximately A.D. 2000. You have brought back some artifacts to your laboratory for study. You will examine the artifacts and determine the ecological niche of *Homo sapiens* in the year A.D. 2000.

You have some prior knowledge of ancient *Homo sapiens,* including the written and spoken language in this part of the world in A.D. 2000.

BIOoccupation

Mel Goodwin: Urban Ecologist

When you think of an ecologist, you probably picture someone studying nature in the rain forest or on the shore of a lake. But Dr. Mel Goodwin is an urban ecologist. He helps people learn ways to make positive contributions to the environment in their communities.

In most urban areas, the basic community sources such as transportation, housing, water, and electricity are managed by separate agencies, even though they are closely related. Ignoring these connections is one of the most common causes of conflict between development and the environment. Dr. Goodwin's non-profit Harmony Project is dedicated to building sustainable communities. The Project's activities involve a partnership among citizens, businesses, community groups, and government agencies.

Just what are sustainable communities? They are communities that are in balance with their surrounding environment. They recycle, protect the local plants and animals, use energy-efficient transportation and housing, and protect their water quality. Citizens work together to make a positive impact on their environment. Dr. Goodwin says, "We often look to nature as a source of models for human systems."

Dr. Goodwin's current mission is to develop projects that show sustainable development in a wide variety of social and economic settings. "In a typical week, I could be working on a project to build affordable housing that is energy-efficient. Or we might look at ways to recycle building materials or provide help with community gardens." Much of Dr. Goodwin's time is spent talking with neighborhood groups and local businesses about environmental friendliness.

The hardest part of Dr. Goodwin's job involves convincing people that humans can have a positive impact on their surrounding environment. He says, "Economic growth and development are often seen only as environmentally destructive." But when he sees people begin to improve their communities and their own lives, he knows it is all worthwhile. He also enjoys the education program that his nonprofit project sponsors, in which students participate in environmental dramas or volunteer as water quality monitors.

How does one become an urban ecologist? Dr. Goodwin worked in natural resource management in several countries before he became an urban ecologist. He recommends a variety of work experiences, starting in high school. Look for internships or summer job experiences, and find local projects that deal with sustainable development. Take college-level courses in ecology, business, and community planning. Although there are no specific requirements, most jobs as an urban ecologist will require a college degree.

Figure 8.6

A possible 40th century view of today's human niche.

However, you are not sure exactly how this ancient civilization coexisted with other organisms. Your team is especially interested in how these interactions occurred.

MATERIALS

- Selected "ancient" artifacts, presumably from remains of a city near you circa A.D. 2000

Procedure

1. Work in research teams of three or four.
2. Examine the ancient artifacts. Note visual clues of how *Homo sapiens* lived. How did these humans get their food? How did they influence other organisms?
3. Determine the identity and possible use of each item.
4. Make a table like the one in Figure 8.7 to organize your observations.

Possible Names of Artifacts	Possible Uses of Artifacts	Evidence of Human Niche

Figure 8.7

A sample artifact inventory data table for Guided Inquiry 8.2.

5. Discuss with your research team how each item might help to define the ecological niche of *Homo sapiens*.

Interpretations: Respond to the following with your group, recording the answers in your *Log:*

1. What did *Homo sapiens* as a species in this community appear to (a) give to and (b) take from the biosphere?

2. What may have been the human impact on other organisms at that time?

3. What effect did these humans likely have on the physical environment?

4. What might have been some unique aspects of the human niche compared to the niches of other organisms?

5. On the basis of your observations, describe the ecological niche of these ancient humans.

Applications: Respond to the following in your *Log:*

1. Write a paragraph evaluating the probable U.S. human niche during the year 2000. You will report this description to your senior archeologist. How did the niche of *Homo sapiens* cause this species to benefit or harm itself, other organisms, and the physical environment?

2. From your knowledge of the human niche in the ear 2000, predict the human niche on the earth in the year 4000. What will the human world be like in A.D. 4000?

3. What evidence from your local community supports your prediction?

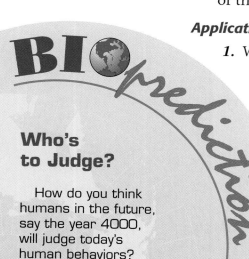

BIO prediction

Who's to Judge?

How do you think humans in the future, say the year 4000, will judge today's human behaviors? How would you want them to judge us? Respond in your *Log.*

BI🌎occupation

The Garcias: Family Sustainable Agriculture

Allen and Sandra Garcia and their daughters, Jennifer (12) and Raquel (15), live in the northern Sacramento Valley of California. They love to talk about rice, wildlife, and their family business: sustainable rice farming.

This landscape now produces more than 200 crops, but it once supported one of the greatest concentrations of migratory waterfowl on the earth. During the 1970s and 1980s, people needed land for agriculture, dams, reservoirs, waterway diversion, and home sites. As a result, many of California's wetlands disappeared. The visits of migratory waterfowl decreased dramatically. People began looking for solutions to the problems created by this rapid development.

The Garcia family participates in a unique alliance of agricultural and environmental interests called the California Ricelands Habitat Partnership. This organization has a plan underway to make the Sacramento Valley home again for migratory waterfowl and, at the same time, to improve farming.

In the valley, rice fields flood naturally with several inches of water from April through October. After a fall harvest, most farmers currently drain the fields and burn the rice stubble to prepare the fields for spring planting. The fields are drained again the following spring, when waterfowl usually visit the wetlands. This practice causes at least three problems:

- The burning causes large-scale air pollution.

- The draining wastes valuable water.

- The crops have to be artificially fertilized.

The new plan lets the rains flood the fields naturally and leaves them undrained, as they were before the rice farmers arrived. The Garcias and others have devised ways that crops can be planted and harvested in undrained fields.

When the fields remain flooded, they become an instant habitat for thousands of waterfowl. The birds flock to the fields in search of leftover rice and natural food such as arthropods and worms. They break up the rice stubble and leave behind natural fertilizer. The results benefit everyone and help to conserve natural resources. The plan also helps endangered bird species to maintain their populations, preserving diversity.

Many farmers are following the Garcias' lead toward a more sustainable future. Jennifer and Raquel Garcia will someday run the family business themselves and carry on a tradition of sustainability.

Energy Consumption

Recall from Guided Inquiry 2.5, "Trophic Scavenger Hunt," that an energy pyramid consists of trophic levels. The pyramid shows the relative amount of food energy available to organisms at each level. Figure 8.8 shows a diagram of an energy pyramid for a typical ecosystem. As a given parcel of energy moves through the ecosystem from producers to consumers, less of it is available to organisms at the next trophic level. Why is this so? Where does the "lost" energy go?

In this Inquiry, you will explore the extent to which available energy is passed along the energy pyramid as it is consumed by organisms at each trophic level. You will also explore some implications of this model for how most effectively to feed hungry populations.

Figure 8.8

An energy pyramid for a typical terrestrial ecosystem.

ENERGY CONTENT OF TROPHIC LEVELS

Decomposers

Tertiary consumers (Top carnivores)

Secondary consumers

Primary consumers

Producers

Energy content

MATERIALS

- Metric ruler

Procedure

1. Copy the diagram in Figure 8.8 into your *Log*. Next to each space on the diagram, write an example of an organism that exists at that trophic level in a terrestrial ecosystem of your choice.

2. Predict what percentage of the energy is transferred up the pyramid from one trophic level to the next. Use the areas of the spaces that represent each trophic level in the diagram to help in your prediction. Write these figures in the appropriate spaces on the pyramid.

3. Now examine some data. Figure 8.9 indicates the amount of energy in Calories that is present in each trophic level in an actual ecosystem. Working from the bottom of the pyramid to the top, calculate the energy that is transferred from level to level. For example, the

Producers	Primary Consumers	Secondary Consumers	Tertiary Consumers
11,206 Calories	1,093 Calories	128.3 Calories	12.1 Calories

Figure 8.9

Amount of energy in Calories present in each trophic level in an ecosystem.

percentage available to the primary consumers is 1,093 Calories ÷ 11,206 Calories. Write this percentage and the percentages for each level above producers on the diagram in your *Log*.

4. Calculate an overall trend by averaging the percentages for primary, secondary, and tertiary consumers.

Interpretations: Respond to the following in your *Log*:

1. What is the pattern for the percentage of energy transferred from one trophic level to another? Express this as a percentage.

2. How close was your prediction in Step 2 to the actual percentage? Explain.

3. Why is a pyramid a reasonable representation of this energy flow?

4. All organisms use energy to metabolize, grow, and reproduce. When organisms die, they are consumed by decomposers and all the remaining energy in their bodies is depleted. What happens to the rest of the energy from each trophic level?

Applications: Respond to the following in your *Log*:

1. Assume that the producer level consists of 1,000 kilograms of grain. *Homo sapiens* can follow either of the following feeding strategies:

   ◆ Strategy 1: *Homo sapiens* feeds at the primary consumer level.

   ◆ Strategy 2: Cattle feed at the primary consumer level, and *Homo sapiens* feeds at the secondary consumer level by eating the meat from the cattle.

   a. How much food energy is available to *Homo sapiens* in these situations?

   b. Why do people in heavily populated countries such as China eat mostly grains rather than meat?

   c. Which strategy should be used during a worldwide shortage of food? Why?

2. What are some other consequences of eating more grain and less meat?

3. Why do some persons choose to follow Strategy 2?

4. The energy pyramid is an example of a model that scientists use to make an abstract idea clear. How is this model valuable to society?

What Is the Best Way to Feed the People of the World?

Ninety million people are born every year, more than double the annual increase of 38 million that was observed in 1950 (Figure 8.10). How can we feed all these people?

To answer this question, we must first explore our three major sources of food: oceans, grazing lands, and croplands.

The annual fish catch from the world's oceans was 100 million tons in 1989. National Marine Fisheries biologists say that this is close to the maximum sustainable annual catch. In fact, some biologists believe that many of the world's major fisheries are in serious decline because of overharvesting. Therefore we cannot look to the oceans for additional food. Similarly, the world's grazing lands are being used at or beyond their capacity.

Can croplands provide enough food for everyone? Consider some of the problems:

1. Croplands throughout the world are rapidly being degraded or converted to living space.

   ◆ In Japan, 52 percent of the land used for basic grain crops was lost in recent years, leading to a 33 percent decrease in grain production. This deficit must be made up by importing food from other countries.

   ◆ Some croplands are being degraded by topsoil loss, as in the Mississippi Valley.

   ◆ Some land in Pakistan has become too salty for crops. This salinization occurs where irrigation is a long-term process.

2. Water will become a limiting resource in years to come. Irrigation water is in short supply; for example, the Ogallala Aquifer east of the Rocky Mountains is shrinking because of irrigation pumping. Communities in the United States, Saudi Arabia, and other countries are already withdrawing water from deep, irreplaceable underground supplies. Add to this the increasing contamination of water, and the prospect of a water shortage is very real.

3. Current technology will not be able to create great increases in food production. Additional fertilizer is no longer increasing crop yields, and biotechnology has not yet come up with products that dramatically increase food production.

Frank and Ernest

THE ENVIRONMENT RESERVES THE RIGHT TO REFUSE SERVICE TO ANYONE.

Figure 8.10

Can we feed all the people on the earth?

What to Do?

What is the world to do? One step is to alter eating patterns, especially in the more affluent countries. Consider the environmental cost of meat consumption. Individuals in low-income countries such as India consume approximately 200 kilograms of grain per year, about one-half kilogram per day. People in affluent countries such as the United States and Canada consume approximately 800 kilograms of grain per year, most of it indirectly as meat, dairy products, and eggs from animals that eat the grain. As countries become more affluent, they use more of their grain to feed livestock. For example, before 1978, only 8 percent of the grain that was produced in China was fed to livestock. By 1990, this figure was 20 percent, mostly due to increased pork production. Look at Figure 8.11 on page 506 to see how much grain is needed to feed livestock to produce meat.

The volume of food that is produced globally could feed all the people in the world for now, if the available food were equally distributed. However, the maximum world food output probably cannot sustain each

Figure 8.11

Efficiency of conversion of grain to meat and dairy products.

MEAT AND DAIRY PRODUCTS	KILOGRAMS OF GRAIN REQUIRED TO ADD 1 KILOGRAM OF LIVE WEIGHT
Beef cattle	7
Hogs	4
Poultry and fish	2

Source: Data excerpted from Lester R. Brown and Hal Kane. 1994. *Full House: Reassessing the Earth's Population Carrying Capacity.* W.W. Norton & Company, New York.

individual at the current U.S. rate. The world grain harvest in 2030 is projected to be 1.9 trillion kilograms. At the U.S. consumption rate of 800 kilograms per year, this grain output could feed approximately 2.5 billion people. At the Indian consumption rate of 200 kilograms per year, it could feed about 10 billion people. The world population is currently 5.5 billion people; and in 2030, it will be 8.9 billion. The projected grain harvest would provide 240 kilograms per year per person, less than the current consumption in China (400 kilograms per year per person) and only slightly more than the current consumption in India. Are you willing to change your eating habits? What else might help to resolve this dilemma? 🌍

Guided Inquiry 8.4

The Last Compost Audit

Months ago, you started a compost column and/or a compost pile. Periodically throughout the year, you have cared for it and analyzed the changes that occurred. Your measurements have been qualitative as well as quantitative, and your *Log* should enable you to see long-term changes that have taken place.

Compost formation models what occurs in natural systems. You have studied the causes and effects of decomposition, living organisms in the compost pile, physical factors that influence composting, and the idea that in natural systems changes occur over time. What has happened in your compost over the school year?

MATERIALS

- Microscope
- Balance
- pH paper or pH meter
- Still camera (analog or digital)
- Moisture meter

Procedure

1. Sample your compost with methods previously used. This is your last chance to collect data on temperature, living things present, moisture, and amount of remaining compost.

2. Take a picture of what is left in your compost pile and put it in your *Log*.

3. Make other observations that seem appropriate.

4. Dispose of your compost column and its contents as indicated by your teacher. In most cases, you will have one of the following options:

   ◆ Take the compost column home and continue adding materials. As compost is formed, add it to a flower bed or garden area. This is the preferred option.

   ◆ Take the compost column home, distribute its contents in a flower bed or garden area, and send the plastic containers to a recycling center.

   ◆ Place the compost and plastic into separate classroom containers, as designated by your teacher. Your teacher will distribute the compost in an appropriate area, and will send the plastic to a recycling center.

Interpretations: Respond to the following in your *Log:*

One of your BioSpecs lenses is a sense of scale; one aspect of this sense is how time affects natural processes. Write a final summary page that describes the changes in the various factors that you studied throughout the year in the compost. Include some of the major changes over time such as living and nonliving factors, nutrient recycling, and the succession of organisms.

Applications: Respond to the following in your *Log:*

Write a paragraph that tells what you think about composting. What value does it have to your community? Give reasons why you would use composting in your future life. What influence would this practice have on the global environment? What sorts of differences could it make?

BI🌐thoughts

How Could Composting Make a Difference?

What do you predict would happen to your compost column if you left it alone for another year?

Would You Make the Investment?

A friend approaches you with a sure-fire money-making scheme. He believes that there is a demand for mink coats. Why not raise minks for coats? These are ranch-raised minks, so you don't need to worry about driving minks to extinction.

Your friend says all you have to do is buy 1,000 kilograms of grain at one dollar a kilogram. Buy a few fertile laboratory rats, feed them some grain, and let them multiply. Then you buy a male and female mink. (The cost of the animals and their shelters won't be over $1,000. Minks are carnivores, so you can eventually feed them rats.)

As the rats multiply, you feed them more grain. As the minks multiply, you feed them more rats. Eventually, you have lots of rats, quite a few minks, and not much grain. No problem your friend says, the 1,000 kg of grain will produce 1,000 kg of minks. You now have 1,000 kg of rats that you can feed to the minks, resulting in the 1,000 kg of minks. The result will be 500 minks, weighing about 2 kilograms each. Sounds great so far.

Then you start selling the mink pelts to the coat manufacturer. The pelts sell for at least $50 each. Five hundred mink pelts will earn you $25,000. But here's the really good news: A mink pelt weighs only 0.2 kilogram (200 grams), 10 percent of the mink's total body, so you still have 1.8 kilograms of mink carcass left over after you skin each mink. Since rats eat almost anything, you can feed them the 900 kilograms of mink carcass. The rats will now support 450 new minks, whose coats you can sell for $22,500.

You can repeat this process over and over, feeding the rats to the minks and the mink carcasses to the rats. Your estimated profit each cycle is $25,000 + $22,500 + $20,250 + $18,225 and so on. The number of minks decreases in each cycle, but before you run out of mink, you will have a huge fortune!

Sound too good to be true? Maybe it is. Would you make the investment? Why or why not? Explain your position in your *Log*. Base your arguments on what you have already learned in this unit, and do some mathematical analysis to support your position.

Self-Check 1

You should by now have completed most or all of Guided Inquiries 8.1 through 8.4. As a result of these experiences and the corresponding readings, you should be able to answer the following questions. Divide the questions below among the members of your group, and work on your questions as homework. Then discuss each question with your group until you reach agreement on all questions. Each member of the group will be responsible for understanding the answers to all questions.

1. In what ways have humans influenced
   ◆ the physical environment in your local community?
   ◆ the organisms in your local community?
   ◆ the physical environment worldwide?
   ◆ all organisms worldwide?

2. What are some important factors that affected the human impact on the environment in the past?

3. What is the ecological niche of *Homo sapiens* worldwide? How does this vary within the species?

4. What have been some of the positive effects of human existence on
   ◆ the physical environment of the world?
   ◆ other organisms?

5. How do China and Mexico feed more people with a given amount of grain than the United States does?

6. As the world population increases, what will happen to our ability to sustain a diet that contains considerable amounts of meat? Explain.

7. What happens to compost over a period of several months?

8. List several benefits of composting at your home. What are possible benefits to your community and to the entire biosphere?

Frank and Ernest

YOU SHOULD HAVE MADE THEM PUT UP A DAMAGE DEPOSIT.

THAVES 4-1

E-Mail: FandE BobT@AOL.COM

Prepare an abstract representing your best research from one of the Guided Inquiries in Unit 8. This abstract should contain:

a. the title of the Inquiry

b. the question being investigated

c. a specific hypothesis being tested, if applicable

d. a summary of results

e. your interpretations

f. applications of your study to your community

Procedure

1. Get together in small groups and present your abstract to your group as the conference proceedings. Each presentation should be about five minutes.

2. At the end of the presentation, ask members of your group for their response to your research. Record this feedback in your *Log*.

Homework

Revise your abstract for homework based upon the feedback from your group. Your teacher may want to inspect your final abstract.

Revisiting My Own Population

In Guided Inquiry 3.1, you began an ongoing experiment in which you cared for the population of an organism. Your goal was to enable the population to survive through the year. If you were successful, now is a great time to make a final observation on your population.

MATERIALS

- A microscope
- Hand lenses
- Forceps

Procedure

Compare the number of individuals in your population now to the number of individuals with which you began. Make a plot in your *Log* of population size versus time. What is the trend?

Observe the appearance of your population (color, shape, smell, activity level of the individuals) and the environment surrounding your population (room temperature, light, food available, moisture). In your *Log*, write a description of the growth and survival of your population. Were you successful in meeting your goal? Why or why not?

Sustainability in My Community

What does *sustainable* mean? Are there any sustainable activities in your community? How are they unique? Why are sustainable activities so important for our survival? In this Inquiry, you will look for a local example of a sustainable activity and determine the extent to which it is having a positive impact on your environment.

MATERIALS

- Telephone and/or public transportation access
- A still or video camera

Day One: In Class

Procedure

1. Make sure you understand what a sustainable activity is and how to recognize one when you see it. To accomplish this, you can:
   - ◆ look up *sustainability* or *sustainable* in an encyclopedia,
   - ◆ find short articles or readings on sustainability,
   - ◆ ask your teacher for clarification,
   - ◆ discuss sustainability with your class or find experts, and/or
   - ◆ read "Is Sustainability a Future Necessity?" on the following page.

2. Find out from your teacher the timeline for completion of this project.

3. Divide into working teams of two to four.

4. Determine the resources your team has for investigating sustainable activities in your community. For example, you may have use of a telephone, e-mail, a fax machine, transportation, a public library, or your Chamber of Commerce. You may also have some experts available, such as environmental scientists, sustainable farmers, university faculty, or business and industry representatives who are very sensitive to the need to preserve environmental resources. Make a list in your *Log* of all the resources available to you.

5. Discuss what data you will want to collect on the sustainable activity observed. Consider such factors as the name, location, visual data, contact person(s), products produced, resources needed to make the product, cost of the product, and what the activity takes and gives back to the environment. What are some other data categories? Write these categories in your *Log* as the possible variables to study.

Subsequent Days: Outside of Class

Procedure

1. Using the resources you identified, collect the data indicated in Step 5 above by making a personal visit to the location of the activity. Not every member of the team needs to visit the actual site. If a personal visit is not practical, try a phone interview with employees. Regardless of how you get your information, be sure to ask for relevant literature about the activity.

2. Get together with your group after data have been collected, and share your observations.

Interpretations: Respond to the following in your *Log:*

1. Make a judgment about the sustainability of the activity that you investigated. Use the following criteria:
   ◆ Does it have a long-term impact on the environment?
   ◆ Does it make minimal use of nonrenewable resources?
   ◆ Could it continue indefinitely using existing natural resources?

2. In your *Log*, describe any clearly unique aspect of the activity that you investigated.

Applications: Respond to the following in your *Log:*

Write a short paragraph discussing the importance of using sustainable activities in your community. Why is it important for human survival? Why is it important on a global level?

Is Sustainability a Future Necessity?

Sustainable development has been defined in hundreds of ways. A popular definition comes from a 1987 report by the World Commission on Environment and Development, *Our Common Future:* "sustainable development . . . meets the needs of the present without compromising the ability of future generations to meet their own needs." This development includes activities such as that shown in Figure 8.12.

Barbara Bramble at the U.S. follow-up conference to the Earth Summit ("From Rio to the Capitols: State Strategies for Sustainable Development," Louisville, Kentucky, 1993) referred to three E's of sustainable development: ecology, economics, and equity. Explained that "'sustainable development' is shorthand for what it really means: 'economically viable, ecologically sustainable, and socially equitable' development."

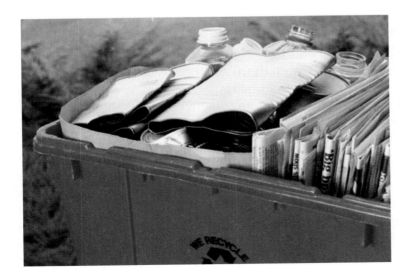

Figure 8.12

What qualifies this activity as sustainable?

Ecology

The first E, *ecology,* stresses environmental sustainability. Generally this includes living on what organisms produce rather than on the organisms themselves and not harvesting resources faster than they are replenished. It also means taking a long-term, global view rather than seeing no farther than your neighborhood's current problems. It requires a holistic perspective on human, biological, and physical systems.

Economics

The second E, *economics,* stresses sustainable development. Economic aid to developing countries has usually aimed to improve quality of life through industrialization and Western agricultural methods. Although the exports resulting from this aid provide increased income, they can also result in pollution and other environmental problems that the United States and other developed countries are confronting. Economic growth alone is not a reliable indicator of improved quality of life. Economic development should lead to sustainable improvements in production and human health.

Equity

The third E is *equity,* which addresses issues of social justice and environmental justice. At the global level, is it just that the 20 percent of the human population that resides in North America and Europe consumes 80 percent of the planet's resources? Equity requires that population, consumption, and distribution patterns change. It is quite probable that we will shift from viewing national and international security as strictly a military issue toward viewing it also as an environmental issue. As this shift occurs, equity issues are likely to become as important as human rights in international relations. As geographical boundaries between nations become less defined, as they have within the European community, issues such as equity in the use of world resources will be examined more as global than as national issues.

Sustainable Methods

Our environment can sustain us if it can tolerate, or recover from, what we do to it. Sustainable methods of working with our environment do not deplete precious environmental resources such as water, topsoil, minerals, or fossil fuels and do not pollute the environment. A sustainable production process could continue indefinitely if it is both environmentally and economically sound.

Some methods of farming can cause erosion, loss of nutrients, and pollution of soil and water. Farmers who use sustainable agriculture practices might not till the soil, thus limiting erosion. Sustainable irrigation techniques such as that shown in Figure 8.13 would preserve fresh water sources. Rotating crops replaces chemicals in the soil naturally, preserving fertility. Cutting back on chemical fertilizers and preventing them from entering local water sources as well as reducing the use of pesticides and finding less harmful alternatives are other sustainable agriculture practices.

Figure 8.13

How would this drip irrigation qualify as sustainable?

Aquaculture is another activity that can be sustainable. Food such as shrimp, oysters, and fish can be cultured in a small area such as a lagoon, a human-made pond, or part of a lake. The food is harvested regularly, and young organisms are reintroduced so that the cycle can continue. The organisms are grown under conditions like those in natural environments. A well-designed aquaculture system can have minimal effects on the environment. Sustainable aquaculture thus contrasts with our usual methods of catching fish, and other marine organisms. These methods deplete natural populations, in some cases to the brink of extinction.

Other potentially sustainable activities include the following:

1. Building a sewage treatment plant that uses methane from biological decomposition of raw sewage to fuel all the energy needs in the plant. The plant could even create extra methane that could be sold for profit.

2. Growing additional plants to help balance carbon dioxide and oxygen in the atmosphere.

3. Composting plant material.

4. Recycling cans and bottles.

5. Recycling used motor oil.

6. Repairing household items.

7. Using household gray water.

8. Recycling newspapers. 🌍

Can Sustainability and Population Growth Work Together?

You learned in Unit 3 about the population increase of *Homo sapiens*. With this growth has come deterioration of the environment. If you use history as a predictor, this trend will continue. However, the idea of sustainability suggests that we can actually improve the environment, not just preserve it. But we can't curb world population growth in just a few decades. Can we actually have sustainability as long as the population increases? Respond in your *Log*.

Trees Versus Lumber: What Is the Difference?

Find a large tree such as the one in Figure 8.14. Touch it, and examine it closely. Think about what functions the tree now performs for organisms in its environment. Compare them to the functions that it would perform if it were cut for lumber.

Lumber and By-Products

For this Inquiry, you will visit your local lumberyard or other industry that uses wood or wood products (such as furniture manufacturers, paper mills, prefabricated buildings factory, etc.). Investigate the number of species of trees that are used for lumber and the role of living things in the production of building material. Find a knowledgeable employee, and make a list of all species that are used in the lumber and wood products in the lumberyard. Find the origin of each product, and determine how each product is used.

Some specific questions to pursue are the following:

1. Which species or products are more expensive and why?

2. How are timber shortages affecting the business that you visited?

3. To what extent does this business depend on imports from other countries?

In addition to recording data in your *Log*, write a summary that reflects on these questions. Include your thoughts on the following:

- Why would you consider lumber a global concern?
- What global factors may affect the availability of future lumber?
- What action can you take to ensure that lumber will be available to your children?

The Earth As an Apple

Our planet, with the help of the sun, is currently meeting the needs of all living things for food, water, and shelter. But what portion of the planet serves as habitat for us and all land-dwelling animals?

Figure 8.14

What are the long-term benefits of this tree to the biosphere?

MATERIALS

- A fresh apple (furnished by you)
- A small knife

Procedure

1. Seventy to seventy-five percent of the earth is covered by oceans. Cut your apple into fourths, and remove three of the pieces, leaving one-quarter of the apple in your hand.
2. Thirty percent of this remaining quarter is desert, too dry for humans to live on. Cut off a third, leaving about two-thirds of the quarter apple.
3. Thirty percent of this remaining area is mountains, too high for humans to live on. Cut off a piece, leaving about 40 percent of the apple quarter.
4. Peel the skin from the small piece of apple. This skin represents the biosphere, that part of the earth and atmosphere which supports life.

SAFETY NOTE

Use care in handling the knife.

Interpretations: Respond to the following in your *Log*:

1. How accurate is this model of the earth?
2. Can you think of any other restrictions that might nibble away more of the skin?
3. How long do you think it will take for humans to consume the skin?

Applications: Choose and complete one of the following activities:

1. Develop a demonstration for an elementary school class that would help the students to understand the limited amount of living space on the earth.

517

2. The apple demonstration applies just to humans and other land-dwelling animals. Investigate living organisms that are hardy enough to live at high altitudes on mountains, in deserts, in ocean trenches, and in freezing water. Prepare a poster presentation that illustrates their habitats.

3. The wax layer on our apple can represent the atmosphere of the earth. We put over 700 million kilograms of pollutants into this layer each year. Investigate what these pollutants are, their effects, and ways that we can reduce them. Prepare an audiovisual presentation aimed at the general public.

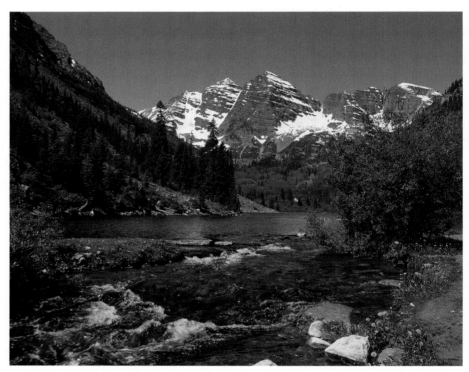

View of the Maroon Bells, Colorado. We want to preserve and protect diverse natural areas such as this.

Self-Check 2

Divide the questions below among the members of your group, and work on your questions as homework. Then discuss each question with your group until you reach agreement on all questions. Each member of the group will be responsible for understanding the answers to all questions.

1. Explain the factors that were responsible for the success (or death) of your own population.

2. Describe the level of comfort in which you live (from basic needs to pure luxury). What are some of the global ecological costs of existing at this level?

3. At which comfort level do you think most of the people in the following geographical regions live? What is significant about their differences?

   ◆ Taiwan
   ◆ Russia
   ◆ Switzerland
   ◆ Argentina

4. We know that three countries—Japan, Germany, and the United States—consume a highly disproportionate amount of the world's resources, such as energy, timber, and minerals. This happens because their citizens, on the average, live at a much higher level of comfort than the people in the rest of the world do. What does this level of comfort cost the rest of the world in ecological terms?

5. What are some of the direct effects on nonhuman life in other countries of importing their materials and products into our country? How do these affect the entire biosphere?

6. How is global cooperation necessary to preserve life in the biosphere?

7. Define sustainability and give an example of a sustainable activity in your community.

8. Explain how your example in #7 meets the criteria for a sustainable activity.

"If the Earth Were a Village of 1000 People"

by Donella H. Meadows
(adapted with permission)

If the world were a village of 1000 people, it would include:

584 Asians

150 East and West Europeans

124 Africans

84 Latin Americans

52 North Americans

6 Australians and New Zealanders

The people of the village would have considerable difficulty in communicating.

165 people would speak Mandarin

86 English

83 Hindu/Urdu

64 Spanish

58 Russian

37 Arabic

That list would account for the mother tongues of only half the villagers. The other half would speak, in descending order of frequency, Bengali, Portuguese, Indonesian, Japanese, German, French, and 200 other languages.

In this village of 1000 there would be:

329 Christians (among them 187 Catholics, 84 Protestants, 31 Orthodox, and 27 others)

178 Moslems

167 "non-religious"

132 Hindus

60 Buddhists

45 atheists

3 Jews

86 all other religions

One-third (330) of the 1000 people in the world village would be children and only 60 would be over the age of 65. Half the children would be immunized against preventable infectious diseases such as measles and polio.

Just under half of the married women in the village would have access to and use modern contraceptives. The first year 28 babies would be born. That year, ten people would die, three for lack of food, one from cancer. Two of 28 babies would die within the year. One person of the 1000 in the village would be infected with the HIV, but that person probably would not yet have developed a full-blown case of AIDS.

With the 28 births and ten deaths, the population of the village in the second year would be 1,018.

In this thousand-person community, 200 people would receive 75 percent of the income; another 200 would receive only two percent of the income.

Only 70 people would own an automobile, although some of the 70 would own more than one automobile.

About one-third would have access to clean, safe drinking water.

Of the 670 adults in the village, half would be illiterate.

The village would have 2.43 hectares of land per person, 2,428 hectares in all, of which

283 hectares would be cropland

567 hectares pasture

769 hectares woodland

809 hectares desert, tundra, pavement, and other wasteland

The woodland would be declining rapidly; the wasteland increasing. The other land categories would be roughly stable.

The village would use 83 percent of its fertilizer on 40 percent of its cropland, the land owned by the richest and best-fed 270 people. Excess fertilizer running off this land would be causing pollution in lakes and wells. The remaining 60 percent of the land, with its 17 percent of the fertilizer, would produce 28 percent of the food grains and feed 73 percent of the people. The average grain yield on that land would be one-third the harvest achieved by the richer villagers.

In the village of 1,000 people there would be:

5 soldiers

7 teachers

1 doctor

3 refugees, driven from home by war or drought

The village has a total budget each year, public and private, of over $3 million—$3,000 per person if it were distributed evenly. It isn't, as we have already seen.

Of the total $3 million:

$181,000 goes to weapons and warfare

$159,000 for education

$132,000 for health care

The remainder goes for a variety of other services and for village government employees. 🌍

For this Congress, your task is to develop a proclamation that will provide global guidelines for sustaining the biosphere. You will present your proclamation at the Forum.

By now you are aware that some of the major biosphere issues facing your generation are atmospheric pollution, loss of biological diversity, deforestation, desertification, global warming, ozone depletion, societal wastes, soil loss, and degradation of water quality.

You also recognize that these nine issues are interrelated. Your job will be to focus on the relationship between two issues. These relationships are both real and complex; the solutions will also be complex.

Consider the following combinations of the global issues. Select a combination that interests you.

- Global warming and ozone depletion
- Deforestation and loss of diversity
- Desertification and soil loss
- Atmospheric pollution and global warming
- Water quality degradation and waste disposal
- Ozone depletion and waste disposal
- Deforestation and global warming
- Soil loss and deforestation
- Loss of diversity and global warming
- Water quality degradation and deforestation

Procedure

Break into groups of two to four students who have selected the same combination of issues. Give your group the name of a nation for which this specific combination of issues may be particularly important. Your teacher may help you select the issues so that all issues are represented.

Your job is to develop a proclamation that addresses a solution to the related pair of issues. (The proclamation is a precise statement that is to be obeyed by all participating nations.) Find supporting documentation to construct your proclamation.

Put on your BioSpecs (Figure 8.15) and proceed:

1. Investigate the two issues, considering causes, relationships, differences, and consequences.

   ◆ Identify the resources that are available to combat the problem. Consider nonliving factors such as energy, water, and atmosphere, as well as organisms.

   ◆ Explain the processes, such as evolution, cycles, and interdependence, in the issue you are investigating.

   ◆ Address the scales—time, space, and cumulative effects—that the issues involve.

   ◆ Consider population growth as a factor.

2. Construct your proclamation so that it is coherent, is well documented, and makes a strong case. The proclamation may have a list of assumptions (given statements) and resolutions (recommendations).

During the Forum, a Gobal Summit, members may choose to use a single recommendation from a group and add it to another group's proclamation. To build support for your recommendations, you may want to negotiate with another group to combine your proclamation with theirs.

Figure 8.15

BioSpecs.

Scale
Processes
Resources

A GLOBAL SUMMIT

This Forum is a global citizens' meeting. The objective is to identify the proclamations from the Congress which have the highest priority for the entire world. Only three proclamations will be selected for implementation.

Procedure

1. Select one representative from each group in the Congress to present the group's proclamation. The remainder of the class will be representatives from other nations of the world.

2. No presider is needed, since each nation has equal stature at the meeting. If your class feels that it needs a presider to keep order, one can be elected.

3. Allow each representative five minutes for the presentation or the proclamation and supporting arguments. Because each nation's proclamation is its highest national priority, presentations need to be as convincing as possible.

4. When all proclamations have been presented, it is time for the global summit to make its decision. Every member of the class (including those who give presentations) should vote for three of the proclamations. Individual votes should be based upon what is believed to be best for the world as a whole.

5. List the three proclamations with the most votes on the board or overhead projector.

6. Copy the three proclamations into your *Log*. Write below these the reasons why you feel they have been selected and what you think their worldwide impact could be.

The Personal Pledge

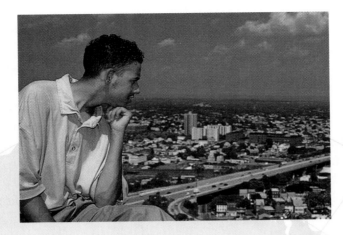

Figure 8.16

This biology student is trying to decide what his personal pledge will be. What will yours be?

This is the grand finale for your biology course. The more freedoms there are in any society, the more its citizens must accept responsibility for their own lives. The Personal Pledge is an opportunity for you to accept some personal responsibility. It also is an opportunity to identify and make a specific, personal contribution to the biosphere. Individual efforts *do* make a difference in preserving and restoring the environment. You should begin preparing for your final commitment several days in advance.

Possible Projects

What can you do? Identify one very specific effort that you will make. Select something that you can do over the next few weeks—or for a year or even longer. It should be constructive, thoughtful, and practical. Here are some possibilities, but you are not limited to them:

◆ Begin a recycling plan at home.
◆ Begin a recycling plan at school.
◆ Set up a worm farm to use home food wastes.
◆ Collect evidence to convince your parents to purchase an environmentally friendly automobile or home appliance.
◆ Set up an organic garden.

◆ Work with young children to increase their understanding of the environment.
◆ Improve the neighborhood's habitat.
◆ Build your own compost pile.
◆ Reduce home water use.
◆ Reduce your energy consumption.
◆ Reduce food waste in cooking and restaurants.
◆ Get an entire group to write to stop receiving junk mail.

Suggested Procedure

1. Do a little thinking and research to verify that your pledge will make an important contribution to the earth.
2. Discuss your ideas with your teacher.
3. Write in your *Log* a plan for your commitment. Describe your pledge—what you are doing and why.
4. Announce your pledge to your class. Be sure that you have completed all preliminary work.

Although you will not execute your entire pledge at this time, seriously consider carrying it out this summer. Remember, you can make a difference in the future of the biosphere.

Summary of Major Concepts

1. Human activities have had unprecedented physical and biological effects on the biosphere.

2. Some of the major types of human influences relate to human overpopulation, pollution, habitat destruction, increased carbon dioxide, ozone depletion, topsoil loss, decreased biodiversity, and energy waste from supporting a luxurious lifestyle.

3. Each time food energy moves up the energy pyramid, less energy is available to the next trophic level because energy transformation is not very efficient.

4. Although many humans are top trophic-level consumers, they can modify their eating habits to eat more economically at lower trophic levels.

5. People in less developed countries tend to make better use of food energy by eating low on the energy pyramid. This means that they eat more plants than animals.

6. Sustainable activities provide for the needs of humans without degrading the potential of the environment to continue providing for these needs over the long term.

7. One example of sustainability is a farm that uses no chemicals, does not break the ground to make it vulnerable to erosion, and does not require external energy other than sunlight to produce crops.

8. The cumulative effects of sustainable human activities may make it possible for humans to provide for themselves in the future without destroying the physical and biological environment of the earth.

9. Highly developed countries consume a vastly disproportionate amount of the world's resources (energy, timber, minerals) because their citizens, on the average, live at a much higher standard of comfort than do the people of the rest of the world. This level of comfort has an ecological cost for the rest of the world.

10. Increased public awareness about ecological and environmental principles is part of the key to protecting and improving our environment.

11. All of us must take steps to preserve the natural world. Our individual contributions are important because they are cumulative. This will benefit not only future humans but most life on the earth.

Suggestions for Further Exploration

Cooper, D.E., and Palmer J.A. 1992. *The Environment in Question: Ethics and Global Issues.* Routledge, London.

Questions about the ethical issues of humans and their environment are addressed by several biologists in the essays in this book. Topics include "What do we owe future generations?" and "The ethics of tourism."

Gould, S.J. 1992. What is a species? *Discover,* 13(12), 40–44.

In this article, Stephen Jay Gould discusses the work of evolutionary biologists as they try to define separate species.

Kellert, S.R., and Wilson, E.O. 1993. *The Biophilia Hypothesis.* Island Press, Washington, D.C.

This book includes essays from many biologists. They are commenting on the philosophy of nature presented by Harvard biologist E.O. Wilson. Topics that are discussed include biophilia and the conservation ethic and the biological basis for human valuing of nature.

Linden, E. 1996. Global fever. *Time,* July 8, p. 56.

Climate change threatens more than megastorms, floods, and droughts. The real peril may be increases in diseases such as cholera, hantavirus, plague, and dengue fever.

Luoma, J.R. 1992. An untidy wonder. *Discover,* 12(10), 86–96.

This article discusses the work of a team of scientists. They have been studying a forest for over 20 years to find out how it works.

Luoma, J.R. 1993. Healing the earth? *Discover,* 14(1), 76–78.

This article discusses the political activities leading to the signing of two environmental treaties at the U.N. Conference on Environment and Development held in Rio de Janeiro in 1992.

Meadows, D.H., Meadows, D.L., Randers, J., Behrens III, W.W. 1972. *The Limits of Growth,* Universe Books, New York.

An examination of the problems facing humans as population size increases.

Plotkin, M.J. 1993. *Tales of a Shaman's Apprentice: An Ethnobotanist Searches for New Medicines in the Amazon Rain Forest.* Viking, New York. (Also available on audiotape from Nova Audio Books, 1-800-222-3225 [$16.95]).

This is a real story about an ethnobotanist's journeys into the Amazon rain forest to try to preserve information about the medicinal uses of a wide variety of plants, most of which were previously unknown outside the Amazonian cultures

Video:

Spaceship Earth. 1991. Worldlink.

This 25-minute video helps viewers to understand the impacts of their everyday actions on the global environment. It features young people from six continents and music from Sting, the B_{52}'s, Ziggy Marley, and Enya in a visually compelling and intellectually challenging exploration of critical environmental issues.

Appendix A: **USING YOUR *BioLog***

Throughout ***Biology: A Community Context***, you will keep a journal that your teacher will review periodically. This *BioLog* provides a means for you to record all your work: notes, data collected, interpretations, questions, and thoughts. Most scientists also keep a log of their work.

The *BioLog* is very important. Here is why:

◆ Effective communication and writing are essential parts of science and life. Writing will make you more aware of your own thought processes and help to correct your misconceptions about science. Sometimes you don't know that you do not understand a concept until you try to express it in writing. Communicating science ideas and concepts through writing and discussion helps you to understand what you are doing.

◆ Your *Log* lets you show your teacher what you have learned, what troubles you about the biology content, and what you think about classroom activities.

◆ Your *Log* is critical for doing the science work of this course. The information in your *Log* not only will help you to learn about biology and how science works, but will be crucial for your participation in the Conference, Congress, and Forum of each unit.

Organizing Your Log

Your *BioLog* will be organized chronologically, with the date indicated for each day's entries. In every entry, you should try to include both thoughts and data. Thoughts are your own personal reflections and comments about assignments, readings, current events, videos, and class discussions. You will want to keep a summary of class discussions, activities, and questions for further research.

The data entries of your *Log* contain laboratory, field, and library data, as well as procedures, calculations, and preliminary conclusions. Working notes, conversations with experts, survey information, worksheets, handouts, and your work on course activities, including "BioIssues" and "BioPredictions," also are data.

You will refer to your *Log* many times during the year. Keep it up to date and thorough, and it will help you to complete many of your assignments.

Writing in Your Log

Try using some of these sentence beginnings as you reflect and write in your *BioLog:*

What I do not understand is . . .

This concept reminds me of . . .

I wonder if . . .

What really surprised me was . . .

The safety concerns with the activity are . . .

I noticed that . . .

I still don't understand . . .

I would predict that . . .

What puzzles me is . . .

Some observations about our discussion are . . .

I used to believe . . .

What would help me is . . .

I learned that . . .

What if . . .

Examples of Log Entries

January 15, 1996   Investigation #1: Observation Skills

Purpose:

1. To learn how I observe and to compare my ways with those of others.
2. To help me be more observant and aware of the things that could be called observations.
3. To check for any safety concerns.

Procedure: We viewed the first video and made as many observations as we could. Then we met in small groups to compare notes and ideas.

Data: I made 27 observations. Our group of five came up with 62 different observations! Angelina didn't make observations like I did. Instead, she wrote a whole bunch of questions about what she observed. Lucas convinced us that even noticing the time of day or seeing that the same thing was happening in different locations were observations. Megan kept talking about my observations being "inferences." For example, I said that the barge smelled bad, but she said we couldn't observe that.

Analysis: I learned that making observations requires more thought and discipline than I realized. Now when I make observations, I will be more creative and include ideas I wouldn't have had before doing this activity. The main thing I learned is that, when making observations, I need to use all my senses.

Summary: Observations are more than just the object you are looking at. Observations are all the things you notice about an object, a situation, or an action. What you observe depends on what you already know and what you expect to see. Observations are useful as a basis for asking questions and testing your ideas.

May 11, 1997

I saw the movie "Jurassic Park" today for the third time. It amazes me how real the dinosaurs look, even though I still think imagination is better than what movie producers can do. But they did a good job of including the recent dinosaur research. Like, Brontosaurus did not live in a swamp, and they really emphasized how some of the dinosaurs acted like birds. Neat how what I've learned in biology helped me see some mistakes in the film, like when it said that red blood cells contain DNA. The red blood cells of reptiles do, but not mature human red blood cells. What I really like about the movie is how it showed that science, technology, and society are all connected. Just because we can do something doesn't mean we should do it. All this stuff about genetic engineering and making ethical choices involving genetic engineering—that stuff will face us all our lives!

Appendix B: HOW TO MAKE A FLOWCHART

A flowchart is a drawing that shows the steps of a process. A simple flowchart for the processing of milk is shown in Figure B.1

Figure B.1

This flowchart helps to explain how milk is processed.

Note that the flowchart contains essentially two ingredients: the product and what happens to produce the product. The product (or whatever is being processed) is boxed and is a noun. What happens during production (the actual process) is described on the arrow and is a verb. Figure B.2 shows a more complex flowchart for the processes that take place in a sewage treatment plant.

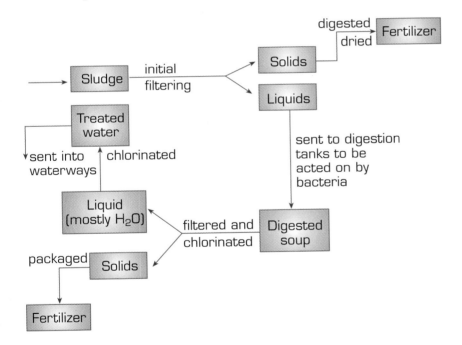

Figure B.2

A flowchart for a sewage treatment plant.

Appendix C: HOW TO MAKE A CONCEPT MAP

Concept maps are tools that help you to learn or clarify relationships between concepts. A concept is an idea, a thought, an object, or a description. Usually, a concept is quite specific. Most concepts are nouns. They can vary from very concrete to very abstract. Some examples of different kinds of concepts are microscope, computer, trash, evaporation, energy, hypothesis, and variable.

A concept statement usually contains a term (the concept) and a description (the definition). Here are some examples of descriptions for the concepts listed above:

◆ A microscope is a tool that is used to magnify objects that are too small to be seen with the unaided eye.

◆ Evaporation is the release of water vapor from an object.

◆ A hypothesis is a prediction of a cause and an effect.

You can make a concept map that shows the connections between concepts. The concept term is usually circled, and lines are drawn connecting the concepts. On the line is a verb that describes the nature of the connection. Figure C.1 is an example of a simple concept map.

Figure C.1

You can "read" this concept map: "Plants require sunlight, plants are colored green, and plants carry out photosynthesis."

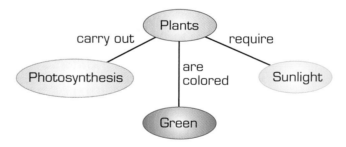

When you make a more involved concept map, you need to obey two rules:

1. Concepts at the top of the drawing are more general or inclusive. As you work your way down the hierarchy of the map, you get more specific or exclusive.

2. Concepts at any level across the map are parallel, or equivalent.

Figure C.2 shows a map that obeys these rules.

Note that the concept terms are connected with lines and that on the lines are verbs that describe the connection. It is best to make the connections functional rather than descriptive. This will tell how the

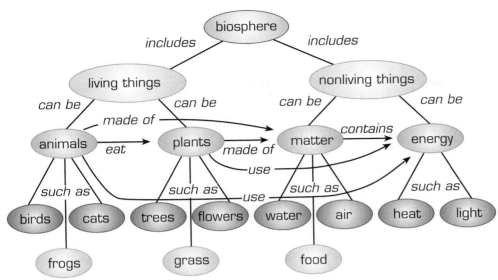

Figure C.2

*A more involved
concept map.*

concepts are connected. You can make concept maps by yourself or in groups. Sometimes group discussions of the relationship between concepts helps to clarify the concepts. This allows you to learn more about the concepts.

You can always change a concept map. As your understanding of concepts gets better, you can improve the verb connectors and make the map more complex.

Some of the uses of concept maps are:

◆ to learn new material,
◆ to review what you have learned,
◆ to present information to others,
◆ to prepare for an exam, and
◆ to check for safety concerns.

You can make a concept map for almost anything. You can even make a concept map of a trip you took or an experiment you did. Concept maps are especially useful for a classification scheme. Some examples are the organization of living things, kinds of cells, bones of the body, and methods of waste disposal. Try making a few concept maps, and share them with your peers or teacher.

Appendix D: HOW TO USE THE MICROSCOPE

Three Basic Properties of Microscopes

Magnification: A means of increasing the apparent size of an object until it is easily visible to the human eye.

Resolution: The capacity to separate adjacent objects so that they are distinct.

Contrast: Aids in distinguishing items.

In the high school biology laboratory, you characteristically use two types of microscopes (see Figure D.1).

Compound microscopes are so named because the simplest compound microscopes use two lenses, placed at either end of a tube. The image of the object is magnified by the first lens (in the objective), the one nearest the specimen, travels through the tube, and is then magnified again by the second lens (in the eyepiece) near the eye. The compound microscope was developed in the late 16th century by two brothers, Dutch eyeglass makers. This original compound microscope had two convex lenses at either end of a tube and was able to magnify an object to ten times (10×) the original diameter. The compound microscopes in today's high school biology classroom may magnify an object up to 430 diameters (430×).

Compound microscopes are characteristically used to observe objects that are very thin; the light from below shines through the specimen. Dissecting microscopes, by contrast, are used to observe larger, thicker, often opaque objects. Two light sources illuminate the object above and below. The magnifying power of dissecting microscopes is usually low; objects are only magnified 10 to 50 diameters.

Figure D.1

The parts of a compound and a stereoscopic (dissecting) microscope.

Compound Microscope   Dissecting Microscope

Eyepiece
Body tube
Arm
Objectives
Stage clips
Focus knob
Fine adjustment knob
Stage
Condenser
Light source
Base
Coarse adjustment knob
Substage light source

Rules For Using A Microscope

1. Always carry a microscope in an upright position. The eyepieces are loose and may fall out if the microscope is tilted. Use both hands. With one hand, hold the arm of the microscope. Place your other hand under the microscope base.

2. Use only lens paper for cleaning the lenses. Your fingers, cloth, paper towels, or tissues may scratch or smear the lenses.

3. Place the microscope in a secure position on the laboratory bench, not too close to the edge. Be sure that the power cord is out of the way so that you don't become entangled in it and pull the microscope off the bench.

4. Before you place a slide on the compound microscope stage, check that the low-power (shortest) objective is rotated into viewing position (pointing straight down).

5. Place the slide on the microscope stage. Be sure that the specimen on the slide is covered by a cover slip. If the microscope has stage clips, gently slip the slide under the clips. If your microscope has a mechanical stage (which moves the slide by means of adjustment knobs), place the slide within (not under) the sides of the mechanical stage.

6. Watch from the side of the stage (not through the eyepiece) as you turn the coarse adjustment knob to lower the low-power objective toward the slide. In which direction did you turn the knob (toward you or away from you) to lower the objective? Record this information in your *Log*.

7. Look through the eyepieces and turn the coarse adjustment knob so that the objective moves upward (away from the slide) until the specimen is visible. Use the fine adjustment knob (again, always move the objective upward, away from the slide) to put the specimen in sharp focus.

8. Once you have located your specimen under low magnification, you can change to a higher-magnification objective. Be sure to move the slide to place your specimen in the center of the field of view before you switch to a higher magnification. Use only the fine adjustment to focus on a specimen at this higher magnification. Be sure the objective lens does not touch the slide.

9. When you have finished observing your specimen, turn the coarse adjustment knob to move the objective up and away from the slide before you attempt to remove the slide from the

stage. Clean the objective lens with a clean piece of lens paper. Lens paper is specially made to avoid scratching the microscope lenses; so don't use tissues, paper towels, or anything else.

10. Always rotate the lowest power (shortest) objective into place before you put the microscope away.

How to Make a Microscope Specimen Slide

To make a prepared slide of a specimen, such as a drop of pond water, begin by placing a clean slide on the table. Check to make certain that the slide is not cracked or broken. Place a drop of the specimen in the middle of the slide. Place a coverslip onto the slide over the drop by laying one edge of the coverslip on the slide near the drop; then let the coverslip fall gently onto the drop of water. Try to avoid forming air bubbles under the coverslip.

Measuring Objects under the Microscope

Because objects that are examined with a microscope are usually quite small, you will find it useful to use units of length smaller than centimeters or millimeters to measure them. One such unit is the micrometer, which is 0.001 millimeter. The symbol for a micrometer is μm.

You can estimate the size of a microscopic object by comparing it with the size of the field of view (Figure D.2). To determine the size of the field, do the following:

1. Place a plastic millimeter ruler on the stage.
2. Focus the low-power objective on the millimeter rulings so that you can see at least two rule lines.
3. Move the rule markers to the center of the field of view with one line barely showing on the left side, as shown in Figure D.2.
4. Count the number of rule lines that you can see going across the center of the circle (an entire diameter of the field).

Figure D.2

Measuring the size of a microscope field of view; one mm is the distance from the rightmost edge of one black line to the rightmost edge of the next black line.

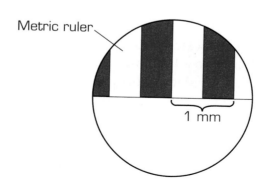

Metric ruler

1 mm

5. Estimate the portion of the space from the last line to the one to the right that cannot be seen. On most microscopes, this is somewhere between four and five millimeter lines under low power.

6. Record your estimate of the diameter of your low power to the nearest tenth of a millimeter.

7. Convert this to micrometers. One millimeter equals 1,000 micrometers.

You can now estimate the diameter of the field of view for your medium- and high-power objectives, as follows:

1. Divide the magnification using your high-power objective by the magnification using your low-power objective. For example, if your low-power magnification is 40× and your medium-power objective is 100×, the factor is 2.5.

2. Divide this factor into the diameter using your low-power field of view. In this example, if the low-power field diameter is 4300 µm, the field of view using the medium-power objective is 4300/2.5, or 1720 µm.

3. To calculate the diameter of your high-power field of view, divide the magnification using your high-power objective by that using your low-power objective. Then divide that factor into the diameter of your low-power objective field of view. You should get a diameter of 300 to 500 micrometers for your high-power field of view.

Appendix E: HOW TO SET UP A DATA TABLE

The information that you gain from an investigation can best be used for analysis when it is properly recorded in a well-thought-out format. A data table or computer spreadsheet provides a way to collect and store data in an easily manageable format.

Examples of data collection tables are presented throughout the eight units of this curriculum. Setting up your own data table requires some thought on your part. It is essential that you make up your data tables before you begin collecting data. In fact, thinking about how you will record data is often useful in conceptualizing the investigation itself.

Consider first the parameters that you will be measuring. For example, you may choose an investigation to determine the effects of various fertilizers on the growth of bean plants. You will measure plant height each day to assess the effects of the fertilizers. You plan to use two different types of fertilizers and test each fertilizer on five plants. You will also grow five plants without fertilizer. You will monitor plant growth for 30 days. What does your data sheet need to include?

First, decide what you will be measuring and when. You will measure plant height on a daily basis for 30 days. Therefore you need 30 rows in which to record data, one row for each day.

Identify the dependent and independent variables. Plant height is the dependent variable. It is what you will measure. Set up the data table so that each plant that you will be measuring has a separate column. In this case, you have 15 plants (five plants for each fertilizer treatment), so you need 15 columns. Add a 16th column to record the date on which you make each measurement. Identify the plants (on their pots as well as on the data table) as A.1, A.2, and so on, so that you can keep track of them. Sort the plants on the data table by the type of fertilizer that they will be getting (fertilizer A, fertilizer B, or no fertilizer).

If you go through this process, you should end up with a data table like the one in Figure E.1.

Figure E.1

This table was developed to record experimental data.

	Plant Heights (in centimeters)														
	Plants in Fertilizer A					Plants in Fertilizer B					Control Plants (no fertilizer)				
Date	A.1	A.2	A.3	A.4	A.5	B.1	B.2	B.3	B.4	B.5	C.1	C.2	C.3	C.4	C.5

(Extend table for 30 rows, one for each day that data is collected.)

Appendix F: HOW TO IDENTIFY COMPOST ORGANISMS

The following drawings and descriptions will assist you in identifying organisms that you find in your compost columns and piles. See also Figure 1.30, the compost food web, on page 43.

KINGDOM: MONERA

ACTINOMYCETES (Figure F.1)

A type of bacteria that forms branching filaments that resemble fungi; important agents in the decomposition of dead organisms and waste materials.

Figure F.1

Actinomycetes.

KINGDOM: FUNGI

MOLDS (Figure F.2)

Fungi made up of fine, branched filaments that penetrate litter and soil breaking down and absorbing nutrients from organic materials such as decomposing plants and animals along with feces and other organic materials. Some are predators that have hooplike filaments specialized to trap animals such as roundworms.

Figure F.2

Fungi.

KINGDOM: ANIMALIA

FLATWORMS (Figure F.3)

Flattened (sometimes ribbonlike), soft-bodied worms that lack segmentation; many are scavengers. Up to several centimeters long.

Figure F.3

A flatworm.

ROUNDWORMS (nematodes) (Figure F.4)

Tiny, slender, unsegmented worms with cylindrical bodies and tapered ends; many nematodes feed on bacteria and fungi. About 1 millimeter long.

Figure F.4

A roundworm.

SNAILS (Figure F.5)

Mollusks with coiled shells that feed on fungi and decaying vegetation using the rasping action of a toothed structure found in their mouths. Approximately 2–25 millimeters long.

Figure F.5

A snail.

SLUGS (Figure F.6)

Mollusks that are similar to snails but possess internal shells. Approximately 2–25 millimeters long.

Figure F.6

A slug.

EARTHWORMS (Figure F.7)

Segmented worms with cylindrical bodies; mature individuals have a short, slightly swollen area on their anterior end that is used in mating; they are scavengers of decomposing organic material, ingesting and mixing soil as they travel through it. Up to several centimeters long.

Figure F.7

An earthworm.

SOWBUGS (Figure F.8)

Land crustaceans; only one pair of their two pairs of antennae is obvious; their segmented, oblong bodies have one pair of legs per segment; they feed as scavengers on organic materials. Approximately 9–16 millimeters long.

Figure F.8

A sowbug.

MILLIPEDES (Figure F.9)

Bodies are composed of many similar segments, with two pairs of legs on most segments; one pair of antennae; like earthworms, they burrow through and ingest both soil and decaying plant material. Up to several centimeters long.

Figure F.9

A millipede.

CENTIPEDES (Figure F.10)

Bodies are composed of many similar segments, with one pair of legs on most segments; one pair of antennae; predators, feeding mostly on other arthropods; all have poison glands associated with their jaws; even small centipedes can produce a bite that is painful to humans. Up to several centimeters long.

Figure F.10

A centipede.

SPRINGTAILS (Figure F.11)

Small wingless insects that have a forked structure on the underside of their abdomen; this structure is folded forward and then released to send them springing into the air; their bodies may be elongate or globular; scavengers of the decaying plant material and fungi. Approximately 0.5–3.0 millimeters long.

Figure F.11

A springtail.

How to Identify Compost Organisms

PSEUDOSCORPIONS (Figure F.12)

Have four pairs of walking legs in addition to a pair of pincerlike pedipalps; poison glands in their pincers aid them in the capture of tiny insects, mites, ants, and small earthworms. Approximately 1–2 millimeters long.

Figure F.12

A pseudoscorpion.

BEETLES (Figure F.13)

Hard-bodied insects; a pair of heavy, modified wings fold down and cover the membranous flight wings when not in use; this diverse group includes scavengers and predators. Up to several centimeters long.

Figure F.13

A ground beetle.

MITES (Figure F.14)

Relatives of spiders, mites have four pairs of legs, although some species have a pair of leglike pedipalps in addition to these; some carnivorous species hunt other arthropods (including other mites) and roundworms, while others feed on fungi and decomposing plant and animal material. Approximately 0.5–1.0 millimeter long.

Figure F.14

A mite.

ANTS (Figure F.15)

Insects with a narrow waist formed by one or two abdominal segments; possess distinctly "elbowed" antennae; predators or scavengers; colonies have a distinct social structure. Up to 10 millimeters long.

Figure F.15

An ant.

APPENDIX G: HOW TO MAKE USEFUL LAB DRAWINGS

Before you start, remind yourself why you are creating a drawing:

◆ Making a carefully done lab drawing will reinforce what you've learned in class by forcing you to review that information as you view an actual specimen.

◆ Carefully done lab drawings can be excellent review materials.

Drawing Hints

1. Create a heading to identify the organism. Identify yourself, and record the date. Include information such as genus, phylum, magnification, living versus preserved specimen, and the like.

2. Familiarize yourself with the subject before you start drawing, like a photographer who surveys all views of an object before taking a photo. Make sense of the organization; don't just draw shapes without understanding what you're drawing. Don't be afraid to ask your teacher for help if you're having problems interpreting the specimen. Organisms can be complicated.

3. Draw what you see, *not* what you think you should see. The structure of your specimen may not be exactly like what you've seen in a book or in class, so you may need to think a bit to figure out the organization.

4. Label important structures. If you are uncertain about a structure, you can label it with a question mark.

5. Make your drawing large enough to cover most of the page to keep from running out of space if you need to add small details.

6. Make notes on features such as the color, appearance, and texture of the organism to supplement your drawing. Use colored pencils if you have them. If your organism is alive and moving, you may wish to do a separate drawing showing its behavior.

7. You create lab drawings to help you learn about organisms by really looking at them. Work to do your best, but don't worry if your drawing is not perfect. This is not an art contest; you are simply making visual notes to help you remember your observations.

See Figure G.1 for an example of a useful lab drawing.

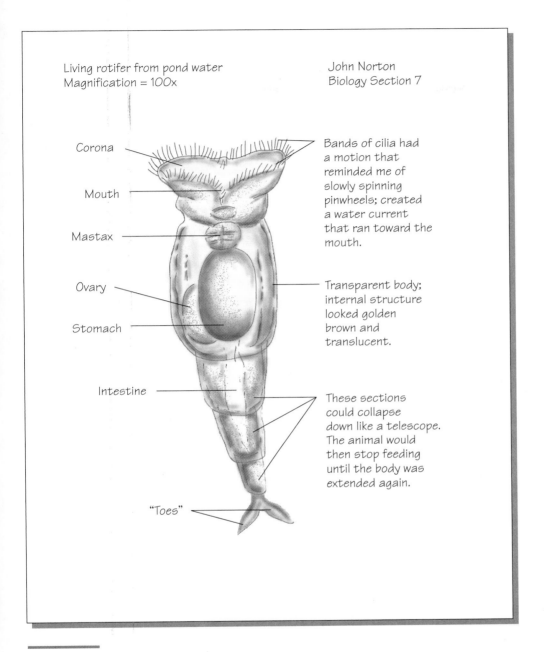

Living rotifer from pond water
Magnification = 100x

John Norton
Biology Section 7

Corona

Mouth

Mastax

Ovary

Stomach

Intestine

"Toes"

Bands of cilia had a motion that reminded me of slowly spinning pinwheels; created a water current that ran toward the mouth.

Transparent body; internal structure looked golden brown and translucent.

These sections could collapse down like a telescope. The animal would then stop feeding until the body was extended again.

Figure G.1

A useful lab drawing.

Appendix H: MATH HINTS

Scientific Notation

Scientists often must use very large or very small numbers to report data. To do so efficiently, they use scientific notation. A number is expressed in scientific notation as the product of a decimal number between 1 and 9 and the number 10 raised to a power. The power that is used indicates how many times the 10 is to be used in the multiplication. For example, 3.6×10^3 is calculated as

$3.6 \times 10 \times 10 \times 10 = 3{,}600$

The power can be either a positive or a negative number. When the power of 10 is a negative number, the multiplication produces a number that is smaller than the original decimal number, by the amount corresponding to the power of 10. You can think of this as multiplication of the decimal number by 0.1 taken one or more times. For example, the number, 4.7×10^{-2} is calculated as

$4.7 \times 0.1 \times 0.1 = 0.047$

You can also think of powers of 10 as indicating how you move the decimal point of a number as a consequence of the multiplication. A positive power indicates that the decimal point moves to the right (to create a larger number). A negative power indicates that the decimal point moves to the left (to create a smaller number).

Understanding Metric System Relationships

The metric system uses a logical sequence of words and prefixes to name quantities. Once you learn these prefixes, using metric calculations is simple. Some of the most common metric prefixes are the following:

Prefix	Decimal Number	Scientific Notation	
tera-	1,000,000,000,000	10^{12}	1 trillion
giga-	1,000,000,000	10^{9}	1 billion
mega-	1,000,000	10^{6}	1 million
kilo-	1,000	10^{3}	1 thousand
hecto-	100	10^{2}	1 hundred
deca-	10	10^{1}	ten
deci-	0.1	10^{-1}	1 tenth
centi-	0.01	10^{-2}	1 one-hundredth
milli-	0.001	10^{-3}	1 one-thousandth
micro-	0.000001	10^{-6}	1 millionth
nano-	0.000000001	10^{-9}	1 billionth
pico-	0.000000000001	10^{-12}	1 trillionth

The logic and universality of the metric system make it the preferred system for communicating numeric data. Current use of numeric units is guided by the International System of Units (SI) (© American Society for Testing and Materials, 1992). However, you will encounter data, especially in historical records, that are expressed in English (non-metric) units. Selected useful factors for conversion between metric and English units (adapted from the SI list of units) are the following:

LENGTH

1 inch = 2.54 centimeters
1 foot = 0.305 meter
1 yard = 0.914 meter
1 mile = 1.609 kilometers

AREA

1 acre = 43,560 square feet = 4,047 square meters = 0.405 hectare
1 square mile = 640 acres = 2.589 square kilometers

VOLUME

1 cubic inch (in^3) = 16.39 cubic centimeters
1 cubic foot (ft^3) = 0.028 cubic meter
1 cubic yard (yd^3) = 0.765 cubic meter

WEIGHT

1 pound = 0.453 kilograms

TO CONVERT FROM:	TO:	MULTIPLY BY:
acre	square meter (m²)	4.05×10^3
degree Fahrenheit (°F)	degree Celsius (°C)	$T_C = (T_F - 32)/1.8$
foot (ft)	meter	3.05×10^{-1}
square foot (ft²)	square meter (m²)	9.29×10^{-2}
square inch (in²)	square meter (m²)	6.45×10^{-4}
mile (mi)	meter (m)	1.61×10^3
square mile (mi²)	square meter (m²)	2.59×10^6
pound (lb)	kilogram (kg)	4.54×10^{-1}

Statistical Methods

It is often difficult to measure an entire large population. In such cases, you must rely on taking a representative sample of the population and making estimations. Once you take a sample, you can calculate a statistic (an estimate about a sample) to describe something about the population that you sampled. Some useful statistical measures are described below. Further information can be obtained from your teacher or a statistics reference.

The *mean* or *average* is calculated by summing all the data for a variable and dividing their total by the number of data items.

The *standard deviation* measures the amount of variance in a sample, that is, how different the data are. Variance is calculated by summing the squares of difference between each observation and the mean, then dividing this value by the sample size minus 1.

Variance $= s^2 = \Sigma(X_i - \text{mean})^2 / (n - 1)$

Standard deviation $= s$

The standard deviation thus estimates how much variance there is in a population and describes limits within which we can make predictions about a population.

The *chi-square test* is used to compare collected data with a predicted or expected value.

Chi-square $= \chi^2 = \Sigma\ [(\text{observed} - \text{expected})^2 /\text{expected}]$

The *t-test* is used to compare the means of two samples from two different populations. It is a method for determining whether or not the two populations are statistically similar for the selected variable.

Appendix I: MAJOR WORLD BIOMES

Tundra (Figure I.1)

This area is characterized by permanently frozen soil, found primarily in the northernmost parts of North America, Europe, and Asia bordering the Arctic Ocean and surrounding the North Pole. The tundra may receive less rainfall than a desert, and its temperatures are usually below freezing. Winter lasts nine months; the growing season, only two. Vegetation includes mosses, lichens, grasses, and shrubs. Some animals—foxes, polar bears, and hares—live here year-round; others—caribou and moose—are migratory.

Figure I.1
Tundra.

Taiga (Figure I.2)

Taiga is found exclusively in the northern hemisphere, often in mountainous regions. The taiga has cold winters and mild summers. Precipitation is low, but the taiga is warmer and wetter than the tundra, causing the soil to be swampy in early summer. The taiga is dominated by dense coniferous forests that block sunlight; its other vegetation is limited to mosses, lichens, and shrubs. This biome is home to many animals, including squirrels, beavers, mice, hares, moose, foxes, wolves, birds, and bear.

Figure I.2
Taiga.

Temperate Deciduous Forest (Figure I.3)

Deciduous forest biomes are found mainly in North America, Europe, and Asia. Although these regions vary, they all have four distinct seasons, during which temperatures range from cold (−30° C) to hot (+35° C), and abundant precipitation, averaging 100 centimeters yearly. The climate is humid, and the soil is deep and rich, making decomposition rates high. Abundant vegetation includes many species of deciduous trees, shrubs, mosses, and ferns. Animals include mice, squirrels, birds, and deer.

Figure I.3

A temperate deciduous forest.

Figure I.4

A tropical rain forest.

Tropical Rain Forest (Figure I.4)

The tropical rain forest biome exists on and around the equator in Africa, Asia, and the Americas. The warm temperature changes very little throughout the year, and rainfall is frequent—usually daily—and plentiful, averaging 200 centimeters yearly. The rain forest has a greater variety of plants than all the other biomes combined, containing more than half of the world's animal and plant species. Vegetation is layered and includes tall trees that emerge above the topmost layer of the rain forest, called the canopy. Below the canopy are layers of shorter trees that can survive in shade. Because of low light intensity, there are few plants on the floor of the rain forest. The animals in the rain forest are also vertically stratified and include jaguars, snakes, monkeys, and many species of birds and insects. Because rain forest soil is not fertile, cutting trees to clear land for agricultural use is not useful in the long-term, as nutrients are quickly exhausted.

Grassland (Figure I.5)

Grassland biomes can be found in the interiors of most continents. Some, like those in the United States, have hot summers and cold winters; while those in tropical areas, called savannas, experience little temperature change. Grassland biomes may receive 25 to 75 centimeters of rain per year but are prone to drought. Low levels of rainfall limit vegetation to grasses of different kinds, which support a variety of plant-eating animals, varying by region but including kangaroos, elk, prairie dogs, and quail.

Figure I.5

Grassland.

Desert (Figure I.6)

Desert biomes are found in North America, South America, Asia, Africa, and Australia. Any areas that receive less than 25 centimeters of rain yearly are classified as deserts, but other characteristics may vary. Plants that live in these dry environments have special features that enable them to absorb water. For example, some have long root systems; while others, such as cacti, store water in thick stems. Desert animals include ants, birds, rodents, and reptiles. Tropical deserts, nearer the equator, have little temperature variation during the year; midlatitude deserts have true winters and summers.

Chaparral (Figure I.7)

Chaparral biomes exist in coastal regions where the climate is moderated by ocean currents. California, Chile, Portugal, and Italy are sites of classic chaparrals. These areas are subject to natural fires, which help to maintain the ecosystem. The dense, spiny shrubs of a chaparral biome have adapted to the long, hot summers and mild winters. Animal life includes deer, birds, rodents, lizards, and snakes. Chaparrals are very popular vacation spots for humans because of their mild, relatively dry climate.

Figure I.7

Chaparral.

Figure I.6

Desert.

Appendix J: FOOD CALORIE INFORMATION

The food Calorie (capital C) that is listed in popular Calorie-counting books and on food labels is the kilocalorie. You should get into the habit of assessing the Calorie content of the foods that you eat, preferably before you eat them. Notice especially the distribution of your food intake Calories among the various types of foods.

Foods, and the Calories in them, can be assigned to three basic categories: proteins, carbohydrates, and fats. Proteins and carbohydrates each provide 4 kilocalories of energy per gram. Fats provide 9 kilocalories of energy per gram. You can assess the Calorie content of your food by determining the relative proportions of carbohydrate, protein, and fat. Some foods with several components are difficult to categorize, but you can solve this problem by reading labels and making judgments. For example, the Calories in most kinds of commercial salad dressings can be divided about half and half between vegetable oil and sugar. Use a Calorie-counting book or chart to look up the foods you eat. The U.S.D.A. handbook entitled *The Nutritional Content of Foods* is an excellent source for Calorie and other nutritional information. Many fast-food restaurants provide booklets that contain nutritional analyses of their foods. If a food that you eat is not listed, look up a similar food. Count everything, not just what you eat at meals; snacks and candy count too! Quantity is important. You need to estimate the quantity of individual foods that you consume.

All processed food that is produced in the United States must list the information in Figure J.1. But what do you do with this information? How can you use this label to guide your food choices?

Current guidelines recommend restricting the fat in our diet to less than 30 percent of our total caloric intake. Some doctors recommend an even lower percentage: less than 20 percent of our food intake.

How would you determine the percentage of fat in macaroni and cheese? First, calculate the caloric percentages of carbohydrate, protein, and fat in one serving when prepared. One gram of either protein or carbohydrate provides 4 Calories. A 3/4 cup serving of prepared macaroni and cheese provides 9 grams of protein at 4 Calories/gram, for a total of 36 Calories of protein. That same serving provides 34 grams of carbohydrate at 4 Calories/gram, for a total of 136 Calories of carbohydrate. One gram of fat provides 9 calories. A serving of prepared macaroni and cheese provides 13 grams of fat at 9 Calories/gram, for a total of 117 Calories of fat.

Nutrition Facts
Serving Size 2.25 oz.
(63g/about 1/4 Box)
(Makes about 3/4 cup)
Servings Per Container 4

Amount Per Serving	In Box	Prepared
Calories	198	289
from Fat	18	117

	% Daily Value**	
Total Fat 2g*	3%	20%
Saturated Fat 1g	5%	23%
Cholesterol 10mg	3%	3%
Sodium 420mg	18%	25%
Total Carbohydrate 34g	11%	9%
Dietary Fiber 1g	4%	4%
Sugars 7g		
Protein 9g		
Vitamin A	0%	15%
Vitamin C	0%	0%
Calcium	10%	10%
Iron	15%	15%

*Amount in Box. When prepared, one serving (about 3/4 cup) contains an additional 11g total fat, 190mg sodium, and 1g total carbohydrate (1g sugars).

**Percent Daily Values are based on a 2,000 calorie diet. Your daily values may be higher or lower depending on your calorie needs.

	Calories	2,000	2,500
Total Fat	Less than	65g	80g
Sat Fat	Less than	20g	25g
Cholest	Less than	300mg	300mg
Sodium	Less than	2,400mg	2,400mg
Total Carb		300g	375g
Fiber		25g	30g

INGREDIENTS: ENRICHED MACARONI PRODUCT (ENRICHED FLOUR [FLOUR NIACIN, FERROUS SULFATE, THIAMINE MONONITRATE, RIBOFLAVIN]); CHEESE SAUCE MIX (WHEY, DRIED CHEESE [GRANULAR AND CHEDDAR (MILK CHEESE CULTURE, SALT, ENZYMES)] WHEY PROTEIN CONCENTRATE, SKIM MILK, CONTAINS LESS THAN 2% OF SALT BUTTERMILK, SODIUM TRIPOLYPHOS-PHATE, SODIUM PHOSPHATE, CITRIC ACID YELLOW 5, YELLOW 6, LACTIC ACID

Figure J.1

A label from a package of macaroni and cheese.

Calculations:

9 grams protein × 4 Calories/gram = 36 Calories of protein

34 grams carbohydrate × 4 Calories/gram = 136 Calories of carbohydrate

13 grams fat × 9 Calories/gram = 117 Calories of fat

Therefore the distribution of Calories in a serving of macaroni and cheese is as follows:

CALORIES

Carbohydrate	136
Protein	36
Fat	117

289 calculated total calories per serving

Check the package label. Does this calculated value match the Calories per serving value on the label? It should. If your calculated value differs by a few calories from the label value, it's usually because the numbers have been rounded off.

Now calculate something that is not always included on the food label. Calculate the percentage of protein, carbohydrate, and fat in macaroni and cheese.

CALCULATIONS:

$$\text{Percent Calories from protein} = \left(\frac{36 \text{ protein/289 total}}{\text{Calories} \quad \text{Calories}}\right) \times 100 = 12.5\% \text{ Calories from protein}$$

$$\text{Percent Calories from carbohydrate} = \left(\frac{136 \text{ carbohydrate/289 Total}}{\text{Calories} \quad \text{Calories}}\right) \times 100 = 47.0\% \text{ Calories from carbohydrate}$$

$$\text{Percent Calories from fat} = \left(\frac{117 \text{ fat/289 total}}{\text{Calories} \quad \text{Calories}}\right) \times 100 = 40.5\% \text{ Calories from fat}$$

Therefore the percent distribution of Calories in one serving is as follows:

Percent of Total Calories

Carbohydrate	47.0%
Protein	12.5%
Fat	40.5%

Try making similar calculations for a few of your favorite foods. Record these calculations as data in your *Log,* and refer to them as you plan your daily diet.

Appendix K: GROWTH AND MAINTENANCE OF LIVE ORGANISMS IN THE CLASSROOM

This appendix gives instructions for maintaining several organisms that are appropriate for use in the Guided Inquiries and Extended Inquiries. This list is by no means comprehensive or restrictive. With the permission of your teacher, seek out and maintain other organisms in which you have a special interest. Check all safety considerations associated with maintaining such living organisms in class. Some present allergy problems. Follow all guidelines provided by your teacher.

Kingdom: MONERA

BACTERIA (various nonpathogenic species) (EUBACTERIA)

Grow bacteria in liquid nutrient broth or on nutrient agar in test tubes or petri plates. Cultures can be stored for extended periods (six months) in a refrigerator.

Autoclave cultures before discarding them. If an autoclave is not available, spray the culture surface or treat the broth with a 10 percent solution of chlorine bleach.

BLUE-GREEN ALGAE (CYANOBACTERIA)

Grow blue-green algae in liquid nutrient media in test tubes, flasks, or a fish tank. Provide a low-intensity light source (less than 10 percent full sunlight). Shade the container with window screening if it is placed near a sunlit window.

Kingdom: PROTISTA

GREEN ALGAE (various genera, including *Scenedesmus, Chlorella, Selanastrum*)

Grow green algae in liquid nutrient media in test tubes, flasks, or a fish tank. Provide a medium-intensity light source (50 to 10 percent full

sunlight). Shade the container with window screening if it is placed near a sunlit window.

Kingdom: FUNGI

BAKER'S YEAST (*Saccharomyces cerevisiae*)

This is one of the simplest of all organisms to grow, but may be difficult to maintain for long periods of time, if only because of the rapid growth rate. Inoculate baker's yeast into a dilute sugar solution, and add sugar periodically to maintain the culture.

Kingdom: PLANTAE

DUCKWEED (*Lemna minor*)

1. Set up a 10-gallon aquarium with a single air pump and a light (or locate the tank near a sunny window). Fill the aquarium with tap water. Operate the pump for several days before adding the *Lemna* to the tank. If you use an aquarium light hood, fill the tank only halfway so that the *Lemna,* which floats on the water surface, will not be too close to the light.

2. Obtain *Lemna* from a field collection, an aquarium supply store, or a scientific supply company.

3. Float *Lemna* plants in the tank.

4. Continue to provide light to the *Lemna,* either continuously or by setting the aquarium light to an 8 hours dark:16 hours light schedule with a timer.

5. If you maintain the *Lemna* population for an extended period of time, add a small amount of plant fertilizer (20:20:20) to the tank on a monthly basis to maintain the nutrient level. Don't overfertilize. If you do, you will encourage algae to grow.

FAST PLANTS® (or other fast-growing plants)

Plants of the genus *Brassica* are well-adapted for classroom use because of their hardiness and rapid growth cycles. Several generations of Fast Plants® can be produced during a school year. Consult the detailed instructions that come with Fast Plants® kits for growing information.

Kingdom: ANIMALIA

PLANARIA

Maintain planaria in spring water or pond water in small, shallow containers at room temperature. Feed them weekly by introducing small strips of fresh liver into jar. Remove uneaten liver.

EARTHWORMS

If you set up a compost pile in Unit 1, you can cultivate earthworms or redworms in the compost. Either add the worms to the class compost or remove some of the compost to a smaller container and add worms. Obtain worms from either local bait shops (the most economical source) or a biological supply company. Maintain the worms just as you maintain the compost pile: Add vegetable material, leaves, and grass, and turn the pile periodically.

To obtain a direct count of the worm population, dump the worms and compost into a white pan, and sort each worm from its surrounding soil. Segregate the worms into a separate pan until they are counted.

If you grow worms in a large compost pile, it may be more practical to estimate the number of worms in the pile by counting only the worms in a sample of the compost. To obtain this estimate, first thoroughly mix the compost.

BUTTERFLIES AND MOTHS

Cultivate butterflies and moths in a screened enclosure or a perforated box covered with muslin netting. The caterpillars should be kept dry and provided with a continuous supply of fresh leaves. Paper egg cartons provide good surfaces for the pupae. Maintain humidity at 60 percent.

Monarch Watch is an excellent source of information for cultivating butterflies and for obtaining monarch butterfly pupae. Contact Monarch Watch, University of Kansas, Department of Entomology, Lawrence, KS 66045. URL: http://monarch.bio.ukans.edu

GRASSHOPPERS, CRICKETS, AND SMALL INSECTS

Maintain populations in glass or plastic containers or a fish tank with a tight-sealing screen top. Provide screen-covered air holes. Egg cartons provide internal living areas. Maintain the temperature at 21–31°C (70–90°F) and humidity at around 60 percent. Feed them dried food pellets, such as those sold for rabbits or dogs. Provide water in the form of a wet sponge in a shallow dish. Small pieces of fresh fruit and vegetables can also be used but should be removed before they rot.

WOWBUGS (*Melittobia digitata*)

Also known as "fast wasps," these blind, flightless insects are quite responsive in behavior experiments and will reproduce quickly enough for inheritance studies. Maintain them at room temperature and humidity. For more information, contact the Riverview Press, P.O. Box 5955, Athens, GA 30604-5955.

TADPOLES AND FROGS

Collect tadpoles from nearshore areas of local shallow bodies of water. Maintain them in a 10-gallon aquarium or similar container that is slightly tilted or that provides both water and dry (pebbles) habitats. Provide about 1 to 2 inches of water at one end of the tank. Feed them small crickets two or three times a week. Keep the tank covered to prevent escape. Place the tank in a suitable location away from direct sunlight and excessive temperature.

GERBILS, HAMSTERS, AND MICE

Maintain the population in a fish tank with a wire-screened lid or a cage. Put cedar shavings to a depth of about 3 centimeters on the bottom of the enclosure. Change the bedding weekly. Provide cotton balls for nest making. House the animals at room temperature, 21–23°C (70–74°F). Use a commercial water bottle introduced through the cage top. Feed the animals commercial pellet food or a mixture of seeds, cereals, and fresh fruit and vegetables.

GOLDFISH

Maintain populations in various sized aquaria (10 to 20 gallons). Allow about 500 cubic centimeters of water for each inch (length) of fish. Aerate the water. Maintain a water temperature of 20–24°C (68–75°F). Feed the fish daily using commercially prepared food. Remove uneaten food.

GUPPIES

Maintain populations in various sized aquaria (10 to 20 gallons). Allow about 500 cubic centimeters of water for each inch (length) of fish. Aerate the water. Maintain water at 24–27°C (70–85°F). Feed the fish daily using commercially prepared food. Remove uneaten food.

Detailed instructions for maintaining populations of various organisms are given in the following manuals from Carolina Biological Supply Company (2700 York Road, Burlington, NC 27215-3398; Phone: 1-800-334-5551):

Techniques for Studying Bacteria and Fungi (order # 45-8296)

Carolina Protozoa and Invertebrates Manual (order # 45-3904)

Culturing Algae (order # 45-8192)

Carolina Arthropods Manual (order # 45-4401)

Carolina's Freshwater Aquarium Handbook (order # 45-1785)

Appendix L: GRAPHING TECHNIQUES

Data from your Inquiries must be presented in a form that allows others to understand your results easily and rapidly. Various forms of graphs can accomplish this. The type of graph that you use depends on the data that you have collected and the hypothesis that you want to illustrate.

You can construct your graphs by hand or with a computer graphing program. The following are useful general rules for constructing graphs:

1. When constructing graphs by hand, always use graph paper.

2. The title of the graph should reflect the hypothesis or the parameters graphed.

3. Place the independent variable on the horizontal (X) axis. Place the dependent variable on the vertical (Y) axis.

4. Adjust the intervals (tick marks) on each axis so that they are evenly distributed.

5. Establish ranges of values on each axis to accommodate the data that you have collected and so that the constructed plot occupies most of the space provided. The maximum value on each axis should be slightly above the maximum values of the data.

Types of Graphs

Scattergram

This type of graph is used when you want to show the relationship between two variables. In this type of graph, you do not connect the data points together with a line. You may choose to draw in a line that describes the general trend of the data. Most computer graphing programs offer this option and will calculate the best-fit straight line or curve for a data set. If you are graphing by hand, you can visually estimate the best-fit line and draw it in.

For example, you might create a scattergram to explore the relationship between students' grades on a test and the hours each student spent studying for the test, as shown in Figure L.1 on page 556.

Figure L.1

The line fitted to these scattered data describes the relationship between study time and test scores. There is a general increase in test scores as study time increases, but this is not consistent for each individual student. Therefore the line describes a trend for the population as a whole.

Sample Data:

Student's Test Grade	Hours of Study
64	0.5
87	4.9
96	6.6
73	4.6
45	1.0
98	5.9
74	4.8
83	3.9

Test Scores and Study Hours

Histogram

This type of graph is useful when you collect data that are in groups or categories. The categories are listed along the horizontal (X) axis. The number of observations in each category is placed on the vertical (Y) axis.

For example, say that you collected the following data on the lengths of cherry tree leaves:

Leaf lengths (cm): 0.91, 0.7, 1.0, 0.85, 0.48, 0.75, 1.15, 1.08, 1.10, 0.84, 1.10, 1.18, 0.77, 0.55, 0.70, 1.22, 0.82, 1.00, 1.05, 0.79, 0.85, 0.83, 0.63, 0.60, 0.94, 0.84, 0.81

To present these data as a histogram, as in Figure L.2, you must first establish size categories:

Size Category	Observations	Number of Observations
0–0.19 cm		0
0.2–0.39 cm	0.39	1
0.4–0.59 cm	0.48, 0.55	2
0.6–0.79 cm	0.7, 0.75, 0.77, 0.70, 0.79, 0.63, 0.60	7
0.8–0.99 cm	0.91, 0.85, 0.84, 0.82, 0.85, 0.94, 0.84, 0.88, 0.81	9
1.0–1.19 cm	1.00, 1.15, 1.08, 1.10, 1.18, 1.00, 1.05	7
1.2–1.39 cm	1.22	1

Time-Course Graphs

You will often need to present data that you have collected over a period of time to show change over time or trends. This type of graph is called a time-course or progress graph. It is made by placing the time intervals on the horizontal (X) axis and the variable that you are measuring on the vertical (Y) axis.

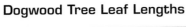

Dogwood Tree Leaf Lengths

Figure L.2

A histogram showing the distribution of dogwood tree leaf lengths.

For example, the following data (from the "World Population" video and teacher's guide) describe the increase in human populations. Beside the data, Figure L.3 shows the completed graph.

World Population Growth

Figure L.3

A time-course graph showing the growth in world population.

Year	Population (in millions)
1 A.D.	170
200	190
400	190
600	220
800	220
1000	265
1100	320
1200	360
1300	360
1400	250
1600	545
1700	610
1750	760
1800	900
1850	1211
1900	1625

Student Resource:
Reference Readings

Glossary

Index

To the Student

The *Student Resource: Reference Readings* will help you expand your understanding and knowledge of biology beyond the information presented in the BioComm: Biology in a Community Context student text. Many of the BioComm: Biology in a Community Context student text activities require you to examine real-world issues relating to the topics discussed. The essays in this section provide additional resources for such issues.

   As you read, remember that knowledge and ideas in science change as scientists gather and consider new information. Some of the ideas presented here may be discarded in a few years, only to be replaced by ideas that better explain the data. Some of the essays in this book present controversial opinions; it is likely that new scientific information will refute some of the ideas in these essays. So watch for new information in newspapers, magazines, and on TV that might support or oppose ideas presented here. Use the skills and knowledge you have acquired to decide if the new information is valid. This is what science and biology are all about!

1.1 When Do We Know Enough to Make a Decision?

Kenneth H. Reckhow, Ph.D.
School of the Environment
Duke University, Durham, North Carolina

Sarah E. Reckhow
Riverside High School, Durham, North Carolina

Dr. Reckhow is a Duke University professor and director of the Water Resources Research Institute at the University of North Carolina. He is an environmental engineer with expertise in water quality modeling, uncertainty analysis, limnology, and environmental statistics. One of his recent projects was the design of Eutromod, a spreadsheet-based model to predict the effects of nutrient runoff on individual lakes.

Ms. Reckhow is a student at Riverside High School in Durham, North Carolina, where her interests include journalism, running, and eating ice cream. She spends a great deal of time outdoors either running cross country or at her favorite place, the beach.

Overview

From a young age, we are taught that scientists are supposed to know the correct answers to our questions. Sometimes they do. An element contains only one type of atom. The earth rotates around the sun. Humans are made up of millions of tiny cells. These are all accepted scientific truths that were reached after many years of careful research. Decision makers such as our elected officials often turn to scientists for facts, especially when they need to make environmental policy decisions.

Global warming is an issue that has baffled decision makers for many years. Is the earth getting warmer? The warmest year on record was reported to be 2005. Is that scientific evidence of global warming? Some scientists are quite convinced that the answer is "yes," while others appear equally confident that the answer is "no."

How can we draw conclusions about scientific issues such as global warming when the scientific experts don't agree? It is confusing and frustrating when the experts disagree, particularly on issues for which corrective actions may be costly and consequences may be severe. How can our political leaders make decisions in the face of this uncertainty? When do we know enough to make a decision?

How can we draw conclusions about scientific issues such as global warming when the scientific experts don't agree?

Decisions about Pollution: A North Carolina Example

Let's think about these questions in the context of some recent water quality events in North Carolina. During the 1990s, there were extensive growths of algae and massive fishkills insw coastal North Carolina. Those have led to public concern about water pollution. Some people are demanding action. They want to control the agricultural and urban activities believed to be responsible. Scientists know that these water quality problems are caused by nitrogen and phosphorus runoff. With this evidence, many people have argued that the solutions are obvious. Other people, including many scientists, caution that we still don't know exactly which sources of nitrogen and phosphorus to control. Nor do we know by how much they should be controlled.

They contend that more scientific study is needed so that decisions are made with confidence.

What should North Carolina do? Scientists' experiences suggest the following principles for making decisions:

(1) There is almost always enough scientific knowledge to make an informed decision. There is no doubt that additional scientific research will improve the scientific basis for decisions. However, it is also true that *we rarely know too little to make a decision.* This is an important message because, as noted, scientists frequently emphasize issues that are not fully understood and are in need of more research.

Here are some examples. What water quality improvements will be achieved if all agricultural fields must be separated from streams by a 100-foot-wide forested buffer strip? Would those forested areas, as shown in Figure 1, prevent pesticides and fertilizers from contaminating the streams? Will urban stormwater detention ponds achieve water quality goals? These are questions that cannot be answered with certainty. However, we still know a great deal about each of these pollution control measures. Scientists could assess the expected improvements in water quality from these control measures and provide a statement of the reliability of this assessment.

Just because scientific analysis cannot give a confident, precise answer to questions like these does not mean that policymakers should defer decisions until additional studies are conducted. We must appreciate the importance of this statement. There will almost always be scientific uncertainty about expected water quality impacts of proposed management actions. However, there is almost always sufficient information to act. Consider that a decision not to act is still a decision.

(2) Decision makers need to understand how to interpret scientific uncertainty so that they can distinguish situations in need of a decision from situations in need of more research. We just noted that we almost always know enough to make a decision and take action. However, there certainly are situations where the uncertainty is so great and the consequences of poor decisions so severe that it is wise to decide to defer action and support more scientific study. We do this in everyday life. All of us have attitudes about risky actions that reflect the uncertainty of the outcome and the cost if we're wrong.

For example, we sometimes make decisions on participation in outdoor activities based on weather predictions. In deciding whether to hold or postpone an outdoor activity, we often check the weather forecast. In doing so we seek (scientific) information on such things as the probability (reflecting uncertainty) of rain or sunshine. Further, it is not uncommon to check the weather forecast on the evening news, but still defer a final decision on the activity until an updated weather prediction in the morning (in other words, get more sample information).

Beyond consideration of the scientific assessment in the weather forecast, we also think about how important the activity is to us. Do we really want to participate in the activity so much that a little rain will not greatly reduce our enjoyment? Or is the activity of only limited value, such that a small probability of rain may be enough to reject participation?

Every day, we make decisions based on a mix of uncertainty in an event occurring (e.g., rain) and value (enjoyment) of an activity. We are accustomed to weighing these issues in our minds and making a decision. These daily strategies we use in making personal decisions, such as getting new information and assessing the value of an activity, are exactly the approaches that our elected decision makers should use in setting environmental policy.

Figure 1 *Forested buffer areas are recommended to prevent contamination of streams.*

When Do We Know Enough to Make a Decision?

(3) Environmental management is most effective when it is not a one-time decision but rather is adaptive, flexible, and continuous. In the North Carolina example—the complex relationships between non-point source pollution and fishkills—it is difficult, if not impossible, to obtain precise scientific knowledge immediately. In addition, management decisions are further complicated by continual changes. The pressure for growth and development in this region of North Carolina will continue. Water pollution technology will improve. And public expectations may change. This situation is clearly dynamic, which suggests that an adaptive, flexible management approach is preferable to a one-time decision.

In North Carolina, decision makers have recognized the value of "adaptive management," or "learning by doing." They have approved an initial management program, while at the same time funding water quality monitoring and research. These scientific efforts will help in the assessment of the water quality response to the initial management actions. The assessments can then provide the scientific basis for "midcourse" improvements in management that are more specifically tailored to the system. For example, it may be discovered through monitoring that certain sources of nitrogen are more (or less) responsible, leading to focused management actions.

No one likes the fact that our science is imperfect, but no one should ignore this fact. When we acknowledge the limitations—the uncertainty—in scientific studies, we end up with more informed and better decisions in the long run.

Additional Resources

Behn, R. D. and J. W. Vaupel. 1982. *Quick Analysis for Busy Decision Makers*. Basic Books, New York.
  The authors of this book use real-life examples to describe how decisions are actually made when information and time are limited.

Novotny, V. and H. Olem. 1994. *Water Quality*. Van Nostrand Reinhold, New York.
  This book presents a detailed, comprehensive assessment of how different land uses and human activities affect surface water quality.

Roth, L (editor). 2004. *Life at the Water's Edge*. Clemson University, South Carolina. 147 pages.
  A guide for planting and mantaining natural lakeshore and stream-side buffer vegetation.

Water Resources Research Institute of North Carolina
  http://www2.ncsu.edu/ncsu/wrri/reckhow.html
  A Director's forum that invites you to respond to various editorials.

Questions for Discussion

1. Why should decisions requiring scientific knowledge not be deferred until <u>all</u> studies are completed?

2. Describe at least one situation where you believe scientists have enough knowledge to make a decision and take action even though they continue to study the problem.

3. Describe the approach that you would take to decide which car insurance to buy. In what ways will this be a flexible versus a one-time decision?

Applications

1. Describe some examples of decisions that you have made recently that were based on the best information available to you at the time. Which of these turned out to be good decisions for you? Which were bad?

2. Choose an essay on a controversial topic from this book or another source. (Possible topics in this book include life on Mars, water from comets, amphibian declines, dam ecosystems, and global warming.) For your chosen topic, do the following:

   ◆ Decide whether there is enough scientific knowledge to make an informed decision about the controversial topic.

   ◆ If you answer yes, list the specific knowledge you would use to make that decision. If you answer no, describe the types of new knowledge that you would need.

   ◆ Develop a plan of action for your community. What decisions and plan of action would you choose based on the knowledge you gained from reading this essay?

1.2 Trash Facts IV

J. Winston Porter, Ph.D.
Waste Policy Center, Leesburg, Virginia
Adapted with permission of the Waste Policy Center.

Dr. Porter is president of the Waste Policy Center, which deals with a wide range of environmental management issues. Dr. Porter was an Environmental Protection Agency (EPA) assistant administrator from 1985 to 1989, serving as national manager for the Superfund and Resource Conservation and Recovery Act (RCRA) programs. In 1988, he set a national recycling goal of 25 percent, which was reached in 1995.

Overview

The United States has made great strides in dealing with municipal solid waste (MSW, trash, garbage) in the last 10 to 15 years. Major accomplishments include:

◆ Attainment of EPA's national recycling goal of 25 percent

◆ Development of stringent regulations for landfills and municipal solid waste combustion units

◆ Significant reduction in the weight of packaging and products

◆ Increased removal of hazardous materials from the waste stream

Nationally, a more balanced mix of waste management methods has been achieved, with recycling at 30 percent, landfilling at 55 percent, and waste combustion at 15 percent of total MSW produced. However, trash management remains a difficult issue at the municipal or county level. Many economic and public policy challenges remain for localities in achieving an appropriate mix of waste management options.

What's in Our Trash?

Municipal solid waste is a complex mixture of waste items, with paper and yard wastes providing the largest fractions. Trash content can be described in terms of basic materials (glass, metals, paper, plastic, etc.) or by the types of used products (appliances, containers, newspapers, etc.) discarded. Figure 1 shows the amounts of various basic materials discarded in 2001. Figure 2 describes the 2001 MSW in terms of the types of products discarded.

How Is Trash Managed?

The nation's trash is managed through landfilling, combustion (usually to make electrical energy), and recycling (includes composting). The EPA refers to the complementary use of these methods, along with source reduction, as Integrated Waste Management (IWM). IWM promotes customized local programs. As shown in Figure 3, recycling in the United States appears to be leveling off after a period of rapid growth from 1980 to 2000. Nationally, MSW generation continues to increase, from 152 million tons by 2001 to a projected 229 million tons by 2001.

MSW by Material in 2001		
	Millions of Tons	**% by Weight**
Paper & paperboard	81.9	35.7%
Yard wastes	29.0	12.2
Plastics	25.4	11.1
Wood	13.2	5.7
Food wastes	26.2	11.4
Glass	12.6	5.5
Ferrous metals	13.5	5.9
Textiles	9.8	4.3
Rubber & leather	6.5	2.8
Aluminum	3.2	2.8
Other wastes	8.9	3.9
Totals	208.0	100.0%

Figure 1 *MSW by material in 2001.*

MSW by Product in 2001		
	Millions of Tons	% by Weight
Containers & Packaging		
Corrugated boxes	29.0	13.5%
Glass	10.9	4.8
Wood	8.2	3.3
Misc. paper	9.4	4.4
Plastics	11.2	4.9
Steel	2.6	1.3
Aluminum	2.0	0.9
	73.5	33.1
Nondurable Goods		
Newspapers	12.2	6.1
Misc. printed matter	10.3	4.4
Misc. nondurables	11.7	5.1
Office paper	7.4	3.4
Clothing & shoes	6.7	2.7
3rd class mail	5.4	2.4
Paper tissue & towels	3.3	1.5
Disposable diapers	3.4	1.4
	60.4	27.0
Durable Goods		
Misc. durables	14.9	6.5
Furniture, furnishings, rugs	10.8	4.4
Tires & batteries	6.6	2.9
Major appliances	4.7	1.6
	37.6	15.4
Yard Wastes	28.0	12.0
Food Wastes	26.2	11.0
Other Wastes	3.5	1.5
Totals	229.2	100.0%

Figure 2 *MSW by product in 2001.*

Source Reduction

Source reduction involves reduction in the quantity or toxicity of materials during the manufacturing process or through product reuse. It can also include, for example, minimizing food spoilage or product damage through effective packaging. While wastes are increasing somewhat due to population growth and our information society, considerable source reduction is also occurring. For example, the weight of a 2-liter plastic soda bottle decreased from 65 grams in 1980 to 47 grams in 2002. Over the same time period, the weight of an aluminum can decreased from 19 to 13 grams, a steel soup can

from 48 to 35 grams, and a glass soda bottle from 255 to 165 grams. Even plastic grocery sacks experienced a weight decrease—from 9 to 6 grams each.

Landfills

Approximately 2000 landfills operate in the United States. About two-thirds of these landfills are owned by public entities, with the remaining one-third belonging to private companies. These landfills vary greatly in size and capacity. About 20 percent receive less than 25 tons of waste per day. Some 17 percent receive more than 500 tons daily. Private sites contain over two-thirds of the remaining capacity.

Modern landfills are designed to minimize potential hazards to public health and the environment. Both existing and new landfills must meet Resource Conservation and Recovery Act (RCRA) "Subtitle D" requirements. States can seek approval from the EPA to enforce these provisions, which include the following landfill regulations:

◆ Restrictions on location of landfills

◆ Operating criteria such as exclusion of hazardous wastes, methane gas controls, and surface water requirements

◆ Design criteria that, in effect, require liners and leachate collection systems for most new landfills

◆ Groundwater monitoring and corrective action when indicated

◆ Closure and postclosure care requirements

◆ Financial assurance provisions

Also, for large landfills, the EPA has issued rules for nonmethane organics emissions under the Clean Air Act.

MSW Management by Percent			
	1990	2000	2002
Landfilling	68.3	57.0	55.5
Combustion	15.5	14.5	14.7
Recycling	16.2	29.2	29.8
Totals	100.0	100.0	100.0

Figure 3 *MSW management by percent of total MSW.*

Waste-to-Energy Combustion

Trash can also be managed in waste-to-energy (WTE) plants, which burn refuse at high temperatures to reduce its volume by up to 90 percent. About 100 of these plants are in use in the United States with over 75 percent of the total capacity located in the states of Florida, New York, Massachusetts, Pennsylvania, Minnesota, Connecticut, Virginia, and New Jersey.

The electricity generated by WTE facilities meets the needs of about 2.4 million homes, replacing the energy equivalent of almost 30 million barrels of crude oil per year. Trash combustors are primarily regulated under the Clean Air Act (CAA) and RCRA. The CAA requires WTE plants to obtain permits whose provisions depend on plant size and other factors. Federal and state regulations under the CAA set emission standards for SO_2, HCl, NO_X, CO, particulates, cadmium lead, mercury, and dioxins/furans. A major RCRA requirement involves determining if combustor ash meets the definition of a hazardous waste. If so, it must be managed as such.

Recycling

MSW recycling is now a mainstream waste management tool with over 9,000 curbside programs; over 4,000 composting facilities; and many thousands of drop-off and buy-back centers, material recovery facilities, and scrap dealers. It is helpful to view recycling from at least two standpoints. The first deals with the percentage of a specific waste that is recycled. Figure 4 shows the percentage of various types of trash recycled in 2002. The second concerns the relative contribution of specific items to the overall recycling rate.

Recycling As a Percentage of Waste Streams	
	2002
Corrugated boxes	70%
Aluminum cans	47
Steel cans	59
Newspapers	62
Office paper	54
Plastic soda bottles	38
Glass containers	27

Figure 4 *Recycling as a percentage of waste streams.*

Recycling As a Percentage of MSW			
	Res.	Comm.	Total
Corrugated boxes	0.1%	8.8%	8.9%
Yard wastes	6.5	0.5	7.0
Newspapers	2.8	0.5	3.3
Other paper	1.4	0.7	2.1
Steel cans & appl.	0.8	0.7	1.5
Glass containers	0.8	0.2	1.0
Office paper	0.1	1.6	1.7
Wood packaging	0.0	0.6	0.6
Aluminum cans	0.2	0.1	0.3
Plastics packaging	0.5	0.0	0.5
Textiles	0.3	0.2	0.5
Food wastes	0.2	0.1	0.3
Rubber & leather	0.1	0.4	0.5
Other wastes	0.4	1.2	1.6
Totals	14.2%	15.6%	29.8%

Figure 5 *Recycling as a percentage of MSW.*

This is shown in Figure 5 for the estimated 68 million tons of recycling in 2002 from residential and commercial sources.

Recycling rates and goals vary in each state and municipality. Each state sets its own recycling goals. The United States Conference of Mayors Recycling Index (CMRI) allows "apples-to-apples" comparisons of recycling rates. To calculate the CMRI for your local area, divide the weight of items recovered to make new products by *all* the MSW produced in your area.

$$\text{CMRI} = \frac{\text{Amount recycled}}{\text{MSW produced}} \times 100$$

For purposes of the above calculation, use the following as MSW: paper (including newspapers, corrugated boxes, office and mixed paper); metal (aluminum and steel cans, appliances); glass; plastics; textiles; batteries; tires; yard wastes; food wastes; and other trash.

Additional Resources

Porter, J. W. Recycling in America . . . the 25% Solution. Jan 1996. Waste Policy Center, Leesburg, Virginia.
   This report summarizes the progress of recycling in America and presents basic principles of recycling.

Porter, J. W. and D. Perchard. Environmental and Public Health Aspects of Reuseable and Disposable Food Service

Packaging. March 1996. Waste Policy Center, Leesburg, Virginia.

This review of 33 independent studies analyzes the environmental trade-offs between reusable and disposable food service packaging.

To purchase individual copies of Trash Facts *or other booklets or reports, contact the Waste Policy Center, 211 Loudoun Street, SW, Leesburg, VA 20175–2718; phone: 703-777-9800; fax: 703-777-3733;* Trash Facts *can be downloaded from the website, www.winporter.com.*

Questions for Discussion

1. Describe the types of materials that are commonly found in municipal solid waste (MSW). How closely does this listing describe the waste produced by your family?

2. Which materials are most likely to be recycled? Of the materials listed in Figure 4, which are recycled in your community? Where do these items go after collection at the recycling center?

Applications

1. How might an Integrated Waste Management plan work in your county? Describe a scheme for managing your local municipal solid wastes that uses landfills, combustion, recycling, and source reduction.

2. Investigate your local landfill. What is its capacity? What types of items and materials are accepted at the landfill? Which items and materials are not permitted to be disposed of in the landfill? Where do these materials wind up?

1.3 Total Recycle

Wayne Fraser
Hudson Bay Mining and Smelting Company
Flin Flon, Manitoba, Canada
Adapted from "Total Recycle" by Wayne Fraser, appearing in Sustainable Development for a New World
Agenda *by Penick, J. E. and J. R. Stiles, (1991). Winnipeg, Canada, STAM/ICASE.*

Mr. Fraser is the director of Environmental and Project Engineering with Hudson Bay Mining and Smelting Company. He has a bachelor's degree in chemical engineering from the University of Saskatchewan and a business administration diploma from the University of Manitoba. Mr. Fraser is a member of the Mineral Processing Committee of the Federal Minister's National Advisory Council of Canada and was the Canadian Mining Industry representative to the United Nations Conference on Environment and Development (UNCED) in Rio de Janeiro, Brazil, in 1992. Mr. Fraser is currently involved in a joint industry–government research program studying acid-generating mine and mill wastes. He also chairs the Mining Association of Canada environmental committee.

Overview

Mr. Fraser suggests that there are some central fallacies in our ideas about recycling, especially the idea that collecting items is the end of the task. He presents an alternative opinion—that we would often be better off burying or burning many items rather than recycling them.

People don't like throwing things away. It's seen as a gross waste of resources and a threat to the environment. However, there is genuine disagreement over the best action, which often leads to measures that turn out to be counterproductive. For example, banning certain types of packaging simply because they cannot easily be recycled could involve an increased use of resources, including fossil fuels.

The field of materials and energy reclamation is dominated by the raw material suppliers and primary manufacturers, the packaging and soft drinks industry, scrap metal and waste paper merchants, local authorities, and voluntary groups. Some of these organizations make a living out of recycling; others see recycling as a potential threat to their business or investment. Environmentalists promote recycling because they believe it saves resources and reduces pollution. Politicians like recycling because it wins votes. With such divergent interests, and differing views as to how best to proceed, it is hardly surprising that the debate over recycling is surrounded by controversy.

Effective Recycling

Recycling must provide a net gain in environmental terms if it is to be worthwhile. Recycling should not be carried out for recycling's sake when overall more fuel, more materials, or more energy are needed to reuse than would be required to make new products from virgin resources. If legitimate technical and economic reasons or threats to the environment don't exist for recycling, then we should not recycle.

If these reasons exist, things should be recycled through as many uses as possible. In many cases where this is possible, reasonable, and affordable, it is not being done because people oppose proper and technically sound recycle schemes and waste destruction. Let me give you a few examples. We have seen several tire dump and chemical fires in the past few years. These fires occurred because so many tires were in

> *Recycling must provide a net gain in environmental terms if it is to be worthwhile.*

one place. When we do not have disposal and destruction plans in place, why do we collect things in central storage areas? Why not leave them where they are until we know what to do with them? Five million tires or flashlight batteries spread out over five million square miles would hardly be noticed. Put them all in one place, though, and the potential for trouble multiplies rapidly.

The environment cannot be considered in isolation from the economy. We must recognize that energy is a major component of everything we use—either as an input or as a potential output. Recycling to energy is as valid as recycling to another product. I recently received a mailing from a major environmental lobbying group about their campaign to stop the incineration of garbage. Why not incinerate garbage? After recycling all we can, why not burn the remainder to recover energy? What could be more elegant than solving a disposal problem, saving fossil fuels that otherwise would be consumed to produce heat or power, and making a dollar on a problem that is so expensive to solve in many jurisdictions?

In past geological times, there were vastly greater amounts of carbon dioxide in our atmosphere than we have now. Limestone beds throughout the world are evidence of this—they have locked up huge amounts of carbon that was not needed to buffer and control the pH of the earth's waters. Similarly, deposits of fossil fuels—coal, oil, natural gas—lock up the carbon residues of huge amounts of incompletely decomposed animal and vegetative matter.

We have been interfering with Mother Nature's carbon cycle for some time. Long-locked carbon in nonrenewable fossil fuel is being released to today's atmosphere when we consume these fuels. Renewable carbon-containing sources, trees and forest products, are excellent candidates for burning with potential heat energy capture and recovery. Products containing hydrocarbons, once their uses have been exhausted, might as well be burned with energy capture. Such approaches save our precious fossil fuels and reduce the amount of carbon we are removing from prehistoric sinks and releasing to today's atmosphere.

There are those who view the metal mining and processing industry as the antithesis of sustainable development. I suggest the opposite is true. With few exceptions, the metals that are produced from mining are never destroyed. Mining continues to produce new metals only to fuel the engine of economic prosperity and growth. Your demands keep us in business. And recycling has always been a cornerstone of our business. What better place to put toxic byproducts, wastes, and secondaries than back into the process that produced them or into an established process that can coreact the material to produce useful products? Why not put cadmium wastes back into cadmium producers, lead batteries back into lead refineries? Aluminum recycling used to be difficult. Early attempts to recycle the metal were frustrated by extensive recovery losses of material through oxidation; economics simply did not support recovery. That problem has since been overcome, and high recovery efficiencies are now possible.

What better place to put toxic byproducts, wastes, and secondaries than back into the process that produced them?

Copper has been recycled since early humans discovered that wood and rock were not the best for utensil and weapon production. The penny in your pocket may well contain atoms from that first piece of native copper worked by that caveman eons ago. And it wasn't necessary for the caveman bureaucracy to impose a cash or perhaps clam deposit system to encourage reuse and recycle of the red metal. Economics and energy balances have always encouraged copper recycling.

Iron, steel, and many nonferrous metals can and have for many years been recycled safely and returned from waste to a useful product. This recycle has been driven by favorable economics and energy balance, the genesis of good recycling. Aluminum drink can recycling is an excellent undertaking. On an energy balance, aluminum can be recycled to a reusable product at less than half the energy input of new metal. On pure economic grounds alone, recycling makes sense. The only technical limitation is that final product can only be composed of 70 percent recycled metal, a ratio not difficult to attain.

Some Problems with Recycling

Recycling paper is nothing new. The Egyptians did it with their papyrus paper; modern paper and paper board making has always utilized recovered fiber. Cardboard is composed nearly entirely of reused material. High-end products—including newsprint—contain very little. Price wise, there is virtually no difference between recycled and virgin paper. Performance wise, recycled paper has presented many problems: mechanical weakness, inconsistency, the fact that it cannot be coated. But if the Canadian and U.S. recycle of paper were doubled to 40 percent, the total amount of timber cut would decrease by only 5 percent.

What could be more environmentally perfect than recycling paper? Well, to begin with, we're not recycling paper—we're only recycling fiber. To get it to that point, we have to take the paper apart, remove the inks and the dyes, and take away the binders and sizers and clay fillers. To do this, we have to use harsh chemicals. Some of the fibers break, and only the long fibers can be reused. The result? Well, I hate to disappoint the environmentalists, but 30 percent of newspaper being recycled ends up as waste. The end product is a toxic waste slurry that is, ton for ton, nearly the same weight as the recycled paper. Some papers even produce 2 or 3 tons of waste for every ton of recovered fiber. Since we can grow new fiber (trees), we are probably better off landfilling paper than producing toxic wastes by trying to recycle fiber.

Certain U.S. states have new rules that require newsprint used in their jurisdiction to contain recycled fiber. For example, in California, 24 percent of newsprint must contain at least 40 percent recycled fiber. We're talking about a lot of newsprint and, therefore, a lot of recycle and an enormous new toxic waste problem. Why don't we burn the paper and recycle it to energy instead? In this way, there is no toxic waste to contend with.

Maybe we can at least feel good about recycling our glass and plastic bottles. Or can we? First, the plastic bottles. You may be aware that health laws prevent the use of most recycled bottles or plastics for direct-contact food packaging. So the original market is gone. Second, plastics are not all the same. Different containers and, in many cases, an individual container may contain several different types of plastics. These have to be separated before anything further can be done. Processes to allow this are being developed as are products for the recovered plastic. So far, we've seen only a few—for example, artificial planks for park benches, flower pots, and the like. We can use a few of these, but we could also burn the bottles and recover the energy directly.

Glass is fused silica, frequently in combination with minor amounts of metals—sodium, potassium, calcium, or lead. Silica, of course, is sand—high-quality sand found in abundance in many places. The major cost input to glass manufacture is energy; the major weight input is the sand. So glass plants locate close to the sand, which as an input is only worth $10–12 per ton. When glass is recycled to glass—as broken glass called cullet—only the raw material cost is saved, not the energy.

Based on pure economics, it makes no sense to move a material to a particular location if it costs more to get it there than it's worth when it arrives. For glass cullet, that is its equivalent in silica sand—about $10–12 per ton. If the cost of collecting, sorting, crushing, and transporting glass containers costs as much as sand, you save nothing but landfill space. Typically, you can only haul about 100 kilometers. Any further and a money loss occurs; that money is principally for the energy consumed by the transport vehicle. Unless we can use the reclaimed glass close to where it is found, it ought not to be bothered with.

Another big push has been switching from plastic to paper bags and wrappers. On the surface, this seems a natural win situation. However, that is not the case. For equivalent use, plastic actually uses less raw material than paper and less energy in production. Because plastic is lighter, it uses less fuel in distribution and, therefore, causes less air pollution. And if the plastic material cannot be recycled, it can be burned with energy recovery—a valid and proper recycling method. The plastic bag,

> *Based on pure economics, it makes no sense to move a material to a particular location if it costs more to get it there than it's worth when it arrives.*

Total Recycle

as with other plastic products, can be viewed as an intermediate (and useful) step between petroleum production and consumption as fuel. For these sorts of reasons, our switch from plastic to paper is currently seeing a reversal.

Many now advocate using cloth diapers. How much of a problem are disposables really? They represent an estimated 1 percent or less of total material going to garbage and landfill sites. I can't believe that this is a sanitary problem. When are garbage dumps sanitary? If you use cloth diapers, those little brown lumps don't just disappear when you flush them. They must be treated in treatment plants. When you wash those cloth diapers, you must use very strong detergents, further adding to the environmental load. Cotton diapers are supposedly much superior to disposables, which contain paper and nondegradable plastic. While cotton is a renewable resource just like the trees that sourced the paper, cotton is grown using herbicides and insecticides and is bleached to make it white. The diapers are washed with detergents and energy-intensive hot water. So what really have we gained in a global context? We're not ahead on energy. We maybe saved a few trees (which can be replaced), but we haven't significantly affected the volume of garbage. In the process, we've possibly introduced health problems for some people where the ability to clean and sterilize cotton diapers is difficult if not impossible.

What of the by-products of vehicle usage—old cars, old tires, old oil, old batteries, to name a few? The cars are, by and large, stripped, sorted, and recycled. During periods of high metal prices, a high percentage of old batteries are recycled back to lead. Tires could be burned. A ton of tires is equivalent in fuel value to about 300 kilograms of oil—about $3–4 per tire. Technology exists to shred these tires and use them as fuel replacement. But we rarely do this.

Why do people oppose the burning of tires? Clouds of black smoke and soot? Residue pooling on the ground? Open burning of fuel oil doesn't look much better. But we all know that controlled combustion of oil is clean and efficient. Those who would choose to burn tires may have to retrofit their operations to do so or may have to design new facilities and new technologies; but it can be done safely, efficiently, and economically.

A company in Canada recently announced interest in building plants to process ten million tires per year. Intended end products include dock bumpers and hockey pucks. Do we need or are we going to revolutionize international hockey with a new steel-belted radial puck? How many do we need? We don't yet have a demand for enough recycled items to use our own waste. Burning tires would save fuel/oil.

Each year Canadians buy one billion liters of lubricating oil. The majority of this use is related to transportation, both public and private. About one-half of this oil is consumed during use; the other half is available for recovery and recycle. Less than half of this is recycled, mostly by industrial users. The remaining 250–300 million liters per year cannot be accounted for. Much of it is simply dumped into the environment—to sewers, to landfills, to the ground. In relative terms, the Exxon *Valdez* spill was only 40 million liters—one-seventh the size of our annual deliberate lubricating oil spill.

Some Final Thoughts

I guess I get a little bothered when I imagine people contentedly and complacently thinking that since they have bundled their papers, sorted their bottles, collected all their flashlight batteries in a box, and squished their aluminum cans, the environmental problems directly associated with their living on this earth have all been taken care of. If only things were so simple.

As a society, we need more and better hazardous waste collection, storage, recycle and recovery, and disposal capacity. Somehow many people seem to be able to divorce themselves from disposal sites. They don't seem to relate these sites to their own wastes. In fact, the majority of material going to landfill sites is not industrial waste—private households produce it. We need to spend as much effort on developing safe disposal methods and sites as we spend on blocking them.

Effective, environmentally sound management of household hazardous waste and other residuals of our modern way of life will require imaginative policies and education programs that can modify consumer behavior. The "not my problem" attitude must change. The task ahead is significant since it has been estimated that every household possesses 50 liters of materials that are hazardous to health or the natural environment. As a consumer product, a portion of this will eventually be used. Much, however, will be disposed.

If every household in North America throws only 1 liter of drain cleaner into their plumbing system each year, that represents over 3,000 tanker truck loads of extremely caustic and hazardous waste. There's not an industry in this land that would get away with dumping that as an industrial discharge.

In summary, there really is only one approach to waste control, and that approach has four steps:

◆ Reduce; where possible

◆ Separate; collect and convert recyclables

◆ Burn combustibles; recycle ash if appropriate

◆ Dispose; nonrecyclable burned waste residue and remaining noncombustibles in safe landfills

Recycling is not just collection. It includes everything from developing technology and processes to creating products and markets. And it must include, as a major component, economic considerations. We must be careful how and where we place artificial economics on wastes and recyclables. Taxes, deposit systems, and incentives only work when they are applied in such a fashion as to reward the proper behavior. Subsidizing disposal or recycling firms promotes sham operations; penalizing producers leads to illegal dumping and disposal to avoid costs. Someplace there is a middle ground that achieves the intent—ensuring proper waste disposal and maximizing recycle.

Additional Resources

Penick, J. E. and J. R. Stiles. 1991. *Sustainable Development for a New World Agenda*. Winnipeg, Canada, STAM/ICASE.
   A series of reports on global issues affecting sustainable development.

Rathje, W. and C. Murphy. 1992. *Rubbish! The Archeology of Garbage*. Harper Collins Publishers, New York, New York.
   An entertaining and informative book describing the types and amounts of garbage that Americans discard.

Questions for Discussion

1. Fraser states that merely collecting items is not recycling. What does he believe must happen to call it "recycling"?

2. What benefits does the author see in burning materials like tires rather than recycling them into new products?

3. Who should be responsible for toxic emissions from factories?

Applications

1. Using Fraser's ideas, how could you improve recycling efforts in your community?

2. What would you say to someone who suggests we ought to collect used flashlight batteries so we could recycle them?

1.4 Turning a Waste into a Resource

E. David Dickens, Ph.D.
Warnell School of Forest Resources
The University of Georgia, Athens, Georgia

Francis J. Wolak, Ph.D.
Agricultural and Biological Engineering
Clemson University, Clemson, South Carolina

Dr. Dickens is a forest ecologist and environmental engineer. He has studied forestland application of biosolids since 1985. His emphasis areas are water quality, waste management, and element cycling. His projects with forestland application of biosolids and, more recently, animal wastes involve determining the effects of these materials on ground and surface water quality, tree growth, and element fate. He published 20 papers on these topics in the last five years.

Dr. Wolak is an agricultural engineer with the Cooperative Extension Service. He works with solid waste, precision farming (the selective placement of fertilizer and pesticides), agriculture, and the environment. He developed the South Carolina Master Waste Educator program to teach homeowners, small businesspeople, and community leaders about appropriate solid waste management practices.

Overview

In the course of normal everyday activities, waste by-products are produced. Human biological activity is no different from any other biological activity except that our activities are often concentrated in cities and towns. Waste by-products produced from the foods we eat and the liquids we drink are excreted from our bodies and enter septic and sewer systems of our cities and towns. We can turn our wastes into useful resources if we use them to fertilize forests.

Human Sewage

A typical family of four generates up to 400 gallons of wastewater a day. After this water has been treated, about one pound of sludge, or biosolids, on a dry weight basis is produced. The term *biosolids* is preferred when sludge is beneficially used. There are approximately 13,000 to 15,000 publicly owned treatment facilities in the United States, which generate 100 to 135 million wet tons of sewage sludge annually. Also entering our waste disposal systems are hair sprays, deodorants, and cosmetics that are washed from our bodies during bathing. Food scraps enter the waste stream from garbage disposals. Cleaning products enter the waste stream as we do our housekeeping chores. Our stores, factories, schools, and merchants also add material to the waste stream. Sewage treatment facilities may also receive runoff from streets, parking lots, and yards.

Sewer and septic systems are designed to break down these waste materials. Sewage sludge is initially a slurry that is 80 percent to 99 percent water. The rest is a mixture of organic and inorganic solids and dissolved substances. Sewage sludge contains nutrients such as nitrogen (N), phosphorus (P), and potassium (K). It also contains pathogens such as bacteria, viruses, and parasites. Some biosolids may also contain small amounts of organic chemicals such as chloroform and inorganic chemicals such as iron.

Sewage sludge must be treated before it can be used or disposed. Treatments include aerobic digestion, which occurs in the presence of oxygen, and anaerobic digestion, which occurs in the absence of oxygen. Other treatments include waste activation, lime stabilization (to increase pH), pasteurization by heating, heat drying, and composting. Biological, chemical, physical, and/or thermal processes are thus used. These treatment processes remove water; reduce the level of pathogens; stabilize volatile solids; and make the biosolids less attractive to rodents, insects, and other disease carriers.

> *A typical family of four generates up to 400 gallons of wastewater a day.*

Where Does Sewage Sludge, or Biosolids, Go Once Treated?

In the past, sewage sludge was considered a liability. It was simply disposed of in landfills, dumped into the ocean, stored in lagoons, or incinerated. However, landfills are filling up, and finding new landfills is becoming difficult and much more expensive; ash from incineration can present a problem; and ocean dumping of sewage sludge was phased out in the mid-1980s. Biosolids have been used with great success on agricultural lands around the world for many decades. As of 1992, it is estimated that approximately 36 percent of the biosolids generated in the United States was beneficially applied to land, 38 percent was landfilled, 10 percent was surface disposed in lagoons or monofills (where only sewage sludge goes), and 16 percent was incinerated.

Land application of biosolids is increasing in the United States, while landfilling and incineration of sewage sludge is declining. Beneficial uses of biosolids include reclaiming disturbed sites, such as strip mines, mine spoils, quarries, and borrow pits. Biosolids are also applied on crop and pasture land, sod farms, golf courses, parks, and forestland. The total macronutrient (nitrogen, phosphorus, and potassium) content for biosolids and effluent (the liquid portion of sewage sludge after solid/liquid separation) was recently estimated to be worth $1 billion per year in the United States. That's 1.4 million tons of nitrogen, 600,000 tons of phosphorus, and 300,000 tons of potassium generated each year in our biosolids.

Criteria for Land Application of Biosolids

The United States Environmental Protection Agency (EPA) has set standards for land application of biosolids in the United States. The Sewage Sludge Use and Disposal Regulation sets national standards for pathogen levels, certain organic compounds, and eight heavy metals in sewage sludge. It also defines standards or management practices for the safe handling and use of sewage sludge. This rule is designed to protect human health and the environment when biosolids are beneficially applied to land or when sewage sludge is placed in a surface disposal site and incinerated. The rule was developed in accordance with the 1987 Amendments to the Clean Water Act and is the product of the EPA's most comprehensive risk assessment to date. It considers the full range of potential impacts biosolids would have on public health and the environment and is based on the

EPA 503 Subpart B Metal Pollutant Limits				
Metal	Class B Ceiling Concentrations	Class A Monthly Avg. Conc.	Cumulative Loading Rates	Annual Loading Rates
	—mg/kg—		—kg/ha—	—kg/ha/yr—
Arsenic	75	41	41	2.0
Cadmium	85	39	39	1.9
Copper	3000	1500	1500	75
Lead	840	300	300	15
Mercury	57	17	17	0.85
Nickel	420	420	420	21
Selenium	100	36	100	5.0
Zinc	7500	2800	2800	140

Notes: Multiply kg/ha by 0.9 to convert to lb/ac.
All values are on dry weight basis.

Figure 1 EPA regulated metals and threshold values for land application.

most current scientific information. It is the first rule that considers the *potential* ecological effects. The rule seeks to protect our surface and groundwater, air, and land. Biosolids are classified either as Class A (Exceptional Quality or EQ biosolids) or Class B for land application. Figure 1 lists the EPA regulated metals and threshold values for land application.

Pathogen populations of fecal coliform, salmonella, certain viruses, and/or parasites are tested in the biosolids and must meet strict criteria for land application.

Estimated Trace Element Ranges and Means in Surface Soils

Element	Range (ppm*)	Mean (ppm)	Pounds/acre
Arsenic	0.100–90	5.80	0.35–100
Cadmium	0.010–2.5	0.53	0.04–5.0+
Chromium	1.400–500	45.0	7.00–160+
Copper	1.000–110	25.0	3.50–90+
Mercury	0.008–4.6	0.17	0.03–1.0
Molybdenum	0.170–17	1.00	0.50–9.5
Nickel	1.000–150	19.0	6.00–110+
Lead	2.300–150	25.0	9.50–100+
Selenium	0.005–3.5	0.33	0.03–4.5
Zinc	3.500–225	74.0	9.50–300+

*ppm = parts per million (on a dry weight basis)

Figure 2 *Estimated concentrations of some heavy metals in surface soils.*

Native Levels of Metals in Our Soil

While many industrial processes contribute to varying amounts of heavy metals in our biosolids, our soils have native levels of heavy metals as well. Animal manure, as well as some fertilizers and pesticides used by humans, also contains heavy metals that have found their way into our soil. Figure 2 lists the concentrations of some heavy metal ranges found in our soils.

Forestland Application of Biosolids Is an Attractive Alternative

Forestland provides an attractive, beneficial alternative use for biosolids application for several reasons. There is an abundance of forestland in the United States. Approximately 40 percent of the United States is forested. In the southeastern United States, almost two-thirds of the land area is forested. For example, South Carolina has 19 million land acres, and 12.3 million acres is forested. Usually only a small percentage of forestland is needed (from 0.01 percent to 2.0 percent) to beneficially use all the biosolids generated in a given area. Therefore, the impact on the forest resource is minimal. Forest products are one step removed from the human food chain. Forest soil fertility is often marginal, and the nutrients in the biosolids have been proven to increase tree growth greatly, as shown in Figure 3, with just one biosolids application. A forest landowner should expect an extra $40,000 of income on a 200-acre loblolly pine tree farm with just a one-time biosolids application.

Benefits of Biosolids

In the past, sewage sludge was often considered to be a waste disposal problem. Now biosolids (the beneficial use term for sewage sludge) are often thought of as a valuable resource. Consider the fact that each year the agricultural industry spends millions of dollars on fertilizer to increase plant and crop growth. At the same time, nitrogen, phosphorus, potassium, and other plant nutrients in biosolids are being landfilled. Doesn't it make more sense to apply biosolids (that meet EPA land application criteria) to the production of plants? This win–win situation would reduce the expense of growing plants and reduce the expense of disposing of biosolids. Pollution potential is reduced since the N, P, K, and other plant nutrients are used for crop production in a controlled environment. Biosolids are used to grow hay crops for animal consumption. More recently, biosolids are applied to forestland to increase tree growth.

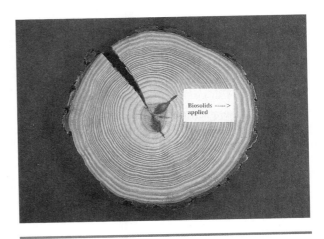

Figure 3 *Growth increment rings of a 31-year-old loblolly pine tree before and after biosolids application.*

A fact of our modern world is that our waste stream can be harmful if not treated properly. Care is taken to ensure biosolids are treated for pathogen, heavy metal, and organic compound control. Modern sewage treatment processes make biosolids safe for use in the environment as a crop and tree fertilizer.

Additional Resources

BioCycle. Journal of Composting and Recycling. 419 State Avenue, Emmaus, PA 18049.
> A great monthly journal on recycling animal waste and biosolids on land and composting waste materials.

Cole, D. W., C. L. Henry, and W. L. Nutter (eds.). 1986. *The Forest Alternative for Treatment and Utilization of Municipal and Industrial Wastes.* Univ. of Washington Press, Seattle, WA.
> Discussion of various subjects including environmental effects, forest response, effects on wildlife, and water quality.

Manahan, S. E. 1993. *Fundamentals of Environmental Chemistry.* Lewis Publishers, Boca Raton, FL.
> Includes a section on water treatment and sludge and is a good general environmental chemistry book.

Overcash, M. R. and D. Pal. 1979. *Design of Land Treatment Systems for Industrial Wastes Theory and Practice.* Ann Arbor Science Publishers, Ann Arbor, MI.
> Describes what is in industrial wastes and land application systems.

Pendias, A. K. and H. Pendias. 1992. *Trace Elements in Soils and Plants,* Second Edition. CRC Press. Boca Raton, FL.
> A good book about native and human-induced levels of trace metals in soils and plants.

The University of Georgia, Warnell School of Forestry and Natural Resources. 2007. *The Bugwood Network.*
> http://www.bugwood.org. A comprehensive website for forest and insects, images and information.

Questions for Discussion

1. List the final "resting spot" alternatives for sewage sludge (biosolids).

2. Rank the alternatives listed above and list advantages and disadvantages for each alternative.

3. The Sewage Sludge Use and Disposal Regulation sets national standards for what components of our biosolids?

4. Which of the regulated metals are also plant micronutrients?

Applications

1. A mass of biosolids meets all Class A criteria for land application and has metal concentrations as described below:

Metal	Concentration (mg/kg dry weight)*
Arsenic	2.01
Cadmium	0.467
Copper	65.7
Lead	4.37
Mercury	0.40
Nickel	16.1
Selenium	0.002
Zinc	119

*Biosolids have 40 percent solids.

How many times could these biosolids be land applied at 10 wet tons per acre? What metal would limit the total number of applications? (Use the data in Figure 1 for these calculations.)

2. Calculate the percent of each of the metals in the biosolids in question 1 after a one-time application of 10 wet tons/acre (4 dry tons/acre) to soil. How do these values compare to the estimated concentrations of heavy metals in the soil (as listed in Figure 2)?

1.5 Living Machines

Ed Edmondson, M.S.
Coneross Creek Wastewater Treatment Facility
Seneca, South Carolina

Mr. Edmondson is an operator at the Coneross Creek Wastewater Treatment Facility. He has a master's degree in biology and is a student in an environmental systems engineering graduate program. He spent a summer engaged in technical and field work at Ocean Arks International, an institute devoted to researching alternative methods for domestic sewage treatment. Ocean Arks has pioneered the use of "Living Machines"—incorporating plants and invertebrate animals into sewage treatment systems. Mr. Edmondson's job at the wastewater treatment facility is to control unit operations and processes such as water flows in and out of the plant. He also participates in water sampling, laboratory analyses, and solids removal. Operators make sure the equipment is operating properly so that the effluent is as clean as possible.

Overview

When you wash dishes or flush your toilet, the water you have used drains from your house. Where does this dirty water, called sewage or wastewater, go? Why does it go there, and what happens to it afterwards? Let's find some answers to these questions. Then you will look at how one group of innovators uses ecologically diverse greenhouse systems to treat sewage. Using plants, snails, fish, and other animals, they produce products for human use and produce clean water as well.

Where Does Sewage Go? Why Does It Go There?

When you flush your toilet, where does the water go? Once this water leaves our homes and businesses, it eventually drains into waterways, such as lakes and streams, and into the groundwater. But first, wastewater drains into a septic tank or is pumped to a conventional wastewater treatment facility. We treat wastewater to remove contaminants such as pathogens, nutrients, and offensive tastes and odors. Pathogens, or disease-causing organisms, may live in the feces in sewage. If we were to wash with or ingest water containing pathogens, we could get sick. Untreated sewage contains both digestible nutrients and indigestible solids. If sewage were untreated, material such as sand, rags, and tree limbs would clog drains and waterways.

The nutrients contained in untreated sewage can be broken down by organisms living in or near the

---

We treat wastewater to remove contaminants such as pathogens, nutrients, and offensive tastes and odors.

---

water. To digest these nutrients, decomposers such as bacteria use oxygen. Often the decomposers use all the available oxygen so that other organisms, such as fish and their prey, cannot live there. When this happens, the decomposers create an anaerobic environment and produce offensive odors. Those undesirable sights and odors reduce our enjoyment of recreational waters. When a beautiful recreational lake is sullied by sewage discharge, people avoid it. Businesses and industries dependent on the clean lake may suffer because of its reduced use. Most importantly, these changes damage aquatic ecosystems.

Conventional Sewage Treatment

As people settled into towns and cities, population size and density increased. Waste concentration also increased. Some of this waste was used to fertilize crops, but much of it was dumped raw into streets and streams. The result was often illness and death from disease organisms in the contaminated water. Cesspools were developed to reduce the impact and offensiveness of raw wastes. Cesspools are simply holes in the ground that contain wastes as they decompose. Flushing human wastes out of homes through a plumbing system is a relatively recent innovation. In rural areas, household wastes flow into buried septic tanks and drainage systems. A home septic system contains wastes and provides an environment for microbial decomposition to occur. In more densely populated areas, collection systems made up of pipes and pumping stations convey sewage to wastewater treatment facilities. Both septic systems and wastewaster treatment plants rely upon bacteria to decompose the digestible material in sewage.

Conventional Wastewater Treatment Facilities

The purpose of these facilities is to remove indigestible solids, suspended and dissolved nutrients, and pathogens. In many instances, these removal processes occur in concrete tanks. In others, ponds fitted with water-impermeable liners are used. A typical wastewater treatment scheme is shown in Figure 1. The first step, once sewage reaches a treatment facility, is to remove heavy debris, such as roots, rags, and sand. This is called grit removal. Materials that settle to the bottom or float to the top are then removed in the gravity separator. In the next step, suspended and dissolved materials are decomposed. Most treatment facilities use bacteria to remove nutrients. Bacteria use the nutrients for growth and reproduction.

The nutrient-depleted water contains some indigestible material, as well as dead or dormant bacteria cells. That material is settled out and returned to the nutrient removal tank to be mixed with incoming sewage. The treated water, called the effluent, is disinfected to kill pathogenic organisms that may be

present. In the United States, chlorine is the primary disinfectant. After disinfection, the treated water is released to the environment.

How Do We Measure Treatment Effectiveness?

Treated water is tested to determine how thoroughly nutrients, solids, pathogens, and undesirable sight and smell characteristics have been removed. Pathogen presence is measured using a fecal coliform test. That test measures the amount of bacteria from the colons of mammals that are present in a water sample. If these coliform bacteria are found, pathogens may also be present.

Another test, for biochemical oxygen demand, measures the amount of oxygen that is used by the bacteria to decompose the organic nutrients in a water sample. Other chemical tests measure the concentration of compounds that contain nitrogen and phosphorus. The concentration of suspended solids is measured by filtering samples of effluent or influent water. Those and other tests are useful because they are directly related to treatment objectives and measure how well treatment works.

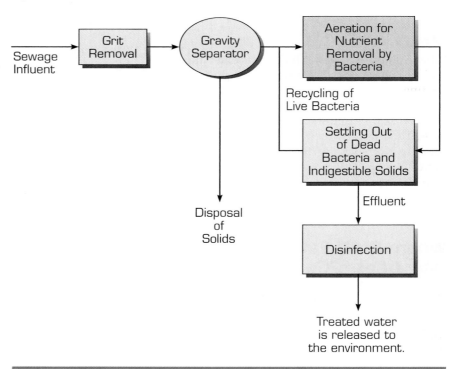

Figure 1 *This schematic shows the flow of wastewater through a conventional treatment facility.*

Living Machines for Wastewater Treatment

We usually treat wastewater from single family homes in septic systems or community wastewater treatment facilities. But there are other ways to handle sewage. In some parts of the world, excrement from cesspools is collected and used fresh as fertilizer. In other areas, this "night soil" (from being collected at night) is composted before it is added to crops. Those methods have been used successfully since the dawn of agriculture. People who use those methods view human waste as a resource that can be recycled into food production.

A group of innovators in New England designs alternative systems, called "Living Machines," for wastewater treatment. A scientist, John Todd, and his colleagues at Ocean Arks combine the benefits of both traditional agricultural and civil engineering approaches to wastewater treatment. They develop systems that treat sewage by recycling the organic and inorganic nutrients into plants using complex ecosystems. An example of a Living Machines treatment system in a greenhouse is shown in Figure 2. The treated water that flows from these greenhouses is as clean as water from a water treatment facility. As an added benefit, the greenhouses produce plants for human use.

Figure 2 *Complex ecosystems, called "Living Machines," can be used as wastewater treatment facilities.*

Greenhouse Ecosystem Design

The Living Machines systems may be located next to conventional systems or may stand alone. Wastewater coming into the system is screened and degritted. The water flow may then be split. In a combined system, a portion of the wastewater is diverted to the greenhouses. The rest goes to conventional wastewater treatment facilities. All of the wastewater flows through the greenhouses in stand-alone systems. Figure 3 shows the plan for a typical greenhouse treatment system. Three stages of treament are used, as shown in Figure 3. Wastewater may recirculate through these three stages to achieve greater cleanliness.

Figure 3 *This schematic of a typical Living Machines greenhouse wastewater treatment facility shows the three stages of treatment used to achieve greater cleanliness.*

The aerated reactors are for organic conversion. Suspended and dissolved materials are decomposed and used to grow plants in these reactors. Note that plants grow hydroponically (without soil) on rafts in the tops of the reactors. Plants are just one part of the complex food webs designed for the greenhouses. The plants' extensive root systems add to the strength of the ecosystem by providing sites for microorganisms to live. Plants also help clean the water by using nitrogen, phosphorus, and other dissolved nutrients.

Additional removal of nitrogen and phosphorus occurs in the stratifiers and marshes. Changing the regime from an aerobic, aquatic one to a more anoxic (low oxygen), benthic one stimulates growth of different types of microorganisms and furthers utilization of nutrients. In the marshes, mollusks control algae populations and filter pathogens. Thus, pathogen and pest populations are controlled by predator–prey interactions. A final treatment uses ultraviolet radiation to ensure that pathogens are removed.

Greenhouses or Conventional Wastewater Treatment Systems?

How do you think these two approaches compare? What differences and similarities do these systems have? The most important difference is the presence of plants, animals, and more complex ecosystems in the greenhouse system. The second difference is the decreased emphasis on settling tanks and less production of solid waste. Third, depending on water flow rate, the greenhouse scheme may use more treatment tanks. Fourth, pathogens are mostly controlled by predator-prey interactions.

At present, the sizes of these two types of systems are different. Greenhouse systems are currently designed to handle wastewater flows of 500 to 1 million gallons per day. Conventional treatment systems can be designed for 10,000 to 100 million gallons per day. Living Machines greenhouse systems can be more economical than are conventional systems for treating wastewater volumes of 30,000 to 1 million gallons per day.

Although the differences between the two approaches are striking, the similarities are important. Both systems remove pathogens, digestible and indigestible material, and offensive odors from wastewater. Solids from both types of systems can be removed and composted. Provided the solids meet pathogen and metals removal criteria, both are high-quality soil amendments. Since water flows into and out of treatment systems, water retention times, tank volumes, solids retention times, and other hydraulic parameters are important design criteria for both. Lastly, communities of microorganisms begin the decomposition process in both types of systems.

References

Todd, J. and B. Josephson. 1994. Living Machines: Part Two. *Annals of Earth*. 12(2): pp. 14–21.

U.S. Environmental Protection Agency. 1992. *Operation of Wastewater Treatment Plants*. 4th ed. U.S. Government Printing Office, Washington, DC. Vol. 1. p. 248.

Additional Resources

Annals of Earth. Ocean Arks International. 233 Hatchville Road., East Falmouth, MA 02536.
   A journal reporting research, environmental awareness, and spiritual issues of interest to Ocean Arks supporters.

Meadows, D. H. 1988. The New Alchemist. *Harrowsmith*. Nov/Dec. pp. 38–47.
   An article about John Todd, greenhouses, and wastewater treatment.

Ocean Arks International. http://www.oceanarks.org.
   Founded in 1981, Ocean Arks develops "Living Machines," technologies for wastewater treatment and environmental restoration.

Todd, N. J. and J. Todd. 1994. *From Eco-Cities to Living Machines: Principles of Ecological Design*. North Atlantic Books, Berkeley, CA.
   The Todds' vision of how cityscapes would look if living technologies were used in urban architecture. Their premise is that humans would be more at ease surrounded by living creatures instead of inanimate steel and concrete. The hope is our society would be more in touch with the limits of our natural resources and, therefore, have a better chance of sustaining ourselves for a long time.

Questions for Discussion

1. Why do we treat sewage?
2. What are two ways sewage is treated conventionally?
3. Why use a septic tank instead of a larger, aboveground facility?

4. The incoming total nitrogen concentration in wastewater is 20 mg/L. If 95 percent of the nitrogen is removed, what is the effluent nitrogen concentration?

5. If in one day 3 million gallons flowed through the facility in question 4, how many pounds of nitrogen would flow out? Hint: Sum the amount in 3 million gallons; then convert from metric to English units.

6. What is the difference between suspended and dissolved particles?

7. Engineers usually choose a biological process to treat sewage. Why might they choose a biological process instead of a chemical one?

8. For domestic use, treatment designers assume each person will produce 100 gallons of wastewater per person each day. How many people will a 50,000-gallons-per-day facility service? How many people will a 7.8 million-gallon-per-day facility service?

Applications

1. Look at the aeration tanks in Figure 1. Nutrient-rich wastewater flows into them and nutrient-poor treated water leaves. These tanks hold a mixture of microbes, nutrients, and water. What happens to the nutrients? (Remember that tank volumes are constant and the effluent must have low nutrient and solids concentrations! Hint: What happens to plants in your garden when you fertilize them?)

2. Look at the flow scheme in Figure 3. Compare this with the conventional system shown in Figure 1. How are the nutrients removed in this system? In what form do they leave?

3. What is the purpose of the biological diversity designed into the Living Machines greenhouse treatment systems?

1.6 Bubble Wrap and Biopolymers

Jonn Foulk, Ph.D.
USDA Agricultural Research Service
Clemson University, Clemson, South Carolina

Mr. Foulk is a research scientist in agricultural and biological engineering. Agricultural engineering integrates knowledge of various techniques used in agricultural crop yields, food production, packaging development, pharmaceutical production, biotechnology improvements, natural resource reserves, and environmental issues. His research integrates studies of agricultural crops with packaging science to derive environmentally degradable materials.

Overview

Current research in agricultural engineering focuses on producing biodegradable biopolymers. These products are made from crops such as corn and soybeans. They can be used instead of the plastics now commonly used in packaging materials. Biopolymers will reduce the amount of packaging materials found in landfills. These new materials may even solve the problem of how to get rid of waste from oceangoing vessels.

Replacing Plastics

Pop! Pop! Pop! We have all probably done it—popped bubble wrap. Of course, bursting those bubbles quickly reduces the packaging's usefulness and hastens its path to the landfill. But a landfill is designed only to contain, not degrade, garbage from our daily lives. All living things, including you and your family, produce waste. The best idea is to recycle, reduce, reuse, and compost so that less waste reaches

the landfill, as shown in Figure 1. About 29.0 million tons of plastic waste are produced each year in the United States. And 18.6 million tons wind up in our landfills where they degrade very slowly, if at all. Plastics occupy 9–12 percent of the volume in U.S. landfills. But what if we could make packaging materials that degrade more readily?

Researchers are looking for ways to replace packaging materials that do not easily break down with biopolymers that are made from naturally renewable agricultural products. Using biopolymers instead of plastics is desirable for four reasons. First, it conserves limited resources of synthetic raw materials. Second, it diverts agriculture and food industry waste from the landfill to use in producing biopolymers. Third, it uses renewable natural resources. And fourth, it hastens biodegradation when a suitable environment is provided. However, the buying public will not easily accept biopolymers if they are not equal to or better than plastics in strength and ease of production. Current research seeks to achieve those goals.

Product Type	Weight Generated (millions of tons)	Weight Recovered (millions of tons)	Percent of Waste Generated
Durable Goods	8.7	0.4	4.2%
Nondurable Goods	6.6	negligible (<50,000 tons or 0.05%)	<1%
Containers and Packaging	13.7	1.3	9.4%
TOTAL	29.0	1.7	3.5%

Figure 1 *Types and amounts of plastic waste generated in the United States in 1993.*

Edible Films

You may not know it, but edible films are already used in products we eat every day. In foods, edible films serve as barriers, glazes, or binding agents. Examples of edible films are sausage casings, coatings on fruits and vegetables, coatings on raisins and nuts in cereals, some candy coatings on chocolate candies, and coatings on reduced-fat fried foods. In reduced-fat fried foods, the edible film is used to reduce fat uptake while frying the foods. Edible films may also be used as a glaze to enhance appearance. In reduced-calorie items, edible films may be used as a binding agent and adhesive instead of fat. The use of edible films in foods is regulated by the Food and Drug Administration (FDA). Edible films, as a food additive, must be Generally Recognized As Safe (GRAS) by the FDA. As with milk and lactose intolerance, allergic reactions and intolerance to the films may occur. Thus, consumption of edible films in so many food items presents real health concerns and safety issues.

You may not know it, but edible films are already used in products we eat every day.

In today's throwaway society, the useful lifespan of more and more products, such as fast-food packaging, is very short. Those items with a short life span will likely be among the first to be made from biopolymers. Bubble wrap is an example of a product that is often thrown away after a single use. Current research may eventually allow us to replace plastic bubble wrap with edible bubble wrap. Bubble wrap could be made from crops, such as corn or wheat, produced on farms around the world. Bubble wrap made from crops is an example of a natural polymer (biopolymer). Even agricultural waste could someday be turned into useful packaging. Producing biopolymers from waste products will help lower the costs to compete better against plastics. This issue is important because the raw materials used to make plastics have in the past been cheap by-products of the petroleum industry.

Biodegradation of Biopolymers

The best reason to use biopolymers is to solve the degradability problems created by polymers. Plastic typically degrades very slowly, if at all. Thus, plastics are often compared to diamonds, which are said to last forever. Look around you at how many items are made of or contain plastic. It's a lot, isn't it? Most of the 19 million tons of plastic that Americans discard each year winds up in landfills where it remains for many years without substantially degrading.

Even when plastics do degrade, they have a bad effect on the environment. Plastics are made from petroleum. Petroleum is a natural resource formed from degradation of plants over millions of years. As plastics degrade, they release the carbon dioxide that was bound up in them millions of years ago. Thus, they introduce new carbon dioxide into the environment. In contrast, the carbon in the agricultural products used to make biopolymers is only recently fixed from the atmosphere. Agricultural products such as plant proteins, meat proteins, structural proteins, carbohydrates, cellulose derivatives, and chitosan derived from the shells of shellfish have all been used to produce biopolymers. When these biopolymers biodegrade, they recycle the carbon dioxide in the environment rather than introduce more, as the petroleum in plastic does.

Biopolymers biodegrade rapidly, which results in less land litter. Biopolymers essentially vanish from the landscape during degradation. This is much better than the situation that exists now. Plastics thrown away in oceans and lakes damage and kill wildlife such as birds, fish, and turtles. Wildlife often becomes entangled in plastics, as shown in Figure 2. As a result, these animals die or experience

Figure 2 *Animals entangled in nonbiodegradable plastics may die or be severely disabled.*

restricted growth and mobility. Sometimes animals eat plastics by mistake, which can cause digestive problems and possibly starvation. Using biopolymers instead of plastic will eliminate many of these problems. The development of biopolymers is an important issue for all oceangoing vessels. These vessels are no longer able to legally dump plastic waste in the ocean. But the vessels would be able to dump biopolymers because they will biodegrade. Biodegradation keeps wildlife safe from entanglement and digestive problems.

Do these new biopolymers really degrade under ocean conditions? For biodegradation to take place, the microorganisms that digest them must have specific levels of water, oxygen, temperature, pH, and growth compounds. If all these are present, the biopolymer becomes the food source. Through a series of chemical reactions created by the microorganisms, the biopolymers are reduced into microscopic particles that are eaten by the microorganisms. Thus, biopolymers provide energy to the microorganisms that, in turn, produce water and carbon dioxide, both acceptable forms of waste.

How Are Biopolymers Formed?

Biopolymer research is a highly competitive market. Thus, specific information about current research is classified top secret. Discussion of how films are formed is not allowed. But the general processes involved can be described. Films are often made by solvent casting where raw material is dissolved in a controlled reaction and spread across a level surface to dry. Specific conditions of temperature, pH, and time are maintained throughout the reaction. After the reaction is complete, liquid is evenly spread across level glass plates and dried at higher temperatures to form a thin biopolymer film. The solvent casting process is illustrated in Figure 3. Films may also be

produced by the process of extrusion, which is the same method often used to produce plastics. To make films by extrusion, raw material is heated and forced through a very narrow opening in a metal plate called a die.

Biodegradation Studies

After producing biopolymer films, the biodegradability of these films must be determined. It is important to understand how the films biodegrade. Right now very little is known about how biopolymers react in the environment. Before biodegradation can take place, microorganisms must be found that will digest and degrade the film. Billions of microorganisms are taken from local environments

Figure 3 *Schematic of spraying apparatus to form film on level glass plate.*

such as lakes, aquaria, sewage water, raw film material, and garden soil. Even bacteria from human mouths are used. This mixture of microorganisms is placed in a circulating aquarium. The aquarium, which has chemical nutrients in it, is kept at the same temperature throughout the process. The biopolymer is the sole organic energy source. Over time the microorganisms recognize the biopolymer as their food source and thrive as the material is digested. The millions of microorganisms must adapt and show they can digest the biopolymer. Then testing of the biodegradation process can begin.

Evaluating biodegradation has in the past been a difficult process. Samples were physically removed from closed reactors to test them. Respirometers have made this task much easier. Electronic controls keep the supply of oxygen the same throughout the process. A respirometer has several sealed bottles. Each bottle functions as a closed environment. The nutrient water in each bottle is kept at a set temperature. Aerobic respiration, or biodegradation, takes place when a known amount of biopolymer material and adapted microorganisms are put in a bottle.

As aerobic respiration takes place, carbon dioxide is produced. Potassium hydroxide absorbs the carbon dioxide to prevent a toxic buildup. A pressure change within each of the bottles is caused by the absorption of carbon dioxide. When the pressure changes in the bottles, more oxygen is added automatically, which helps with the biodegradation process. Researchers record the amount of oxygen delivered to each bottle. From that data, we learn important information about how fast or slow biodegradation takes place. Knowing how long it takes for a biopolymer to degrade helps us understand how biopolymers and the environment react with each other. The time it takes for a biopolymer film to biodegrade varies. But compared to plastics, they are readily and smoothly changed into carbon dioxide and water.

Future Uses for Biopolymers

In the future, the use of biopolymers such as edible films and coatings may be quite widespread. As discussed, various edible films and coatings are currently used in foods we eat every day. Research is now under way at universities such as Clemson University. Industry is also involved in this research. The research will help us understand how to produce different films and alter film properties.

We will also learn more about degradation in various environments. If we use biopolymers to make packaging materials, we can conserve our limited resources.

Additional Resources

O'Hara K., S. J. Iudicello, and J. Zilligen. 1994. *A Citizens Guide to Plastics in the Ocean: More Than a Litter Problem* (4th edition). Center for Marine Conservation. Washington, DC.
  This book reviews the success of plastic, how improper disposal affects marine animals and birds, sources of plastic waste, plastic waste laws, and what individuals can do as well as what involved groups to contact. Information is available on the Web at http://www.cmc-ocean.org/mdio/teacher.html.

Congressional Office of Technology Assessment. 1993. *Biopolymers: Making Materials Nature's Way*—Background Paper. OTA - BP - E - 102. U. S. Government Printing Office. Washington, DC.
  This background paper provides an introduction to biopolymer technology, new biopolymer materials, and new laws affecting biopolymer production.

US EPA. 2005. Municipal Solid Waste in the United States.
  http://www.epa.gov/msw/msw99.htm

Questions for Discussion

1. What environmental conditions are necessary for microorganisms to degrade materials?

2. What are some advantages to pursuing future research on biopolymer materials?

3. Name the current functions and examples of edible films in foods we eat every day.

4. Compare and contrast advantages and disadvantages of synthetic polymers and biopolymers.

Applications

1. Make a list of places where synthetic polymers could be replaced with biopolymers. (Hint: Visualize the items you viewed, used, or discarded yesterday.)

2. Of the laboratory methods to produce biopolymer films discussed, which has the best opportunity of being used in industry and why?

3. How could a respirometer be used to measure the degradation of a biopolymer shampoo bottle placed in a compost pile?

2.1 The World Is Coming to an End—So What Are You Going to Do about It?

Steven B. Case, M.S.
University of Kansas, Lawrence, Kansas

Dr. Case is currently associate director of the Center for Research and Learning at the University of Kansas. He has taught in a variety of settings and uses computer technology as an integral part of his science teaching. He was instrumental in establishing the Kansas Environmental Monitoring Network, a grassroots computer network of teachers, students, and scientists across the state dedicated to monitoring changes in the regional and global environments.

Dr. Case, in addition to education, has maintained a personal research agenda that ranges from habitat management of tallgrass prairie to work in protein engineering for a biotechnology company.

Overview

The environmental problems we face today are complex global issues. It is important that we develop a deeper understanding of these problems and then act to correct these problems based on that knowledge. Developing research communities through the Internet allows students to develop and play a critical role in this process.

Information Overload and Science As a Way of Knowing

Every time you turn on the news or pick up a newspaper or magazine to read, there is another story about the latest pending global disaster. These stories discuss many environmental issues. Some are about global warming. Another may be about the decreasing ozone or maybe too much ozone. Others may discuss the increasing levels of ultraviolet light or acid rain. Habitat loss may be the focus of another; while the loss of biodiversity is the focus of the next. Still another may be about the decreasing water quality or the effect of the increasing human population. All these stories create such a jumble of information that the real information may be lost. Instead only a few simple messages emerge that make environmental problems appear to be overwhelming and difficult to work on. The main message seems to be that if one of these problems does not wipe out the human species, one of the others will!

It is easy for young people facing this jumbled mess of information to have a dark view of their future. It appears that no matter what we try, all we do is make things worse. Many people choose to become environmental activists. On the first Earth Day in 1970, environmental activists took action to cause change in the way human beings behave toward the planet. We have learned that other citizens and government agencies are environmental activists too. Everyone wants clean water and clean air. Partially as a result of these desires, the Clean Water Act and Clean Air Act were passed, and the Environmental Protection Agency was founded.

Today we realize that while this activism was very important, it is not enough. While that may sound like we need to do even more, we don't necessarily need to do more work. It is necessary to take a step beyond being an environmental activist and become an environmental decision maker. Since we will all make this change together, it requires less work by individuals and relies on the power of collaboration. Decision makers first collect information. Then they analyze that information. Finally, they develop a social action plan based on that information, as described in Figure 1. That process becomes an ongoing cycle for environmental decision makers. They continue to

> *It is necessary to take a step beyond being an environmental activist and become an environmental decision maker.*

584

The World Is Coming to an End—So What Are You Going to Do about It?

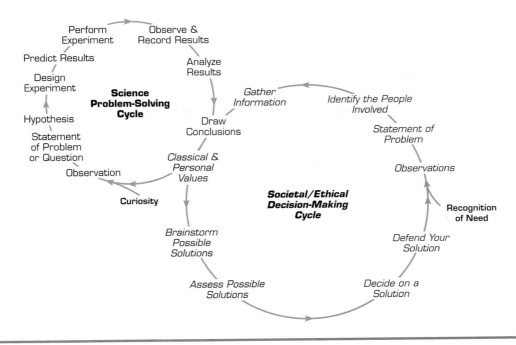

Figure 1 *Decision makers use the information they collect to create a social action plan.*

collect information and evaluate the effect of the social action plan. Decision makers use science, data collection, analysis, social sciences, and social action plans to attack global problems. Decisions are based on knowledge.

Gathering Information

So how do we generate this information on which we are going to act? Science is one way of knowing things, a way of ordering nature in a search for laws (models) on which to base predictions (future events). We must not assume that science is only a search for laws of cause and effect. Science begins with the belief that the world is orderly—or at least our knowledge of it can be made orderly by scientific activity. The better our understanding of the natural world, the better the quality of our predictions. Research to improve our understanding can take place in a variety of ways, including the Internet.

The Internet As a Scientific Tool

The Internet is a powerful tool that helps students work together as part of the science community. Powerful collaborative research can be done using the Internet. For instance, collecting enough data

to really understand global change issues is a challenge for all in science. One or two samples of the atmosphere do not give us enough information to order knowledge or to make predictions. In the case of the atmosphere, even hundreds of samples may not be enough. Now imagine if every secondary classroom in the United States, around 1.2 million, contributed one sample to an atmospheric database. Very quickly we would have enough data to begin the analysis. We could develop models of what we have observed and make accurate predictions.

The Kansas Collaborative Research Network, KanCRN (http://kancrn.org), uses the Internet to build a research community. The KanCRN project involves using leaf stomata as indicators of environmental change. Several researchers have evidence that indicates that stomatal densities change in response to changing atmospheric levels of carbon dioxide. This observation has been developed into an area of research that may allow the use of stomatal densities to monitor increasing levels of carbon dioxide. Since this work involves climatic variations, it requires many geographically dispersed sites to collect and share data. The Internet allows this work to be done by a research community. For these students, the Internet has become a great deal more than a place to go to look things up. It has become an interactive research environment where students work together to generate new understandings of the natural world. They contribute to what we know. In discussion forums, students discuss their data, work out ways to analyze their data, make predictions, and work toward appropriate social action based on their knowledge.

The National Science Foundation's Student Scientist Partnerships are helping science classrooms make this transition from learning about science to doing science. Dr. Neal Lane, former director of the National Science Foundation, said students need to "look beyond the traditions of research in higher education and to understand and explore the possibilities of new partnerships between research and education at the primary and secondary levels." Opportunities for student-scientist partnerships, like the KanCRN project, are increasing as schools across the country try to make these changes. Again they are assisted by the Internet, which has extended their ability to share and work with data and to communicate long distance. The Internet allows for the establishment of a virtual community that is dedicated to research. It is a community in which everyone is welcome; and because of the complexity of the problems we are facing, everyone is necessary.

Additional Resources

Aquanaut Program
   http://www.ap.nurc.uconn.edu
   Students are part of a marine science research team.

Cornell Laboratory of Ornithology
   http://www.birds.cornell.edu
   A membership organization for the study, appreciation, and conservation of birds. Find out how classrooms across the country are helping Cornell scientists learn about birds through FeederWatch.

GLOBE
   http://www.globe.gov
   Find out how students and teachers from more than 4,000 schools in over 60 countries are working with research scientists to learn more about our planet.

GREEN
   http://www.green.org
   Global Rivers Environmental Education Network. Students examine local water quality and discuss policy implications.

Hands On Universe
   http://handsonuniverse.org
   Students investigate the universe.

Journey North
   http://www.learner.org/jnorth/
   Students can observe global wildlife migration and seasonal changes.

The Kansas Collaborative Research Network
   http://kancrn.org
   The Kansas Collaborative Research Network is a community of researchers, teachers, and students interested in conducting collaborative research. It is an open community, and anyone that enjoys doing research is welcome to participate.

Monarch Watch
   http://www.MonarchWatch.org/
   Students follow monarch migrations from Canada to Mexico.

Questions for Discussion

1. What is the advantage of having a large amount of data?

2. If you were taking temperatures around the globe to see if temperatures were going up, how many would you take? Would you take all the temperatures at the same time or take one and move on to another? If you took 10,000 temperature readings, including over the ocean, approximately how much area would each temperature represent?

3. What is the standard for really knowing something? What is the difference between what we "believe" and what we "know"?

Applications

1. Do some basic calculations, and see if you can determine if it is better to have a data sample of 30 points in which you have a lot of confidence or 1,000 data points that give you greater variation.

2. Explore a research project listed in the Additional Resources. Make a poster that explains the project. What are they trying to find out, why is it interesting, what have they found out so far, and what do they still need to find out? Is there enough information to propose a social solution to this problem?

586

The World Is Coming to an End—So What Are You Going to Do about It?

2.2 Dam Ecosystems

John J. Hains, Ph.D.
U.S. Army Corps of Engineers
Waterways Experiment Station, Vicksburg, Mississippi

Dr. Hains is a limnologist, a scientist who studies aquatic systems. His interest in lakes and reservoirs began in his teens as he canoed and fished the rivers and lakes of the southeastern United States. After college, he was hired as a biologist by a local power company where he learned to characterize aquatic communities by identifying algae. In his work with the United States Army Corps of Engineers, Dr. Hains works to answer environmental questions about reservoirs throughout the United States. His most recent major project is the study of an artificially oxygenated reservoir.

Overview

At a location along a river where the waters are clear and cool, a smell of rotten eggs permeates the air, coming from the water released from a dam. How can apparently clean water smell so bad? In another region, coots (a type of waterfowl) become debilitated and die. Eagles scavenge the carcasses and also die. No other life seems to be affected. What is the cause? Elsewhere, in the Southeast, trucks laden with thousands of tons of liquid oxygen travel to impoundments where the oxygen is bubbled into lakes. For what purpose?

When a river is impounded, what is the nature of the resulting reservoir that makes it different from other lakes? And what factors and processes contribute to so many problems? Are problems inevitable?

Dams and Their Functions

Why build a dam? Reservoirs always represent substantial economic investment; thus, their intended purposes are well-defined. The major purposes for constructing dams are simple. One reason is flood control. Dams store water to compensate for seasonal or occasional fluctuations in river flow. By storing or impounding water, rivers are prevented from flooding inhabited land.

Another major reason for constructing a dam is to provide hydroelectric power. In a hydroelectric dam, water flows through large turbines. These turbines convert the energy of water flowing through them into electrical energy. Worldwide, hydroelectric power produces almost one-fifth of all electricity. Aside from these major uses, the reservoirs formed by dams also provide fishing, housing sites, and recreation opportunities.

Dam History

Throughout history, humans have constructed reservoirs in areas where there are few large natural lakes but substantial water needs. These reservoirs served to make water more readily available to local populations. The first archeological evidence of dams dates from about 3,000 B.C.E. in the area that is now Jordan. There an elaborate system of canals and small reservoirs provided a water supply to nearby towns. Similar historical evidence of earthen and stone dams is found in many areas of the world, including Europe, the Middle East, Southeast Asia, China, and Central America. The reservoirs created by these dams were used for drinking water and to irrigate crops.

Hydropower from dams has long been used to ease people's workload. Watermills, which used the power of flowing water to turn massive stone wheels, have been used to grind grains since the first century B.C.E. As the industrial revolution began, hydropower supplied the energy to run factories and other industries. In the United States, the need to bring hydroelectric power to rural communities in the Tennessee Valley resulted in the building of a complex system of large dams and reservoirs.

In the United States, dam building provided irrigation water and thus encouraged settlement in areas of the dry western states. The first very large project was construction of Hoover Dam, begun in 1931. At the time, that was by far the largest dam

Figure 1 *The Richard B. Russell Dam was constructed in 1983 to provide flood control and hydroelectric power.*

on earth. Since then hundreds of dams have been built in the United States. The reservoirs thus formed now serve multiple purposes. For example, the Richard B. Russell Dam in South Carolina, shown in Figure 1, was constructed in 1983 to provide flood control and hydroelectric power. Reservoirs help to provide drinking water; irrigation of crops; flood control; navigation; fishing; and, more recently, recreation and home sites.

Anatomy of a Dam

Figure 2 diagrams the basic features of a large hydropower dam and lake. Water flowing downstream through the reservoir enters the penstocks, the tubes that are open to the lake and deliver water to the turbines. The force of the water passing through the penstock tubes turns the turbine blades, much as a stream might turn a waterwheel. In a dam, however, the turbines generate electricity. After passing through the turbines, water exits the dam into the downstream river or lake.

Some dams, such as the one shown in Figure 2, can also pump water upstream. The purpose of this reverse pumping is to store water in the upstream reservoir, then allow it to flow back through the turbines when electricity is needed. Pump storage, as this process is called, provides extra power for peak demand times—such as a hot summer afternoon when everyone is running an air conditioner.

Pumping of water between upstream and downstream reservoirs is not typical of a natural aquatic system. The abnormal motion of the water may change the habitats of many organisms. The most significant changes are in the water temperature and the amount of dissolved gases in the water. Water flow through dams may alter the natural gradients of both.

The passage of fish through dams presents another problem. When water flows through turbines, so do organisms living in the water. Fish that go through the turbines may be killed, and such fish kills are a source of much public interest and concern.

Competing Interests Influence Dam Construction

Opposing views often exist regarding decisions to build reservoirs. This is due to the competing interests in our natural resources as well as potential problems associated with reservoirs.

Figure 2 *Diagram of a hydropower dam and lake. Arrows show directions of water flow.*

Dam Ecosystems

A group of reservoirs on the Chattahoochee River, in the southeastern United States, illustrates some of the potential problems. The Chattahoochee watershed includes the Atlanta, Georgia, metropolitan area. Wastewater from sewage treatment plants and industries in Atlanta eventually flows into the Chattahoochee River and then into West Point Lake, which is the first major reservoir downstream of Atlanta. Wastewater contains high concentrations of organic materials and nutrients. Thus, the biological productivity, or amount of living organisms in West Point Lake, is greatly enhanced by the wastewater inflows. Fish production in West Point Lake is great! People who like to fish recognize the tremendous resource this lake represents.

However, organisms other than fish also grow prolifically. Bacteria in the deep waters of West Point Lake decompose the organic material flowing into the lake. As a result, the water flowing out of the lake below the dam sometimes has a very bad smell. People who use West Point Lake as their drinking water supply may regard the organic loading from the Chattahoochee River as undesirable.

Human Error

Just as competing public interests influence decisions to build dams, people may decide in retrospect that a dam was not such a good idea after all. Dam builders are beginning to recognize mistakes and to seek ways to repair damaged ecosystems. For example, several dams on the Snake River in Oregon are under serious consideration for removal. If the dams are removed, it will be because there was a change in human priorities for the Snake River water resources. The potential benefits of improvements to the fisheries and recreation may be greater than benefits from the power produced by the dams. Such decisions are made by consideration of the often competing local and national interests.

Glen Canyon Dam, on the Colorado River, provides a similar example of a change in priorities. Lake Powell, which was created when the Glen Canyon Dam was built, serves several purposes. The lake helps to prevent downstream flooding. It provides water for drinking and irrigation. Anglers and tourists flock to the lake for recreation, and hydropower generates electricity. All of these features have been good for the economy of the Glen Canyon Dam area.

The change in priorities for the Glen Canyon Dam and Lake Powell reflect recent public interest in ecosystem restoration. In 1997, for the first time, water from Glen Canyon Reservoir was intentionally released to simulate natural flooding. Such floods occurred naturally before the dam was constructed. Fast-flowing water can carry sand, gravel, and even large boulders as it moves downstream. The periodic high flows of sediment-laden water had created the original river habitats, which supported a unique community of organisms. Deprived of these periodic flows, the river habitats below the dam diminished. The 1997 release of water was an experiment. Reservoir managers are considering releasing large flows of water from Glen Canyon Dam on a regular basis. By doing so, they will help restore and maintain downstream habitats.

Altered Ecosystems

Reservoirs always greatly alter the land, the watershed, the organisms living within them, and the streams they impound. Despite these alterations, reservoirs are important for the aquatic ecosystems they support. The chemical content of the water in a lake is initially determined by the nature of the watershed through which the water flows. This, in turn, depends on its geological characteristics and the biota and human development occurring in the watershed. Climate acting on the watershed determines the amount of water available as well as the types of organisms living in the watershed.

The basic features of natural lakes are independent of any human design although human activities in the watershed, such as agriculture or urban development, are important. Reservoir design usually incorporates factors such as climate (water balance), geology (basin shape and dam type), and political and economic factors. Land use and development practices have only recently become recognized as important factors in lake and reservoir management, often too late to be used for the reservoir design.

What Is Distinctive about Reservoirs?

Reservoirs are often very different from natural lakes in their shapes and water characteristics. Some reservoirs have water flowing swiftly through them. They are slow places along rivers caused by dams. Water may take years to pass through other reservoirs. Reservoirs are often shaped differently from natural lakes. Natural lakes often have their greatest depth away from the shore, often near the middle. Reservoirs usually are deepest near the dam. Natural lakes are often more rounded than reservoirs. The shape of a reservoir depends on the topography of the land and on design features such as the height of its dams. On maps, many reservoirs look tree-shaped, or dendritic, with a main stem and tributary branches.

Water levels in reservoirs may fluctuate greatly and frequently. Reservoir outflows often occur at great depths and can allow dramatic "drawdowns" of the water level or lake surface elevation. Some flood control reservoirs can fluctuate 100 feet or more, and this creates a new set of problems to be managed, such as bank erosion due to exposure to rainfall or wind. In contrast, most natural lakes experience very modest changes in water level.

Natural lakes are also older than reservoirs. Most of the large reservoirs in the United States were built within the last 150 years. Almost any natural lake larger than a beaver pond is at least 1,000 years old; some may be 50,000 years old or older.

The watersheds of most reservoirs are large compared to most natural lakes. More material is available from these larger watersheds to be transported into reservoirs. Such material input to a lake or reservoir is called loading. Although reservoirs may be young in age compared to natural lakes, reservoirs may fill quickly with accumulated sediment. Sometimes this filling occurs too quickly. In the Tennessee Copper Basin, excessive erosion from many acres of bare soil caused several reservoirs on the Ocoee River to nearly fill with sediment. This rapid filling in, or sedimentation, of local reservoirs encouraged community members to revegetate the Copper Basin.

Dams Alter Aquatic Habitats

Scientists have observed that dams may adversely affect fish populations. Water in contact with air will tend to absorb gases in air, including oxygen. Sometimes too much air is absorbed, producing

The watersheds of most reservoirs are large compared to most natural lakes.

water in which the air tends to bubble out. Fish living in this overly aerated water may die as the air bubbles out inside their bodies. This happens on the Columbia River and other places where dams release well-aerated water into deep downstream basins.

Alternatively, microorganisms such as bacteria may use all of the oxygen in the deep water of the reservoir. Chemicals produced in poorly aerated water can be detrimental to life in the water. Metals in the sediments may dissolve into the water. Waste products such as ammonia or methane may be produced. Proteins in decomposing organic material may contribute to the production of poisonous hydrogen sulfide, producing a rotten egg smell. Because of this, the deepest waters of stratified lakes can contain chemicals that would be considered poisonous to many aerobic organisms.

In most natural lakes, these chemicals would tend to stay there until mixing and aeration slowly converted them to their aerobic forms. In Richard B. Russell Lake and other southeastern reservoirs, the quality of the water is improved by artificially adding pure oxygen to the lake. Imagine pumping thousands of tons of pure oxygen into a reservoir! This expense must be offset by some benefit. In most cases, that benefit is increased habitat in the reservoir or in the waters released from the dam.

New Ecosystems

Both natural lakes and reservoirs formed by dams support ecosystems in which organisms live and interact and are supported by energy from the sun. Materials enter the lakes from the watershed; and many different things can happen depending on the shape of the lake or reservoir, energy exchanges, water movements, the types and numbers of organisms living there, and the depth of the water outlet if the lake is a reservoir. Natural lakes tend to have characteristics that are less dependent than are reservoirs on their watersheds. Reservoirs contain all of the characteristics and processes of natural lakes and are even more complicated because of their relationship to the watershed and the types of operation of the dams.

References and Additional Resources

International Rivers Network. Dams: What they are and what they do
   http://www.irn.org/basics/ard
   This Web site provides an informative history of dam construction and discusses the detrimental impacts of some large dams.

Thorton, K. W., B. L. Kimmel, and F. E. Payne. 1990. *Reservoir Ecology: Ecological Perspectives.* John Wiley & Sons, Inc.
   Research articles describing the limnology of reservoirs.

United States Geological Survey, 1998. Controlled Flood—Can Large Releases of Water Restore Habitats in the Grand Canyon?
   http://www.walrus.wr.usgs.gov/grandcan/flood.html

Bureau of Reclamation, 1998. Operation of Glen Canyon Dam.
   http://www.usbr.gov/uc/library/envdocs/eis/gc/gcdOpsFEIS.html

Questions for Discussion

1. How does a reservoir formed by the damming of a stream or river differ from a natural lake?
2. Describe two ways in which the aquatic habitat may be altered by construction of a dam.

Applications

1. Find out if you have a dam and reservoir in your local community. If so, when and why was the dam built? Are the original purposes for which the dam was built still community priorities? If not, how have priorities changed since the dam was constructed?
2. Relatively few large dams have been built in the United States in recent years, but several major dams are planned for river systems outside of the United States. Research one of these projects. Describe the potential environmental and economic effects of one planned dam project.

2.3 How Does Water Get to the Top of a Tree?

William C. Olien, Ph.D.
Shenandoah University, Winchester, Virginia

Dr. Olien received his B.S. degree in biological science and then earned his M.S. and Ph.D. degrees in horticulture at Michigan State University with specialization in the physiology of woody plants. After receiving his Ph.D. in 1980, he has been active in research and teaching in the area of plant responses to environmental conditions. He is especially interested in effects of environmental stresses on plants and the role of the plant vascular system in responses to these stresses. His work with cooperators on environment-genotype interactions was awarded the Paul Howe Shepard Publication Award by the American Pomological Society in 1992.

Overview

Have you ever wondered about how water moves from tree roots through the trunk and on up into the leaves? You may observe that tree leaves dry up and fall off during droughts or when the tree doesn't receive adequate water. So you know that the roots and leaves are somehow connected. What internal structures in the tree provide this connection, and how do they interact? Moving water up a tree is real work, and work requires energy input. Where does this energy come from, and how is it used?

Calculating Water Movement in a Tree

It doesn't look like tall trees have much trouble getting water to the shoots and leaves at the very top. Look at the tallest trees around your home or school in summer, trees like pine or maple or oak. Way at the top, maybe 18 meters or more above the ground, the leaves look green and healthy, just like the leaves low in the tree near your reach. Eighteen meters high is like a five-story building. Stomates, microscopic openings in the leaf surfaces, allow water to evaporate from inside the leaves. On a nice summer day, the leaves of a maple tree might be evaporating water to the air (by the process of transpiration) at the rate of 80 g of water per square meter of leaf surface each hour (or in other words, 80 g $H_2O/m^2/hr$). Just how much water loss is this for the entire tree?

To calculate the total amount of water lost, or transpired, from the leaves of a tree, you first need to know the amount of leaf area. You can estimate the total leaf area on a big tree as three times the amount of ground area that the tree canopy covers. The area of a circle = πr^2. Thus, if a tree's canopy is 40 feet wide (12.2 meters), then the ground area covered is equal to:

$$3.14 \times (6.1 \text{ m})^2 = 116.8 \text{ m}^2$$

The estimated total area of all leaves on the tree is then:

$$3 \times 116.8 \text{ m}^2 = 350 \text{ m}^2$$

This ratio of total leaf area to ground area covered is called the leaf area index, and it is an important number in understanding how trees and forests grow.

If all the leaves are transpiring at the same rate, then our tree is losing a total of:

$$(80 \text{ g } H_2O/m^2/hr) \times (350 \text{ m}^2 \text{ leaf area}) = 28,000 \text{ g of water every hour}$$

That is a lot of water, more than 7 gallons (28 liters). There is an old saying about water that "a pint is a pound the world around." Since a pint of water weighs a pound, then a gallon weighs 8 pounds; and 7 gallons weighs 56 pounds.

Think about putting 7 gallons of water in a large bucket and carrying it up five floors by climbing the stairs. That is a lot of work. The tree is releasing that much water to the air every hour during the middle of the day. On a hot summer day, a tree may lose more than 50 gallons in a day.

But it's worse than that. The tree does not have a convenient bucket system. Before it can transpire any water from its top-most leaves, it must first get an entire column of water from the roots to those thirsty leaves at the top—a water column as high as the tree, about 18 meters in our example. All of that water is transported through the xylem system, which contains cells called vessels and tracheids. How much water is that?

Since one cm³ of water weighs 1 gram, then a square water column 1 cm by 1 cm and 60 feet (18.3 meters) tall weighs 1.83 kg/cm², or about 4 pounds/cm². Now suppose the trunk of our tree has a diameter of 30 inches (or 76 cm). Only part of that trunk will contain functional xylem vessels that can carry water up the tree. As shown in Figure 1, the rest of the trunk is made up of dead cells, or nonfunctional xylem.

Let's estimate that one-fourth of the trunk area is made of functional xylem. Since the area of a circle equals πr^2, the area of functional vessels in our tree would equal:

$$(3.14 \times (38 \text{ cm})^2) \times 0.25 = 1140 \text{ cm}^2$$

If the tree were shaped like a straight post (just to keep this simple), the total weight of the water columns in the tree would be:

$$1140 \text{ cm}^2 \times 1.8 \text{ kg/cm}^2 = 2052 \text{ kg}$$

That equals over 4,500 pounds, or 2.25 tons, of water! That is the amount of water that the tree must hold before any water reaches the leaf surface to evaporate. No wonder a falling tree sounds like an earthquake when it hits the ground.

Think of this also. The tree must counteract the force of gravity to move water up the trunk.

Bark

Functional Xylem

Functional Phloem

Figure 1 *Only a small portion of the cells in this tree trunk are alive and functional.*

Gravity is pulling 1.47 pounds of force down per cm² area of water column for each meter of tree height. This is the force that the tree must counteract in order to move water up.

Any way you look at it, our tree has a big job. But fortunately, it has a lot of roots, xylem vessels, and leaves to do the job. How specifically does this process of water movement work?

Several Theories Describe Water Movement in Trees

You know that water movement in trees is a fact, but from where does the needed energy come and how does it accomplish the water movement? There are several ways that water can move in plants; but moving water is always work, and doing work takes energy. In some cases, the driving energy comes from internal chemical energy; and in some cases, the driving energy comes from external heat energy. But in all cases, nothing moves without energy. Several different theories describe the mechanism of water movement in trees. Let's look at these and see which methods might be most important in carrying water up our tree.

Capillary Rise

The spaces between plant cells and inside xylem vessels are small. People have compared water movement in these spaces to the rise of water in a small diameter tube (a capillary). If you put a small diameter glass tube into a cup of water, you can see water rise in the tube above the level of water in the cup. Look at the top of the water column. The thick, curved surface of the water, called a meniscus, is where water molecules interact with air and the walls of the tube. Water wets the side of the tube and is pulled up. The pull of water up the wall of the tube is greater than the force of gravity pulling it down. Thus, the water level is highest along the inside wall of the tube and lowest in the center of the tube. Try some different diameter tubes. The smaller the tube diameter, the higher the water will rise because smaller diameter tubes interact more strongly with the water surface and because the weight of water in a small tube is less than in a larger tube. Capillary rise alone will lift water less than half a meter in tubes the size of plant xylem vessels.

But xylem vessels and spaces between cells in plants do not have surfaces open to the air; so the internal pressure would change if water moved, counteracting the energy for capillary rise. Seal the end of one of your glass capillary tubes, and see if capillary rise still happens when you put it in water. Capillary rise won't get us very far in moving water up our 18 meter tall tree. But the meniscus that water forms between cell walls and air spaces is important in holding water in plant tissues. The same principle holds water in small spaces between particles in the soil.

The Push of Root Pressure

Cells that have more salts (greater osmotic potential) than the surrounding solution can draw water into them. When water uptake is slow, plant roots can accumulate salts from the water passing through them. Increased salt concentrations increase the osmotic potential in root cells. Thus, the root cells more readily attract water and draw water in from the soil by osmosis. Sugars can also accumulate in root cells, further increasing the root osmotic potential.

As water continues to be drawn in by the root cells, it begins to build up pressure. This pressure pushes the water in the path of least resistance, that is, up the xylem vessels. Water will not move very fast this way; but this force can move water up the trunks of grape vines and some trees (such as birch trees) to cells that are just beginning to grow in the spring, the cells that will make the first leaves and shoots of the new season. Root pressure increases as the soil warms in the spring and continues to increase until the new leaves unfold and begin to transpire.

Stem Pressure Can Push Too—and Thanks for the Maple Syrup!

Some trees, such as maples, can use the osmotic principle in xylem ray cells and vessels to move water all the way up the tree trunk in spring. Again water does not move very fast this way, but stem pressure is another way to get things going in the spring. This is the mechanism by which the sap that is used to make maple syrup is produced.

Maple sap flow can occur any time from October to April if freezing nights are followed by warm days. The sap will not flow if temperatures are constantly warm or constantly below freezing. Cold temperatures increase the conversion of stored starch into sugar. The next morning warm temperatures start the sap flowing. The osmotic gradient between sugar in the plant and water in the soil drives water up the tree. It has been suggested that sap flow may also be driven by carbon dioxide gas that accumulates from rapid cell respiration as the temperatures warm.

In New England, people have collected sap from maple trees for centuries. Traditionally, a hole is bored (tapped) in the trunk in late winter and a bucket is hung to catch the sap. The sap is then boiled down to reduce the water content. The resulting thick syrup, or sugar, is used to make maple syrup and maple sugar candy. Harvesting the sap does not seem to hurt the tree; sap is collected from the same trees year after year. It has been estimated that tapping removes less than 10 percent of the tree's sap, so the tree has plenty left for its own needs. The average yield of sap from a maple tree is 40 to 75 liters in a year and can be as high as 150 liters. Raw sap usually contains 2 percent to 3 percent sugar, so it takes a lot of sap to boil down for sweets. Other compounds in the sap, like certain amino acids, give maple syrup its special flavor.

Cohesion of Water and the Pull of Transpiration

When the leaves are out and the sun is shining, the main method of moving water up our tall tree is transpiration from the leaf surfaces. Heat from the sun evaporates a lot of water from inside the leaf, through the stomates, and out to the air. Surfaces of the leaf cells become dryer when water is evaporated away. This dryness pulls water from the xylem, which in turn pulls water up the trunk, which then pulls water into the roots from the soil. It's like a long, continuous rope of water. The pull on this "rope" of water by transpiration is tremendous, creating a huge tension on the water column in conducting vessels and forcing water up the trunk, as shown in Figure 2.

Forces that act against the flow of water are gravity (weight of the water column), resistance to water intake by the roots, and resistance to water flow in xylem vessels and tracheids. The total speed of water moving up the trunk can be quite fast on a sunny day, as high as 6 meters per hour in narrow xylem vessels and 45 meters per hour in wide vessels.

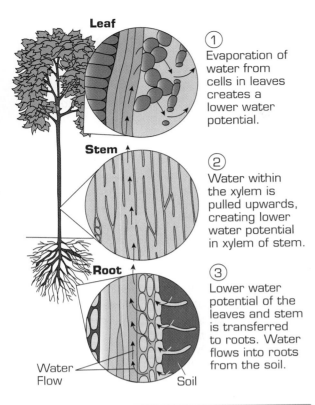

Leaf

① Evaporation of water from cells in leaves creates a lower water potential.

Stem

② Water within the xylem is pulled upwards, creating lower water potential in xylem of stem.

Root

③ Lower water potential of the leaves and stem is transferred to roots. Water flows into roots from the soil.

Water Flow

Soil

Figure 2 *Transpiration and water molecule cohesion affect water flow through the xylem. Evaporation from leaves lowers water potential [1] pulling water up through the stem [2] from the roots [3] and soil.*

Xylem Vessel Size: Fast Flow Versus Blockage of Vessels

Flow of water in wide vessels is faster than in narrow vessels or tracheids because there is less resistance to flow in wider vessels. For smooth flow that does not tumble, like the flow in xylem, flow rate increases in proportion to the fourth power of capillary radius. So a small increase in vessel radius makes a big difference.

Water columns in small tubes, like narrow xylem vessels and tracheids, can stand very great tension without breaking. The more narrow the tube, the more tension the water column can stand. But when enough water is not coming in through the roots, the tension builds to the point where the water column breaks. Larger diameter tubes are much riskier because their water columns will break more easily than water columns in narrow tubes. When the water column in a vessel breaks, the "rope" is broken and water can no longer move up in that vessel. The plant must use the remaining vessels to move water. The drier the plant becomes, the more vessels and tracheids snap their water columns. Once the water column in a vessel is broken, that vessel cannot transport water again until it is refilled by positive root or stem pressure next spring. Or the vessel may become plugged with materials deposited from other cells, and the vessel then becomes part of the colored heartwood in the center of the trunk.

Wide Vessels or Narrow Vessels?

So which is better, wide vessels or narrow vessels? Some flowering trees, like oak, use both strategies. They make large vessels in the spring when the tree has a high water demand for new growth and the risk of drought is very low. Then in the summer, they make narrow vessels and tracheids and so play it safe when the risk of drought is greater. The growth rings are very clear when you look at the end of a log from this kind of a tree. You can clearly see the large spring vessels as small holes in the wood. This kind of tree is called ring porous because of the annual rings of spring xylem "pores," as shown in Figure 3.

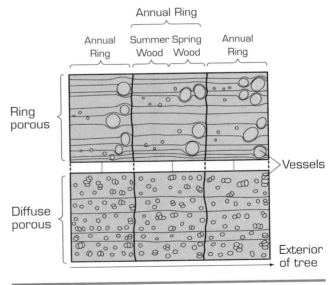

Figure 3 *Stem cross sections from ring porous and diffuse porous trees. Ring pourous trees produce narrow xylem vessels early in the growing season and wider vessels later each year. Diffuse porous trees have only evenly distributed narrow vessels.*

Some flowering trees, like birch and apple trees, choose the safe route. They make only narrow tracheids and xylem vessels. When you look at the end of a log from this kind of a tree, the wood looks quite uniform. It is hard to see the annual rings because there are no large "spring" vessels; so this kind of wood is called diffuse porous, as shown in Figure 3. Conifer trees, such as pine and fir trees, make only narrow tracheids; so they also use the safe route. Conifers also have narrow leaves to reduce the amount of water demanded by transpiration. Annual growth rings are clearly seen in conifers like longleaf pine because lignin, a reddish-brown material, is laid down in cell walls in the late-season part of the growth ring.

Additional Resources

Kramer, P. J. 1983. *Water Relations of Plants*. Academic Press, New York.
   This is a classic and very readable text on all aspects of the use and needs of water by plants.
Kramer, P. J. and T. T. Kozlowski. 1979. *Physiology of Woody Plants*. Academic Press, New York.
   A classic book with broad coverage of the function and development of woody plants.
Salisbury, F. B. and C. W. Ross. 1992. *Plant Physiology*, 4th ed. Wadsworth Publishing Company, Belmont, CA.
   This is a well-written basic text on the growth and function of all plants, not just trees; it contains many helpful diagrams and pictures.
Zimmermann, M. H. 1983. *Xylem Structure and the Ascent of Sap*. Springer-Verlag, NY.
   A short book focused on how water movement in trees is related to the structure and function of the xylem.
Zimmermann, M. H. and C. L. Brown. 1980. *Trees: Structure and Function*. Springer-Verlag, NY.
   An excellent advanced text with good diagrams and pictures on the internal structure and function of trees.

Questions for Discussion

1. A water molecule is evaporated from the topmost leaf of a tree. What were the factors that the water molecule had to overcome to arrive at the top leaf?

2. What are the sources of energy that can move a water molecule to the top of a tree? Describe this for (*a*) the spring before the leaves are out and (*b*) a hot day in July.

3. How does the tree balance safety versus efficiency of water movement? What are the strategies of ring porous and diffuse porous trees?

4. What might cause the water column in a xylem vessel to break? What is the consequence of this for supplying the top of the tree with water over the summer?

Applications

1. List as many ways you can think of to estimate the total leaf area of a tree.

2. List as many ways you can think of to estimate both the total amount of water used by a tree in a day as well as the water used in a day by one square mile of forest.

3. You can determine how much rain fell by putting an empty soup can out on the lawn and measuring how deep the water is in the can after the rain. How can you relate this number to how many gallons of water the tree lost by evaporation on the day before the rain? For example, how many inches (or cm) of rain would be needed to completely replace the 50 gallons (or 189 liters) lost per day by our example tree (2.54 cm/inch; 3.79 liter/gallon)?

4. You can estimate the dryness of the air, and the amount of evaporation, by filling a soup can with water and placing it out in the yard in the morning and then measuring how far the water level dropped in the can at the end of the day. Suppose you keep track of water evaporated, or rain gained, for every day during the summer. How could you use your two-soup-can method to determine how much to irrigate your lawn (or flower bed or garden or apple orchard)?

5. What characteristics would make a good drought-resistant tree? Consider internal and external structure of roots, trunk, branches, and leaves.

2.4 Populations under Control: Catfish Farming

William "Rockie" English, Ph.D.
Clemson University, Clemson, South Carolina

Catherine Ann English, M.L.S.
Pickens Co. School System, Clemson, South Carolina

Dr. English helps fish farmers to become established and to keep their fish healthy and growing rapidly without polluting surrounding water. He also develops and teaches water quality education classes for children and adults including the popular "Stream Watch" program.

Mrs. English manages information resources and dissemination of materials for Morrison Elementary School. She worked as an aquaculture technician during her college years and continues to work with her husband on aquatic invertebrate projects.

Overview

Aquaculture (aqua = water) is the culture, or growing, of plants and animals in fresh, brackish, or salty waters. Aquaculture is considered the fastest growing segment of agriculture in the United States. The United States Department of Agriculture reports that nearly 70 percent of the world's conventional, commercially caught fish species are reported to be fully exploited, depleted, or recovering from depletion. According to the Western Regional Aquaculture Center, the need for cultured seafood will grow to keep pace with our rapidly expanding human population.

Aquaculture is accomplished through the management of fish populations using ecosystem knowledge and manipulation of natural resources. In aquaculture, a fish farmer harvests fish that have been stocked and managed. This is different from commercial fishing where hooks or nets are set to capture wild fish. A successful fish grower will apply principles learned in studies of ecosystems, populations, biology, chemistry, physics, and economics.

Types of Aquaculture

Aquaculture practices can be considered extensive or intensive. Extensive culture is the growing of fish with low input and management from humans. With this type of aquaculture, the density of animals and biomass (weight of fish) is low. Aquaculture of this type is often used to provide food for a small family or as a supplemental income. Intensive culture maximizes the quantity and weight of fish grown in a limited space. Intensive culture systems (commercial fish farms) and extensive culture, or wild, systems (lakes, farm ponds) can be compared using examples primarily from catfish farming, which is the largest aquaculture industry in the United States. More than 460 million pounds (209 million kg) of catfish are produced annually, providing revenue of over $352 million directly to catfish farmers.

Intensive fish culture systems require considerable external input and management to increase the natural carrying capacity of a pond. The carrying capacity of a pond is the maximum number or weight of fish that can be sustained in a given area. Many environmental pressures set the carrying capacity of wild ponds. The most important of these include competition, predation, food abundance, and water quality. By reducing the impact of these limiting environmental pressures, aquaculture practices increase the carrying capacity of ponds. With catfish culture, a single species of fish is grown at a very high density. This practice eliminates competition between fish species (interspecific competition) and predation. Formulated feed is provided once or twice daily, and mechanical aeration is commonly used to supplement natural oxygen production. All these practices increase the carrying capacity of ponds where fish are cultured.

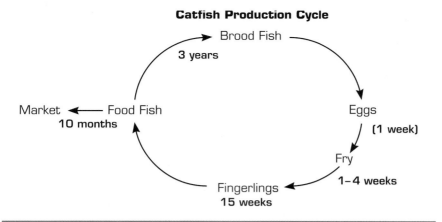

Catfish Production Cycle

Brood Fish

3 years

Market ← Food Fish
10 months

Eggs

(1 week)

Fry

1–4 weeks

Fingerlings
15 weeks

Figure 1 *Fish population growth in a wild pond compared to cultured fish population numbers. The cultivated fish pond was managed to maximize production by removing competition and predators and providing supplemental feed. Fish in the cultured pond are stocked and harvested annually.*

A description of the production cycle or life cycle of a cultured catfish shows how culturing of a species increases birth rate and survival. Human manipulation of the environment further increases the carrying capacity of catfish ponds.

Catfish Farming

The catfish reproduction cycle, as shown in Figure 1, begins with brood fish that spawn primarily in the spring of the year when water temperatures are between 23° and 30°C. The length and date of spawning season varies with location. Catfish are cavity spawners. In natural systems, the male builds a nest in a submerged hollow log, undercut bank, or other secluded, semidark cavity. The male selects and prepares the nest by fanning out silt and debris. The female then enters the nest and deposits eggs in a

gelatinous mass on the bottom. The male fertilizes the eggs and remains in the nest after the female leaves. The male constantly fans the eggs, providing fresh water circulation through the nest area and removal of waste products given off by the eggs. In the wild, the male defends the cavity from predators until spawning is complete and the fry (baby fish) leave the nest.

In commercial ponds, spawning containers about the size of 40-liter wastepaper baskets are used to satisfy the cavity-breeding behavior. Fertilized eggs are moved from spawning containers to a hatchery where optimal temperature, oxygen level, and waste removal are provided artificially. Cultured catfish reach prime breeding condition at three to four years and range in size from 1.4 to 4.5 kg. Wild catfish may not spawn until the fifth year of their life, as shown in Figure 2. Cultured brood catfish are fed a nutritionally complete diet having 36 percent protein and produce about 6,667 eggs per kg of spawning female. A typical 1.8-kg female may lay 12,000 eggs. Wild fish may go for days without feeding and have a nutritionally poor diet. This results in low growth rates for fish that spawn and poor health condition at spawning time. On average, smaller and fewer eggs are produced in wild spawns.

Water quality is critical for egg hatching success. Ideal water temperatures for hatching are between

	Brood Fish Age	Eggs Hatched	%	Fry Survived	%	Fingerlings Survived	%	Food-size to Processor
Wild Fish	4–5 months	4,000–10,000	(0–60)	0–6,000	(0–60)	0–3,600	(0–60)	0–2,100
Cultured Fish	3–4 months	10,000–12,000	(95)	9,500	(95)	9,025	(95)	8,573

Figure 2 *Expected survival of fish in wild ponds compared to cultured ponds. Percentage survival (%) between growth stages is in parentheses. The best situation in wild ponds and the worst in cultured ponds were used to calculate these values.*

24°C and 28°C. Fungus growth is common on eggs kept below 24°C, and bacterial egg rot often appears on the eggs when temperatures are over 28°C. Dissolved oxygen in hatchery water should remain about 6 mg/l, and pH should be near neutral. Oxygen levels below 4 mg/l are extremely stressful, and immediate death results when levels reach 2 mg/l. Oxygen levels near pond bottoms often approach 2 mg/l.

Egg hatching success in the wild is low and extremely variable because there are no controls on the environmental variables affecting success. In contrast, approximately 95 percent of the eggs in commercial hatcheries will hatch. This contrast between hatching success in the wild versus cultured conditions is detailed in Figure 2. Eggs kept at 26°C will hatch into sac fry in 7–8 days. Sac fry are tiny fish that swim about with their yolk sac still attached. They receive nourishment from the yolk sac. After three days, the yolk sac is absorbed and the fry swim up to the surface searching for food. In hatcheries, fry are fed finely ground high protein (45 percent) feed to insure good health and rapid growth. In wild ponds, fry feed on bottom dwelling worms, insects, and free-swimming, microscopic animals called zooplankton. These wild food sources are not reliable and may require much energy to capture.

Survival is imperiled in wild ponds because eggs and fry are easy prey for predators such as bass, bluegill, and aquatic insects. All fish are highly susceptible to predation until they reach about 5 inches. In contrast, hatcheries do not have predators and thus provide ideal conditions for survival and growth. Newly hatched fry usually stay in the hatchery for 10 days before being moved to a fingerling production pond. Fingerling is a name given to small fish approximately the length of your finger. All other fish are removed from these fingerling ponds before stocking. This practice eliminates competition for food, predation, and the introduction of diseases carried by wild fish. Predatory aquatic insects are also removed and controlled continuously for the first three weeks or until fry are bigger than the insects. In wild ponds, the fry-to-fingerling survival is very low; fish density by the end of the production cycle may be less than 250 fish per hectare. In contrast, 95 percent of the fry survive to reach fingerling size in culture ponds, as shown in Figure 2.

Fry are stocked at a very high density. The number of fish stocked per pond (density) is dependent on the size of fingerling desired at harvest. If a 6-inch (15 cm) fingerling fish is desired at the end of the fingerling production period, then the stocking rate is 58,333 fry/acre (23,607 fry/hectare). To produce a 4-inch (10-cm) fingerling fish, the stocking rate is 175,000 fry/acre.

After competition, predation, and food limitations are controlled, the two major environmental factors limiting the carrying capacity in aquaculture ponds are dissolved oxygen and waste assimilation capacity. Aeration, the mixing of water to introduce air into it, can maintain oxygen concentrations at 4 mg/l, the requirement to keep fish healthy. Aeration is economical, costing less than $0.03 per pound of fish produced.

Ultimately, the carrying capacity in a culture pond is limited by fish waste products primarily. Excessive waste products degrade water and kill fish. Waste assimilation capacity in aquaculture ponds is the main determinant of carrying capacity, uneaten food, and excreted ammonia.

The amount of waste in intensive culture ponds is determined by the amount of fish food added. Normally, fish are fed 2 to 4 percent of their body weight daily. The eventual size of fingerlings (10–15 cm) is dependent on amount of feed provided. A critical point is that the amount of feed the fish farmer can provide is dependent on the waste assimilation capacity of the pond. The maximum feeding rate for ponds receiving artificial aeration is 113 kg of feed per day for each hectare of pond surface area. Higher feeding rates cause water quality to degrade and fish to die.

High feeding rates are necessary for rapid growth. Thus, when small fish are first introduced into culture ponds, they are fed two to three times daily. As they grow, larger fingerlings eat less food in proportion to their body weight and more efficiently convert food to fish biomass. Small fingerlings require 4 mg of feed to gain 1 mg of weight. Fish larger than 0.22 kg require about 1.5 mg feed to gain 1 mg of body weight. This is called a 1.5:1 feed conversion ratio. Fish have a high conversion ratio relative to other cultured animals. For example, chickens have a 6:1 conversion ratio, swine converts at 5:1, and beef cattle have a 7.5:1 conversion ratio. Fingerlings reach 10–15 cm in 100 to 150 days. Fingerlings are removed from the fingerling ponds when maximum feeding rates are reached and stocked into food-fish production ponds. Ideally, feeding rate for fingerling culture ponds at this time is 113 kg of feed/hectare/day.

Stocking density for food-fish production ponds is about 9,800 fish per hectare. These fish are provided supplemental aeration when needed and fed a 32 percent protein feed at 2 percent of biomass given daily until harvest time (9 to 12 months). Fish should be about 0.5–0.6 kg at harvest time, and feeding rates should be about 113 kg of feed/hectare/day. Survivorship should be about 90 percent. Wild pond survivorship to this age is usually less than 10 percent, as shown in Figure 2.

Catfish ponds are artificial human-controlled systems. The carrying capacity for a catfish population in a culture pond is artificially raised through elimination of predation, competition, disease management, supplemental aeration, and feeding. This contrasts with catfish populations living in natural wild systems. In wild ponds or systems, fish population numbers and weight tend to stabilize in a few years at the pond carrying capacity, as shown in Figures 3 and 4. Catfish culture ponds are usually harvested each year. Annual restocking weight of fish is below carrying capacity so that environmental pressures are low and maximum growth rate is achieved, as shown in Figure 4. Ideally, cultured fish are harvested just as they reach the carrying capacity of the culture pond. Wild populations of fish are seldom composed of a single species and will reach the carrying capacity of a pond in two to three years. Typical carrying capacity of wild ponds is less than 450 kg, as shown in Figure 4, and the age structure is a mix of different ages but is dominated by young of

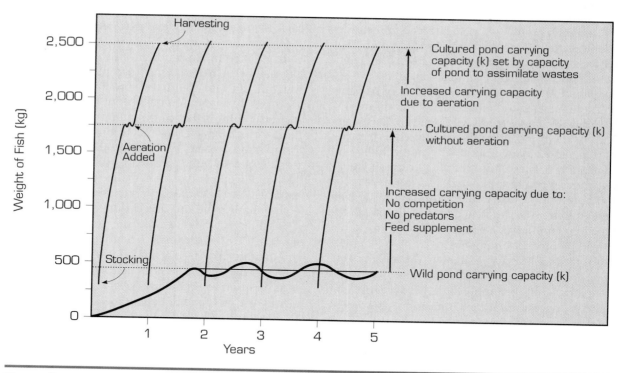

Figure 3 *Fish weight changes in wild pond populations compared to weight changes in cultured fish ponds. Competition, predation, and availability of feed all limit the carrying capacity of wild ponds. Because fish in cultured ponds have these limitations removed, the next limitation becomes dissolved oxygen. The dissolved oxygen limitation is removed by artificial aeration. Ultimately, the pond carrying capacity of an aquaculture pond is limited by the rate of assimilation of fish waste products. This waste is equivalent to feeding 113 kg of feed/hectare/day.*

Populations under Control: Catfish Farming

the year. Ever notice that all fish in the store are the same size? In cultured populations, fish ages are all the same. This reduces competition within species (intraspecific competition) and provides the fish processing plant and fish market a standard-sized fish.

By design, cultured systems control population numbers, biomass, competition, predation, food supply, and dissolved oxygen. They are limited primarily by the waste assimilative capacity of the pond. All these factors interplay in wild ponds.

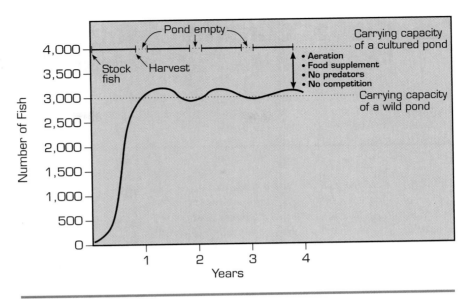

Figure 4 *The difference in carrying capacities in cultured and wild fish ponds.*

Additional Resources

Avault, J. W. Jr. 1996. *Fundamentals of Aquaculture*. AVA Publishing Co. Baton Rouge, LA.
    General text covering all aspects of aquaculture. It is a step-by-step guide.
Bardach, J. E. 1997. *Sustainable Aquaculture*. John Wiley & Sons, Inc., New York, NY.
    Collection of essays on sustainable aquaculture practices.
Mathias, J. A., A. T. Charles, and H. Baotong. 1997. *Integrated Fish Farming*. CRC Press, New York, NY.
    Covers the integration of aquaculture with agriculture and inland fisheries.
Tucker, C. S. 1985. *Channel Catfish Culture*. Elsevier Publishing Co., New York, NY.
    Covers all you will ever want to know about catfish culture. It's very technical.

Questions for Discussion

1. Why would you expect the number of fish in wild ponds at carrying capacity to be more variable than the weight at carrying capacity?
2. Why do fish have such good food conversion ratios?
3. What would it take to raise fish in wastewater treatment plants?

Applications

1. Discuss the reasons why you should eat cultured fish or wild caught fish.
2. What is the probability of catching all the fish in a pond with a fishing pole or net?
3. How does intensive fishing change the size of fish you see in the grocery store?

2.5 Global Climate Change: Does Raising Food Cause Part of the Problem?

Marilyn Swisher, Ph.D.
Department of Home Economics, Institute of Food and Agricultural Sciences
University of Florida, Gainesville, Florida

Dr. Swisher's academic degrees are in the areas of geography, soil science, and biology. Combining those topics with agricultural and international experiences, she has developed sustainable agriculture programs and courses in the United States, Central America, and Africa. She has considerable experience working with limited resource farmers internationally and in the United States. In Florida, Dr. Swisher is a cooperative extension specialist and statewide leader in sustainable agriculture and sustainable development. She specializes in developing educational programs and materials for adult learners. She regularly teaches sustainable agriculture courses—both in the field and on-line—in Central America and at the University of Florida.

Overview

Food production may be a cause of global warming. Many farmers in Asia, Africa, and Central and South America often use a practice called slash-and-burn to create new farmland. They do not have the necessary resources to maintain the nutrient levels in existing farmland, so they cut down and burn sections of rain forest to grow crops on the land. When they burn the rain forest, carbon dioxide is released into the atmosphere. Carbon dioxide (CO_2) is known to prevent energy from escaping into space and is thus implicated in the rise of average atmospheric temperature worldwide.

Industrialized production of food uses electricity and gas. Processing, packaging, transporting, storing, and cooking food also require electricity and gas. Petroleum and coal used to produce electricity and gas have a high carbon content. When those fuels are used, carbon dioxide is released into the atmosphere with the same potential result as slash-and-burn agriculture—global warming.

Who Farms?

Before you do anything else, take a couple of minutes to think about your mental picture of a farmer. Who do you see? What is this person doing? What does the landscape around the person look like? If you are like most people in the United States, you are likely to have an image of a man using some piece of machinery, maybe a tractor. Most of us will also imagine this person in some kind of temperate zone setting, maybe in a field with oak or pine trees around the edge.

The Real Picture of a Farmer

This mental picture of a farmer does not match most of the farmers in the world very well. First, a large percentage of the world's farmers are women. In many parts of Africa, for example, farming is a woman's, not a man's, job, as can be seen in Figure 1. Women are often more likely to

Figure 1 *These vegetable farmers in Cameroon, West Africa, are women. Few men in this area farm.*

602

Global Climate Change: Does Raising Food Cause Part of the Problem?

farm than men in some parts of Central and South America and Asia, and even in the United States many farms are run by women.

Second, most farmers in the world do not have any machinery. They use simple hand tools, such as a hoe or an axe. Even where machinery is used, it is more likely to be pulled by an ox than a tractor.

Finally, most of the world's farmers live in the tropics. In fact, most of the world's population live in the tropics, and most of these people are farmers. Unlike the United States, where less than 10 percent of the population lives on farms, it is common for 50, 60, or even 90 percent of the population in many tropical countries to be farmers, as shown in Figure 2.

These farmers raise food primarily to feed their families. They have few of the modern tools and chemicals that farmers use in the United States. Even so, some of the practices they use to grow their food contribute to our global environmental problems. For example, tropical farming activities, such as slash-and-burn, add carbon dioxide to the atmosphere and thus help cause global climate change.

Essential Plant Nutrients

One of the biggest problems faced by many farmers is that they cannot afford to buy fertilizer. Plants need several elements to grow well. Plants must have nitrogen (N) to make proteins and chlorophyll. They also need phosphorus (P), potassium (K), magnesium (Mg), and calcium (Ca) in large amounts. They require some other elements, such as zinc (Zn), copper (Cu), and iron (Fe), in much smaller quantities. These elements are present naturally in the soil, but they are gradually removed when a piece of land is farmed. The plant nutrients in the soil are taken up by the plants. When we harvest and eat the plants, instead of allowing the plant to die and return the nutrients it has captured to the soil, we gradually deplete the natural nutrient stores in the soil.

There are several ways to replace these nutrients. One way is simply to apply them in a concentrated form. The atmosphere contains large amounts of nitrogen. We can extract this nitrogen from the atmosphere and turn it into a solid form and then apply it to the soil. Some parts of the world

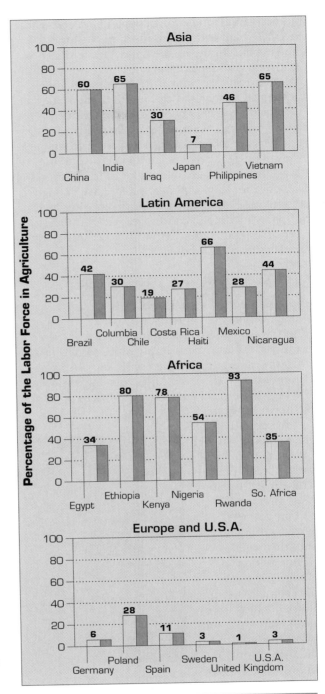

Figure 2 As the bars show, many African countries have a high percentage of the population working in agriculture whereas most European countries and the United States have low percentages.

(Morocco and Florida, for example) have soils with extremely high concentrations of phosphorus. We mine it, concentrate it, and apply it as fertilizer too. Another way to replace the nutrients is to recycle them. We can take human feces, animal manures, and vegetative material and return them to the soil.

Unfortunately, many of the world's farmers cannot use these ways of replacing nutrients. Fertilizers are too expensive for many of them, even though they may seem inexpensive to us. Recycling nutrients requires a lot of labor, and many of the world's farmers barely have enough labor to raise and harvest a crop. They simply do not have the time to collect and recycle human feces or animal manure. How do you think these farmers solve this problem?

Slash-and-Burn Agriculture

The solution used by many of these farmers is simple. Unlike the United States, where we may farm the same piece of land for decades or even centuries, these farmers simply move to new land. This way of farming is called slash-and-burn agriculture because the farmer first cuts down (slashes) the vegetation on the new field and then burns it, as shown in Figure 3.

The vegetation the farmers slash is often the trees in tropical rain forests. These trees contain large amounts of carbon that they have incorporated into their cells during photosynthesis. The trees also contain all the nutrients they have taken out of the soil over a period of decades, centuries, or even thousands of years. When the farmer cuts down the trees and burns them, the nutrients are released back into the soil where

Figure 3 *This Guatemalan farmer is planting corn in the new field that he just created by clearing tropical forest.*

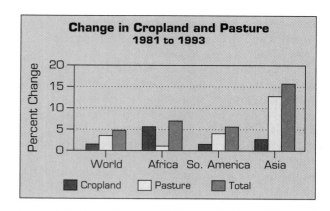

Figure 4 *The land area used for pasture and crop production in Asia, Africa, and South America increased between 1981 and 1993.*

they can be taken up by the farmer's crop. This "new" land can be very productive for at least a few years, until the nutrient supply is depleted by farming.

Slash-and-burn agriculture is a major cause of the rain forest destruction in tropical countries, as shown in Figure 4. As population grows, poor farmers must find new land to raise livestock and produce crops. While the amount of land that each farmer deforests is small, the total destruction is great.

Carbon Dioxide and Global Climate Change

The carbon in the trees is not important to the farmer. However, the amount of carbon contained in the forest that is cut down and burned can be large, especially when farmers cut down tropical rain forest. This carbon is released into the atmosphere as carbon dioxide. Japanese government agencies estimate that each hectare of tropical forest that is cut down contains 250 tons of carbon.

Carbon dioxide is one of the major "greenhouse warming gases." Carbon dioxide in the atmosphere helps trap long-wave radiation. Each day, the earth's atmosphere receives energy, primarily as short-wave radiation, from the sun. Most of that

Global Climate Change: Does Raising Food Cause Part of the Problem?

energy is returned to space, or reradiated, as long-wave radiation. Long-wave radiation, however, is easily reflected back to earth by molecules in the atmosphere, including carbon dioxide, and is thus prevented from escaping into space. When we increase the carbon dioxide levels in the atmosphere, less energy reradiates into space, potentially increasing the average atmospheric temperature worldwide.

Scientific evidence indicates that the average carbon dioxide content of the earth's atmosphere has increased. Scientists debate the effects this will have on the world's climate. Some models show important changes, such as a warming trend that could melt the world's icecaps and raise the sea level, flooding many coastal areas.

According to the Intergovernmental Panel on Climate Change, the level of carbon dioxide in the atmosphere has increased roughly 30 percent since the beginning of the industrial revolution, about 1750. Most of the increase is believed to be due to human activities, mostly fossil fuel use, land use changes, and agriculture.

Erosion and Water Pollution

Cutting down tropical forests adds to erosion and water pollution. Trees protect the soil and prevent erosion. The amount of soil that is lost by erosion when trees are cut down is high, especially in areas that receive large amounts of rainfall. The soil loss itself is important because it takes decades or even centuries to form an inch of soil. The soil particles wash into streams and rivers where they become a pollutant. They can prevent aquatic macroinvertebrates (large "bugs" that spend their entire life in the water) or fish from reproducing. Eventually the soil particles wash into the ocean where they may cause further damage to another very diverse tropical ecosystem, the coral reef.

Reduced Biodiversity

Slash-and-burn agriculture also reduces biodiversity. Tropical rain forests are some of the world's most diverse ecosystems. According to the National Geographic Society, more than 1,000 species of trees have been identified in a single square kilometer of tropical rain forest. One rain forest in the

South American country of Ecuador has 20,000 species of flowering plants. California, although about one-third larger than Ecuador, has only 5,000 species of flowering plants.

Is Slash-and-Burn Agriculture Acceptable Today?

Because slash-and-burn agriculture has destructive results, it may seem illogical for farmers to use those practices. The "new" farmlands often last for only a few years for many reasons. Once the soil nutrients are depleted, the land is no longer productive. Perhaps as important, weeds and insect pests become a problem. These farmers are often forced to move to a new piece of land every few years.

When the population level in these tropical regions was low, this way of farming was probably very sustainable. With only a few people, the amount of forest cut down to farm was small. The overall impact on biodiversity was not important. An abandoned plot might be left for decades or even centuries before it was used for agriculture again. This gave the forest plenty of time to regrow. The erosion from small, isolated plots was probably not great. And the amount of carbon dioxide added to the atmosphere was small.

Tropical rain forests are some of the world's most diverse ecosystems.

Today, however, the situation is different. Population levels are high. Entire forests are cut down, not just small patches in the forest. Abandoned plots are allowed to regrow for shorter and shorter periods of time, sometimes less than a decade. What was once a sustainable way of producing food has become unsustainable.

How Much Tropical Rain Forest Have We Cleared?

According to Malcolm Gillis, president of Rice University, tropical forests in Asia, Africa, and Latin America originally covered about 15 million square kilometers of land area, or about 12 percent of the earth's land surface. Today they have been reduced to half that, or 7.5 million square kilometers. According to the Food and Agriculture Organization of the United Nations, conversion of forest to agricultural land is a major cause of destruction in Africa, Asia, and Latin America.

Does Slash-and-Burn Agriculture Really Add Much Carbon Dioxide?

We are adding to the atmosphere's carbon dioxide levels in many ways. Our use of fossil fuels is probably the most important, as shown in Figure 5. These fuels, such as petroleum or coal, are really just the remains of plants that lived on the earth in previous geological periods. Just like the trees in the rain forest, they contain large amounts of carbon. When we burn gasoline in our cars or coal in electric power plants, we release carbon dioxide into the atmosphere, just as slash-and-burn farmers in the tropics do. Further, this carbon dioxide has been in storage, locked away, for millions of years, not hundreds or thousands of years like the carbon dioxide in the rain forest trees. Therefore, on a global scale, the addition of carbon dioxide by people living in industrialized midlatitude countries is much greater than that of farmers in the tropics and potentially much more important because it has been in storage for so long.

Figure 5 *The carbon dioxide emitted from burning fossil fuels, gas flares at wells, and cement manufacturing, the three biggest contributors to atmospheric carbon dioxide levels, has increased sharply since 1950.*

How Much Carbon Dioxide Comes from Land Use Change?

In 1991, carbon dioxide emissions from industrial processes worldwide were 22,339,408 metric tons. Land use changes (largely deforestation) accounted for only 4,100,000 metric tons, or only about one-fifth of the total. However, almost all the carbon dioxide emitted due to land use changes came from Asia, Africa, and South America—1,300,000 for Asia, 730,000 for Africa, and 1,800,000 for South America.

Farming in Our Own Backyard

Before we condemn the millions of tropical farmers for adding to global climate change, we should think about our own food production system. It may not be any more sustainable than slash-and-burn agriculture because it adds to the carbon dioxide released by industrialized countries. Our tractors burn diesel fuel. The trucks that bring the food from the farm to the supermarket use petroleum. We burn yet more gasoline in our cars to bring food home from the store. Then we use electricity or gas to cook the food. Studies show that we use more energy—and, therefore, release more carbon dioxide—to process, transport, store, and package food products than we do to produce them. In some cases, we can use more energy to drive to the grocery store and get the food than what it took to produce it.

Finding ways to produce enough food to feed the world's population without causing irreparable damage to the environment is one of the major challenges facing us today. Both the slash-and-burn agriculture of the tropics and the industrialized system we use in the United States cause serious problems.

Scientists are searching for answers. Some plants have a symbiotic relationship with bacteria that can extract nitrogen from the atmosphere, for example. We do not need to apply nitrogen fertilizer to these plants. The common bean, *Phaseolus vulgaris,* is an example of one of these leguminous plants. Can we use genetic engineering to make more plants capable of having these kinds of symbiotic relationships? There are also naturally occurring pesticides. *Bacillus thuringiensis* is an example. We have already learned to splice the gene responsible for its pesticidal action into plants, making them resistant to attack by many kinds of pests. However, some also criticize this approach, arguing that the potential hazards from genetic engineering outweigh the potential advantages. And if we do decide to use these new tools, tropical farmers may be the last to get them because they are often too poor to afford them.

Global Climate Change: Does Raising Food Cause Part of the Problem?

What Can We Do?

Any food production system causes some environmental damage, although it may be minimal, and produces some carbon dioxide. None of us can avoid completely any negative impact on the environment. But there are things we can do to help reduce our personal carbon dioxide emission.

◆ Buy food products with minimal packaging. Many of our food products come in two, three, or even more layers of packaging. Often the packaging is plastic that is made from petroleum. We should try to avoid buying those products that have many layers of packaging.

◆ Eat locally grown foods when we can. Transporting foods for long distances is one of the biggest energy costs in our food production system. We should act a little more like a farmer in a tropical country by eating things grown near our homes.

◆ Recycle all the packaging that we possibly can, especially things like aluminum cans. Manufacturing new aluminum cans takes much more energy—and, therefore, releases much more carbon dioxide into the atmosphere—than remaking cans from used aluminum.

◆ Compost or recycle organic wastes, like food wastes. Solid waste disposal adds to the atmospheric carbon dioxide load too, and landfills are filling rapidly.

We all want a sustainable food production system. Farmers today are doing a great deal to make their farms more environmentally sound by reducing fertilizer, pesticide, and water use, for example. But a sustainable food production system means that both farmers and consumers must do their part. Be a sustainable consumer!

Additional Resources

Edwards, C, R. Lal, P. Madden, R. Miller, and G. House (eds.). 1990. *Sustainable Agricultural Systems.* St. Lucie Press, Delray Beach, FL.
   A collection of articles on various topics and issues in sustainable agriculture.

Peterson, W. 1995. Farm Programs and the Environment: The Case for a Limited Land Payment. *Journal of Sustainable Agriculture,* Vol. 6 (2/3), pp. 123–134.
   This discussion of the history and effects of price support/crop diversification programs in the United States argues that these programs have harmed the environment. The author advocates a limited land payment program that would be neutral in its effects on the environment while helping to preserve the family farms and rural communities.

Pimental, J., A. Beers, L. Guinard, et al. 1987. World Agriculture and Soil Erosion. *BioScience* ,Vol. 37, pp. 277–283.
   A discussion of the magnitude of the problem of soil erosion worldwide and its impact on world food production.

Questions for Discussion

1. Describe a typical farmer in our world.

2. Why do many farmers use slash-and-burn techniques?

3. What are the consequences of slash-and-burn farming?

4. Why are the results of slash-and-burn farming different today from 10 to 20 years ago?

Applications

1. What can be done to reduce slash-and-burn farming techniques?

2. Compare the cost of producing food in the United States to that of underdeveloped countries.

3. What are some alternatives to the use of chemical fertilizers?

4. Which of the suggestions given at the end of this essay are ones you can do yourself? Explain how you could implement at least one of these suggested actions.

2.6 The Environmental History of a New England Lake

Richard B. Brugam, Ph.D.
Department of Biological Sciences
Southern Illinois University, Edwardsville, Illinois

Dr. Brugam has studied many aspects of the biological communities of lakes. He studied the impacts of watershed development on lakes in Connecticut, Minnesota, and the Pacific Northwest. He has examined the long-term recovery of lakes acidified by coal mining. Most recently, he has studied the impacts of postglacial climatic change on lakes and peatlands of the Upper Peninsula of Michigan in the Sylvania Wilderness Area.

Overview

We all have heard that the earth's environment is changing. Have you ever wondered how scientists document this change? One way is to study the remains of organisms found in lake and ocean sediments. These water bodies preserve a historical record of past environmental contamination and climatic change. A technique called coring can recover this record. We will examine how this technique was used to understand the history of a small pond in Connecticut.

Lakes Mirror Human Activities

Global environmental change is a major modern problem. Most biological communities have been strongly impacted by humans. Lakes are particularly sensitive to human activities. Increases in plant nutrients from sewage, improper land management practices, or industrial processes degrade lakes by clouding the water with excesses of plant growth. This accumulation of nutrients and resultant growth of organisms is called eutrophication.

Lakes accumulate sediment that contains the remains of past lake communities. We can read the fossil record found in lake bottom sediments to determine how a particular lake changed in the past. The record is especially sensitive to eutrophication.

Linsley Pond is a small lake in North Branford, Connecticut—just east of New Haven. It was one of the first lakes in North America to be affected by colonial settlers. The sedimentary record of this lake records the history of human impact from the time of the earliest colonial settlers in New England to the present time.

Lakes are particularly sensitive to human activities.

Cores Sample Lake History

The sediment of a lake is sampled by coring. Scientists push a hollow tube into the soft sediment of the lake bottom (just like a corer into a ripe apple). The tube can be pushed into the lake bottom by a scuba diver, on the end of long sturdy steel rods, or by a heavy weight. The tube full of mud is capped and pulled from the lake bottom. The coring process is described in Figure 1. The mud in the tube is sampled just as it was deposited—oldest at the bottom and youngest at the top. We can date the sediment using radioactive elements like radiocarbon. Some lake cores show horizontal banding, which further aids in dating sediment samples.

The sediment sample is cut into pieces 1 cm long. The pieces are processed chemically to reveal the microfossils that are present. Micropaleontologists examine and count these microfossils under a compound light microscope or under a scanning electron microscope (SEM). The light microscope is able to magnify objects up to about 1,000 times. An SEM can magnify objects up to 100,000 times. Thus, the SEM allows us to look at the surface design of a tiny object. This level of detail is often needed to accurately identify microfossils.

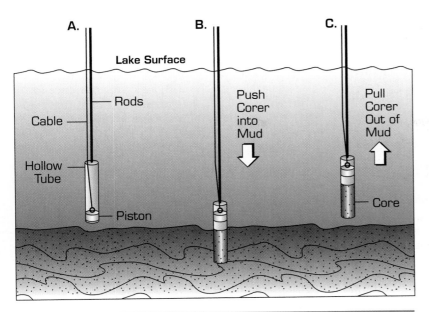

Figure 1 *The coring process. The corer is positioned about 1 meter above the mud surface (Panel A). The core tube is pushed into the lake mud using the rods while the cable is used to hold the piston steady (Panel B). The corer is pulled out of the mud. Note that the core tube is now filled with mud. The piston keeps the mud from slipping out of the core tube.*

In Figure 2, depths have been converted to dates. From radioactive dating, we know the dates when each core level was laid down so we can determine when changes happened in the lake and the surrounding forest.

Evidence for change in the lake itself comes from diatom fossils found in the sediment. Diatoms are microscopic algae that have shells made of a natural form of glass. As seen in Figure 4, the shells are highly ornamented. There are many species of diatoms, and each one has particular environmental preferences. Some species of diatom float in the water of a lake, getting their mineral nutrients from dissolved chemicals in the water and their energy from sunlight. Plants that have this lifestyle are called phytoplankton. Other diatom species live on

What do sediment cores tell us about the history of Linsley Pond?

Colonial Times

The area around Linsley Pond was settled by colonial farmers in 1700. They cleared the forest and planted corn. The evidence for these changes comes from the pollen of terrestrial plants found in the lake sediment. Figure 2 graphs the historical abundances of selected species of plants, as evidenced by the gravity of pollen in lake sediment layers. In the sediment laid down in 1700, there is a decline in pollen from forest trees (oaks). It is replaced by pollen from ragweed and grass. The ragweed pollen pictured in Figure 3 is a weed of cornfields. The grass grows in cow pastures.

Pollen diagrams (Figure 2) are often difficult to read. The diagrams show the percentages of different species of pollen (or diatoms) as they change at different levels in the core. The different core levels represent different dates in history.

Figure 2 *Changes in the abundance of selected microfossils in the Linsley Pond core.*

Figure 3 *Scanning electron microscope (SEM) photograph of ragweed pollen (magnified 4,000X).*

larger plants, rocks, and mud. Since each diatom species has a unique set of living requirements, shifts in diatom species indicate changes in the lake environment.

The species of diatoms have no common names in English. Biologists have given each species a scientific name derived from the Latin or Greek language. A scientific name is indicated by italics.

In 1700, when colonial farmers colonized the Linsley Pond watershed, a few species of diatoms such as *Cyclotella* died out, as shown in Figure 2. *Cyclotella,* shown in Figure 4, is a diatom species that is characteristically found in lakes that are low in plant nutrients. The loss of this species indicates the beginning of eutrophication. Eutrophication reduces the clarity of a lake because of the increased growth of phytoplankton. The diatom species *Aulacoseira* grew better with the increased nutrients.

Modern Times

A major change in the forests around the lake came in 1912 when the chestnut blight, a disease, killed all chestnut trees. The death of chestnut trees occurred throughout the range of the tree (Alabama to Connecticut). The blight was brought to the United States on contaminated wood from Europe. It escaped and destroyed trees throughout eastern North America. At Linsley Pond, the results of the chestnut blight can be seen in the loss of chestnut pollen from the sedimentary record.

Industrial development hit the watershed of the lake in 1914 when a quarry was established about one-half mile north of the lake. The quarry

produced stone that was used to build houses in New York City. Pollution from the quarry changed the lake. The diatoms changed when the quarry was established. *Aulacoseira* was replaced by *Asterionella,* a species with a strong preference for nutrient-rich lakes. Its presence indicates that the lake became even more eutrophic than before.

Cores Provide Records of Diverse Ecological Communities

The changes at Linsley Pond show how human activities can change a lake. This historical record is representative of many small natural lakes throughout North America. Each has a similar story. Pollution and its effects are not new. The story of human-caused environmental change is recorded in the lake sediments.

Scientists can use coring to document other environmental changes. Cores like those from Linsley Pond have been used to show that some lakes have become more acidic because of acid rain. Scientists have used pollen microfossils from lake sediment cores to show how forests in North America have changed since the last ice age. Dr. Margaret Davis, at the University of Minnesota, used cores that are much longer than the cores from Linsley Pond to reconstruct changes in forests over the last 10,000 years. She also showed that the ranges of forest tree species have changed due to historical changes in climate.

Figure 4 *SEM photograph of the inside of a* Cyclotella *shell (magnified 4,200X). Notice the intricate ornamentation of the shell.*

We can also core the ocean bottom. These cores have shown that there have been enormous changes in the earth's climate over the last two million years. Ice ages have buried northern latitudes under huge glaciers every 100,000 years.

Glaciers in Greenland accumulate ice year by year just as does lake sediment. These glaciers can be cored just like lake and ocean sediment. Cores from Camp Century in Greenland have shown that the levels of carbon dioxide in the atmosphere were lower during the last glacial age and have increased dramatically over the past one hundred years. These cores also show recent increases in air pollutants like lead and mercury that date from the beginning of human use of these metals in Greek and Roman times.

Cores from glacial ice, lake, and ocean sediment allow us to study environmental changes over long periods of time. This record helps us to understand the origins of modern ecological communities.

Additional Resources

Colinvaux, P. 1978. *Why Big, Fierce Animals Are Rare: An Ecologist's Perspective*. Princeton University Press, 256 pp.
    This book is a layperson's summary of an earlier edition of Colinvaux's ecology text. While it does not have specific chapters on paleoecology, it is a good summary of ecological ideas.

Colinvaux, P. 1993. *Ecology 2* Chapter 17: The Ecologist's Time Machine. John Wiley & Sons, Inc., 338–362.
    Colinvaux's ecology text is a well-written summary of ecology for first-year college students. His chapter on paleoecology is a particularly fine summary of the field.

Delcourt, H. and P. A. Delcourt. 1991. *Quaternary Ecology: A Paleoecological Perspective*. Chapman and Hall. 200 pp.
    This book summarizes paleoecological studies in North America and the light they shed on long-term climatic change.

Imbrie, J. and K. P. Imbrie. 1979. *Ice Ages: Solving the Mystery*. Enslow Publishers, 205 pp.
    This book presents theories on the causes of glacial ages in language that is easy for the layperson to understand.

Russell, Emily W. B. 1997. *People and Land Through Time: Linking Ecology and History*. Yale University Press, 388 pp.
    This book presents recent information on the long-term impacts of human activities on North American ecosystems. It skillfully combines historical research with paleoecological research.

Questions for Discussion

1. What are diatoms and where do they live?

2. How might a lake become eutrophic?

3. What happened to chestnut trees in the forests of eastern North America?

4. What was the impact of the first colonial farmers on Linsley Pond and its surrounding landscape?

5. How would you apply the technique of coring to find out if global warming is actually happening?

6. What do you think the disposal of sewage into a lake would do? Remember that sewage is full of mineral nutrients.

7. Lake Washington is a very large lake just east of Seattle, Washington. In the 1950s, the people of the Seattle metropolitan area built a large ring sewer around the lake, preventing sewage from entering the lake. What do you think happened to the lake?

8. What would happen if we reintroduced chestnut trees into the forests of the eastern United States?

Applications

1. In some places (like Sudbury, Ontario), air pollution from smelters was a major environmental problem. These smelters released large amounts of metal vapor into the air. These metal contaminants in the atmosphere fell to earth around the smelter. What sort of record would you expect to see in cores taken from lakes near such a smelter? How would you use this record to track the history of pollution from the smelter?

2. How might you use the technique of coring and microfossil analysis to test the hypothesis that lakes on coal mine sites were acid when formed, but neutralized over time?

3. Like the smelter at Sudbury, the explosion of the Chernobyl nuclear reactor contaminated the atmosphere. Unlike the smelter, the nuclear reactor released large amounts of radioactive elements. Do you think these could be found in lake sediment? What might influence how far away the pollution traveled from the reactor?

3.1 Essay on Population

Thomas Robert Malthus
1766–1834

Reprinted from: An Essay on the Principle of Population as it Affects the Future Improvement of Society. *1798.*

Thomas Robert Malthus was a political economist in England. He was concerned about what he saw as a decline in the living conditions in England during the early 19th century. In expressing this concern, he identified three causes of this decline: overpopulation, lack of adequate resources to feed the increasing population, and social irresponsibility. In the course of his An Essay on the Principle of Population, *Malthus advanced these ideas, which were unpopular at the time, and his proposed remedies.*

This essay is reprinted, in the original language, from Chapter II in Malthus' An Essay on the Principle of Population. *The late 18th-century English writing style and some words may require extra attention and a slower reading pace.*

Overview

Malthus' *An Essay on the Principle of Population,* written in 1798, was controversial in its time but has since become a cornerstone for modern population ecology and evolutionary biology. Malthus' intent in writing this essay was to demonstrate that the ultimate consequence of unchecked population growth would be poverty and human suffering. Malthus observed that, in nature, all organisms produced many more offspring than could survive and that humans were equally liable to suffer the same fate. He concluded that human populations could be checked by controls on family size or by the ravages of poverty and famine. Charles Darwin based his description of the mechanism for natural selection, detailed in his book *On the Origin of Species,* on the principles set forth in this chapter from Malthus' *An Essay on the Principle of Population.*

Chapter II

I said that population, when unchecked, increased in a geometrical ratio; and subsistence for man in an arithmetical ratio.

Let us examine whether this proposition be just.

I think it will be allowed, that no state has hitherto existed (at least that we have any account of) where the manners were so pure and simple, and the means of subsistence so abundant, that no check; whatever has existed to early marriages; among the lower classes, from a fear of not providing well for their families; or among the higher classes, from a fear of lowering their condition in life. Consequently in no state that we have yet known, has the power of population been left to exert itself with perfect freedom.

Whether the law of marriage be instituted or not, the dictate of nature and virtue, seems to be an early attachment to one woman. Supposing the liberty of changing in the case of an unfortunate choice, this liberty would not affect population till it arose to a height greatly vicious; and we are now supposing the existence of a society where vice is scarcely known.

In a state therefore of great equality and virtue, where pure and simple manners prevailed, and where the means of subsistence were so abundant, that no part of the society could have any fears about providing empty for a family, the power of population being left to exert itself unchecked, the increase of the human species would evidently be much greater than any increase that has been hitherto known.

In the United States of America, where the means of subsistence have been more ample, the manners of the people more pure, and consequently the checks to early marriages fewer, than in any of the modern states of Europe, the population has been found to double itself in twenty-five years.

This ratio of increase, though short of the utmost power of population, yet as the result of actual experience, we will take as our rule; and say, that population, when unchecked, goes on doubling itself every twenty-five years, or increases in a geometrical ratio. Let us now take any spot of earth, this Island for instance, and see in what ratio the subsistence it affords can be supposed to increase. We will begin with it under its present state of cultivation.

If I allow that by the best possible policy, by breaking up more land, and by great encouragements to agriculture, the produce of this Island may be doubled in the first twenty-five years, I think it will be allowing as much as any person can well demand.

In the next twenty-five years, it is impossible to suppose that the produce could be quadrupled. It would be contrary to all our knowledge of the qualities of land. The very utmost that we can conceive, is, that the increase in the second twenty-five years might equal the present produce. Let us then take this for our rule, though certainly far beyond the truth; and allow that by great exertion, the whole produce of the Island might be increased every twenty-five years, by a quantity of subsistence equal to what it at present produces. The most enthusiastic speculator cannot suppose a greater increase than this. In a few centuries it would make every acre of land in the Island like a garden.

Yet this ratio of increase is evidently arithmetical. It may be fairly said, therefore, that the means of subsistence increase in an arithmetical ratio.

Let us now bring the effects of these two ratios together (Figure 1).

The population of the Island is computed to be about seven millions; and we will suppose the present produce equal to the support of such a number. In the first twenty-five years the population would be fourteen millions; and the food being also doubled, the means of subsistence would be equal to this increase. In the next twenty-five years the population would be twenty-eight millions; and the means of subsistence only equal to the support of twenty-one millions. In the

next period, the population would be fifty-six millions, and the means of subsistence just sufficient for half that number. And at the conclusion of the first century, the population would be one hundred and twelve millions, and the means of subsistence only equal to the support of thirty-five millions; which would leave a population of seventy-seven millions totally unprovided for.

A great emigration necessarily implies unhappiness of some kind or other in the country that is deserted. For few persons will leave their families, connections, friends, and native land, to seek a settlement in untried foreign climes, without some strong subsisting causes of uneasiness where they are, or the hope of some-great advantages in the place to which they are going.

But to make the argument more general, and less interrupted by the partial views of emigration, let us take the whole earth, instead of one spot, and suppose that the restraints to population were universally removed. If the subsistence for man that the earth affords was to be increased every twenty-five years by a quantity equal to what the whole world at present produces, this would allow the power of production in the earth to be absolutely unlimited, and its ratio of increase much greater than we can conceive that any possible exertions of mankind could make it.

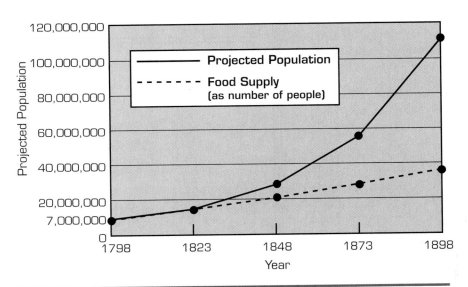

Figure 1   *This graph presents Malthus' predictions for increases in population size and food supply of Great Britain during the 100 years following publication of his* Essay.

Taking the population of the world at any number, a thousand millions, for instance, the human species would increase in the ratio of—1, 2, 4, 8, 16, 32, 64, 128, 256, 512, etc., and subsistence as—1, 2, 3, 4, 5, 6, 7, 8, 9, 10, etc. In two centuries and a quarter the population would be to the means of subsistence as 512 to 10; in three centuries, as 4096 to 13; and in two thousand years the difference would be almost incalculable, though the produce in that time would have increased to an immense extent.

No limits whatever are placed to the productions of the earth; they may increase forever and be greater than any assignable quantity; yet still the power of population being a power of superior order, the increase of the human species can only be kept commensurate to the increase of the means of subsistence, by the constant operation of the strong law of necessity acting as a check upon the greater power.

The effects of this check remain now to be considered.

Among plants and animals the view of the subject is simple. They are all impelled by a powerful instinct to the increase of their species; and this instinct is interrupted by no reasoning, or doubts about providing for their offspring. Wherever therefore there is liberty, the power of increase is exerted; and the superabundant effects are repressed afterwards by want of room and nourishment, which is common to animals and plants; and among animals, by becoming the prey of others.

The effects of this check on man are more complicated.

Impelled to the increase of his species by an equally powerful instinct, reason interrupts his career, and asks him whether he may not bring beings into the world, for whom he cannot provide the means of subsistence. In a state of equality, this would be the simple question. In the present state of society, other considerations occur. Will he not lower his rank in life? Will he not subject himself to greater difficulties than he at present feels? Will he not be obliged to labour harder? And if he has a large family, will his utmost exertions enable him to support them?

No limits whatever are placed to the productions of the earth.

May he not see his offspring in rags and misery, and clamouring for bread that he cannot give them? And may he not be reduced to the grating necessity of forfeiting his independence, and of being obliged to the sparing hand of charity for support?

These considerations are calculated to prevent, and certainly do prevent, a very great number in all civilized nations from pursuing the dictate of nature in an early attachment to one woman. And this restraint almost necessarily, though not absolutely so, produces vice. Yet in all societies, even those that are most vicious, the tendency to a virtuous attachment is so strong that there is a constant effort towards an increase of population. This constant effort as constantly tends to subject the lower classes of the society to distress, and to prevent any great permanent amelioration of their condition.

The way in which these effects are produced seems to be this.

We will suppose the means of subsistence in any country just equal to the easy support of its inhabitants. The constant effort towards population, which is found to act even in the most vicious societies increases the number of people before the means of subsistence are increased. The food therefore which before supported seven millions, must now be divided among seven millions and a half, or eight millions. The poor consequently must live much worse, and many of them be reduced to severe distress. The number of labourers also being above the proportion of the work in the market, the price of labour must tend toward a decrease; while the price of provisions would at the same time tend to rise. The labourer therefore must work harder to earn the same as he did before. During this season of distress, the discouragements to marriage, and the difficulty of rearing a family are so great, that population is at a stand. In the meantime the cheapness of labour, the plenty of labourers, and the necessity of an increased industry amongst them, encourage cultivators to employ more labour upon their land; to turn up fresh soil, and to manure and improve more completely what is already in tillage; till ultimately the means of subsistence become in the same proportion to the population as at the period from which we set out. The situation of the labourer being then again tolerably comfortable, the restraints to population are in some degree loosened; and the same retrograde and progressive movements with respect to happiness are repeated.

This sort of oscillation will not be remarked by superficial observers; and it may be difficult even for the most penetrating mind to calculate its periods. Yet that in all old states some such vibration does exist; though from various transverse causes, in a much less marked, and in a much more irregular manner than I have described it, no reflecting man who considers the subject deeply can well doubt.

Many reasons occur why this oscillation has been less obvious, and less decidedly confirmed by experience, than might naturally be expected.

One principal reason is, that the histories of mankind that we possess are histories only of the higher classes. We have but few accounts that can be depended upon of the manners and customs of that part of mankind, where these retrograde and progressive movements chiefly take place. A satisfactory history of this kind, of one people, and of one period, would require the constant and minute attention of an observing mind during a long life. Some of the objects of inquiry would be, in what proportion to the number of adults was the number of marriages: to what extent vicious customs prevailed in consequence of the restraints upon matrimony: what was the comparative mortality among the children of the most distressed part of the community, and those who lived rather more at their ease: what were the variations in the real price of labour: and what were the observable differences in the state of the lower classes of society, with respect to ease and happiness, at different times during a certain period.

Such a history would tend greatly to elucidate the manner in which the constant check; upon population acts; and would probably prove the existence of the retrograde and progressive movements that have been mentioned; though the times of their vibration must necessarily be rendered irregular, from the operation of many interrupting causes; such as, the introduction or failure of certain manufactures: a greater or less prevalent spirit of agricultural enterprise: years of plenty, or years of scarcity: wars and pestilence: poor laws: the invention of processes for shortening labour without the proportional extension of the market for the commodity: and, particularly, the difference between the nominal and real price of labour; a circumstance which has perhaps more than any other contributed to conceal this oscillation from common view.

It very rarely happens that the nominal price of labour universally falls: but we well know that it frequently remains the same, while the nominal price of provisions has been gradually increasing. This is, in effect, a real fall in the price of labour; and during this period, the condition of the lower orders of the community must gradually grow worse and worse. But the farmers and capitalists are growing rich from the real cheapness of labour. Their increased capitals enable them to employ a greater number of men. Work, therefore, may be plentiful; and the price of labour would consequently rise. But the want of freedom in the market of labour, which occurs more or less in all communities, either from parish laws, or the more general cause of the facility of combination among the rich, and its difficulty among the poor, operates to prevent the price of labour from rising at the natural period, and keeps it down some time longer; perhaps till a year of scarcity, when the clamour is too loud, and the necessity too apparent to be resisted.

The true cause of the advance in the price of labour is thus concealed; and the rich affect to grant it as an act of compassion and favour to the poor, in consideration of a year of scarcity; and when plenty returns, indulge themselves in the most unreasonable of all complaints, that the price does not again fall; when a little reflection would shew, them that it must have risen long before, but from an unjust conspiracy of their own.

But though the rich by unfair combinations, contribute frequently to prolong a season of

> **The histories of mankind that we possess are histories only of the higher classes.**

distress among the poor; yet no possible form of society could prevent the almost constant action of misery upon a great part of mankind, if in a state of inequality, and upon all, if all were equal.

The theory on which the truth of this position depends appears to me so extremely clear, that I feel at a loss to conjecture what part of it can be denied:

◆ That population cannot increase without the means of subsistence is a proposition so evident that it needs no illustration

◆ That population does invariably increase where there are the means of subsistence, the history of every people that have ever existed will abundantly prove

◆ And, that the superior power of population cannot be checked without producing misery or vice the ample portion of these two bitter ingredients in the cup of human life, and the continuance of the physical causes that seem to have produced them, bear too convincing a testimony.

But in order more fully to ascertain the validity of these three propositions, let us examine the different states in which mankind have been known to exist. Even a cursory view will, I think, be sufficient to convince us that these propositions are incontrovertible truths.

Additional Resources

Malthus, T. R. 1798. *An Essay on the Principle of Population as it Affects the Future Improvement of Society. With Remarks on the Speculations of Mr. Godwin, M. Condorcet and other Writers*. Printed for J. Johnson, in St. Paul's Church-Yard.
    Chapter two of this original Malthus essay is reprinted here.

Questions for Discussion

1. What is Malthus' premise regarding the production of food for humans?
2. What is Malthus' premise regarding the growth of human populations?
3. What problem does he present?
4. What does Malthus see as a consequence of the problem so far as human living conditions are concerned?
5. What does Malthus seem to suggest as possible solutions to the problem?

Applications

1. Make a graph with *time* across the x-axis and *number* across the y-axis. Plot one line to represent the human species numbers using Malthus' values 1, 2, 4, 8, . . . 512. Plot another line using his values for subsistence (food) 1, 2, 3, 4, . . . 10.
2. What hypothesis does this graph suggest?
3. Extrapolate the graph to a population value of 4096 and a subsistance value of 13, as Malthus proposes in his essay. How does this extrapolation support your hypothesis?

616

Essay on Population

3.2 America in the 21st Century

Kimberly Crews, M.A.
Public Education Programs
Population Reference Bureau, Washington, DC

Ms. Crews received her master's degree in demography from Georgetown University in 1985. As a demographer, she studies the causes and consequences of changes in population size, distribution, and structure and their interrelationships. She is now the director of Public Education Programs at the Population Reference Bureau, Inc., in Washington, DC. Ms. Crews develops materials and conducts seminars to help educators and community leaders understand population trends and the implications of population change. She examines global and United States population trends and often works with groups such as the National Geographic Society, the Smithsonian Institution, and national teachers' associations.

Overview

Throughout the history of the United States, population growth and redistribution has had dramatic impacts on societal development and the environment. Such impacts will become even greater as the population continues to grow and to become more diverse. This exploration of population trends in the United States provides a basis for speculation as to the changes that can be expected in the 21st century.

How Big Are We?

On April 1, 2000, the United States will conduct the official count of its population for the 22nd time in its history. You and your parents will complete a form to provide the United States Bureau of the Census with information about the people who live in your household. This information will be tabulated along with the information from approximately 103 million other households so we will have a snapshot of the size, geographic distribution, age, and social and economic characteristics of the whole nation.

When the census was taken in 2000, the United States population was approximately 281 million. Many Americans do not realize that the United States has the third largest population in the world. According to the Population Reference Bureau 299 million people in 2006. Only China and India have larger populations.

> *Americans do not realize that the United States has the third largest population in the world.*

During the 1990s, the population of the United States grew by about 1 percent each year. This does not seem like a large number, but it means that the United States is adding more than 2 million people to its population each year. This is more than the total population of many countries. At this rate, the United States is one of the fastest growing industrialized nations but is growing more slowly than most countries in Africa, Asia, and Latin America.

How Are We Growing?

In 2006, 4.2 million babies were born in the United States, 2.4 million people died, and 897,300 more people moved to this country than moved out. So how many people were added to the United States population in 2006?

Many people think that most of the growth in the United States is from immigration. But you can see that about two-thirds of the population growth in 2006 was from natural increase (the excess of births minus deaths). The other third was from net immigration. During the 1990s, 6.1 million people were admitted to the United States as immigrants.

Imagine what the population of the United States will be like when you have children your age. It is important to consider how the population will grow in the future so that your family's housing, transportation, education, and job needs can be met. Projecting future growth is tricky because demographers must speculate about future births, deaths, and immigration patterns. In order to think about the possible course of population growth, demographers have to consider things such as the number of children that people will have, how long people will live, and the number of people that will move to the United States from other countries.

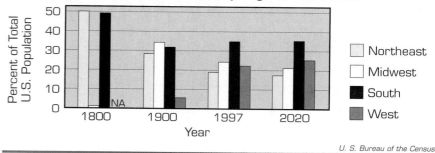

Figure 1 *Population distribution (percentages) of the United States by region, 1800–2020.*

As we move into the 21st century, it is expected that the population growth rate will continue to slow down because the population of the United States is aging and the number of deaths will most likely increase. By the time you are a grandparent, say in 2050, the population will have increased to 420 million. This is almost 50 percent greater than the current population size.

Where Do We Live?

When the first census was taken in 1790, most of the population (excluding Native Americans who were not counted) lived east of the Mississippi River, up and down the East Coast. Since then the population has been spreading to the South and West as Americans search for open space to settle. By 1900, 34 percent of the population was living in the Midwest. For the past few decades, the population has been moving from the northern Frostbelt states to the southern and western Sunbelt areas. Today nearly one-quarter of the population lives in the West, as shown in Figure 1.

In the 21st century, the population continues to grow fastest in the West and South. The five states that grew the fastest between 1990 and 2000 were the mountain states of Nevada, Idaho, Arizona, Colorado, and Utah. The West and South are expected to continue to lead the nation in growth into the next century.

While the West and South are growing most rapidly, Figure 2 shows that the most densely populated areas are still in the East and Midwest. The five most densely populated states are on the eastern seaboard—New Jersey, Rhode Island, Massachusetts, Connecticut, and Maryland. The map also shows that most of the people in the United States live in clusters; three out of every four Americans live in urban areas, defined as those with populations greater than 2,500.

The Changing Face of America

People moving from the Midwest and the East is one reason for the changing distribution of the United States population. Another reason is that immigrants are more likely to come from Latin America and Asia and are, therefore, more likely to settle in the South and West. These changing immigration trends contribute to another significant change that will occur during your lifetime— the continued shift in the racial and ethnic makeup of the United States population. The major racial and ethnic groups that are identified are non-Hispanic white, black, American Indian, Asian, and Hispanic.[1]

Historically, the majority of immigrants to the United States came from Europe; so the population has, until recently, been largely white. In 1900, one in eight Americans was nonwhite, mostly

---

[1] Persons of Hispanic origin may be of any race.

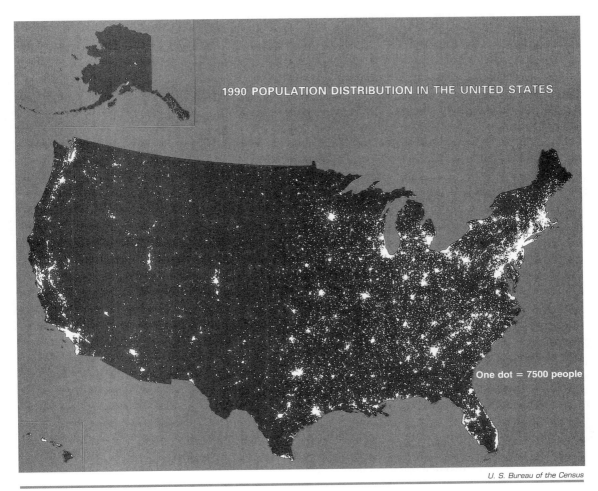

1990 POPULATION DISTRIBUTION IN THE UNITED STATES

One dot = 7500 people

U. S. Bureau of the Census

Figure 2 *1990 population distribution of the United States.*

African-Americans. In the past 50 years, the population has become more diverse with more people of color and non-European backgrounds. Today one of every four Americans is a "minority." By 2020, about one in three Americans will come from a non-European background.

The minority population, particularly Asians and Latinos, is expected to grow because of changing immigration and fertility patterns. For most of this century, most immigrants came from Europe. Now about three of every four immigrants comes from Asia and Latin America. In addition to higher immigration, the rates of natural increase are higher for nonwhites because the number of births is greater among these groups. Consequently, Asians and Hispanics will continue to make up a greater portion of the population, and Hispanics are expected to outnumber blacks early in the 21st century, as shown in Figure 3.

When you and your parents fill out the census form for your family, your responses become part of the national historical record. While demographers today speculate about how the actions of you and your cohorts will contribute to future population change, your grandchildren will look at historical statistics and wonder at the social and economic trends that affected demographic trends at the turn of the 21st century.

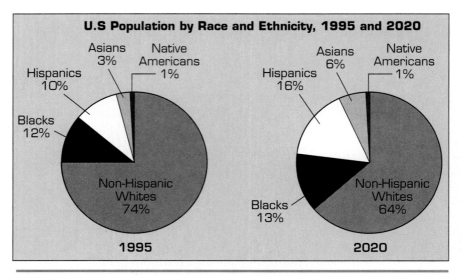

Figure 3 *U.S. population by race and ethnicity, 1995 and 2020.*
(Source: U.S. Bureau of the Census, Current Population Reports.)

Additional Resources

De Vita, C. J. 1996. *The United States at Mid-Decade,*
Population Bulletin Vol. 50, No. 4 Population Reference
Bureau, Washington, DC. (http://www.prb.org)
   A profile of the United States during the first half of
   the 1990s focusing on regional patterns of population
   growth and change and their implications. It also
   examines the aging of the population, racial and
   ethnic diversity, immigration, changing family
   patterns, and the distribution of income and poverty.

U.S. Census Bureau (http://www.census.gov)
   The Census Bureau is the preeminent collector and
   provider of timely, relevant, and quality data about the
   people and economy of the United States. In more
   than 100 surveys annually and 20 censuses a decade,
   evolving from the first census in 1790, the Census
   Bureau provides official information about America's
   people, businesses, industries, and institutions.

Questions for Discussion

1. How much is the population projected to
   change between now and 2050?

2. Describe the density and distribution of the
   United States population today.

3. How does the size, distribution, growth, and
   diversity of the United States population
   today compare to the population in 1900?

Applications

1 What are the components of change about
   which demographers must make assumptions in order to project the course of future
   population change?

2. Plot the three data points for the minority
   percentage in the United States population
   given on page 61 in "The Changing Face of
   America" section. What do you predict will
   happen to the minority percentages for the
   years 2040 and 2060?

3.3 Population and Nutrition

Kailash Mathur, Ph.D.
Nutritional Sciences, Department of Family and Consumer Sciences
School of Applied Professional Sciences, South Carolina State University, Orangeburg, South Carolina

Dr. Mathur is professor of nutrition and advisor to the Nutritional Sciences graduate program in the Department of Family and Consumer Sciences at South Carolina State University. He was born in Jodhpur, Rajasthan, in India. His education includes B.S. and DVM degrees in India, a M.S. degree in dairy science from North Carolina State University, and a Ph.D. degree in nutritional sciences from the University of Illinois. Dr. Mathur has conducted research in the field of human nutrition for the United States Department of Agriculture (USDA), has presented at professional meetings, and has published many articles about his research findings. He was appointed as a member of the National Nutrition Monitoring Advisory Council by President Clinton. Recently he was honored by the Senate and House of Representatives of South Carolina.

Overview

The sex drive is the strongest human drive after hunger. It is nature's way of continuing the human race. The world's population is increasing rapidly, the developing countries contributing greatly to this increase. A study done at Johns Hopkins University reveals that unless population growth slows and farm production increases dramatically, by 2025 there won't be enough food for the world's projected 8 billion mouths. If this continues, there may not be enough natural resources to meet the demand of every person. That seems especially possible because we expect many generations of humans to come. We must appreciate that the earth's resources are limited and that the quality of life for each individual decreases as population on earth increases. A broad understanding of culture, society, and politics is needed to understand population growth and policies.

The State of the World

Our forests are shrinking. Water tables are falling. Soils are eroding. Wetlands are disappearing. Fisheries are collapsing. Rangelands are deteriorating. Rivers are running dry. Temperatures are rising. Coral reefs are dying. And plant and animal species are disappearing. From 1950 to 1997, the use of lumber tripled. The use of paper increased sixfold. The fish catch increased nearly fivefold. Grain consumption nearly tripled. The burning of fossil fuel nearly quadrupled. And air and water pollutants multiplied several times. All are consequences of increasing population. However, if we can control population growth, we can potentially avoid what appears to be impending disaster.

Population and Nutrition

Nutrition is more than just the food we choose to eat. It is a science that includes all the interactions between living organisms and food. These interactions include the physiological processes by which an organism ingests, digests, absorbs, transports, and uses food. Nutrition includes the biological actions and interactions of food with the body and their consequences for health and disease. It also includes the physiological, social, cultural, economic, and technological factors that influence which foods we choose to eat.

The good news is that the per capita food supply has increased despite unprecedented population growth. Human health and welfare have also improved throughout much of the world. But there are warning signs that we may be reaching the limits of agricultural expansion. The amount of land available to produce crops may be shrinking, and even current production may not be enough. Erosion, desertification, and salinization all contribute to the reduction of available farmland. At the same time, the unequal distribution of food within and among countries is a problem. About 840 million people worldwide, including 200 million children, do not have enough to eat. The balance between population size and food supply is the most basic challenge humans face. We produce enough food for the nearly 6 billion people today. But the bad news is that poverty, natural disaster, political violence, and geopolitical factors prevent at least one-seventh of the world from getting enough to eat.

Nutrition and diet play important roles in health promotion and chronic disease prevention. The changing health care environment makes clear that preventive health care services are needed. The roles of diet, food choices, and physical activity need to be emphasized to reduce the cost of health care in traditional, public health, and managed care settings.

Availability of Food

The availability of food is affected by geography, socioeconomic issues, and health status. In some parts of the world, the foods consumed are limited to those produced locally. Survival depends on making the correct choices from a limited selection of foods. Nutrients that are lacking in local foods will be lacking in the population's diet.

In developed nations, the ability to store, transport, and process food allows year-round access to seasonal foods and foods grown and produced at distant locations. Even if foods are available in a store or market, it doesn't mean that they are available to everyone. Socioeconomic factors such as income level, living conditions, education, and life-style affect the types and amounts of foods that are available. Individuals living in poverty can choose only the types and amounts of foods that are available and that they can afford.

A goal should be to make sure all people have adequate nutrition for a normal, active life. This goal was reaffirmed by people from around the world at the 1996 World Food Summit in Rome. Even though the number of people suffering from malnourishment has fallen, the task of ending world hunger remains difficult. Extra-

Nutrition and diet play important roles in health promotion and chronic disease prevention.

ordinary efforts are needed to make sure the world's poor and disadvantaged have enough of the right foods.

Food Supply and Malnutrition

About 90 percent of the world's food energy intake is provided by just 15 crop plants. Relatively inexpensive starch foods are the major staples dominating the world's food supply. Rice is the primary food. It is the staple for about half of the world's people; and along with maize and wheat, it provides two-thirds of all food energy, as shown in Figure 1. These three cereals (rice, wheat, and maize) and root crops that are high in carbohydrates and protein are the basic elements in the diets of many countries. Fruits, vegetables, and animal products provide variety and vital nutrients. However, they form a relatively small share of the diet in most countries, especially in the developing countries where three-fourths of the earth's population lives.

Poverty is the main cause of world hunger. Developing countries do not grow enough food to feed their people and cannot afford to import food. According to the Food and Agriculture Organization (FAO), as shown in Figure 2, some 43 percent of the population in Sub-Saharan Africa and 22 percent of the population in South Asia are malnourished. Millions more people do not get the necessary protein and essential vitamins and minerals to lead a healthy life.

Rural people are more likely to be poor, and they are more prone to malnourishment and malnutrition. However, in developing countries, urban poverty is increasing rapidly. Children living in the countryside are more likely than those in urban areas to be underweight for their age, a sign of malnutrition. Malnutrition takes its heaviest toll on children, and the health damage can begin before birth. Mothers who receive inadequate nourishment are most likely to have underweight babies. Those underweight babies are vulnerable to infections and parasites that can cause early death. Malnourished children who survive the first

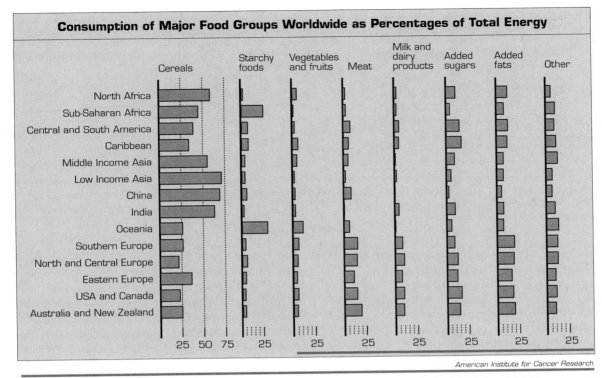

Figure 1 *Cereals make up the major part of human diets worldwide, particularly in Asia and Africa.*

five years of life may suffer permanent stunting of their physical growth. According to the Food and Agriculture Organization, 60 percent of children in South Asia have stunted growth, as do 39 percent of children in Sub-Saharan Africa and 33 percent in East and Southeast Asia. As shown in Figure 2, the percentage of underweight children in developing countries ranges from 12 percent in Latin America and the Caribbean to 58 percent in South Asia. The percentage of people suffering from severe malnutrition is greater in Sub-Saharan Africa than in any other region.

Population Size

The United Nations predicts that the global population—5.8 billion at the beginning of 1997—is likely to reach 9.4 billion around the middle of the 21st century. Population growth over the next 50 years will affect every facet of life, including housing, income, education, health care, the environment, and the demand for food.

Even using the lowest United Nations projections, the world is expected to have another billion people to feed within 13 years. Nearly all the additional people will live in developing countries. The populations of those countries are growing at nearly 1.6 percent each year in the 1990s; and according to UN projections, those populations will continue to expand well into the next century. Improved nutrition and sanitation, as well as expanded health programs worldwide, have led to a rapid increase in the time a person is expected to live. Because people are living longer, the population growth rate is higher.

Physiological Food Requirements

The number of calories a person needs every day ranges from less than 1,000 for an infant to about 3,900 for an adult man under extreme physical stress. The minimum calories a person needs is primarily determined by body weight. Other factors

Region	Daily Calorie Supply (kcal/person)	Total Population (millions)	Malnourished Population (millions)	Malnourished Population (percent)	Underweight Children (millions)	Underweight Children (percent)
Developing countries	2,500	4,200	840	20	179	34
Sub-Saharan Africa	2,100	500	220	43	26	30
Near East/North Africa	3,000	310	40	12	13	25
East & Southeast Asia	2,500	1,680	270	16	43	24
South Asia	2,500	1,160	260	22	91	58
Latin American/Caribbean	2,700	430	60	15	7	12

Figure 2 *Daily Per Capita Calorie Supply and Malnourishment in Selected Developing Regions, 1990–1992. (Source: FAO Food Security and Nutrition, WF596/TECH/9: 8, 130; and N. Alexandratos. World Agriculture— Towards 2010 [1995]: 433.)*

(such as level of physical activity; health problems; and for women, pregnancy or lactation) can increase needs. Age and gender have the greatest impact on caloric consumption. Body weight and height directly affect the basal metabolic rate and, therefore, the food needs of individuals. If all children received adequate nutrition and stunting were eliminated from the planet, the average height and weight of the world population would increase— and food needs would grow. The global food supply would need to expand 8 percent to maintain a healthy weight at the taller heights. On the other hand, the demand for food would drop by 1 percent if obesity were eliminated and no one ate more than he or she needed.

Continued migration of people from rural to urban areas also affects food consumption. Between 1995 and 2025, the percentage of developing-country residents living in urban areas is projected to rise from 38 percent to 57 percent. City dwellers tend to be less physically active than rural residents. Thus, this shift of population from rural to urban areas around the world decreases the number of calories needed to sustain a healthy life.

Between 1995 and 2050, fertility reductions, population aging, and urbanization are expected to increase food needs from 2 to 7 percent in the major developing regions. They will also reduce food needs by 1 or 2 percent in the developed regions. At the same time, projected population growth will nearly triple food requirements in Africa. The amount of food needed will be about three-fourths greater in Latin America and the Caribbean. Asia's food needs will be two-thirds greater. Only in Europe, where the population is projected to decline, will food requirements be lower in 2050 than in the 1990s. Worldwide the amount of food required for a healthy population will increase by 75 percent over the next 50 years as the global population climbs from nearly 5.8 billion to over 8 billion.

Amount of Food Waste

National incomes appear to affect the amount of food lost or wasted. Low-income countries lose minimal amounts of food—less than 10 percent. The percentage of food wasted is estimated at 40 percent in middle-income countries such as Greece, Ireland, and Libya and 25 to 30 percent in higher-income countries such as the United States. If food losses were kept at 23 percent or less in all countries, nearly 13 percent of global food consumption would be saved, reducing per capita demand for grain and other food.

The minimum calories a person needs is primarily determined by body weight.

Accepting the Challenge

Balancing population size with food supply is a complex issue. The task requires people from a wide range of disciplines and positions from around the world. National leaders, farmers, nutritionists, local politicians, doctors, nurses, teachers, school children, moms and dads, and many others will all be needed to meet the challenge. A good place to start helping is in learning more about the issue. With a better understanding of the causes and effects, individuals, communities, nations, and the world can make wise decisions in the policies we set, the money we spend, the foods we produce, the food we waste, and more.

References

Bender, W. and M. Smith. (1997). Population, food, and nutrition. *Bulletin*, 51 (4).

Falkenmark, M. and C. Widstrand. (1992). Population and water resources: A delicate balance. *Population Bulletin*, 47 (3).

Position of the American Dietetic Association: The role of nutrition in health promotion and disease prevention program. (1998, February). *Journal of the American Dietetic Association*, p. 205.

Rockett, J. R. (1994). Population and Health: An introduction to epidemiology. Bulletin, 49, (3).

Smohn, L. A. and Mary B. Grosvenor. (1997). *Nutrition Science and Application* (2nd edition). Saunders College Publishing. Philadelphia, PA.

The Rotarian. (1997, December). *Rotary International.*

Additional Resources

Brown, L. R. 1997. *State of the World: A WorldWatch Institute Report on Progress Toward a Sustainable Society*. W.W. Norton & Company, New York.
> One of a series of annual reports on global issues affecting population growth and resource utilization by the WorldWatch Institute.

Crews, K. A. and P. Cancellier. 1991. *Connections: Linking Population and the Environment.* The Population Reference Bureau, Inc., Washington, DC.
> A curriculum that explores population issues and teaches demographic skills.

Food, Nutrition and the Prevention of Cancer: A Global Perspective. 1997. American Institute for Cancer Research, Washington, DC.
> A review of the scientific literature on foods, nutrition, and the worldwide occurrence of human cancer.

Weeks, J. R. 1996. *Population: An Introduction to Concepts and Issues.* Wadsworth Publishing Company, Belmont, CA.
> A comprehensive textbook dealing with the methods of population studies.

Questions for Discussion

1. Which crops form the basis of the world food supply and why? How do the amounts of these crops consumed—as a percentage of a population's total energy (calorie) intake—vary in different regions of the world?

2. Describe the social factors that play a role in determining whether a population is well-nourished or malnourished.

3. Describe the projections for food needs by the year 2050 in various regions of the world.

Applications

1. How does the typical United States diet compare to diets in other parts of the world in terms of consumption of the major types of foods? Create a table that shows how global differences in diet may affect population health.

2. Compare the projections for population growth and anticipated food supply in various regions of the world. Discuss any problems you may see. How might the observed discrepancies between the needs of local populations and available food supplies be handled on a global basis? Describe some of the changes that might be necessary to achieve adequate nourishment for every person on earth.

3.4 Balancing the Desires of People with the Needs of Fish

Bradley B. Shepard, M.S.
Montana Cooperative Fishery Research Unit
Biology Department, Montana State University, Bozeman, Montana

Mr. Shepard has worked for the Montana Department of Fish, Wildlife and Parks for 20 years. A biologist since 1981, he works on many aspects of fish biology and management. He has done considerable work on the effects of habitat alteration and angler use on trout populations. Mr. Shepard's research, as an adjunct professor at Montana State University, evaluates the effects of habitat enhancement projects on fish populations and strategies for conserving native fishes. The opinions expressed in this essay are those of Mr. Shepard and not necessarily those of the Montana Department of Fish, Wildlife and Parks.

Overview

When growing up in Ohio during the 1960s, Mr. Shepard enjoyed fishing more than any other activity. He dreamed of becoming a fisheries biologist. He wanted to work on the fabled "blue ribbon" trout waters in Montana that he read about in outdoor magazines. He worked to make his dream come true. He still enjoys his career and the opportunities he has to work with the amazing fish resources Montana supports. Unfortunately, Montana and most of the West is changing fairly fast. The demands people are making on fish resources and the habitats supporting these fish have steadily increased. Fish management in Montana can be used as an example of how fish managers in the West are trying to balance the desires of people with the needs of fish.

Historical Perspective

The aboriginal peoples who inhabited Montana (nomadic American Indian tribes such as the Crow, Blackfeet, Kootenai, and Salish) harvested and ate fish that they considered a bounty from the "earth mother." The earliest written records describing the species of fish inhabiting Montana are from Lewis and Clark's famous 1804 to 1806 journey. They described several previously undescribed fish species including cutthroat trout, longnose sucker, and sauger. One such excerpt from their journals, a description of a fish later to be named the westslope cutthroat trout, *Oncorhynchus clarki lewisi,* is shown in Figure 1. Early historical accounts reported that native fish were eaten by soldiers stationed at many of the forts throughout Montana. The fish were a welcome change from standard army rations. By the mid-1800s, stocking of fish raised in eastern hatcheries had begun. The United States Biological Survey raised the fish and transported them in railroad cars to waters near new settlements in Montana. A bill passed by the first Montana Territorial Legislature of 1864 stipulated that "a rod or pole, line or hook, shall be the only

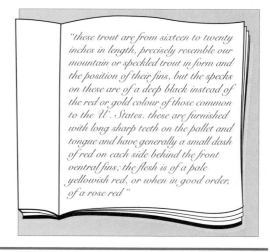

"these trout are from sixteen to twenty inches in length, precisely resemble our mountain or speckled trout in form and the position of their fins, but the specks on these are of a deep black instead of the red or gold colour of those common to the U. States. these are furnished with long sharp teeth on the pallet and tongue and have generally a small dash of red on each side behind the front ventral fins; the flesh is of a pale yellowish red, or when in good order, of a rose red"

Figure 1 *This excerpt from the* Original Journals of the Lewis and Clark Expedition 1804–1806, *(Volume 2) edited by Reuben Gold Thwaites, 1904, is the first description of the westslope cutthroat trout,* Oncorhynchus clarki lewisi.

lawful way trout may be caught in any of the streams of the territory." This law made it illegal to use dynamite to harvest fish, which had been a relatively common practice by early miners.

The Montana Fish and Game Commission was founded in 1895. At that time, their primary role was to enforce game and angling laws. The first state fish hatchery was constructed in 1908 with the fish and game commissioners and state game warden deciding which waters were to be stocked. Professionally trained fishery biologists were not hired as part of the Montana Fish and Game Department until the 1950s.

Management Tools

Fish managers have four main tools for managing fish resources:

- ◆ Data collection—Biological and ecological information is necessary to understand what a species or community of fish needs to survive and prosper.
- ◆ Habitat protection—Habitats, including water quantity and quality critical to fish, must be protected or enhanced.
- ◆ Fish stocking—Hatcheries are needed to produce fish to stock, especially into waters that do not have habitats that can support much natural reproduction.
- ◆ Regulations—Fishing regulations are used to limit the number and/or size of fish harvested by anglers.

Funding of sport fish management by state agencies in the United States is unique. Funding is provided by an excise tax on equipment used in angling combined with angler license fees. This funding scheme ensures that the users of the resource pay for its management. These excise taxes are collected by the federal government and distributed to the states based on fishing license sales and each state's population.

Managing Sport Fisheries

Many sport fisheries in the West were traditionally maintained by stocking hatchery fish. Montana began to eliminate stocking of hatchery fish from its trout streams and rivers in 1967. This was done after a study showed that stocked hatchery fish had a negative impact on wild trout. Montana now manages almost all of its trout streams and rivers for wild trout. Fish population surveys are conducted periodically. Knowledge gained from these surveys is used to modify angling regulations. The modifications ensure that enough wild fish survive to reproduce and maintain fish populations. They also maintain angling opportunity. Most fish populations have very high reproductive and survival rates. Thus, they produce more adult fish than are needed to perpetuate the population. These "excess" adult fish are called the "harvestable surplus." Harvesting of these "excess" fish by anglers does not damage the fish population. Regulations are used to restrict the type of terminal gear used. For example, anglers are only permitted to use artificial flies or lures. Regulations may also restrict the number and size of fish that anglers can keep. This regulation ensures that enough adults survive to spawn and maintain the population.

Montana's "wild trout" management has been implemented in many other states. However, some states still rely heavily on hatchery stocking due to the high fishing pressure their waters receive. Montana's excellent hatchery system now maintains some of our native fish, such as the westslope cutthroat trout pictured in Figure 2. State hatcheries stock game fish primarily into lakes and reservoirs. In these environments, natural reproduction may be limited. Also, fishing pressure may be so high that wild reproduction alone cannot meet angling demand.

Figure 2 *This westslope cutthroat trout is one of the fish species that is now raised in state fish hatcheries and stocked in Montana's lakes and reservoirs.*

Fish Management Concerns

Illegal introductions of fish by people can disrupt an aquatic ecosystem that provides good fishing. These people usually want to see their particular favorite fish species in waters close to their homes. Another problem that has recently surfaced in Montana and other western states is "whirling disease." This disease infects young trout and can cause them to "whirl" (thus, its name), preventing them from feeding effectively. Stress and lack of food can weaken infected fish, and many of these fish eventually die. This disease threatens the wild trout fisheries in many western rivers. Research is under way to solve this problem.

Conserving Native Fishes

A major issue facing fish managers in the West is how to prevent many of our native fish from going extinct. Various factors contribute to the decline and potential extinction of many once abundant native fish species. These include introductions of nonnative fish, degradation of habitat and water quality, changes in stream flows, construction of structures that prevent unrestricted fish movement, and excessive angler harvest. Hatcheries are sometimes used as homes to preserve native fish species when wild populations get too low. Conservation of native fish species will require protection of their habitats and removal of nonnative fish species in some locations. Regulating angler impacts on native fish has already been done for most native species presently at risk in Montana.

Some people use potentially threatened native fish and wildlife species as an issue when they want to prevent land management activities. In many cases, their real concern is more about stopping development of lands than preserving species. On the other side, natural resource extraction industries, such as timber, mining, and livestock grazing, don't want to see any further restrictions placed on their development and use of private and public lands in the West. Fish managers are often caught in the middle of this controversy—with no money dedicated specifically for conserving and restoring native fishes. This issue is also very controversial because it involves the state's right versus the federal government's right to manage fish and wildlife species within the state.

Changing Public Demands

Angler demands are constantly changing, and angler interest groups have become much more focused. Historically anglers belonged to general fish and wildlife organizations like rod and gun clubs. Now specific groups of anglers have individual organizations like the Federation of Fly Fishers, Trout Unlimited, Walleye Unlimited, etc. These groups often have narrow views of what they want. The desires of different groups often conflict with each other.

Commercial users of sport fisheries, guides and outfitters, have dramatically increased during the past 15 years. These commercial users are primarily interested in making money from sport fish resources. The increase in commercial use, along with an increase in nonguided anglers, has resulted in crowding of many popular fishing waters. Many Montana anglers no longer fish waters they traditionally fished because these waters have become too crowded. Many private lands historically open to fishing are being purchased by individuals who no longer allow fishing access. This further restricts angling opportunities.

Some people believe any type of angling is morally inappropriate.

Some people believe any type of angling is morally inappropriate. They worry about possible pain a hooked fish might experience. They also worry about the possible impacts of harvest on fish populations. Many of these people don't recognize that habitat availability and quality controls fish populations. Nor are they willing to acknowledge that humans are omnivores. Thus, we are designed to be predators on other life forms.

How Management Decisions Are Made—The Balancing Act

Fish managers usually consider biological, social, and economic components when they make management decisions. The biological component consists of the scientific information. It tells us what is biologically feasible and what biological impacts might be expected as a result of a decision. The social component recognizes that different people have different desires. The economic component acknowledges that decisions will affect different economic sectors in different ways.

Biologically some fish management decisions are not the very best for the fish population. Compromises are often made based on social and economic components. The job of fish biologists and fish management agencies is to explain clearly how decisions might affect fish populations. A clear understanding of the possible consequences of a management decision on a particular fish population is necessary. This is important for both the person making the decision and those people who are interested in the decision itself. Only when all people involved are well informed can a reasonable decision be made.

Fish managers must balance the many conflicting desires: (1) Commercial guides want to make money, (2) the public wants to catch and harvest fish for sport, (3) various industries want to extract natural resources from the land, and (4) many members of an expanding human population want to live near their favorite fishing spot. The desires of these different people can conflict with what is best for the fish population. As fish habitats are degraded by human activities, the number of fish these habitats can support declines. Fish managers and the public must work together to preserve and improve fish habitats, ensure that anglers do not harvest more fish than a fish population can support, and provide different types of angling opportunities for different groups of anglers. Balancing these uses is what fish management is all about.

References and Additional Resources

Alvord, B. 1991. *A History of Montana's Fish Division From 1890 to 1958*. Montana Fish, Wildlife and Parks, Helena, MT.
    Presents a brief history of Montana's fish management.

Moring, J. R. 1996. Fish discoveries by the Lewis and Clark and Red River Expeditions. *Fisheries* 21: 6–12.
    Documents the fish discovered during these two historic expeditions.

Newman, C. 1996. A passion for trout. *National Geographic* 189: pp. 64–85.
    Reviews why people across the world like to angle for trout. An excellent map on pages 77 and 78 shows human threats to fish habitat.

Vincent, E. R. 1987. Effects of stocking catchable-size hatchery rainbow trout on two wild trout species in the Madison River and O'Dell Creek, Montana. *North American Journal of Fisheries Management* 7: pp. 91–105.
    Documents how stocking hatchery fish had negative impacts on wild trout populations.

Questions for Discussion

1. What tools are available to fish managers for managing fish populations and angler use?

2. What are the main components of fish management?

3. Why are some fish management decisions not always the best decisions for fish populations?

Applications

1. Think about a fish population in a body of water near where you live. List things that might be impacting habitats used by this fish population, and make suggestions on how you might reduce these impacts. List the different types of users of this fish population, both anglers and others, who affect this population.

2. What happens to a fish population if its habitat shrinks or is degraded by human activities?

3. Get a copy of your state's current fishing regulations. Find examples of regulations that you think might help protect fish populations. How do some of these regulations limit harvest? Why do you think different regulations are imposed on different waters?

3.5 The Science of Declining Amphibian Populations

Paul E. Brunkow, Ph.D.
Department of Biological Sciences
Southern Illinois University, Edwardsville, Illinois

Dr. Brunkow studies the conservation biology of mole salamanders in southern Illinois. He is especially interested in how these animals might be affected by large-scale flooding along the Mississippi River. He also studies the ecology of shallow pond communities, from the daily dynamics of dissolved oxygen and carbon dioxide to predator-prey interactions between larval insects, fish, and amphibians.

Overview

Many biologists are alarmed by recent reports that amphibian populations are declining around the world. Some scientists think that these declines indicate the magnitude of changes in environmental quality brought about by human activities. Others claim that many cases of declines in amphibian populations are not adequately documented. Those scientists believe that we need to better understand the dynamics of amphibian populations before we can make such conclusions. In order to appreciate this scientific debate, people need to understand more about amphibians. Why are they good indicators of environmental change? What are the main hypotheses to explain why amphibian populations may be declining?

What Are Amphibians?

Amphibians include frogs, salamanders, newts, and another little known group called caecilians. Amphibians were the first animals to evolve to live on land. They were, therefore, around a long time before the dinosaurs. There are presently about 5,000 species of amphibians. Almost 4,000 of these species are frogs. Some of these species can be found in very large numbers during the breeding season, whereas others are more rare and very difficult to find.

As their name suggests, amphibians commonly inhabit both land and water habitats. Amphibians are unique in that they do not possess any protective scales, fur, or feathers. In this way, they are very different from fish, reptiles, mammals, and birds. Amphibians usually lay their eggs in aquatic environments like ponds, lakes, and streams. Amphibian eggs are unprotected by any shell or covering. Because they lack protection during all stages of their lives, amphibians are sensitive to many environmental conditions. Changes in moisture, temperature, acidity, and the presence of pollutants in the environment all affect amphibians. Because of their lifestyle, amphibians are impacted by environmental changes in both land and water habitats.

Amphibian skin is very permeable to water. Therefore, even though some amphibians are purely terrestrial, they all need some kind of moisture in the soil or in ponds, lakes, and streams to survive. Amphibians are found in a very wide variety of habitats. They live in areas from mountainous temperate and tropical forests to prairies to low deserts. About the only places you will not find amphibians is near

> *Because of their lifestyle, amphibians are impacted by environmental changes in both land and water habitats.*

sea shores and the high Arctic and Antarctic. They cannot survive near the salty water or in extreme cold. Because amphibians are found in so many different habitats and because they are sensitive to a wide variety of environmental factors, they can possibly tell scientists something about environmental change in a wide variety of environments.

Over the past several years, many biologists have observed declines in some populations of amphibians throughout the world. Many of these species were common at one time but are now difficult to find or have not been seen in several years. Examples of such species from the United States include the mountain yellow-legged frog, the Yosemite toad and the Santa Cruz long-toed salamander in California, the Wyoming toad in Wyoming, and the Huachuca tiger salamander and Chiricahua leopard frog in Arizona. The gastric brooding frog (it raises its young in its stomach!) of Australia and the golden toad of Costa Rica are two such species from other countries.

Why Are Amphibian Populations Declining?

Four main hypotheses explain why amphibian populations might be declining:

◆ Natural habitats required by amphibians are disappearing due to human activities.

◆ Certain fatal diseases are becoming more common in amphibian populations.

◆ Nonnative species introduced to amphibian habitats are excluding native amphibians from those habitats.

◆ Increases in ultraviolet radiation caused by pollution kill amphibian eggs and young.

Habitat Destruction

Humans alter amphibian habitats for a wide variety of reasons. Forests are cut for timber and residential or commercial development. Wetlands are drained for agriculture. Streams and rivers are dammed for water supplies or power production. All of these activities can alter natural habitats to the extent that native amphibian species are unable to live or reproduce. Cutting timber and draining wetlands reduce the amount of moisture in the soil. These sites then dry out more quickly in the spring and summer when most amphibian species breed. Damming streams and rivers submerges natural ponds and wetlands. Under so much water, frogs and salamanders cannot breed and are forced to move. Many studies show that amphibian populations may decline after such human activities begin in an area.

Fatal Diseases

Amphibians, like other organisms, are susceptible to many bacterial, fungal, and viral diseases. Some biologists have found dead or dying individuals in amphibian populations that were at one time quite healthy. This was observed even in areas that were relatively free of human influence. When scientists examined these amphibians in laboratories, some contained lethal bacteria, viruses, or parasitic protozoans. The scientists concluded that disease may have caused the decline of these populations. In these cases, there did not appear to be any other factors that might have caused the decline. Many times diseased amphibians have been found in areas that were free of pollutants and had little or no human habitation. Examples of such areas include mountain forest reserves in Costa Rica and Panama, the mountains of Colorado, and rain forest preserves in Australia. These biologists also pointed out that some amphibians may get sick after some other factor has reduced the capability of their immune system to ward off disease.

Parasite infection that causes deformities in frogs and salamanders is another potential cause of amphibian decline. Some parasites, called flukes, can burrow into the skin of immature frogs and salamanders. This causes multiple legs to form where only one would have developed normally, as shown in Figure 1. These abnormal animals then usually die as juveniles or adults. Do you remember seeing stories in the news about deformed frogs found by school children in Minnesota, Michigan, and Oregon?

Figure 1 *This frog has an extra set of front legs.*

Introduced Species

Humans move many species of organisms around the world. They do so either intentionally or unintentionally. For example, many fish species were introduced to lakes and rivers to improve sport fishing. Many other species have invaded new habitats when human activities made the habitat more suitable for them. Humans also accidentally introduce nonnative species to a habitat on boats, earth-moving equipment, or even clothing or car tires. Introduced species can quickly reduce or eliminate native populations of amphibians. For example, crayfish and nonnative fish, such as trout and bass, are effective predators on amphibians. Bullfrogs, which have been widely introduced to habitats where they are not native, have completely eliminated some populations of the endangered Huachuca tiger salamander in southern Arizona. Thus, competitive and predatory effects of introduced species can have very negative effects on native amphibian populations.

Ultraviolet Radiation

Ultraviolet (UV) radiation is very high energy light that is always emitted by the sun. This is the light that gives you a sunburn if you stay in the sun too long. Over the past several years, pollution worldwide (especially from industrial countries) has increased the amount of UV light penetrating our atmosphere and striking the earth. Figure 2 illustrates the effects of increased UV light on amphibian eggs. Frog and salamander eggs protected from UV radiation hatch more successfully. They also develop fewer deformities than eggs that hatch while exposed to UV radiation. Thus, increases in UV radiation reaching the earth may contribute to some of the declines in amphibian populations. Interestingly, UV radiation is more severe at higher elevations. Sunburns are

worse for skiers in the mountains than for hikers at lower elevations. Many declining amphibian populations are also found in higher elevation habitats. This fact lends support to the UV hypothesis.

Are the Amphibian Declines Real?

Multiple observations suggest that amphibian populations are declining throughout the world. However, many biologists contend that additional study of amphibian populations is needed. They cannot yet confidently conclude that these declines are real.

Amphibian populations fluctuate widely even under normal circumstances. A study lasting nearly 20 years in eastern North America concluded that there were no significant declines in the populations of frogs and salamanders studied. Figure 3 shows

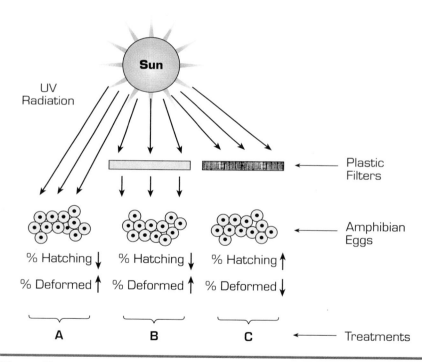

Figure 2 *In this experiment, scientists used various densities of plastic filters to reduce the quantity of UV light on some amphibian eggs. Others were exposed to full-intensity UV light from the sun. Fewer of the eggs in full sunlight hatched sucessfully, and more of the hatchlings were deformed.*

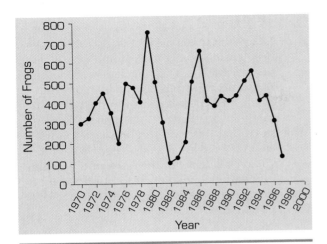

Figure 3 *This example shows the types of fluctuations in amphibian population numbers that may be observed.*

potential results from long-term studies. Frogs, and especially salamanders, can be very hard to observe under natural conditions. This is because they hide under rocks and logs and in holes in the ground. Therefore, studying amphibian population dynamics can be very difficult. Frogs and salamanders can also live for a long time as adults, sometimes up to 30 years. In some cases, these adults may simply be waiting for conditions to improve before coming out to breed again. Thus, the fact that biologists haven't seen some of these amphibian species in the wild for several years may simply reflect the fact that they are hiding out, waiting for better environmental conditions.

Scientists' Dilemma

Amphibians may be good indicators of environmental change because of their life-styles and their presence in many kinds of habitats. Because amphibian populations fluctuate widely, many long-term studies are needed for scientists to assess accurately the impact humans have had on the environment by using amphibians as "indicator species." Clear indications are that at least some frog and salamander populations have declined to critically low levels. These population changes alert scientists to the need to determine the cause of these declines. Amphibians may be sensitive indicators of the quality of our environment. They thus provide us with an opportunity to correct these environmental problems before these factors affect human welfare.

References and Additional Resources

Blaustein, A. R., P. D. Hoffman, D. G. Hokit, J. M. Kiesecker, S. C. Walls, and J. B. Hays. 1994. UV repair and resistance to solar UV-B in amphibian eggs: A link to population declines? *Proceedings of the National Academy of Sciences* USA 91: pp. 1791-1795.
    This short paper describes the experiments that show an effect of solar ultraviolet radiation on the survivorship of amphibian eggs.

Duellman, W. E. and L. Trueb. 1986. *Biology of Amphibians.* McGraw-Hill Publishing Company, New York.
    This is a very general reference book describing everything you could want to know about amphibians.

Gamradt, S. C., L. B. Kats, and C. B. Anzalone. 1997. Aggression by non-native crayfish deters breeding in California newts. *Conservation Biology* 11: pp. 793–796.
    This study used survey and experimental techniques to demonstrate the effect that introduced crayfish had on a native salamander species in streams in California.

Index to Deformed Frog Research
    http://www.hartwick.edu/biology/def_frogs/index.html
    This site contains many excellent pictures of deformed frogs and salamanders and micrographs of the parasite that causes the deformities.

Laurance, W. F., K. R. McDonald, and R. Speare. 1996. Epidemic disease and the catastrophic decline of Australian rain forest frogs. *Conservation Biolog* 10: pp. 406–413.
    The authors of this paper analyze many different types of evidence suggesting that declines in frog populations in the rain forests of Australia could be due to a highly virulent disease organism.

Means, D. B., J. G. Palis, and M. Baggett. 1996. Effects of slash pine agriculture on a Florida population of flatwoods salamander. *Conservation Biology* 10: pp. 426–437.
    This study looks at the population dynamics of a forest salamander species. The potential effects of human activities in forests in Florida on this salamander are discussed.

North American Reporting Center for Amphibian Malformations
    http://www.npsc.nbs.gov/narcam/
    Includes a discussion of the problem of amphibian malformations, a clickable map showing where malformations have been discovered, and images of various types of malformations.

Sessions, S. K. and S. B. Ruth. 1990. Explanation for naturally occurring supernumerary limbs in amphibians. *Journal of Experimental Zoology* 254: pp. 38–47.
In this paper, the authors make a series of detailed observations on deformed frogs found in California and discover that the likely culprit is a naturally occurring parasite. A series of laboratory experiments lend support to this hypothesis.

Questions for Discussion

1. Why is it that amphibians might be particularly sensitive to environmental changes?

2. Summarize in your own words the major hypotheses proposed to explain declines in amphibian populations.

3. What is controversial about the conclusion that amphibian populations are declining?

Applications

1. Imagine that you are a biologist who has been given the task of determining the cause of a decline in a frog population at Johnson Marsh. As you study this population, you realize that there is a virus in the water that can kill frogs. Further experiments demonstrate that this virus can only attack frogs when UV radiation is increased. What do you conclude about the cause of the decline in the frog population at Johnson Marsh: Is it due to the virus or is it due to increased UV radiation? Justify your answer.

2. Describe what you know about salamander or frog populations that have declined in recent years. Have you ever found frogs or salamanders with extra legs around where you live?

3.6 Harmful Algae Blooms: What Do We Know?

Barbara Doll, M.C.E.
North Carolina State University, Raleigh, North Carolina
Originally printed in the Fall 1997 issue of WaterWise, *a quarterly publication of North Carolina Sea Grant, Box 8605, North Carolina State University, Raleigh, North Carolina 27695-8605.*

Ms. Doll is a water quality specialist for North Carolina Sea Grant, which is a federal/state program that promotes the wise use of coastal resources. She has a master's degree in civil engineering. Based at North Carolina State University, Ms. Doll provides information to the public and local governments about water quality status, research, and regulations. Much of her work is focused on reducing the impacts of stormwater runoff and nonpoint source pollution and repairing degraded ecosystems.

Overview

Pfiesteria *outbreaks in the Neuse River.*
Red tides off the coast of Florida.
Fish and shellfish poisonings in Canada, California, and overseas.
What do these events have in common?
They all result from hazardous blooms of toxic marine algae.

Thousands of species of microscopic algae form the base of the marine food chain. Of those, only a few dozen species produce potent toxins. Virtually invisible, small numbers of toxic algal species may be present in coastal waters at any time. In the right environment, however, they can form large colonies or blooms that pose harm to fish, shellfish, marine mammals, and humans. Some species of microalgae can produce toxic effects in concentrations of only a few cells per liter. In recent decades, the United States has witnessed an escalating and worrisome trend in the incidence of harmful algal blooms.

Many of the toxins produced by these blooms are both waterborne and airborne. This increases the opportunities for humans to be exposed to the toxins. Algae that form red tides produce aerosol toxins that can blow ashore and irritate people's eyes and respiratory systems. Toxins can also accumulate in fish and shellfish that eat the algae. If, in turn, humans or shorebirds consume the seafood, they can become ill or die. Likewise, the toxins can harm or kill fish, shellfish, porpoises, whales, manatees, and other sea life. Aquaculture fish are especially vulnerable to toxins since they cannot escape.

Toxic algae have been around for thousands of years. The Old Testament of the Bible contains the first known description of a red tide. And Native Americans in the Pacific Northwest were aware of shellfish poisonings centuries ago. But before the early 1970s, only a few regions of the United States were affected by toxic algae. Now virtually every coastal state is threatened by at least one toxic species that can be found over large geographic areas. This trend gives rise to concern. Outbreaks can cause millions of dollars in economic losses to coastal communities. The 1987 red tide that closed shellfishing along more than 250 miles of North Carolina shore during peak harvest season caused $25 million in losses to the seafood and tourism industries.

Possible Causes of Toxic Algal Blooms

Scientists are searching for the causes of the increase and spread of toxic algal species. There are many possibilities.

Some evidence points to widespread eutrophication of coastal waters as the problem. Eutrophication is the accumulation of excessive amounts of nutrients, especially nitrogen and phosphorus, in lakes and rivers. Nutrients come from wastewater treatment plants, cropland, livestock facilities, and urban runoff. Excess nutrients stimulate the growth of algae and aquatic plants. They may also help harmful algal species thrive. Research has shown that reducing the supply of nutrients can dramatically decrease the amount of toxin produced.

Humans are also responsible for transporting these organisms. In Australia, researchers have learned that toxic algae can be spread by ships. This happens when a ship takes on ballast water in one port and dumps the extra water into another port.

Climate change may be another culprit. Changes in sea surface temperature and elevation may create an environment more suitable for harmful algae. Even periodic climate shifts could contribute to increases in harmful algal blooms. One example of a periodic climate shift is El Niño, which forces masses of warm water up the Pacific coast.

Finally, some scientists suspect that the increase may be partially because people are more aware of the problem and reporting is better.

Which Algae Produce Toxins?

Three groups of marine organisms produce toxins: diatoms, dinoflagellates, and cyanobacteria. All are microscopic single-celled algae. The following further describes the three groups:

◆ Diatoms have yellow pigments and a cell wall made of silica. Species from only one genus produce toxins.

◆ Dinoflagellates have both plant and animal traits. Only a couple dozen of them make toxins.

◆ Cyanobacteria are blue-green algae that spend much of their time photosynthesizing. Almost all of them produce toxins.

Health Effects of Toxic Algae

Toxins from several species of dinoflagellates and diatoms can accumulate in fish and shellfish, causing human and animal poisonings.

The accumulation of toxic algae in seafood can adversely affect humans. It can cause paralysis, loss of memory, damage to the nervous system, and

The accumulation of toxic algae in seafood can cause many problems.

intestinal disorders. What makes these toxins so serious to human health is that they are not killed by cooking. About 2,000 cases of human poisoning caused by eating fish or shellfish are reported each year. Except for amnesic shellfish poisoning, all are caused by dinoflagellates.

Amnesic shellfish poisoning (ASP) was identified in 1987 in Prince Edward Island, Canada, after four people died from eating mussels. ASP is caused by domoic acid. It is produced by several species of diatoms of the genus *Pseudonitzschia*. Domoic acid can accumulate in fish and shellfish. In rare cases, it can cause permanent short-term memory loss if consumed by humans. Since 1987, domoic acid poisoning has shown up in northern California, Oregon, and Washington. It continues to be a serious problem in razor clams and dungeness crabs.

Toxic *Pseudonitzschia* species are also in the Northeast and Gulf of Mexico. Low levels of domoic acid have been found in shellfish on the East Coast, but not at levels that require quarantine.

Paralytic shellfish poisoning (PSP) is caused by several closely related dinoflagellate species in the genus *Alexandrium*. PSP toxins can be fatal to humans in small doses. In 1942, three people and masses of seabirds were killed by an outbreak of PSP near the Columbia River. Every year since then, portions of the West Coast are closed to shellfish harvest for more than half the year. PSP is a problem every year along the coast of northern California, Oregon, Washington, and Alaska. The toxin also repeatedly shows up along the coast from Maine to Massachusetts. Connecticut, Long Island (New York), and New Jersey sometimes experience the toxin at low levels. But these states seem to define the southern extreme of its geographic distribution. Crabs and fish (herring, mackerel, or sardines) are also known to accumulate PSP toxins.

Neurologic shellfish poisoning (NSP) is caused by *Gymnodinium breve*, a dinoflagellate that frequently forms red tides in the Gulf of Mexico and on rare occasions along the southeastern Atlantic Ocean. NSP was first documented in Florida in 1880. In 1987, a *G. breve* red tide reached North Carolina's coast through the Gulf Stream.

But no cases of NSP were reported in North Carolina because the bloom was closely tracked and affected shellfish beds were closed to harvesting. A *G. breve* bloom was also reported in New Zealand in 1992. Unlike PSP, NSP is not fatal and its health effects last only a few days.

Diarrhetic shellfish poisoning (DSP) is mainly a problem in Europe and Japan. It is caused by dinoflagellate species of the genus *Dinophysis*. Like ASP, DSP is caused by an acid rather than a toxin. Okadaic acid accumulates in fish and shellfish. When humans eat the tainted fish and shellfish, the acid can be passed to them. Blooms of dinoflagellate species associated with diarrhetic shellfish poisoning have appeared along the United States West Coast. But no cases of DSP have yet been verified.

Ciguatera fish poisoning was first recorded in 1511. It is caused by several dinoflagellate species that grow with coral reef macroalgae in tropical areas. Macroalgae include seaweeds and other aquatic algae that are large enough to be seen with the naked eye. Herbivorous tropical fish that graze on the macroalgae also eat the dinoflagellates. As a result, they accumulate the two ciguatoxins. Air and ground shipping can now move fresh catch from overseas ports to world markets within hours. Therefore, the risk of human illness from toxic marine algae is not limited to any location. Recently a case of ciguatera poisoning was reported in North Carolina. The poisoning was traced to an out-of-state grouper served in a restaurant. People and fishers who live in the tropics know where ciguatera dinoflagellates are and can avoid them. But seafood is not tagged with location of harvest. The only consumer protection against ciguatera is for seafood dealers to buy tropical reef fish from reliable brokers.

Red Tides

Red tides are dinoflagellate blooms that occur in coastal waters most often during winter. They can consist of several different species. One red tide organism, *Gymnodinium breve*, is pictured in Figure 1. The name arises from pigment in the dinoflagellate cells that can color the marsh or ocean red, yellow, orange, or brown. These blooms consist of local algae or species that travel with the Gulf Stream and move across the continental shelf with the help of wind and currents. This was the case in North

Carolina's 1987 red tide bloom. When they die, the dinoflagellates release neurotoxins that damage the nervous systems of nearby fish and shellfish and often paralyze their respiratory systems. Sessile animals such as clams and oysters often suffocate because they cannot escape the toxins. Those that do survive accumulate toxins that can cause several types of shellfish poisonings in humans, seabirds, and other animals.

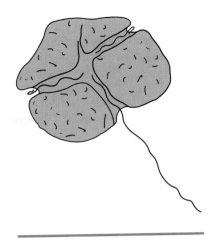

Figure 1 *The red tide dinoflagellate* Gymnodinium breve.

Cyanobacteria

Cyanobacteria are commonly known as blue-green algae. They are the oldest known group of photosynthetic organisms. Blue-green algae thrive in marine and fresh waters. Recently they expanded into the lower estuaries in North Carolina and other states. In many cases, organisms produce toxins to ward off predators. Oddly, blue-green algae produce toxins even though few animals eat them. Scientists think that cyanobacteria may make toxins to create a suitable microenvironment for themselves. Humans are rarely poisoned by blue-green algae because the algae produce surface scums, foul odors, and tastes that deter drinking and swimming. Livestock, however, have become sick or died from drinking the algae. Cyanobacteria toxins can affect other mammals, birds, fish, and aquatic invertebrates. And once they die, their decomposition can deplete oxygen levels and kill fish and shellfish.

Pfiesteria

In 1991, *Pfiesteria piscicida* became the newest toxic dinoflagellate on the world scene. It has been found from the Gulf of Mexico to inland bays in Delaware, and it is the leading suspect for many large fish kills in North Carolina's estuarine waters and tributaries of the Chesapeake Bay. Close study of water samples from Maryland, North Carolina, and various research laboratories has revealed the existence of two species of *Pfiesteria* and at least two other *Pfiesteria*-like organisms. Differentiation is difficult. Researchers don't know yet if all of these species produce toxins and are capable of killing fish.

Although *Pfiesteria* is also a dinoflagellate, it behaves differently from the organisms that form red tides. Most dinoflagellates contain toxins that are not released until the cell dies and breaks up. *Pfiesteria,* on the other hand, appears to use its toxins to stun fish before feeding on them. *Pfiesteria* can assume more than 20 forms. Scientists think *Pfiesteria* may transform when certain environments and food sources are available. Scientists have verified these transformations in laboratory studies. One example occurs when *Pfiesteria* is in the presence of fish; it transforms from a cyst to a zoospore. Then it swims into the water column and releases toxins that affect the fish's nervous system. The toxins cause the fish to become lethargic, paralyze its respiratory system, and cause it to suffocate if it cannot escape. The zoospore then consumes fish tissue and reproduces. A zoospore form of *Pfiesteria,* which has been implicated in fish kills, is shown in Figure 2.

Scientists are currently searching for a quick way to identify the species and to determine which species produce toxins. Right now the only way to tell *Pfiesteria* from *Pfiesteria*-like dinoflagellates is to strip their outer cell membranes. Then scientists examine the outer cellulose deposits near the surface with an electron microscope. They look at the number and arrangement of the deposits. Few labs in

Figure 2 Pfiesteria, *in its toxic zoospore stage, has been implicated in fish kills.*

the country can perform this difficult and time-consuming work. Scientists are also working to isolate and characterize all toxins produced by the organisms. If species produce different toxins, then toxin isolation may be a way to distinguish them. Understanding the environmental parameters that stimulate *Pfiesteria* to proliferate and to produce toxins is another goal. Scientists want to know what environmental conditions may be working together with *Pfiesteria* to kill fish. One condition that may contribute is low dissolved oxygen. Scientists also want to know if toxins accumulate in fish and shellfish tissue. Learning what potential health effects threaten fishers, swimmers, and others exposed to the toxins is important as well.

Pfiesteria has only recently been identified, and other toxic algae species have expanded their ranges. As a result, harmful algal blooms have become an issue of national importance. Federal agencies have collaborated to develop a research plan. The National Science Foundation and several agencies within the National Oceanic and Atmospheric Administration are involved, including the National Marine Fisheries Service, Sea Grant, and the Coastal Ocean Program. This national program has three goals. The first goal is to better characterize the harmful algal bloom species. The second goal is to identify similarities among ecosystems that experience these blooms. And the third goal is to determine the effect of the algal blooms on the food web.

References and Additional Resources

Anderson, C. M. 1997. Bloom dynamics of toxic *Alexandrium* species in the northeastern U. S. *Limnology and Oceanography* Vol. 42 (No. 5):1009–1022.

A review of the ecology of toxic *Alexandrium* species and a discussion of issues relating to paralytic shellfish poisoning.

Anderson, D. M., A. D. Cemballa, and G. M. Hallegraeff (eds.): 1998. *Physiological Ecology of Harmful Algal Blooms. Proceedings of the NATO Advanced Study Institute on "The Physiological Ecology of Harmful Algal Blooms," held at Bermuda Biological Station for Research, Bermuda, USA, May 27th–June 6th, 1996.* NATO ASI Series, Series G: Ecological Sciences, Volume 41. 662 pages.

This book reviews all of the major topics relevant to the ecology and physiology of harmful algal bloom (HAB) organisms. Each HAB species is described; and its growth, bloom development, and production of toxins are discussed.

Burkholder, J. M. and H. B. Glasgow. 1997. *Pfiesteria piscicida* and other *Pfiesteria*-like dinoflagellates: Behavior, impacts, and environmental controls. *Limnology and Oceanography* Vol. 42 (No. 5):1052–1075.

    This article is an excellent compendium of available information on the life cycle stages, environmental preferences, and impacts of *Pfiesteria piscicida*. It includes detailed diagrams of the life cycle and electron micrographs of various forms.

ECOHAB, *The Ecology and Oceanography of Harmful Algal Blooms, A National Research Agenda*, Woods Hole Oceanographic Institution (published and distributed by WHOI) Dec. 1995.

    This report from a symposium on Harmful Algal Blooms (HABs) describes the known extent of the problem and discusses current research.

Lewitus, A. J., R. V. Jesien, T. M. Kana, J. M. Burkholder, H. B. Glasgow, and E. May. 1995. Discovery of the "Phantom" Dinoflagellate in Chesapeake Bay. *Estuaries* Vol. 18 (No. 2):373–378.

    This report on the discovery of *Pfiesteria piscicida* in the Chesapeake Bay supports the speculation that the organism can have a dramatic impact on fish populations in shallow eutrophic estuaries.

NCSU Center for Applied Aquatic Ecology.
Pfiesteria piscicida
Web site.

    http://www.ncsu.edu/wq

    One of the most comprehensive *Pfiesteria* Web sites with background information, research reports, and downloadable images.

Questions for Discussion

1. Which groups of algae produce toxins? Within which kingdoms are these algae classified?

2. In what sort of environment are most toxic algae found?

3. Describe the human health effects of two types of toxic algae.

Applications

1. How might human activities affect the growth of toxic algae? What steps can be taken to limit human enhancement of toxic algal blooms?

2. Have you heard of a toxic algae problem in your community? If so, collect newspaper clippings and present a report to your class on the nature of the problem and its potential causes.

3. The toxic algae described in this article are members of two kingdoms. What does this mean with regards to the taxonomic utility of the word *algae*?

4.1 Neural Tube Defects: Prevention Is at Hand

Roger E. Stevenson, M.D., and Jane H. Dean, R.N.
South Carolina Neural Tube Defects Prevention Initiative
Greenwood Genetic Center, Greenwood, South Carolina

Dr. Stevenson is a physician and the director of the Greenwood Genetic Center. His professional career has been devoted to the study of birth defects and developmental impairments. He has many publications on the cytogenetic, metabolic, molecular, and environmental causes of disabilities, including the textbook The Fetus and Newly Born Infant: Influences of the Prenatal Environment *and a two-volume treatise entitled* Human Malformations and Related Anomalies. *As director of research at the Greenwood Genetic Center's J.C. Self Research Institute of Human Genetics, Dr. Stevenson is responsible for focusing research efforts on problems of birth defects and developmental impairments.*

Ms. Dean received her nursing degree from Lander University in Greenwood, South Carolina. After graduating, she worked as a labor and delivery and pediatric nurse. Since entering the field of genetics, she has worked as coordinator of the David W. Smith Workshop, in the Maternal Serum Alpha-Feto Protein (MSAFP) program, and in Fragile X research. She is currently the statewide coordinator of the South Carolina Neural Tube Defects Surveillance Initiative at the Greenwood Genetic Center in Greenwood, South Carolina, where she tracks neural tube defects in the state and is working to help prevent the recurrence of these defects in South Carolina. She is a member of the International Society of Nurses in Genetics.

Overview

Birth defects are common in the general population and, for the most part, are unpredictable. About 3 out of 100 newborns have significant birth defects. An equal number of additional individuals will be identified as having birth defects by their fifth birthday. Neural tube defects represent one of the most common congenital anomalies. A neural tube defect is a birth defect of the brain or spinal cord. Ninety-five percent of individuals who have offspring with a neural tube defect (NTD) have no family history of neural tube defects.

Prevalence

Over the past 50 years, there has been a decline in NTDs in most areas of the world. In the United States, a peak incidence of about 4 per 1,000 births occurred in the late 1930s. Now there is less than 1 case per 1,000. Whites have a several times higher incidence than blacks. Early in development, an infant's brain and spinal cord are open but normally close during the fourth week of the pregnancy. A neural tube defect occurs when the brain and spine do not close completely. These defects are usually obvious because of an opening in the skull or spinal column (backbone).

Types of Defects

The most frequent neural tube defects are spina bifida, anencephaly, and encephalocele. Spina bifida occurs when there is an opening along the spine. As shown in Figure 1, a lump is present on the back that contains part of the spinal cord. The lump may be very small or as large as a grapefruit. Sometimes the defect does not have a skin covering. When this happens, spinal fluid may leak from the

Figure 1 *In this infant afflicted with spina bifida, a section of spinal cord protrudes, causing a large lump on the lower back.*

surface. Infection is always a danger until surgery and healing take place. The baby may have weak or totally paralyzed legs and may develop hydrocephalus, otherwise known as "water on the head." Later lack of feeling in the legs and poor bladder and bowel control may become obvious.

Anencephaly, depicted in Figure 2, is caused by partial or complete absence of the baby's skull. The baby's brain is damaged without

Figure 2   *In this infant afflicted with anencephaly, the skull is almost entirely absent.*

this protection and does not develop as it should. These babies die shortly after birth. An encephalocele, as shown in Figure 3, is caused by a defect in the baby's skull. The baby's brain and its membranes push through the defect. Most affected babies will have mental retardation.

Cause of Neural Tube Defects

It is believed that both genetic and environmental exposures or deficiencies contribute to the formation of neural tube defects. Since the causes of neural tube defects have not been specifically identified, prevention measures have usually been severely limited. When there was a known genetic risk, such as a previous neural tube defect in the family, genetic counseling was recommended and recurrence could be prevented only by family limitation or prenatal diagnosis with therapeutic interruption of an affected pregnancy. Known teratogens, chemicals that may cause birth defects, such as valproic acid and carbamazepine, should be avoided during pregnancy when possible. However, 90 to 95 percent of newborns with neural tube defects are born into families with no known risk factors.

A number of observations have suggested that inadequate nutrition, particularly certain vitamin deficiencies, may contribute to the causation of neural tube defects. A deficiency of folic acid, in

particular, has been considered because aminopterin, a folic acid antagonist, can cause neural tube defects. In addition, it has been found that folic acid blood levels are lower in women who have had a baby with a neural tube defect.

Prevention of Neural Tube Defects

A study completed in 1991 by the Medical Research Council (United Kingdom) found that folic acid (a B vitamin) supplementation prior to conception and until 12 weeks' gestation reduced recurrence of neural tube defects in a high risk group, namely women who had previous pregnancies with neural tube defects. In fact, in this controlled study, high-risk women supplemented with 4 milligrams of folic acid had a 72 percent reduction in the recurrence of neural tube defects compared to the control groups of women, also at high risk, who received placebos or a multivitamin without folate. The risk factors for having a pregnancy with a neural tube defect are presumably the same for high-risk women who have already had a child with a neural tube defect and the far greater number of women in the general population who are at risk but have not had a baby with a neural tube defect. A Hungarian study by Czeizel has confirmed that taking folic acid and multivitamin supplements prior to conception and during the first trimester of pregnancy reduces first occurrences of neural tube defects. Based on data from these and other studies, the Centers for Disease Control (CDC) recommends that all women of childbearing age take 0.4 milligram of folic acid daily and that all women with a previous pregnancy with a neural tube defect increase

Figure 3   *In this infant afflicted with an encephalocele, a portion of the brain has protruded ouside the improperly formed skull.*

the dose of folic acid when they are actively trying to conceive. Folic acid may also be consumed through the intake of leafy green vegetables, liver, legumes, nuts, orange juice, and certain cereals that now contain 0.4 milligram of folic acid in each serving. The FDA authorized the fortification of cereal grain flours with folic acid. All of these products (including grits, corn meal, and wheat flour) have been fortified as of January 1, 1998. The level of fortification, however, is inadequate to protect most pregnancies against NTDs. Therefore, it is still important for all women of childbearing age to take a multivitamin with 0.4 milligram of folic acid every day.

References

Centers for Disease Control. Use of folic acid for prevention of spina bifida and other neural tube defects—1983–1991. MMWR 1991; 40: pp. 513–516.

Medical Research Council Vitamin Research Study Group. Prevention of neural tube defects: Results of the Medical Research Council Vitamin Study. *Lancet* 1991; 338: pp. 131–137.

Smithells, R. W., S. Shepard, C. J. Schorah, et al. Apparent prevention of neural tube defects by periconceptional vitamin supplementation. *Arch Dis Child* 1981; 56: pp. 991–998.

Additional Resources

Exceptional Parent magazine and the Family Education Network
    555 Kinderamack Road
    Oradell, NJ 07649
    800-562-1973
    http://www.familyeducation.com
    This magazine and associated Web site frequently have articles on specific birth defects such as spina bifida.

March of Dimes Birth Defects Foundation, National Office
    1275 Mamaroneck Avenue
    White Plains, NY 10605
    888-MODIMES (663-4637)
    http://www.marchofdimes.com/pnhec/4439_4137.asp
    The Web site provides a number of spina bifida facts that describe the condition, prenatal diagnosis, treatments, and preventative measures. The Web site and the March of Dimes Foundation also provide links to resources for families affected by spina bifida.

Spina Bifida Association of America (SBAA)

4590 MacArthur Boulevard NW, Suite 250
Washington, DC 20007-4226
202-944-3285; 800-621-3141
spinabifda@aol.com
http://www.babycenter.com/refcap/
1424.html
SBAA provides general public services such as bimonthly newsletters, publications, referral services, individual and systems advocacy, and current research applications.

Questions for Discussion

1. What is a neural tube defect?
2. How has the incidence of neural tube defects in the United States changed?
3. Which type of defect is characterized by the partial or complete absence of the skull?
4. What type of foods contain folic acid? How much of each food would you have to eat to get 0.4 milligram of folic acid per day?
5. Who should take folic acid?

Applications

1. How can the risk for birth defects of the spine or brain (neural tube defects) be reduced by consuming folic acid? Describe the importance of the timing of the folic acid supplements to the development of the fetus.
2. What is the easiest way to get folic acid in your diet?
3. How often should you take folic acid?
4. What types of foods may be fortified with the correct amount of folic acid needed?

4.2 The Human Body and Shock

George E. Tempel, Ph.D.
Department of Physiology
Medical University of South Carolina (MUSC), Charleston, South Carolina

Physiology is the science of living systems—the study of how things work. As a physiologist, Dr. Tempel studies how the body's systems change during shock. He hopes that greater understanding will lead to better treatment and increased survival. He also recruits students for MUSC's College of Graduate Studies by describing the school's programs leading to careers in research to interested young people.

Overview

Both of Dr. Tempel's sons played soccer in middle and high school on competitive teams. The coach of his sons' classic soccer team was involved in a car accident, developed an infection, and died. Like Jim Henson, the creator of Big Bird and Ernie, his boys' soccer coach and tens of thousands of Americans in intensive care units have died from shock. This essay explains two kinds of shock, the body's response to shock, and how the body's response to shock may be both helpful and harmful.

What Is Shock?

Maybe the first thing that comes to mind when you read the word *shock* is what would happen if you were to touch a bare electrical wire. Or maybe you think of a time when you felt a static electricity jolt after pulling off a sweater and touching a metal object. You might also think of shock waves from an earthquake or a car shock absorber. Shock to the biologist and the families of hospital patients is a physiological condition. Shock occurs when the blood pressure falls so low that the body's cells, tissues, and organs fail to get an adequate blood flow to meet their needs. This general failure of the circulatory system to supply oxygen and fuel to the cells and to remove carbon dioxide and wastes may result in a vicious cycle of continued cell destruction and death.

> *Shock occurs when the blood pressure falls so low that the body's cells, tissues, and organs fail to get an adequate blood flow to meet their needs.*

Normal Blood Flow

The force developed by a normally contracting heart produces a blood pressure that is the driving force for blood flow to and through tissues. This pressure is maintained by a reflex, called the baroreceptor reflex, that provides for rapid control of arterial pressure, as shown in Figure 1.

Just as a weather barometer measures atmospheric pressure, the baroreceptors in the body are affected by pressure—in this case, arterial pressure. The baroreceptors are located in the walls of the largest blood vessels of the body, the aorta and the carotid arteries. As blood pressure increases, the baroreceptors are stretched. This stretching sends messages to the central nervous system. These messages affect the activity of a special branch of the nervous system, the autonomic nervous system (ANS). The autonomic nervous system conveys messages between the central nervous system and the various body organs.

There are two main components to the autonomic nervous system. The parasympathetic nervous system acts mainly when the body is in a state of relaxation. The sympathetic nervous system is active when the body is stressed. An increase in pressure in the blood vessels activates the parasympathetic division of the ANS and decreases the activity of the sympathetic division. The net result is a decrease in the amount of blood pumped out by

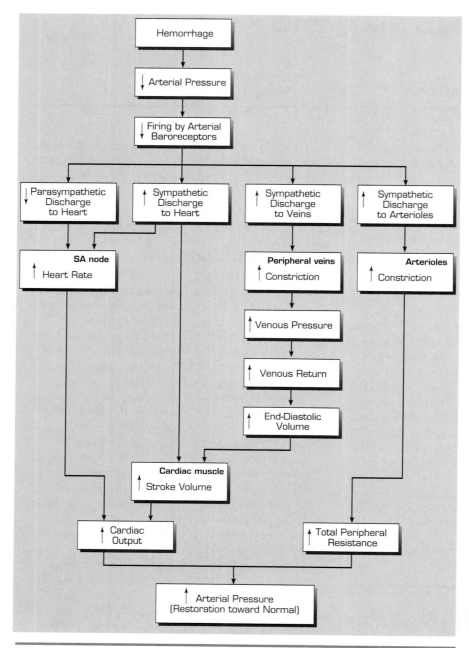

Figure 1 *The baroreceptor reflex, described above, controls blood pressure. The arrows in each box indicate an increase (↑) or decrease (↓) in the described action.*

Cardiogenic Shock: Shock from Diminished Function of the Heart

Shock results when the body fails to provide enough blood to its tissues and organs. This failure of the body to match blood flow to the tissues' needs arises for a variety of reasons. The most obvious reason is that the heart's ability to pump blood has decreased. Impaired pump function could occur because of problems with the heart itself, such as a heart attack (myocardial infarction). Heart arrhythmias or decreases in the amount of blood returning to the heart may also cause a decrease in the heart's ability to pump blood.

Hypovolemic shock (reduced blood volume) is one of the most common types of shock. It arises most often from a hemorrhage, a massive flow of blood from damaged blood vessels. If the loss of blood is small, the baroreceptor reflex and other mechanisms enable the body to compensate. These mechanisms usually maintain cardiac output, blood pressure, and the needed blood flow to the tissues.

If instead the person lost a lot of blood, the system would attempt to compensate but might fail. Then a vicious cycle called progressive shock could occur. Due to poor blood flow to the tissues, the smaller blood vessels may become blocked.

the heart (cardiac output) and an increase in blood vessel diameter. Both of those actions decrease the mean arterial pressure, returning it to its normal value of approximately 100 millimeters of mercury.

Next, inflammatory mediators and toxins would be released. They further impair heart, blood vessel, and tissue functions. Finally, beyond a certain point, tissue damage is so great that even if pressure is temporarily restored, shock is irreversible and death occurs.

The body's response to damage is an inflammatory process that is necessary for recovery. But in the case of massive damage, the body's attempts to compensate actually become overwhelming. Continued release of inflammatory mediators and toxins leads to remote organ injury with even more release of mediators and toxins. The result is not recovery and survival, but continued deterioration and death.

Septic Shock

Septic shock is the second most common form of shock. This form of shock caused the death of my sons' soccer coach. It used to be called blood poisoning. Sepsis is the leading cause of death for critically ill patients. In the United States alone, it is estimated that there are over 500,000 cases of sepsis annually that result in over 100,000 deaths from septic shock. It can result from an abdominal infection that occurs when the gut ruptures from intestinal disease or trauma. A simple streptococcal or staphylococcal skin infection may also result in a generalized infection leading to septic shock. Although cardiac output may be normal or even elevated at first, it is not adequate for the tissues. Bacterial toxins and mediators from the body's own cells cause vasodilatation in infected tissues and elsewhere. Inadequate blood flow, sludging of blood, and intravascular coagulation worsen the situation. Like cardiogenic shock, the symptoms are progressive and the result can be death.

Continued Research

Through continued medical research, we can learn more about how the body reacts to shock and discover better ways of treating patients in shock. Our goal is to increase the survival rate until shock is no longer a threat to the lives of educational entertainers, soccer coaches, or anyone else.

Additional Resources

Guyton, A. C. and J. E. Hall. 1996. *Textbook of Medical Physiology.* W. B. Saunders Co. Philadelphia, PA.
   This text is used by most medical school students in their first-year physiology classes.

Okada, K. and H. Ogata (eds.). 1996. *Shock: From Molecular and Cellular Level to Whole Body.* Elsevier Science B. V. Amsterdam, The Netherlands.
   Want to find out what's going on at the forefront? What current areas of research are hot and what new treatments might be? Then this is it.

Vander, A. J., J. H. Sherman, and D. S. Luciano. 1998. *Human Physiology: The Mechanisms of Body Function.* WCB/McGraw-Hill. Boston, MA.
   A good college text in which you can learn more about the body's short-term regulation of arterial pressure as well as satisfy your curiosity about shock.

Questions for Discussion

1. What is shock? Why is it best called "cardio-vascular" shock?

2. Describe two causes of shock.

3. How can shock be prevented?

Applications

1. If you were a physician and saw a patient in hemorrhagic shock in the emergency room, what would be the first thing you might do?

2. You have been lying down for a while and suddenly stand up. How does your body respond?

3. Blood flow to an arm has been reduced for awhile by a tourniquet. What problems might occur when the tourniquet is released?

4.3 Dinosaurs: Jocks or Couch Potatoes?

Renee Wagenseil

Clemson University, Clemson, South Carolina

Ms. Wagenseil is an analytical chemist in an agricultural support lab. She is also pursuing a graduate degree in Professional Communications, which will allow her to combine a talent for languages with her interests in chemistry and biology.

Overview

Until recently, scientists were generally in agreement that dinosaurs were cold-blooded animals. Discoveries in the 1960s demonstrated that dinosaurs may well have been far more physiologically active than was previously believed. But was this evidence of warm-bloodedness? The debate over whether dinosaurs were cold-blooded or warm-blooded spans discussions of feathers, bone microstructure, and nasal canal structure. Though it is difficult to ever know with certainty the physiology of an extinct animal, evidence both for and against warm-bloodedness continues to accrue.

Warm-Blooded Dinosaurs?

Remember that scene in *Jurassic Park* when the *Velociraptor* steps into the walk-in refrigerator and you can see its breath? Only a warm-blooded dinosaur would have such hot breath, but some scientists are not sure that is right. In fact, there is a fierce debate whether dinosaurs were warm-blooded or cold-blooded.

In 1825, when dinosaurs were first discovered, they were characterized as huge, slow-moving, tail-dragging lizards. The idea of a giant cold-blooded reptile seemed logical. The earth they inhabited, from about 228 to 65 million years ago, was believed to have been a hot, tropical climate ideal for reptiles with no internal heat source to get them going. Pictures of dinosaurs showed them with their legs splayed out sideways and their tails dragging along the ground like lizards.

Then in the late 1960s, two researchers at Yale University challenged this theory. One of them, John Ostrom, found a fossil of *Deinonychus* that showed it to be an animal designed for speed and agility. It was designed to run and jump, using the long claws on its hind feet like daggers. This implied an active hunter with a fast metabolism. Ostrum contended that an animal with such a high metabolic rate would not likely rely on the sun for warmth. Ostrom believed this supported his vision of a fast-moving, agile, and active predator and one that was warm-blooded.

Robert Bakker, also at Yale, called for a complete revision of current theories regarding dinosaur behavior and physiology. Like Ostrom, he believed that endothermy, or warm-bloodedness, was a key element in the success of the dinosaurs during their more than 100 million years on earth. During the 1980s, other paleontologists joined the warm-blooded side of the debate. Jack Horner of Montana State University found several dinosaur nesting sites with well-preserved fossilized remains of eggs, embryos, and young. His investigations showed that the baby dinosaurs' bones developed as speedily as those of baby ostriches, a strong indication of endothermy.

Chinese researchers recently described two specimens of *Sinosauropteryx prima,* both discovered by farmers northeast of Beijing. The dinosaur was basically the size of a turkey with a long lizardlike tail. One specimen measures about 2 feet long from the snout to the tip of the tail, and the other is somewhat larger. The dinosaur walked on its hind legs and had short, stout forelimbs. Scientists are debating how old the fossils are, with estimates ranging from around 120 million years to about 140 million or older. The specimens are compressed fossilized remains pressed into slabs of rock, showing the dinosaur in profile. The featherlike features appear along the neck, back, and tail.

Scientists have two main theories about why feathers first evolved—flight and insulation. The featherlike features on the Chinese dinosaur give no sign of being useful for flying. At the same time, other researchers were making a strong evolutionary connection between birds and dinosaurs. Birds are warm-blooded; and if dinosaurs are their closest kin, it would make sense that they shared this trait.

The warm-blooded camp has held sway for the last 10 years, but a new generation of researchers is taking a fresh look at the fossil record and questioning the warm-blooded theory. A group of paleontologists and physiologists are working to find solid proof that dinosaurs were cold-blooded, as originally believed.

Physiological Evidence

What does the activity level in an animal tell us about its internal physiology? Cold-blooded (or exothermic) and warm-blooded (or endothermic) animals employ different metabolic strategies. Reptiles have no internal way to raise or lower their body temperature. They warm themselves by basking in the sun and cool off by hiding in the shade. These temperature adjustments take time, and a slower life-style is the result. Mammals, on the other hand, maintain a relatively constant body temperature as a result of the chemical reactions that make up their faster metabolisms. Mammals and birds have an average metabolic rate four times higher than that of reptiles. There is no waiting period for activity; they live at a faster pace, moving more and eating more.

Scientists have two main theories about why feathers first evolved—flight and insulation.

The evidence for endothermy was strong, yet most of it was indirect. Scientists wanted further proof to support the theory. This search led them to a paleontologist and anatomist at the University of Paris, Armand De Ricqles. He claimed to be able to see strong similarities in the bone tissue of dinosaurs and that of warm-blooded animals.

As young warm-blooded animals develop, fast-growing bone matter intrudes into areas of connective tissue, trapping the fibers and blood vessels already there, creating a thick mat called haversian canals. (Look for haversian canals the next time you gnaw on a steak bone.) According to De Ricqles, the texture of the bone and the presence of the canals would indicate quick growth, such as could only be supported by the fast metabolism of a warm-blooded creature.

Skeletal development in reptiles takes place at a slower pace. Reptile bones have fewer haversian canals, and their bones often show layered growth rings, such as one might see in a cross-section of a tree. De Ricqles' analysis of dinosaur bones found patterns similar to those of birds and mammals and none of the growth rings usually found in reptiles. This led him to conclude that dinosaurs were most likely warm-blooded.

Comparisons to Living Animals

At Harvard University, graduate student Tomasz Owerkowiczk set out to check De Ricqles' theory by examining the bones of living animals. Owerkowiczk chose three species of similar size— monitor lizards, ground squirrels, and hedgehogs. Each species represented a distinct point on the warm-to-cold-blooded spectrum. At one end were the cold-blooded lizards, at the other end were the warm-blooded squirrels, and somewhere in the middle were the slow-pokey hedgehogs.

The animals were divided into two sets: "couch potatoes" and athletes. The athletic set ran on a treadmill 20 minutes every day for six months; the couch potatoes rested. Every six weeks all the animals were injected with fluorescent dye. As their bone tissue grew, small amounts of dye were deposited in layers on the bone. The layering gave Owerkowiczk a way to calculate the rate of bone growth. This could be used to compare bone growth in reptiles to that of mammals.

Owerkowiczk found that the bone growth in "couch potatoes," both cold- and warm-blooded alike, remained very similar; this was also true of the athletic set. The real difference was whether the animals had exercised or not. All the animals that worked out on the treadmill had bones full of haversian canals; the unexercised animals did not.

Owerkowiczk concluded that the microstructure of an animal's bone is shaped by exercise, not metabolism. Bones that are subjected to exercise are dense with haversian canals as the bones are stressed, built-up, and remodeled. Thus, bone that is dense with these canals shows that the animal was active. Unfortunately, it does not tell us whether the animal was warm- or cold-blooded.

The Nose Knows?

John Ruben, a physiologist at Oregon State University, also believes that dinosaurs were cold-blooded and that the proof may be in their noses. Ruben and graduate student Willem Hillenius examined a large database of living animals and found that exotherms and endotherms have very different noses.

Warm-blooded mammals, with their fast rate of metabolism, must breathe at a very fast rate. Inside their noses are coils of cartilage or bone covered with membranes called respiratory turbinates. As moist, warm air is released from the lungs, it passes over the turbinates, cools, and condenses. By recycling water in this manner, warm-blooded animals can save almost 75 percent of their daily water intake. Cold-blooded animals, who live and breathe at a slower rate, sometimes only about 5 percent the rate of similarly sized warm-blooded animals, have little need to conserve water and have no turbinates in their nasal passages.

Hellenius examined fossil skulls looking for evidence of turbinates. Since the turbinate structures are fragile and not well-preserved in fossil skulls, he looked instead for evidence of the bony ridge on the skull where the turbinate tissue would normally be attached. He found them in fossil mammals, but in dinosaurs they were absent.

Hillenius and his colleagues also found that the size of the nasal cavity itself is a strong indicator of metabolism. Working with an expert in CAT-scanning, they determined that warm-blooded birds and mammals have nasal cavities that are four times bigger than those of similar-sized reptiles. The researchers then looked at CAT-scans of four dinosaur skulls. Results showed that

Clues to dinosaur behavior may be found in the behavior of modern reptiles.

dinosaurs had nasal-cavity-to-body-mass ratios like those of modern day crocodiles or lizards. They thus concluded that the nasal structures in dinosaur fossils could not have accommodated the higher breathing rate of a warm-blooded animal.

Can We Ever Know for Sure?

Does this new research prove that dinosaurs were really slow-moving, slow-witted, cold-blooded reptiles? Not necessarily. Scientists believe that dinosaurs may have been endotherms that acted like mammals. Clues to dinosaur behavior may be found in the behavior of modern reptiles. The feisty Komodo dragon bites his prey with infectious saliva, then tracks it for hours until it falls. Pit vipers and pythons defend their offspring from predators. Leatherback turtles swim for hours in the chilly North Atlantic ocean, maintaining a high body temperature.

Large dinosaurs may have held enough heat in their massive bodies to energize them for 24 hours a day, even in a cold climate. This would have enabled them to travel long distances, stalk prey, and lead a life with a level of activity not unlike that of the lion, a top predator who spends only a few hours hunting, then sleeps away the rest of the day. Smaller dinosaurs were probably agile and fast-moving runners, chasing down prey and living life at the pace of some present day mammals.

New research has widened and fueled the debate, which will continue to evolve as more scientists approach the question of dinosaur physiology from different perspectives. One thing is clear: Our fascination with dinosaurs is far from over.

References

Associated Press. 1998. Boost for Warm-Blooded Dinosaur—Feather-Like Features are Seen in Fossils Found in China. *Boston Globe*, January 9, 1998. Globe Newspaper Company.

Morell, V. 1996. A Cold, Hard Look at Dinosaurs. *Discover*, December 1996, pp. 98–108.

Stauth, D. 1996. Dino-Noses Suggest Cold-Blooded Dinosaurs. Oregon State University, News and Communications Serives, August 29, 1996.

Additional Resources

Braginetz, Donna. 1993. *Audubon Society Pocket Guide to Dinosaurs*. Alfred A. Knopf, Inc.
   Full-color paintings and skeletal line drawings taken from actual museum specimens around the world illustrate this book that explains the lives, behavior, and habits of the world's favorite prehistoric animals and the circumstances surrounding their eventual extinction.

Fastovsky, D. and D. Weishampel. 1996. *The Evolution & Extinction of the Dinosaurs*. Cambridge.
   Many illustrations; good taxonomic and general subject indexing. Very well written and informative.

Questions for Discussion

1. Why did scientists initially conclude that dinosaurs were cold-blooded?

2. What features of dinosaurs first led scientists to consider that they may have been warm-blooded?

3. How does dinosaur bone structure support the theory that they were warm-blooded?

4. How does nasal anatomy support the warm-blooded hypothesis?

Applications

1. Since the only remains we have of dinosaurs are their bones, how can we justify hypotheses about physiological processes?

2. If you unearthed an animal fossil, how might you go about the process of determining how that animal lived?

4.4 Physiological Limits of Athletic Ability

Sandra Winicur, Ph.D.

Indiana University, South Bend, Indiana

Dr. Winicur teaches anatomy and physiology to nursing students and general biology to premedical students. She lectures widely in the community on the effects of aging on physiological performance. She has done research with students on the effect of different behaviors on the enzyme activity of saliva.

Overview

Since humans started performing in athletic events, they have been trying to surpass previous records. However, only when accurate techniques of measurement and record keeping were devised did competitive sport begin pushing the physiological limits.

Historical Perspective

The Olympian wrestler of ancient Greece, Milon of Croton, is said to have developed his strength by carrying a calf every day since its birth. When the calf was a full-grown cow, he could carry it with ease. Since then people have been trying to develop better techniques for training athletes. Somewhere between Milon's cow and the mythological Atlas, who carried the world on his shoulders, there is a real physiological limit to the amount of weight a human can lift. But that limit has not yet been reached.

For a long time, people believed in the absolute limit of the four-minute mile; but in 1954, Sir Roger Bannister of England ran the mile in 3 minutes 59.4 seconds. The current record is faster than 3 minutes 45 seconds.

In 1932, the Olympic competitions used stopwatches and cameras to record results to a fraction of a second. Technology and medical science are developing ways to make sports training more efficient. Equipment that changes the way almost all sports are being played is being designed. Records in all sports are being broken steadily by fractions of a second. With new shoe design, better-engineered equipment, and sophisticated training procedures, no one now knows what human limits are.

> *Somewhere between Milon's cow and the mythological Atlas, who carried the world on his shoulders, there is a real physiological limit to the amount of weight a human can lift.*

Maximum Oxygen Uptake

The oxygen supplied by the respiratory and circulatory systems makes the body able to turn its fuel into energy. Exercise physiologists have determined that the limit of the body's work capacity is the maximum uptake of oxygen available to the body, a quantity called VO_{2max}. It is influenced by heredity, sex, age, and body condition. Figure 1 shows the limits of oxygen uptake as it changes with age. You can only control body condition. The efforts of exercise physiologists are in this direction.

Exercise physiology is the study of two separate situations. One is how the body restores homeostasis during a single exercise session. The second is how the body conditions itself during repeated exercise.

When exercise begins, muscle cells use more oxygen. The heart works harder to send oxygen-carrying blood to the muscles. The lungs take in more oxygen to supply the blood. With regular exercise, the heart becomes stronger and pumps more blood with every beat. Then it does not have to work as hard or beat as fast as formerly. The lungs do not have to work as strenuously to take in oxygen.

The muscles use a substance called ATP (adenosine triphosphate) for energy. There are only a few seconds worth of ATP stored in the muscle cells. After that, the body has two methods for generating more ATP. One method does not require oxygen and is called anaerobic. The other more efficient method does require oxygen and is called aerobic.

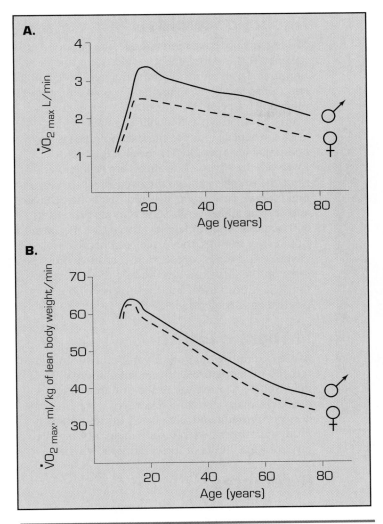

A.

(graph: y-axis "$\dot{V}O_{2\,max}$ L/min" ranging 1 to 4; x-axis "Age (years)" marked 20, 40, 60, 80; solid line marked ♂, dashed line marked ♀)

B.

(graph: y-axis "$\dot{V}O_{2\,max}$ ml/kg of lean body weight/min" ranging 30 to 70; x-axis "Age (years)" marked 20, 40, 60, 80; solid line marked ♂, dashed line marked ♀)

Figure 1 *This graph shows how maximum oxygen uptake changes with age.*

Skeletal muscle contains two types of fibers. One type is the glycolytic fiber. It is specialized for fast twitches and is highest in muscles that perform rapid responses, such as sprinting (Figure 2) or weight lifting. The other type is the oxidative fiber. It is specialized for slow movements and is highest in muscles that perform endurance activities, such as cycling or marathon running. Depending on what kind of activity is being considered, there are two different kinds of training to develop these fibers.

Glycolytic fast-twitch fibers are pale. They use a stored fuel called glycogen. They do not completely burn the glycogen but provide a rapid but limited source of ATP without using oxygen (anaerobic). This process produces lactic acid, a material that tires muscle when it accumulates and causes the muscle to ache.

Strength training acts on fast muscle fibers. Weight lifting can accomplish this. It increases muscle bulk and muscle response.

Conditioning exercises involve developing these fibers and increasing the muscle's ability to tolerate lactic acid. In addition, physical endurance can be increased by an eating and exercise plan called carbohydrate loading. This can increase muscle tolerance for lactic acid, perhaps as much as doubling it. Athletes involved in sports requiring short, intense bursts of activity such as sprinting can train to tolerate high lactic acid levels in their muscles.

Oxidative slow-twitch fibers depend on oxygen (aerobic). Muscles high in slow fibers are very red because they need an adequate supply of blood and oxygen-carrying pigments. These are the fibers needed for continued activity and can keep going for a long time as long as large amounts of ATP are supplied.

Endurance training acts on slow fibers. It increases the athlete's ability to keep going and raises the $VO_{2\,max}$. This kind of training can be achieved by about 30 minutes of exercise three or four times per week if it raises the heart rate to between 60 and 90 percent of the maximum. Your theoretical maximum heart rate is determined by subtracting your age from 220.

The circulatory system brings oxygen to the muscles. At rest, the heart delivers 5 to 6 liters of oxygen per minute. In extreme exercise, this may rise sixfold. Training increases the heart's ability to supply more oxygen at a lower rate. Athletes have low resting heart rates so that the rise during exercise does not become dangerously high.

Energy use can increase about 13 times over normal during marathon running and as much as 50 times during an intense activity such as sprinting. At rest, the body uses about 250 milliliters of oxygen/minute. Under maximum exercise,

Figure 2 *Sir Roger Bannister was the first person documented to run a mile in less than four minutes.*

Anabolic Steroids

Males generally have more muscle mass than females. This is partly due to testosterone, a male sex hormone. In an effort to mimic the muscle-building effect of testosterone, many professional and student athletes have been taking synthetic testosterone compounds known as anabolic steroids.

The beneficial effect of these compounds is very questionable, especially for the average athlete. However, the adverse side effects are well-known. Anabolic steroids damage the liver, affect the sex organs, may cause aggressive and psychotic behavior, and may be addictive. Because of these side effects and because of the unfair advantage that may result from use of steroids, they have been banned from Olympic and other competitions. Sensitive drug tests done on the urine can determine if these or other drugs have been used, and the athletes who test positive have been disqualified.

Is There a Limit?

Athletic training has gotten very sophisticated, and records are being broken by small amounts. We may well be nearing the limits of human performance in many activities. However, as technology keeps improving and as research in training techniques continues, we can only imagine what the physiological limits of future athletes will be.

References

Australian Sports Commission. Olympic Facts. 1997. http://www.ausport.gov.au/factmenu.html

Kearney, J. T. Training the Olympic Athlete. 1996. *Scientific American*. p. 274.

McDonald, M. Pushing the Envelope. 1996. *Civilization, the Magazine of the Library of Congress*. 3.

Moffett, D. E., S. B. Moffett, and C. L. Schauf. 1993. *Human Physiology: Foundations and Frontiers*, 2/e. Mosby.

Vander, A. J., J. H. Sherman, and D. S. Luciano. 1998. *Human Physiology: The Mechanics of Body Function*, 6/e. WCB/McGraw-Hill.

Additional Resources

McArdle, M. D., F. I. Katch, and V. L. Katch. 1996. *Exercise Physiology: Energy, Nutrition, and Human Performance*. Williams & Wilkins.
  Addresses nutrition, energy, and systems of energy delivery and use. Focuses on applications. Covers enhancement of energy capacity; exercise performance

oxygen use rises 20 times, to 5 liters/minute. For athletes in training, the $VO_{2\,max}$ can go up much higher. However, it decreases with age, perhaps 10 percent for every decade after age 25.

High-Altitude Training

According to a NOVA television interview with Dr. Brownie Schoene, an expert in high-altitude medicine, studies on a 1997 team of Mount Everest climbers indicated they were probably operating at the limit of human capacity. At sea level, the blood is 98 percent saturated with oxygen; but at the top of Mount Everest, it is below 70 percent saturated. Often athletes will train at high altitudes in an effort to increase the number of red blood cells and their ability to get oxygen to their cells.

and environmental stress; and body composition, energy balance, and the health-related aspects of exercise.

Plowman, S. A. and D. L. Smith. 1997. *Exercise Physiology: For Health, Fitness and Performance,* 1/e. Allyn & Bacon. Explains principles of exercise physiology for undergraduates in kinesiology, physical education, exercise, and sport science.

Questions for Discussion

1. How did modern technology affect the establishment of record keeping at the Olympics?

2. New nutritional programs and training procedures are pushing the limits of human activity. Why is the use of drugs different than the use of these other factors in determining eligibility for competition?

3. On what factors do human physiological limits depend?

4. How does the body change under conditioning for aerobic training? for strength training?

Applications

1. Obtain and graph Olympic records in various sports over the years to see how and at what rate they are changing with time.

2. After first getting approval from your physician, set up an aerobic exercise program for yourself as suggested in this article and see if your heart rate and respiratory rate change at rest and during exercise after several weeks.

4.5 So What about Life on Mars?

Debbie M. Swift, Ph.D.
Cary, North Carolina

Dr. Swift has a diverse background driven by diverse interests. She holds a B.S. in marine science and biology, an M.S. in biology, and a Ph.D. in zoology. Her research areas have included biochemical measures of aging; mineral formation in larval and adult sea urchins, adult oysters, and diatoms; and the study of genetic control of fatty acid synthesis in peanuts.

Overview

A small rock found in the Antarctic ice 10 years ago has stirred up a storm of interest among biologists, chemists, geologists, and planetary scientists. The rock, a meteorite from Mars, weighs about 4 pounds and is fairly unremarkable—on the outside. Inside, one group of scientists believe they have found the remains of Martian life. Their evidence and the arguments of those who oppose their interpretation have been marking a hot new scientific controversy. The implications are far-reaching. The Mars missions, long on the back burners due to poor public interest, have been given a new high priority. If there are living organisms on Mars, what does this mean for the stability of our world? Many public policy makers are concerned about just this issue. It is up to the scientists to determine if we are or are not alone.

The Meteorite and Its History

It all started with the examination of a meteorite, shown in Figure 1, the size of a softball with the not-so-glamorous name ALH84001. This particular meteorite had been buried in the Antarctic ice for 13,000 years before it was found in 1984. Before that, it had cruised around in space for about 16 million years. The earth has lots of meteorites, and there didn't seem to be anything special about this one until David Mittlefehldt at Lockheed Martin in Houston determined that there was indeed something different about ALH84001. In 1994, he deter-

mined that it was from Mars. Only 11 other meteorites are known at this time to be from Mars.

After examination, a little more about the history of this particular piece of Mars was known. For starters, it's the oldest rock ever examined, clocking in at 4.5 billion years old. It was hit by yet another meteorite while it was still on Mars and only 900 million years old. This is important because it developed fractures from that impact. The fractures were the nesting place for what came later. For the next 3.5 billion years, the rock stayed on Mars. Back then Mars was very different; it was much wetter and warmer. Planetary scientists determined that instead of the dusty, bone dry surface and $-55°C$ temperatures that Mars has on average today, there used to be flowing rivers, lakes, and maybe even oceans. But that was all a long time ago—about 4 billion years. Mars dried up, perhaps because it lacks plate tectonics, its volcanoes became extinct, or some really big meteors crashed into the surface and vaporized all the water. Without any volcanoes to generate a new atmosphere, the planet slowly died—on the surface. Before that happened, were there any organisms that got a foothold on life?

Figure 1   *Meteorite ALH84001.*

The Evidence for Life

David McKay and his colleagues at the NASA Johnson Space Center in Houston think they have found evidence that maybe there was life on Mars. There are three main reasons that they think so. First, organic molecules called PAHs, specific highly structured mineral deposits, and possible fossils have all been identified in those fractures that the meteorite developed when it was struck back on Mars. PAHs are organic molecules that can be found from organisms that have died and broken down. They were found in high concentrations along the fractures inside the meteorite, and none were found on the exterior of the meteorite.

Incidentally, while the meteorite was entering the earth's atmosphere, it heat sealed itself. The rock essentially melted on the surface and formed a glaze. None of the Antarctic meteorites examined had PAHs on their surfaces. McKay's group interprets this to mean that the PAHs found did not get there by contamination from the Antarctic ice.

Secondly, the meteorite contains several different types of organized mineral structures. The two most interesting and significant ones, carbonate globules about 50 microns in size and even smaller pieces of magnetic minerals, are often found associated with living organisms on earth. The carbonate minerals were thought to have been made when the water they developed from was changed by the bacteria living there, causing the mineral to precipitate out. The magnetite they found resembled the same type of fossil material found on earth by bacteria that use the mineral to stay oriented in a specific direction relative to the earth's magnetic field. These minerals can be found together in nature on earth due to the presence of organisms but do not form in the same location if there are no organisms present.

Third are the objects believed to be fossils of actual Martian organisms. As shown in Figure 2, McKay's group found some very small oval-shaped objects clustered along the fractures. These were no bigger than 0.1 micrometer in length and as small as 0.02 micrometer. These relics would be much smaller (by 100 times) than any bacterial fossils previously found on earth, but McKay's group pointed out that there have been recent reports of potential terrestrial nanofossils (extremely small microscopic fossils) that would be approximately in the same size range.

The Opposing View

All lines of evidence McKay's group offered could be explained without mentioning Martian life-forms. For example, PAH molecules could have been deposited within the rock while still on Mars through nonbiological processes.

Both the carbonate globules and magnetite and iron monosulfide are commonly precipitated in nature. Biologically, processes take place at temperatures generally below 115°C; while abiologically, deposited minerals arise at much higher temperatures. The signature of living intervention in terrestrial deposits is a skewed ratio of some elemental isotopes including sulfur and oxygen. However, examination of the ratios of these elements has not clarified the temperature issue at all. No one group has been able to convincingly determine the temperature of the rock when the minerals precipitated.

The presence of certain types of amino acids in the rocks appears to suggest that they derived from terrestrial contamination processes as they seem to be skewed towards the kind biologically produced here on earth. The carbon isotopes found in the carbonate globules seem to suggest that they were formed when the meteorite sat in the Antarctic ice for 13,000 years.

Still there are those possible fossil bacteria. Current tests are under way to determine if the fossils have the trademarks of terrestrial bacteria or have any structure at all. All terrestrial bacteria have, at the very least, a rigid cell wall that is often preserved when the fossil forms. It's possible that

Figure 2   *The elongated structure in the center of this photo may be a Martian microfossil.*

some organic material is even trapped in the fossils. There have been proteins and even DNA found in some fossils from earth, so why not from Martian bacteria? Newer studies on the shapes McKay's group called nanofossils suggest that they are merely interesting geologically formed minerals.

The answer to the question of life on Mars, as it turns out, will not in all likelihood be answered by ALH84001. The ultimate answer will hopefully come when the Martian exploration voyages are completed with some native rocks as souvenirs—rocks with no earth history.

Additional Resources

Ancient Life on Mars, *Science*, 16 August 1996, Vol. 273, No. 5277, p. 864.
> Summary of the original article where the Martian meteorite thought to have fossil life-forms is discussed.

Mars
> http://seds.lpl.arizona.edu/nineplanets/nineplanets/mars.html
> An Internet Web site with good general information about Mars. The site has links to pages with additional information about meteorites and NASA exploration missions. Great pictures.

Martian Microbes Cover Their Tracks, *Science,* 4 April 1997, Vol. 276, No. 5309, pp. 30–31.
> Summary of the difficulty in determining whether or not the evidence from the meteorite indicates that a life-form created the artifacts.

NASA's Ask the Space Scientist
> http://image.gsfc.nasa.gov/poetry/ask/amars.html
> Good specific answers to specific questions. Interactive site where you can ask questions.

Questions for Discussion

1. What are the three main findings that convinced McKay and his colleagues that the Martian meteorite showed evidence of life from Mars?

2. What type of organism did the group think the meteorite showed fossil evidence of?

3. What is the sinificance of where the meteorite was originally found?

4. What kinds of mineral formations did the meteorite contain?

Applications

1. What do you think the scientists should look for to determine if a living organism was ever in the meteorite?

2. Where would life on Mars most likely have occurred? What characterizes the Martian environment and atmosphere?

3. What life-forms from Earth could survive on Mars?

4. What impact would discovering life on Mars have on you, your government, or the world?

4.6 Blood, a Great Natural Resource

Mary Ann Spivey, M.H.S.
Department of Pathology and Laboratory Medicine
Medical University of South Carolina, Charleston, South Carolina

Ms. Spivey is a medical technologist (MT), a specialist in blood banking (SBB), an educator, and a former blood bank supervisor. She has a master's degree in health science (M.H.S.). Since 1976, she has been an educator with both the American Red Cross and the Medical University of South Carolina. She has taught blood bank specialist students and currently teaches clinical pathology residents. Ms. Spivey recently coauthored the textbook Introduction to Transfusion Medicine: A Case Study Approach *with Dr. Elaine Jeter.*

Overview

We all carry a great renewable natural resource, our blood, within our bodies. It has the power to save lives, but it took almost a century and several important discoveries by outstanding scientists of various nationalities to make blood transfusion safe. Finally, when Dr. Charles Drew created the modern blood bank system, we had an essential ingredient for much of modern medicine.

History

Blood has held a fascination for people since ancient times. From the time when people noticed that extreme blood loss led to death, blood was recognized as the body's life force. During ancient times and into the Middle Ages, blood was valued as a tonic. Drinking it was thought to make a person young and strong again and even to cure madness.

According to legend, the first transfusion may have occurred in 1492. Pope Innocent VIII was dying.

A mystic promised to cure the pope by exchanging his blood with blood from three boys. Though details of the account vary, it was recorded that the pope and all three boys died. During the following centuries, transfusions were attempted in several countries using both human and animal blood. It was soon recognized that humans had violent reactions to animal blood and sometimes to human blood. James Blundell, a 19th-century British obstetrician, has been called the father of modern blood transfusion therapy. He recognized the need for replacing shed blood with human blood and transfused at least 10 patients. Early transfusionists also observed that blood had to be transfused rapidly and directly from the donor to the patient, as shown in Figure 1, or it would clot.

Discoveries

In 1900 in Vienna, Austria, Karl Landsteiner discovered three of the major blood groups, which came to be known as A, B, and O. One of his students soon discovered the fourth, AB. Blood

Figure 1 *Direct transfusion was practiced in the 1800s. A tubing, with a rubber bulb to provide pumping action, connected the donor artery to the recipient vein.*

type is determined by its antigens, which are structures on the surfaces of red blood cells, and antibodies, which are molecules in the blood that react with specific antigens. Individuals with Type A blood have A antigens on their red blood cells and antibodies that react with B antigens. Individuals with Type B blood have B antigens on their red blood cells and antibodies that react with A antigens. Type O individuals have neither A nor B antigens and both types of antibodies. Type AB individuals have A and B antigens and neither type of antibody. Although hundreds of blood group antigens have been discovered since 1900, incompatibility in the ABO system has caused most transfusion reactions. Thus, the routine ABO typing now performed prior to all transfusions has gone a long way toward solving one major problem.

Albert Hustin, a Belgian, began resolving a second major problem by developing the first effective solution used to prepare blood for transfusion. His solution had three major components. He used citrate, which is an anticoagulant, to prevent the blood from clotting. The citrate was added to a salt solution that had a concentration similar to that of body fluids. This salt concentration prevented lysing, or rupture, of the red blood cells. The third important component of the solution was glucose, which served as a nutrient. Hustin's original solution led to modern anticoagulant-preservative solutions that allowed blood to be collected and stored prior to transfusion. The development of electrical refrigeration made it possible to store blood for long periods. The first United States blood bank was organized at Cook County Hospital in Chicago in 1937.

Charles Drew, the first African-American certified by the American Board of Surgery and a former biology teacher, was the founder of the modern blood banking system. World War II created a greatly increased demand for blood and plasma, its liquid portion. Dr. Drew, pictured in Figure 2, became the medical director of the Plasma for Britain Project. In 1941, he was appointed as director of the first Red Cross blood program, which became the model for a national all-volunteer program.

In the earliest collections from donors, blood was drawn into bottles. That made it difficult to separate the blood cells from the liquid plasma. The development of plastic blood bags with attached smaller bags and high-speed refrigerated

Figure 2 *Dr. Charles Drew, Founder of the Modern Blood Banking System.*

centrifuges made it possible to separate out the components of blood. When a blood bag is spun in a centrifuge, the heavier cellular components move to the bottom of the bag. Most of the lighter liquid plasma remains at the top of the bag. Thus, as shown in Figure 3, several components can be isolated from one donation and transfused into several patients. Each patient would receive only the specific blood component needed. For example, an anemic patient might receive the red blood cells. A cancer patient on chemotherapy might receive the platelets, which aid in clotting. Finally, a hemophiliac might receive a specific clotting factor product prepared from the fresh plasma.

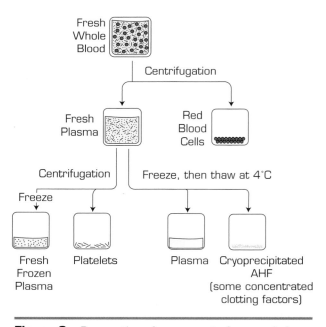

Figure 3 *Preparation of components from a whole blood donation.*

Blood, a Great Natural Resource

Blood Supply

There are currently no adequate substitutes for blood or its components. You may have heard of artificial blood. Several products have been developed that are able to carry and deliver oxygen to the tissues. However, none of these synthetic products do this as efficiently as the hemoglobin in red blood cells. Artificial blood products have not been approved for general use in the United States. Researchers are also working on developing artificial platelets. Another research approach is the development of growth factors that cause patients to produce red blood cells, white blood cells, and platelets at an increased rate.

Despite these advances, blood used for transfusions must still be provided by donation from healthy individuals who are 17 years old or older. Donation is a safe process. Most donors replace their donated blood quickly and can give blood about every two months. The need for blood has increased as complex surgical procedures such as liver transplantation become more common. However, donations have actually decreased in the last 10 years. Especially during vacation periods, when many people are traveling and many accidents occur, you may hear reports of blood shortages on the radio or in local newspapers.

Blood Supply Safety

Once blood transfusion became common, it was realized that blood could transmit certain infectious diseases such as serum hepatitis, which damages the liver. In the 1980s, physicians discovered that the HIV virus, which causes AIDS, could be acquired by transfusion of HIV-contaminated blood. That discovery sparked massive public concern about blood supply safety. Concerns about blood supply safety encouraged patients to use their own blood, in a process known as an autologous transfusion, for elective surgery. This option is available to patients only if the patient is healthy enough to donate blood.

Two blood tests developed since 1985 have made the blood supply safer. A new test for HIV has reduced the risk of HIV transmission to about two in a million. The new tests for hepatitis reduced the risk of contracting this disease from a transfusion to about one in 100,000. The remaining risks are due to the presence of donors who may not test positive even with these new tests. Therefore, the risk from receiving properly tested donor blood is minimal.

In the 1990s, both donating and receiving blood have become very safe procedures due to multiple discoveries and advances made in this century. Although research continues in the area of blood substitutes, human donation of this valuable natural resource is more important than ever before.

Additional Resources

American Association of Blood Banks. Facts About Blood
  http://www.aabb.org/docs/facts.html
    Provides excellent discussions of the blood banking process.

Jeter, E. K. and M. A. Spivey. 1996. *Introduction to Transfusion Medicine: A Case Study Approach.* American Association of Blood Banks, Bethesda, MD.
    This book is an introductory text for medical students and outlines basic concepts in transfusion therapy.

Petz, L. D. and S. N. Swisher et al. (eds). 1996. *Clinical Practice of Transfusion Medicine.* 3rd ed. Churchill Livingstone Inc., New York, NY.
    This book has an excellent chapter on the history of transfusion.

Questions for Discussion

1. Describe the discoveries that:
   - prevented most serious transfusion reactions;
   - led to the formation of blood banks; and
   - led to providing several transfusions from one donation.

2. Why has disease transmission by blood transfusion become rare?

Applications

1. How can high school students (older than 17, of course) be encouraged to become regular blood donors to help ensure an adequate supply of blood for the future?

2. How would you feel about receiving blood from the following blood donors:
   - a volunteer donor;
   - a paid donor;
   - an autologous donor?

3. In designing a blood substitute, what do you believe would be some important considerations?

5.1 Analyzing Neandertal DNA

Anne Stone, Ph.D.
Department of Ecology and Evolutionary Biology
University of Arizona, Tucson, Arizona

Dr. Stone is a post-doctoral fellow at the University of Arizona in the Department of Ecology and Evolutionary Biology. She is studying Y chromosome variation in chimpanzees and bonobo, or pygmy chimpanzees, to better understand their population history and structure. Her Ph.D. work in anthropology at the Pennsylvania State University focused on analyzing genetic and archaeological data from a prehistoric Native American community. While a graduate student, she received a Fulbright scholarship to study in Germany for one year. During that time, she was able to participate in a study of the 5,000-year-old mummy found in the Alps and known as the Iceman. She learned new techniques for studying ancient DNA and collaborated with Dr. Svante Pääbo's laboratory to examine Neandertal DNA.

Overview

Who were the Neandertals? Were they our ancestors? These questions have puzzled anthropologists since the first Neandertal skeleton was found in 1856 in the Neander Valley near Dusseldorf, Germany. Anthropologists have studied the shape, or morphology, of Neandertal bones and the remains of shelters and hunting sites left by the Neandertals. Those anthropologists want to determine how the Neandertals lived and adapted to their environment. Some anthropologists argue that Neandertals should be considered a subspecies of our species, *Homo sapiens*. Therefore, they should be called *Homo sapiens neandertalensis*. Others think that the differences between modern humans and Neandertals indicate they are a separate species and should be called *Homo neandertalensis*. The former group of researchers sees Neandertals as ancestral to the populations found in that region today. The latter group thinks that the Neandertals went extinct and were replaced by modern *H. sapiens* from Africa. Recently I collaborated with other scientists working in Dr. Svante Pääbo's laboratory in Germany. We extracted DNA from the upper arm bone of the first Neandertal found in 1856. The information we gained is now being used to try to settle this debate.

Who Were the Neandertals and When Did They Live?

The Neandertals lived in Europe and western Asia from about 300,000 years ago to 33,000 years ago. During most of that period, glacial climate conditions were present in Europe. The landscape was more open than forested with herds of large mammals such as deer, bison, mammoths, and antelope. Predators included cave lions, leopards, wolves, and the giant cave bear. The Neandertals lived by hunting and gathering and often used caves for shelter from the cold. Physically the Neandertals appear to be adapted to their cold, dry environment. They were stocky and very muscular. They had bigger noses, which may have helped warm the air before breathing it in; and they had very large browridges, as shown in Figure 1. Although their skulls were more "loaf-shaped" than humans, their brains were the same size.

Figure 1 *This reconstruction of a Neandertal shows the characteristically large browridges and nose.*

How Do We Get DNA from a Fossil?

Actually we can't get DNA from a fossil because a fossil is a bone that has mineralized into stone. However, most of the Neandertal bones are "sub-fossils." That means they have not yet turned to stone, so there is the possibility that some will still contain DNA. While working in Germany, I learned new techniques to examine Neandertal DNA.

Our first step to extract DNA from a bone was to grind it into powder. This increased the surface area of the bone. We then mixed the bone powder with detergents and chemicals to break up the proteins and separate the DNA from the cellular debris. When we finished the DNA extraction, we had a small amount of DNA in water.

We used a portion of this DNA in a procedure called the polymerase chain reaction (PCR). This reaction is essentially the genetic version of a photocopy machine. PCR made millions of copies of a specific fragment of DNA that we could then use for other analyses. We used this DNA to test for restriction fragment length polymorphisms (RFLPs) and for sequencing the DNA. Because PCR only needs a few molecules of DNA to start with, this technique made our study of ancient DNA possible.

One difficulty, however, was that any modern DNA (from dandruff or skin cells) would have been preferentially amplified if it contaminated the sample. Modern DNA would be more easily copied because there usually would be much more of it and it would not be damaged or broken into small pieces. To prevent contamination, we worked in a clean room away from the main genetics lab and wore lab coats, gloves, and face shields. We also removed the outer layer of the bone before we ground it up. It had been handled previously in the museum and might have contained shed cells from other scientists.

Finally, we extracted DNA from one piece of bone at the University of Munich and from another piece at Pennsylvania State University. We then compared our results and found that each group had the same DNA sequence for the region we analyzed.

Since the Human Genome Is So Large, Which Part Did We Study?

Each cell in the body contains two types of DNA. One type is nuclear DNA, which makes up the 23 pairs of chromosomes and found in the nucleus. The second type is mitochondrial DNA, which are small circular pieces of DNA that are found in the mitochondria. Mitochondria are organelles in the cytoplasm that transform the energy for the cell. Each cell contains hundreds of mitochondria. Thus, each cell contains hundreds of copies of mitochondrial DNA (mtDNA). Most ancient DNA research examines mtDNA.

Because mtDNA is present in larger amounts than nuclear DNA, it has a greater chance of being preserved. Several other features of mtDNA make it useful for analysis. Unlike nuclear DNA, the mitochondria are inherited solely from the mother and the mtDNA does not recombine. In addition, mtDNA is typically more variable than nuclear mtDNA. Some highly variable portions of mtDNA have been used extensively to study human population history. To learn how closely related humans are to Neandertals, we examined the sequence of the mtDNA from a region called the hypervariable region I (HVI) of the mitochondrial DNA genome.

> *Each cell in the body contains two types of DNA.*

The Comparison of Chimpanzee, Neandertal, and Modern Human mtDNA Sequences

We amplified the Neandertal mtDNA HVI region in small fragments and determined the sequence of a total of 379 bases. This sequence was compared to the sequences of 59 chimpanzees and over two thousand people from throughout the world. On average, there were 27 differences between the Neandertal and modern human sequences and 55 differences between the Neandertal and chimpanzee sequences, as shown in Figure 2. Among modern humans, there are typically eight differences. Although Neandertals lived in Europe and western Asia, modern human mtDNA sequences from this region of the world differ from Neandertals by about 28 bases. This indicates that Neandertals are not more closely related to modern Europeans than to other populations. It also argues for the idea that they were not the ancestors of modern humans but instead were close "cousins" who became extinct.

A note of caution about these results should be made, however. These results are from a sample of one—a very small sample! By chance, it could represent a rare sequence in the Neandertal population. Therefore, we need more data from other individuals to confirm these results. This confirmation will depend on finding other Neandertal skeletons that contain preserved DNA. Also, the genetic locus examined is only one part of the genome, and that part may have a different history from other parts (such as nuclear genes). It would be best to examine many parts of the genome to get a fuller picture; however, the difficulty of recovering ancient nuclear DNA may make this impossible.

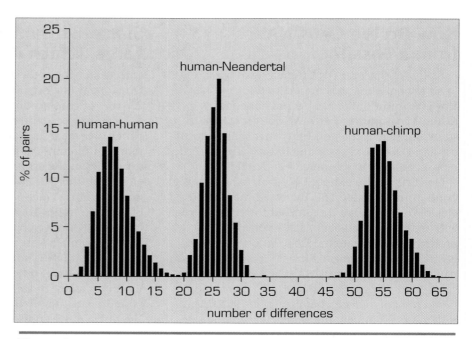

Figure 2 *A comparison of DNA sequences from modern humans, chimpanzees, and the one Neandertal sample.*

Additional Resources

Stringer, C. and C. Gamble. *In Search of the Neanderthals.* 1993. Thames and Hudson, New York.
    This book provides an excellent overview of what we know about Neandertals (and how we know it).

The Great DNA Hunt Part I and II, Archaeology Magazine. September/October and November/December 1996 issues.
    These articles reveal the difficulty of working with ancient DNA and discuss the research that has been done to answer archaeological questions. Such research includes DNA analysis of the Tyrolean Iceman and Egyptian mummies, examines the history of the initial colonization of the New World, and determines when and where cattle and wheat were first domesticated.

Trinkaus, E. and P. Shipman. *The Neandertals: of Skeletons, Scientists and Scandal.* 1992. Vintage Books, New York.
    Trinkhaus and Shipman discuss the history and controversies in the study of Neandertals (and how we know it).

Questions for Discussion

1. Where did Neandertals live and what was their life like?
2. How did the scientists make sure that their mtDNA results were authentic?
3. What are mitochondria?
4. How do these mtDNA analyses indicate that Neandertals might not be the ancestors of modern humans?

Applications

1. What other questions could ancient DNA be used to answer?
2. What other types of evidence could tell us if Neandertals and modern humans are the same species?

Analyzing Neandertal DNA

5.2 Inherited Mental Retardation: The Fragile X Syndrome

Gail Anderson, M.S.
Greenwood Genetic Center, Greenwood, South Carolina

Ms. Anderson is a genetic counselor for the Greenwood Genetic Center in Greenville, South Carolina. Genetic counselors are trained in both medical genetics and psychological counseling and combine these skills to help patients and their families understand and cope with the diagnosis of a genetic condition or birth defect. Ms. Anderson has worked with many families who have received the diagnosis of Fragile X syndrome. In 1996, she helped organize the Carolinas Fragile X Support Group, which serves families in the upstate of South Carolina as well as western North Carolina.

Overview

It has been known for over 100 years that more males than females have mental retardation. The reason for this is that many genetic conditions that cause mental retardation are sex-linked (or X-linked), meaning that the gene involved is located on the X chromosome. One of these conditions is Fragile X syndrome (FXS), which is the most common inherited cause of mental retardation. We are not sure exactly how often this condition happens because a lot of people have FXS in their families but don't know it. FXS is an important condition to diagnose because it does run in a family and other family members may want to be tested to see if they carry the gene and are at risk for having children with the condition.

Features of FXS

The most important feature of FXS is mental retardation. Boys with FXS usually walk late and talk late and often have behavior problems. Their speech may be difficult to understand, and sometimes they repeat the same word or phrase over and over. As men they have moderate to severe

mental retardation. Many men with FXS, such as the young man pictured in Figure 1, have certain physical features, such as a long, thin face, large ears, prominent forehead and jaw, enlarged testes, and large hands. Girls can also have FXS, though they usually are not as severely affected. In both men and women, the features of FXS vary; so not everyone who has this condition will be affected in exactly the same way.

Figure 1   *This young man's appearance is typical of FXS.*

The Fragile X Gene—FMR1

The Fragile X Mental Retardation gene (FMR1) was discovered in 1991. FXS is caused by a trinucleotide repeat amplification, a duplication of multiple copies of three nucleotide sequences, in this gene. Figure 2 shows the nucleotide sequence of the FMR1 gene. In a normal FMR1 gene, a person will have around 30 repeats of the nucleotides cytosine-guanine-guanine (CGG). If a person has too many

Most common alleles have 29 or 30 repeats

....GCAGCGCGG CGG CGG CGG CGG CGG CGG CGG CGG CGG CGG CGG CGG CGG CGG CGG CGG CGG CGG CGG CGG CGG CGG CGG CGG CGG CGG CGG CGG CGG CGG CGG GCGG GGC CTG CGG CGG CGGCGG....

Figure 2 *This normal FMR1 gene has about 30 repeats of the CGG trinucleotide sequence.*

of these CGG repeats, the gene gets too big and cannot function normally. A full mutation is present when the number of repeats is more than 230. Males who have the full mutation will usually have the full-blown syndrome, including moderate to severe mental retardation, no matter how much higher the number of repeats. About half of females with the full mutation have IQs in the borderline or mildly mentally retarded range, and those with a normal IQ may have learning disabilities or emotional problems.

A person who has between 54 and 230 of these repeats in FMR1 has a "premutation." A person with a premutation, whether they be male or female, will usually not show signs or symptoms of FXS. However, when a woman with the premutation has children, the number of repeats can actually increase (a "repeat expansion") and she could have a child with the full mutation for FXS. Premutations usually do not develop into full mutations when inherited from the father.

Scientists have discovered many other genetic conditions that are caused by a trinucleotide repeat amplification. One of these is Huntington's disease. Other conditions include myotonic dystrophy, Kennedy's disease, and Friedreich ataxia.

Genetics of Fragile X

The FMR1 gene is located near the bottom of the X chromosome just above the genes for color blindness, hemophilia A, and Lorenzo's oil. Remember that humans have 23 pairs of chromo-

somes for a total of 46. One of these pairs is called the sex chromosomes, which determine if a person is male or female. Females have two X chromosomes, and males have one X chromosome and one Y chromosome. This is why more boys than girls have FXS. Girls who have the gene for Fragile X often do not show severe symptoms of the condition (although it is possible) because they have a normal gene on their other X chromosome that helps protect them from its effects. Boys do not have a second X chromosome and, therefore, will more likely have symptoms.

Women who have the FMR1 gene, whether they have the premutation or the full mutation, are called "carriers" of FXS. When a female carrier of FXS has children, there is a 50 percent chance the baby will get the X chromosome with the FMR1 gene and a 50 percent chance the baby will get the X chromosome with the normal gene, as shown in Figure 3. The odds are much like flipping a coin. If the child does inherit the FMR1 gene, the sex of the child and the size of the trinucleotide repeat will determine the odds that he or she will be affected with FXS. Unaffected males who have the premutation will pass the premutation to all of their daughters but will not pass it to any of their sons, as shown in Figure 4. Testing can be done during a pregnancy to determine if the fetus has the FMR1 gene. The test will also show the number of repeated nucleotide sequences in the gene.

Genetic Counseling Issues

When the diagnosis of FXS is made in a family, many issues can arise. Although parents often feel relief when they find out the cause of their child's learning problems, they may also start to grieve for the loss of their "normal" child. They may have feelings of denial, anger, disappointment, and low self-esteem. The counselor will discuss with the family the psychological issues they may face and reassure them that these responses are perfectly normal and healthy. The mother may also feel guilt for passing the Fragile X gene on to her child. The genetic counselor will emphasize to the parents that there is no way for her to have known that she carried this gene (unless there is a positive family history). Support groups are often helpful to families because they help the families realize they are not alone. These groups give them someone to talk to who really understands what they are going through. With information and ongoing support, most parents eventually accept the diagnosis and begin to focus on the needs of their child.

The family may also be faced with certain decisions to make, such as whether or not to have more children, considering the risk of having another child with FXS. They must also decide how and when to inform other family members at risk for carrying the FMR1 gene. The genetic counselor can discuss these situations with the family and help them make the decisions that are best for them. There are no right or wrong answers here because every family is unique and has differing needs and desires.

Segregation of X-Linked Recessive Trait (Carrier Mother)

Figure 3 *A woman who carries the FMR1 gene on her X chromosome (x') has a 50 percent chance of passing that gene to her children. A child's sex and the size of the trinucleotide repeat region determine whether a child will be affected with FXS.*

Additional Resources

FRAXA Research Foundation. PO Box 935, Newbury, MA, 01985-0935. 508-462-1990. Email: fraxa@seacoast.com Web site: www.fraxa.org
FRAXA promotes and funds research aimed at finding a cure for Fragile X and is also a good resource for both parents and professionals.

Hagerman, R. J. and A. Cronister. 1996. *Fragile X Syndrome*. The Johns Hopkins Press, London.
This book reviews in detail all aspects of Fragile X syndrome, including diagnosis, inheritance, physical and behavioral aspects, treatments and therapies, and research.

National Fragile X Foundation. 1441 York Street, Suite 303, Denver, CO, 80206-2127. 1-800-688-8765.
The National Fragile X Foundation is a nonprofit organization promoting awareness, research, and education of Fragile X syndrome. It is a vital resource for both parents and professionals. Information is available on Fragile X through the foundation, which includes fact sheets, videos, booklets, and a quarterly newsletter.

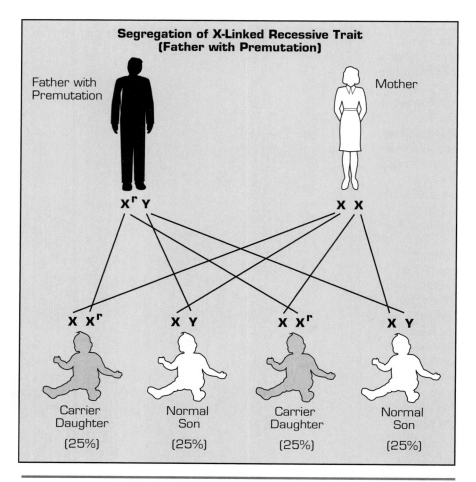

Figure 4 *Fathers carrying the FMR1 premutation will pass it to all of their daughters but none of their sons.*

Questions for Discussion

1. What are some features of Fragile X syndrome?

2. Why are boys more likely to show symptoms of the FMR1 gene than girls?

3. Explain trinucleotide repeat amplification.

4. What determines whether or not a child with the FMR1 gene will have Fragile X syndrome?

Applications

1. How do you think the diagnosis of Fragile X or any other inherited condition might impact a family? How do you think it might cause stress on a marriage?

2. Why don't fathers with FXS or FXS premutations pass these conditions to their sons?

3. If someone in your family were diagnosed with Fragile X syndrome, would you want to know whether or not you carried the FMR1 gene? If you knew you had the gene, how might the information impact your family planning?

4. An 8-year-old girl has a brother with Fragile X syndrome. Her parents want to know whether or not she carries the FMR1 gene. Should they have her tested now, or should they wait until she is old enough to make her own decision about being tested?

5.3 Twins—Twice the Fun or Double the Trouble?

Mary C. "Katy" Phelan, Ph.D.
Cytogenetics Laboratory
Greenwood Genetic Center, Greenwood, South Carolina

Dr. Phelan received her Ph.D. in human genetics from the Medical College of Virginia in Richmond. She is currently the director of the cytogenetics laboratory at the Greenwood Genetic Center in Greenwood, South Carolina. Dr. Phelan is certified as a diplomate of the American Board of Medical Genetics, as a Ph.D. medical geneticist, and as a clinical cytogeneticist. In addition, she is a founding fellow of the American College of Medical Genetics. Dr. Phelan is a member of several professional societies, including the American Society of Human Genetics, the Teratology Society, and the International Society for Twin Studies. Her primary interest is the diagnosis of chromosome defects that may lead to mental retardation and/or birth defects.

Overview

In many ancient cultures, twins were viewed with caution and fear. Although the birth of two or more babies was accepted in lower animals, such an event in humans was considered with suspicion. In certain cultures, the twins were honored; while in other cultures, they were punished or killed. Among some primitive African tribes, twins were thought to be associated with evil spirits and the mother of the twins was said to be cursed. "May you become the mother of twins" were the most dreaded words a woman might hear. An American Indian myth viewed the firstborn twin as heroic and good, while the second born twin was thought to be villainous and evil. Some California Indians smothered either both twins at birth or only the second born twin; if the twins were of opposite sex, the female twin was killed. In contrast, Mohave Indians believed that twins were the reincarnation of an old person in double form; hence, twins were treated with the same respect as the elderly members of the tribe. Certain West African tribes also viewed twins favorably. A joyous celebration was held when twins were born, and the mother of the twins wore special ornaments and baubles. Twins were associated with fertility, and parents of twins were asked to preside over rituals to ensure successful crops and fertile animals.

Fortunately in our society today, twins are viewed with excitement and interest. But why do twins happen? How often does twinning occur? Why do some twins look so much alike while others do not?

Identical or Fraternal?

About one-third of all twins are "identical"—they look so much alike that it is often very difficult to tell them apart. The remaining two-thirds of twins are nonidentical, or "fraternal"—these twins show the usual family resemblance but look no more alike than ordinary brothers or sisters.

Fraternal twinning can be viewed as a duplication of the usual process of conception. Typically, when a single infant is conceived, one egg is released from one of the mother's ovaries and is subsequently fertilized by one of the father's sperm. In fraternal twinning, two eggs are released by the mother and the eggs are fertilized by two different sperm. The result is that fraternal twins are no more alike genetically than ordinary brothers and sisters—the twins arose from two eggs fertilized by two separate sperm. Unlike most brothers and sisters, fraternal twins share the same birth date and, therefore, are the same age. Fraternal twins can be of the same sex (both twins are boys or both twins are girls) or of different sexes (one twin is a boy and one twin is a girl). Because they arise from two separate fertilized eggs, or zygotes, fraternal twins are also called dizygotic (or DZ) twins.

Identical twinning results when a single egg is fertilized by a single sperm and the zygote

667

Figure 1 *Identical twins.*

subsequently splits to form two separate zygotes. As such, identical twins develop from the same fertilized egg and thus share all their genes in common. Since identical twins share the same genes, they look very much alike and may often be mistaken for one another. Can you discern any physical differences between the twins pictured in Figure 1? Identical twins are also known as monozygotic (or MZ) twins. Can you explain why? Can you imagine the confusion you could cause for your friends or teachers if you had an identical twin?

Incomplete Twinning

Identical twinning usually occurs within 12 to 13 days after fertilization. If the zygote splits at a later stage, the separation of the embryonic disk may be incomplete, resulting in conjoined, or Siamese, twins. The incidence of conjoined twins is about 1 in 50,000 births. The most common type of conjoined twins are those joined at the chest or thorax, so-called thoracopagus twins. Other types of conjoined twins are united at the head, at the hip, at the abdomen, or along the entire body. Surgery can be performed to separate conjoined twins, but the success of the surgery depends upon the degree of fusion and the extent to which vital organs are shared by the twins.

Late division of the embryo is the current explanation for conjoined twins. When twinning occurs near the end of the second week of development, the embryonic disk does not separate completely, resulting in conjoined twins. Experimental studies in chicks, amphibians, and other organisms have suggested that a defect in the primitive streak, aging of the ovum, and environmental factors may contribute to the formation of conjoined twins. The primitive streak is formed by the movement of cells within the early embryo and precedes the development of the embryonic axis. If two embryonic axes form within one ovum but fail to separate completely, conjoined twinning may result. Aging of the ovum could result in a reduced ability of the ovum to differentiate normally; one consequence of abnormal differentiation would be conjoined twinning. Environmental factors such as low oxygen supply and low temperature have been shown to lead to conjoined twinning in certain types of fish.

Why are conjoined twins also called Siamese twins? Figure 2 shows a famous pair of conjoined twins—Chang and Eng Bunker—who were born in Siam in 1811. The Bunkers joined the circus of P.T. Barnum and were exhibited around the world as his famous "Siamese twins." The name was popularized and is now used to refer to any pair of conjoined twins.

How Often Does Twinning Occur?

Twinning occurs in about 1 in 80 births in the United States and Europe. The incidence of twinning varies in different populations, with a higher incidence among some populations than others. For example, the twinning rate in Africa is higher than that in the United States and Europe while the twinning rate in Asia is lower. The variation in the twinning rate is attributable to variation in the incidence of fraternal twins; the incidence of identical twins tends to remain constant across populations.

Many factors influence the incidence of fraternal twins: the mother's height, weight, age, and use of fertility drugs. Tall women are more likely than short women to have fraternal twins, and heavy women are more likely than thin women to have fraternal twins. Similarly, the twinning rate peaks in women between 35 and 40 years of age. Mothers who take fertility drugs may ovulate more than one egg per reproductive cycle. If two or more eggs are ovulated and fertilized, then twins, triplets, or higher multiple births may result.

Twins—Twice the Fun or Double the Trouble?

Figure 2 *Here are the original "Siamese Twins," who startled the world with their birth in Siam in 1829. Chang & Eng were world-famous when touring with Barnum's colossal collection of curios. With the profits of their tours they settled down as farmers, married sisters, and had children. In this picture taken about 1871, Chang & Eng are shown with their children.*

Higher Multiple Births

In 1997, a mother in Iowa gave birth to septuplets—seven babies delivered from a single pregnancy. How can this be possible? With the popular use of fertility drugs, women may release multiple eggs within one reproductive cycle; and if several of the eggs are fertilized and implanted, the mother may give birth to more than one baby.

Many complications can arise in a twin pregnancy; and the problems are even greater when three, four, or more babies are present. Twins and higher multiple births tend to weigh less at birth and be born earlier than single infants. The more babies present, the lower the birth weight tends to be. The septuplets weighed less than 3 1/2 pounds each and were born nine weeks early. Low birth weight and premature delivery are two serious problems that can lead to illness or death in multiple pregnancies. Premature babies are at an increased risk for respiratory, neurologic, and infectious complications, often requiring prolonged and intensive hospital care.

Birth Defects and Twins

Certain birth defects, such as conjoined twinning, are a result of the twinning process itself and, therefore, occur only in multiple pregnancies. Other abnormalities unique to twins result from abnormal blood flow within the placenta. The placenta is the fetal organ through which nutrients and waste products are exchanged between the mother and the baby. Birth defects related to abnormal placental blood flow are generally seen in identical twins but not in fraternal twins. Whereas fraternal twins each have their own placenta, identical twins may each have their own placenta or may share a single placenta.

The type of placenta of identical twins is determined by the timing at which the twinning event occurred. When twinning occurs one to three days after fertilization, each twin will have its own placenta with its own inner and outer birth sacs. This type of placentation, pictured in Figure 3, is referred to as dichorionic diamnionic and is the same type of placentation as seen in fraternal twins. Sometimes, as shown in Figure 4, the two zygotes will implant adjacent to each other in the uterus and the placentas may grow together, even showing some fusion of the placental discs. Nonetheless, careful examination of the placentas will demonstrate the presence of two chorions (outer membranes) and two amnions (inner membranes) characteristic of dichorionic diamnionic placentation.

When twinning occurs between four and eight days postfertilization, the twins will share a common placenta with a single outer birth sac but

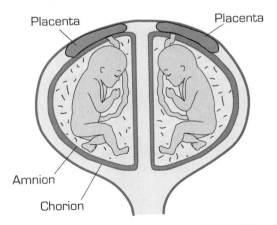

Figure 3 *These identical twins have separate placentas and birth sacs (amnion and chorion).*

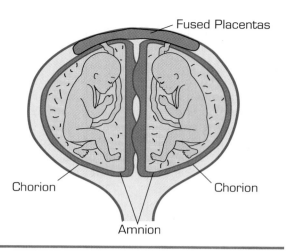

Figure 4 *These twins have separate placentas and birth sacs, but the placentas have grown together.*

separate inner birth sacs. This type of placentation, shown in Figure 5, is called monochorionic diamnionic and occurs in 70 to 75 percent of identical twins. Later twinning, between 8 and 13 days postfertilization, results in monochorionic monoamnionic placentation, as shown in Figure 6. In this case, the twins have a single placenta with single inner and outer birth sacs. This type of placentation is found in only 1 to 2 percent of identical twins.

The blood vessels in monochorionic placentas frequently grow together and fuse, permitting the exchange of blood between the twins. Normally the blood flow within the placenta remains balanced and these shared blood vessels do not cause any problems for the twins. On occasion, however, the blood flow within the placenta becomes imbalanced, resulting in serious problems, such as the twin transfusion syndrome. In this disorder, one twin (the recipient) receives a greater supply of blood than the other twin (the donor). In extreme cases, the donor twin is growth retarded, severely anemic, and has small and underdeveloped organs. In contrast, the recipient twin has enlarged organs, an increased blood volume, and increased blood viscosity. While the donor twin frequently has a reduced amount of amniotic fluid (oligohydramnios), the recipient twin often has an excess amount of amniotic fluid (polyhydramnios). Polyhydramnios can be a serious problem that can lead to preterm labor and delivery. One or both twins may die from complications related to abnormal organ development and premature birth.

In general, fraternal twins have a similar rate of birth defects as single infants, while identical twins have a higher rate than single infants. Examples of birth defects that occur more frequently in identical twins are neural tube (open spine) defects and microcephaly (small head). Birth defects may occur in one or both members of a twin pair. If both twins have a similar defect, they are said to be "concordant" for the abnormality. If only one twin is affected, the twins are "discordant."

Nature's Experiment

Twinning is truly an experiment of nature; and the study of twins allows us to learn more about many complex traits such as growth, intelligence, and behavior. An interesting model for examining behavioral tendencies in twins is the study of identical twins "reared apart." These are identical twins who were separated soon after birth and raised by different families—perhaps because their mother was unable to bear the burden of caring for two babies. Oftentimes each twin is unaware of his cotwin's existence until they are united many years later. There are many anecdotal tales in which the twins show up at their reunion with the same hairstyle or in very similar clothing and, upon getting acquainted, find that they are alike in many of their habits and preferences. Comparing differences and similarities between identical twins reared together and reared apart can help estimate the contributions of genetic and environmental factors to a variety of traits.

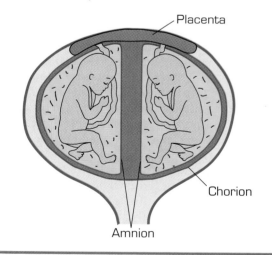

Figure 5 *These twins share a common placenta but have separate inner birth sacs (amnion).*

Twins—Twice the Fun or Double the Trouble?

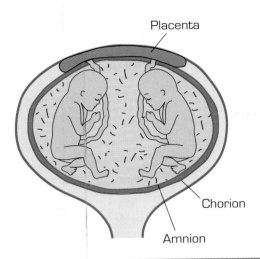

Placenta

Chorion

Amnion

Figure 6 *These twins share a single placenta and are contained within single outer and inner birth sacs (chorion/amnion).*

Comparisons between the two types of twins—identical and fraternal—also provide insight into the complex interactions between genetics and environment. Because identical twins are alike in their genetic makeup, any differences between identical twins are attributable to environmental influences. On the other hand, fraternal twins are no more alike genetically than ordinary brothers and sisters; therefore, differences between fraternal twins are due to both genetic and environmental factors. The classic twin method exploits this unique relationship between identical and fraternal twins to study disease states as well as normal development.

References

Bulmer, M. G. 1970. *The Biology of Twinning in Man.* Clarendon Press, Oxford.

MacGillivray, I., P. P. S. Nylander, and G. Corney. 1975. *Human Multiple Reproduction.* W. B. Saunders Company Ltd, London.

Phelan, M. C. 1993. Twins. *Congenital Malformations.* Oxford University Press, New York. pp. 1047–1079.

Scheinfeld, A. 1967. *Twins and Supertwins.* J. B. Lippincott Co., Philadelphia.

Additional Resources

http://www.twinspace.com/
   A comprehensive Web site with much information and links to other sites of interest to twins, including frequently asked questions (FAQs) about twins, twin bookstore, twin organizations, and parenting twins. The site even has a bulletin board that lists twins' casting calls.

Questions for Discussion

1. Knowing that the overall incidence of twins is about 1 in 80 births, what is the incidence of monozygotic (MZ) twins? Of dizygotic (DZ) twins?

2. Triplets are born—one boy and two identical girls. Explain how this could happen.

3. The incidence of twins is $1/n$, where n is the number of live births. The incidence of triplets is $1/n^2$ and the incidence of quadruplets $1/n^3$. If the incidence of twins is 1/80, what is the incidence of triplets? Of quadruplets? How does this compare to the incidence of triplets and quadruplets when $n = 20$?

4. One complication of twin pregnancy is crowding in the mother's uterus (womb). Crowding can result in positional birth defects, such as clubfoot, in the baby. The effects of intrauterine crowding seem to be independent of whether a single or double placenta is present. What differences would you expect between identical and fraternal twins in terms of positional defects? What about between triplets and quadruplets?

Applications

1. Do you know a set of twins? Are they fraternal or identical? Explain how you arrived at this answer.

2. If you had a same-sex fraternal twin, how might it change your life at home? At school? What if you and your twin were identical?

3. Although identical twins have the same genetic makeup, they are not always exactly the same height and weight. What other factors might lead to differences in height and weight between identical twins?

4. Identical twins are born at a local hospital. One twin is found to have a genetic disorder, while the other twin is not affected by the disorder. Explain how a genetic disease may be present in only one of the twins.

5.4 Two's Company and Three's a Crowd: Uniparental Disomy and Imprinted Genes

Ron C. Michaelis, Ph.D.
J. C. Self Research Institute
Greenwood Genetic Center, Greenwood, South Carolina

Although he now does genetic research, Dr. Michaelis received his Ph.D. in psychology. His first interest was in the neurochemistry of behavior. Some of his work involved the loss of memory and learning ability as people aged. However, the work he found most interesting involved the neurochemistry of drug abuse, especially stimulants. Today he combines his training in the field of drugs and behavior with his knowledge of genetics to search for genes that may be responsible for disorders such as mental retardation or autism.

Overview

You already know that your chromosomes come in pairs with one member of each pair inherited from your mother and the other from your father. Sometimes, though, people inherit both members of a pair of chromosomes from only one parent. This occurrence is called uniparental disomy, or UPD, which means two chromosomes (disomy) from one parent (uniparental). UPD sometimes has no effect at all but also can result in severe disorders including seizures, mental retardation, or cancer in babies. The effect of UPD depends on which chromosomes are involved and sometimes which parent contributed the two copies of the chromosome. This essay also shows how the discovery of UPD led to the discovery of a class of genes called imprinted genes.

Two from One Cell and One from the Other—the Cause of Trisomies

Mendel's Law of Segregation states that the two chromosomes in a homologous pair separate during meiosis. Sometimes, however, the chromosome pair experiences what is called a nondisjunction in which the chromosomes do not separate and the entire pair moves into one of the two daughter cells. Nondisjunction can occur during either the first or second meiotic division and can involve any of the chromosome pairs. Nondisjunction produces either an egg or a sperm cell that contains two copies of a particular chromosome in it along with a single copy of each of the other chromosomes. Fertilization that involves this egg or sperm and a normal cell produces a fertilized egg cell, or zygote, that is trisomic. In other words, it has three copies of the particular chromosome.

When trisomy occurs with almost any one of the human chromosomes, the fetus does not survive. However, there is a rescue mechanism that can eliminate one of the three chromosomes during the first few mitotic divisions after fertilization. Research shows that the eliminated chromosome is chosen at random. Two-thirds of the time the mechanism discards one of the pair of chromosomes that resulted from nondisjunction. The fertilized egg cell ends up with a normal pair containing one chromosome from the mother and one from the father. This biparental inheritance pattern is shown in Figure 1. The other one-third of the time the rescue mechanism discards the single chromosome that came from one parent. Thus, the zygote ends up with the pair of chromosomes that came from the other parent, as shown in Figure 1. The resulting condition is called uniparental disomy, UPD, because both chromosomes of the pair are from the same parent.

A Mysterious Case of Cystic Fibrosis Linked to UPD

A little girl who had cystic fibrosis (CF) was the first person in whom UPD was shown to result in a genetic disease. Doctors knew that her mother carried a mutation in the gene for cystic fibrosis on

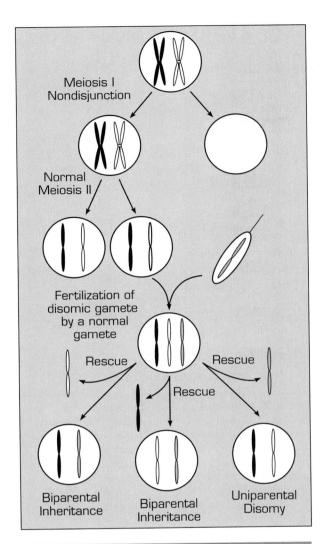

Meiosis I
Nondisjunction

Normal
Meiosis II

Fertilization of
disomic gamete
by a normal
gamete

Rescue   Rescue

Rescue

Biparental
Inheritance

Biparental
Inheritance

Uniparental
Disomy

Figure 1 *When a disomic gamete is involved in fertilization, there are three possible outcomes after the rescue mechanism has done its work. The outcome depends on which extra chromosome is lost. Either UPD or biparental (normal) inheritance results.*

two chromosomes that are the same. Besides CF, the girl suffered from growth retardation as well.

A patient with UPD can alternatively inherit one copy of each of the two chromosomes in a pair from a single parent. The term for this is heterodisomy, which literally means two chromosomes that are different. When scientists first became aware of UPD, they believed that heterodisomy was harmless. If these chromosomes worked correctly in the parent, why shouldn't they work correctly in the offspring? In time, scientists discovered that some genetic disorders could be linked to heterodisomy, and they puzzled over the possible causes. Their research led to the discovery of a class of genes called imprinted genes. With imprinted genes, either the gene from the patient's mother or the gene from the patient's father is active, but not both.

Thus, a person with UPD might inherit either a pair of identical chromosomes or a pair of different chromosomes from the same parent. In either case, the person will have only one set of active genes because there is no balancing set of genes from the other parent.

A Bigger Mystery: Two Disorders from the Same Genetic Defect

One of the biggest mysteries solved by the discovery of UPD involves two disorders whose genes lie very close to each other on chromosome 15. These disorders are called Angelman syndrome (AS) and Prader-Willi syndrome (PWS). AS results from the loss of one or more genes that are expressed only from the chromosome 15 that came from the mother. On the other hand, PWS is caused by the loss of one or more genes that are expressed only from the chromosome 15 that came from the father. AS and PWS are two very different disorders with different effects on the body, as you can see in Figures 2 a and b. AS causes devastating mental retardation; lack of speech; seizures; jerky, stiff-jointed movements; and repeated outbursts of laughter, hand-wringing, or flapping. PWS causes mild to moderate mental retardation, a ravenous appetite, obesity, and impaired sexual development.

These two genetic diseases, AS and PWS, mystified scientists for a long time until they learned how to determine the origin of a chromosome by analyzing its DNA. Before that time, researchers could use microscopes to view the general structure

chromosome 7, but the mutated gene that produces CF is recessive. This means that a child would have to inherit one CF gene from the mother and a second CF gene from the father. However, the girl's father did not have a mutated CF gene on chromosome 7. Because of this finding, the parents were told that their daughter could not inherit CF. Unfortunately, scientists found that the girl had inherited two identical copies of chromosome 7 from her mother and none from her father. This situation is called isodisomy, which literally means of chromosomes. They observed that chromosome 15 from both AS and PWS patients were missing the same genes. How could the same missing genes on a chromosome cause two very different types of genetic diseases?

As scientists learned how to analyze DNA, molecular techniques were applied to the mystery of AS and PWS. The locations of the imprinted genes on chromosome 15 were mapped, as shown in Figure 3. A new method of analysis allowed scientists to determine whether an individual chromosome came from the mother or the father. When the DNA in chromosome 15 was analyzed, scientists found that AS resulted when one of two conditions occurred. Either a defective chromosome 15 was inherited from the mother or the individual had UPD involving chromosome 15 and both chromosomes came from the father. PWS occurred when either of the opposite conditions occurred. Either a defective chromosome 15 was inherited from the father or the individual had UPD involving chromosome 15 and both chromosomes came from the mother.

Findings such as these show that the mother's and father's contributions to an individual's genetic makeup are not always equivalent. Whether a certain chromosome comes from the mother or the father can be critical in determining the physical effects of a defective chromosome.

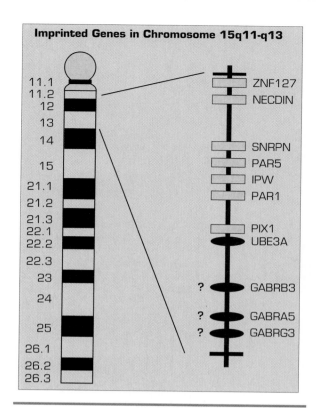

Figure 3 *Imprinted genes in chromosome 15. Genes designated by rectangles are expressed only from the chromosome 15 that comes from the father. Genes designated by ovals are expressed only from the chromosome 15 from the mother. Question marks indicate genes that scientists think are expressed from the chromosome 15 from the mother, but only in cells from certain tissues including nerve cells.*

Figure 2 *Patients with Angelman (a) and Prader-Willi (b) syndromes.*

Additional Resources

Butler, M. G. 1990. Prader-Willi Syndrome: Current Understanding of Cause and Diagnosis. *American Journal of Human Genetics,* 35: pp. 319–332.

> Several important discoveries have been made about the genes responsible for Prader-Willi syndrome since this paper was published. However, this paper still stands as an excellent, thorough review of the Prader-Willi syndrome and the chromosome abnormalities that have been found in Prader-Willi syndrome patients.

Chan, C-T. J., J. Clayton-Smith, X-J. Cheng, J. Buxton, T. Webb, M. E. Pembrey, and S. Malcolm. 1993. Molecular Mechanisms in Angelman Syndrome: A Survey of 93 Patients. *Journal of Medical Genetics,* 30: pp. 895–902.

> This paper presents a good discussion of the several different ways in which Angelman syndrome can be produced and includes a brief but good description of the features of the syndrome.

Driscoll, D. J. 1994. Genomic Imprinting In Humans. *Molecular Genetic Medicine,* Vol. 4. T. Friedman, (ed.). Academic Press, San Diego, CA.

    This chapter is a readable review of imprinting in humans with an emphasis on Prader-Willi and Angelman syndromes. It is written by one of the leading research scientists in the field of these syndromes.

Ledbetter, D. H. and E. Engel. 1995. Uniparental Disomy in Humans: Development of an Imprinting Map and its Implications for Prenatal Diagnosis. *Human Molecular Genetics,* 4: pp. 1757–1764.

    Dr. Engel was the first person to suggest that uniparental disomy was not only possible, but was the mechanism by which some patients acquired certain genetic disorders. His classic original article was published in 1980, eight years before the first report of a patient whose disease was caused by UPD. This paper summarizes the cases of UPD reported before 1995 and lists the chromosomes that are either known or suspected to contain imprinted genes.

Questions for Discussion

1. What is the difference between heterodisomy and isodisomy?

2. What extra risk is present in isodisomy that is not present in heterodisomy?

3. Why did Angelman and Prader-Willi syndromes present such a mystery to the people who first discovered that the two disorders were associated with a defect in chromosome 15?

Applications

1. Draw a three-generation pedigree. Assume that each couple in the pedigree produces two children, one male and one female. This should result in a total of ten people in the pedigree, five male and five female. At the top level of the pedigree, choose either the male or female to have a deletion of the Angelman/Prader-Willi syndrome region on chromosome 15. Assume that Angelman and Prader-Willi syndrome patients reproduce normally. (In reality, they do not.) Indicate which members of the pedigree will be unaffected and which will be affected with either Angelman or Prader-Willi syndrome.

2. Do research to learn about the genetic diseases Down syndrome, Edwards syndrome, Patau syndrome, and Klinefelter syndrome. Also, learn about Turner syndrome, and tell how its cause differs from the other syndromes mentioned. Describe the symptoms of each and the defect that causes each disease.

5.5 Genetic Engineering in Agriculture: A Technology with Roots Deep in the Past

Nancy H. Ferguson, Ph.D.
Department of Crop and Soil Environmental Science
Clemson University, Clemson, South Carolina

Dr. Ferguson teaches introductory genetics and a humanities class on modern genetics and human values. Her research is on the most important cool-season grass in the United States, tall fescue grass, and the fungus that infects it. Strong chemicals called alkaloids produced by this fungus can cause reproductive problems, severe illness, or death in horses and cattle.

Overview

"The roots of the present are deep in the past" is a concept central to any high school world history class. To understand modern genetic engineering, one must recognize how deeply modern science and technology are rooted in past discoveries. This essay mentions several important past scientific discoveries and explains how they relate to modern genetic technology. It also gives examples of how this technology is now used to improve agricultural crop plants and how it has the potential of improving the quality of life for billions of people.

Discoveries before the 20th Century

As long ago as 2000 B.C.E., during the reign of the Babylonian king Hammurabi, date palms were artificially fertilized or pollinated. Carvings from 880 B.C.E. illustrate artificial pollination and show that improvement of date varieties was considered extremely important in that society. The biological basis for plant improvement through artificial pollination was recognized in the mid-1800s when experiments done by the Austrian monk Gregor Mendel with the garden pea showed that inheritance was based on the transmission of separate, discrete factors. We now call these factors "genes."

Other important discoveries toward the end of the 19th century included the invention of the modern form of the microscope, which led to the realization of the universal existence of cells in all organisms and the observation of chromosomes within cells. In this century, plant breeders have used those discoveries to improve dramatically the quality and yield of cultivated crop plants. Occasionally there have been surprises, such as in the attempt to cross a cabbage and radish in the hopes of producing a plant with the head of a cabbage and root of the radish. Unfortunately, the resulting plants had the leaves of a radish and the roots of a cabbage and were, therefore, agriculturally worthless.

Discoveries during the 20th Century

In 1952, James Watson and Francis Crick published their landmark paper, based in part on the work of Rosalind Franklin, describing the structure of DNA. This began a new era in genetic technology. Within two decades, scientists discovered restriction enzymes, which are enzymes that allowed scientists to move genes around and to manipulate the genetic composition of organisms. We thus entered an era of biotechnology and genetic engineering.

Biotechnology uses biological organisms or products in commercial and/or industrial processes. Genetic engineering refers to a series of techniques that allows us to alter the genetic makeup of cells or entire organisms by selecting, removing, inserting, or modifying individual genes. When a gene from one organism is inserted into a different organism, the resulting offspring is referred to as transgenic.

The goal of agricultural biotechnology and genetic engineering is the improvement of the quality of crop plants. This is the same goal that the Babylonians had in 2000 B.C.E. with their efforts to improve date palms and as the people in this century had who crossed a radish with a cabbage.

However, since we can now identify specific genes prior to inserting them into plants, we can see rapid changes in one generation and decrease the likelihood of getting unexpected negative results. The most important objectives for improving crop plants through genetic engineering are increasing their nutritional value, conferring resistance to disease and insects (and in some cases herbicides), and developing the ability of a plant to grow in marginal environments.

Improved Nutrition

Iron is a required nutrient that is often deficient in the human diet. Iron deficiency affects an estimated 1 to 2 billion people. Increasing the iron content in rice is an appealing strategy to supply the mineral inexpensively and effortlessly to a large sector of the world's population. Rice feeds half of the world and is eaten every day in those parts of the world where iron deficiency is most common. Research groups from Japan and Switzerland are using genetic engineering to develop rice plants with increased iron content.

Vitamin A also is essential for the human body; and widespread dietary deficiency of that vitamin also occurs in Asian countries, where the main food supply is rice. Vitamin A is a compound based on a universal plant pigment; flowers and fruits owe their dazzling colors to orange-colored pigments related to vitamin A. Scientists have inserted a gene from the daffodil, *Narcissus,* that codes for formation of a compound related to vitamin A into rice. The success of that work could have significant implications for reducing vitamin A deficiency in the developing world. Who would have thought that daffodils, the beautiful flowers that have inspired poets for centuries, may, in the future, also lead to a healthier world?

Insect Resistance

Feeding by insects causes significant damage to crop plants. The development of insect-resistant crop varieties has been the most successful application of biotechnology research in agriculture to date. *Bacillus thuringiensis* (Bt) is a bacterium that produces a protein that kills detrimental insects, such as boll weevils or the tomato moth caterpillar,

shown in Figure 1, but does not harm the plant or useful insects, such as ladybugs. The bacterial gene that codes for this protein has been inserted into several plant species, and Bt transgenic crops containing this gene can resist damage from insects. Cotton, corn, and potatoes engineered with such genes were grown commercially for the first time in 1996. A major worry that

Figure 1 *Tomato moth caterpillar five days after feeding on plant treated with* Bacillus thuringiensis.

lurks behind this success, however, is whether insects will develop immunity to the protein as they have to many chemical insecticides.

Marginal Environments

Aluminum is the most abundant metal on earth and is used in products such as beverage cans, kitchen utensils, and aircraft. However, the element aluminum is very unfriendly to agriculture because too much of it in the soil injures plant root cells and thus interferes with root growth and nutrient uptake in crops. Aluminum's harmful effects are worst under acidic conditions since aluminum becomes soluble in acid. More than one-third of the arable land in the world (i.e., land suitable for agriculture) suffers from soil acidity and aluminum toxicity. Therefore, low agricultural productivity in acid soils sometimes can be directly attributed to the effects of aluminum.

Some research that was done in Mexico may provide a breakthrough in solving the problem of aluminum effect on crops. By introducing a specific bacterial gene into tobacco and papaya, Mexican scientists have genetically engineered plants to be more tolerant to this metal, as shown in Figure 2.

Figure 2 *Genetic engineering has produced plants, as shown above (CS-5), that grow normal roots in soil having high aluminum concentrations.*

can test transgenic plants for suspected allergens during development of the plant and alert people to the possible risk.

Public Awareness

The sale of transgenic corn and soybeans has been prohibited in Europe largely due to public outcry against the consumption and planting of genetically engineered products. Although it is important to be aware of potential problems, the public needs to be educated about the positive aspects of genetic engineering in the production of a safe and sound food supply so that people can make informed decisions about the safety of transgenic plants.

Herbicide Resistance

Weeds will grow wherever the soil has been disturbed by cultivation. Weeds are a major problem in crop production because they compete with crops for light, water, and nutrients. Unfortunately, chemical herbicides may kill the crop along with the weeds. There are bacteria that have genes that make them immune to chemical herbicides, and these genes have been introduced into transgenic soybeans. Farmers who grow these transgenic soybeans can apply herbicides to their fields and kill the weeds but not the soybeans.

Potential Problems

A major fear with the current success of agricultural biotechnology is the potential risk that genes from transgenic crops might somehow be transferred to weeds. Introduction of genes for disease or pest resistance into weedy relatives could make them more invasive. That fear is especially troublesome with herbicide-resistance genes because the addition of such a trait could make the weeds impossible to control by application of herbicides.

The development of transgenic food crops to enhance production of food or desirable traits in a plant presents a potential health concern; some protein products of these genes may cause allergic reactions in sensitive individuals. Fortunately, we

Potential Benefits

Biotechnology and genetic engineering can result in rapid improvement in the quality of crops and increased yields. Better nutrition and better availability of food in marginal environments throughout the world can enhance the quality of life of the world's population.

References

Astwood, J. D., J. N. Leach, and R. L. Fuchs. 1996. Stability of food allergens to digestion in vitro. *Nature Biotechnology* 14: pp. 1269–1273.

Barinaga, M. 1997. Making plants aluminum tolerant. *Science* 276: p. 1497.

Burkhardt, P. K., P. Beyer, J. Wunn, A. Kloti, G. A. Armstrong, M. Schledz, J. von Lintig, and I. Potrykus. 1997. Transgenic rice *(Oryza sativa)* endosperm expressing daffodil *(Narcissus psuedonarcissus)* phytoene synthase accumulates phytoene, a ket intermediate of provitamin A biosynthesis. *The Plant Journal*. 11: pp. 1071–1078.

Chevre, A. M., F. Eber, A. Baranger, and M. Renard. 1997. Gene flow from transgenic crops. *Nature* 389: p. 924.

de la Fuente, J. M., V. Ramirez-Rodriguez, J. L. Cabrera-Ponce, and L. Herrera-Estrella. 1997. Aluminum tolerance in transgenic plants by alteration of citrate synthesis. *Science* 276: pp. 1566–1568.

Gould, F., A. Anderson, A. Jones, D. Sumerford, D. G. Heckel, J. Lopez, S. Micinski, R. Leonard, and M. Laster. 1997. Initial frequency of alleles for resistance to *Bacillus thuringiensis* toxins infield populations of *Heliothis virescens. Proceedings of the National Academy of Science*, USA 94: pp. 3519–3523.

Genetic Engineering in Agriculture: A Technology with Roots Deep in the Past

Additional Resources

Watson, J. D., M. Gilman, J. Witkowski, and M. Zoller. 1992. *Recombinant DNA*. W. H. Freeman and Company, New York.

This book reviews the biology of genetic engineering. A chapter on the genetic engineering of plants describes how recombinant DNA technology is used in plants.

Questions for Discussion

1. What are some of the important discoveries in biology that were required before genetic engineering of plants became possible?

2. What are the major ways we can improve crop plants through genetic engineering?

3. What are some potential problems that may result from the use of genetically engineered plants?

Applications

1. Think of your least favorite vegetable. What factor would you change to make it more likable (for example, taste, texture, color, odor)? Now think of a vegetable that has a more desirable factor than the one you would like to change. Describe what your least favorite vegetable would be like if you could move a gene or genes to make that change.

2. Describe what might happen if herbicide-resistance genes were somehow transferred to weeds that grew adjacent to a field of soybeans.

3. What might be the consequences of providing genetically engineered food to malnourished people?

6.1 What's That Blob of Mud on the Wall?

Robert W. Matthews, Ph.D.
Department of Entomology
The University of Georgia, Athens, Georgia

Dr. Matthews is an entomologist who teaches, writes books, and does research on the behavior of insects. He specializes in the study of stinging insects—bees, wasps, and hornets. His most recent work is the development of activities for high school classrooms using the parasitic wasp Melittobia *as a model system for studying insect behavior.*

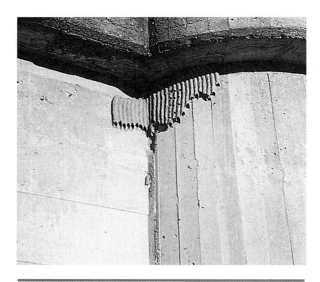

Figure 1 *Each mud dauber tube is a single nest.*

Overview

Mud dauber nests are familiar sights on the walls of barns, under bridges, and on picnic shelters. In this essay, you will discover that these nests house a fascinating group of seldom-seen organisms. Scientists are just beginning to unravel the complex ecological relationships of these organisms. One of these intriguing creatures is a small wasp that turns out to be the major killer of mud dauber larvae. Given the name "WOWBugs," these parasitoid wasps have many strange behaviors.

Nests and Tubes

Most people have seen structures like the one pictured in Figure 1. On the walls of buildings, they may last for years. Long before houses and picnic shelters, they appeared on rock faces that were protected from rain and sun. Now they can also be found almost anywhere that is similarly protected from the elements, as long as mud and spiders are nearby. Why? Who or what made them?

Mud tubes show the efforts of organ pipe mud dauber wasps. (In some parts of the country they are called dirt daubers.) Each tube is a single nest built by one individual. Unlike social wasps such as hornets, these "solitary" wasps do not cooperate with each other to build large nests

> *Given the name "WOWBugs," these parasitoid wasps have many strange behaviors.*

together or rear their young together. Having no community nest to defend, solitary wasps also are not inclined to sting.

A Good Nursery and Cafeteria . . .

If you were to watch one of these beautiful, relatively shy creatures during the summer, you would see that building a single mud tube can take days of work. It looks like a wonderful home. Yet as soon as it is finished, the mud dauber flies off and never returns. If she's not going to live in it, why does a wasp go to all this trouble? The mud structure is a shelter all right, but not for the wasp that built it. Instead, a female mud dauber builds the nest as a nursery for her young. Within its walls, she constructs a series of separate rooms, or cells. In each one, she

Figure 2 *The back side of a mud nest shows individual cells. The top one contains fresh paralyzed spiders. The middle cell contains a feeding larva. The lower one shows the cocoon in which the winter is spent. When next summer comes, new adult mud daubers will chew out through the nest walls and fly off to make new nests.*

places spiders she has stung and carried back to the nest, as shown in Figure 2. The stung spiders are still alive but paralyzed so they cannot get up and run away. It's a good answer to the problem of how to keep food fresh for one's young when there's no refrigerator!

In each cell, the mother mud dauber lays a single egg. If all goes well, it will soon hatch into a grublike larva. It will grow up with fresh spider meat to feed on. The thick walls of the mud nest will safely protect it from enemies, and the cell partitions will isolate it from its brothers and sisters—an important consideration since wasp larvae are cannibals!

It sounds like a good plan. How well does it work?

. . . But Not a Very Good Fortress

Mud dauber nests turn out to hold much more than young mud daubers and their spider food. For example, when scientists opened large series of nests from Missouri, Mississippi, and Alabama, they found that in almost half of the nest cells, something had attacked the immature mud dauber. What happened?

By careful observation and dissection, scientists have shown that many animals, large and small, find food in a mud dauber nest. Together they make up a little community tied together by a web of energy transfers. A typical food web is described in Figure 3. It is a complex world, and describing these interactions can be more difficult than it would seem.

Predators

Many of the mud dauber's enemies are clearly predators. A predator is a meat-eater that is larger than its prey. During its lifetime, it attacks more than one individual, which it kills and devours outright. For example, birds such as tufted titmice peck into nests to feed on the larvae during the lean winter months. Certain kinds of flies sneak in while the tube is still open and lay their eggs next to those of the wasp. The maggots of these "pirates" hatch more quickly than the wasp eggs do, and they devour the spiders' plump bodies, leaving only a pile of legs behind for the starving larva. If the maggots' hunger is still unsatisfied, they will move on from one cell to the next to find more spiders.

Scavengers

Other enemies of the mud dauber are scavenger insects that feed upon waste materials. Book lice and carpet beetles are examples of scavengers. These insects quickly move into cells where young mud daubers have died or been destroyed.

Parasites

The mud dauber is frequently prey for parasites. WOWBugs are one example of a parasite that feeds on the larvae of the mud dauber. Parasites are organisms that live in or on other living organisms (hosts) from which their food is obtained. The hosts are usually larger and are not destroyed directly by the feeding of the parasites. Tapeworms and ticks are familiar examples.

All species of insects and all stages of their development probably are subject to parasitism, but the true parasites of insects are poorly known. Instead, scientists say, the most important types of insect parasites are the ones known as parasitoids. These are the organisms most often used in the natural pest control methods called "biological control."

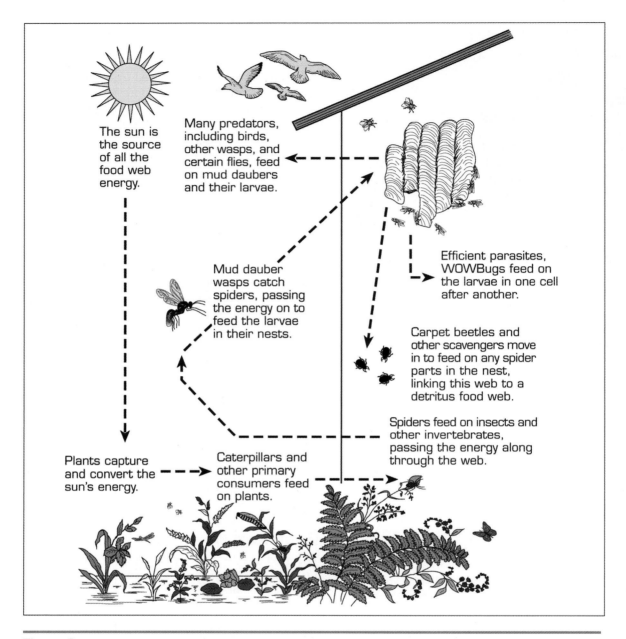

Figure 3 *A simplified representation of the food web that centers around a mud dauber's nest.*

Parasitoids

Like a predator, a parasitoid kills its host. Like a parasite, a parasitoid is smaller than that host and lives on or in a single host for its entire life. The most important enemies of mud daubers are parasitoids that kill the larva by feeding upon it.

The most common of them all is *Melittobia*, a little wasp no bigger than an ant or a fruit fly. *Melittobia* are parasitic wasps found all around the world. There are at least six different species in North America. All of them are about 1 millimeter long and live fairly similar lives.

What's That Blob of Mud on the Wall?

The Wondrous WOWBug

In one study after another, tiny *Melittobia* has been the major killer of mud dauber larvae. Scientists and naturalists routinely find them in about one-third of all the cells they investigate.

When it comes to taking advantage of a host, *Melittobia* is a real powerhouse of a parasitoid. One female can produce more than 500 offspring in under three weeks at normal room temperatures. Under normal conditions, about 95 percent of these offspring will be females who can each go on to produce 500 more. By the time a mud dauber has finished building one summer's nests, a single female *Melittobia* could have given rise to more than a million descendants! This is just one of many reasons why people call these insects WOWBugs.

Although mud dauber larvae are a favorite host, WOWBugs can also feed on the young of over 20 other insect species. Two things about a host are especially important to them. First, the hosts have to be in a helpless condition, such as a larva or pupa trapped inside a cocoon. Second, the hosts have to have fairly thin skin. Why?

A wasp's stinger is really an egg-laying tube called an ovipositor. In many species, it has become adapted to also deliver venom. Social wasps, such as hornets, use this venom to defend their nests. Solitary wasps use venom to paralyze other invertebrates to use as food for their young. WOWBugs use their stinger to puncture their host in order to get the fluids they need to begin maturing eggs. (They can't sting through people's tough skin; their stinger is much too tiny and weak for that.)

After a female WOWBug has found a host and stung it, she begins to mature her eggs. She spends several days laying batches of eggs all over the outside of the insect larva or pupa. Three days after they are laid, WOWBug eggs hatch into larvae with voracious appetites. In a week or less, nothing is left of the host but dust, and the larvae begin to pupate.

Adults

By 17 to 21 days from the time their mother first found the host, new adult WOWBugs emerge. The first to appear are honey-colored males with

Figure 4 *These electronmicrographs show female (left) and male (right) WOWBugs, whose scientific name is* Melittobia digitata.

stumpy wings, antler-shaped antennae, and no compound eyes. Next come jet black females with normal compound eyes and fully developed wings. Both female and male WOWBugs are pictured in Figure 4.

The blind males almost never leave their birth site. Within the darkness of the cocoon, they produce an odor, or sex pheromone, that is highly attractive to unmated females. Mated females simply ignore them. When, instead of a female, a male finds another male, the result is a vicious battle that often leaves one or the other dismembered or dead.

Even though they have wings, female WOWBugs apparently seldom fly. Instead they spread out from the original nest by walking, running, and hopping. Adult WOWBugs live for two to three weeks without food or water before they finally run out of energy and die. But during this time, the mated females search avidly for new hosts. Since 500 or more female WOWBugs may emerge from a single mud dauber nest cell, it isn't long before at least some of them find any other suitable hosts that may be nearby.

> *Even though they have wings, female WOWBugs apparently seldom fly.*

Unanswered WOWBug Questions

Many different questions about *Melittobia* still need answers. For example, do these tiny parasites actually seek out their hosts? Or do they just bumble into them by chance? No one knows. What determines the way a WOWBug moves? Do they ever fly? When? And what makes them decide to hop?

When you look at them under a microscope, WOWBugs don't seem to have any special adaptations for hopping. How do they do it? Remember, the female lays eggs only on fully grown larvae that are about to pupate. How does she know they're ready? Do they smell different to her then?

Do WOWBugs have other strange behaviors that haven't been discovered yet? A final question hints that they do. Almost always, female *Melittobia* have quite normal-looking wings. However, under some conditions, a population of *Melittobia* that usually has long-winged females will suddenly give rise to a generation of short-winged females. No one has figured out why this happens.

WOWBugs are easy to handle, and no expensive equipment is needed to raise them or to study them. One doesn't have to be a professional scientist to learn more about them. Many science teachers have begun helping students do classroom activities with them. WOWBugs are also good for science fair experiments. Even though they are found almost everywhere that mud dauber wasps build their nests, many questions remain about WOWBugs. Perhaps you are the person who could answer some of them!

Additional Resources

Matthews, R. W. 1997. Teaching ecological interactions with mud dauber nests. *American Biology Teacher* 59: pp. 152–158.
   A "how-to-do-it" activity that includes instructions for dissecting nests of mud dauber wasps and using a dichotomous key to identify nest inhabitants.

Matthews, R. W. 1997. Weird wonderful WOWBugs. *Carolina Tips* vol. 60, no. 2, pp. 9–11. Carolina Biological Supply Co., Burlington, NC.
   A brief pictorial essay on the biology and habits of the WOWBug, *Melittobia digitata,* with information on how to obtain them.

Matthews, R. W., T. R. Koballa, Jr., L. R. Flage, and E. J. Pyle. 1996. *WOWBugs: New Life for Life Science.* Riverview Press, Athens, GA.
   Includes 20 activities using WOWBugs with numerous suggestions for extended independent investigations and extensive background information on WOWBugs and mud daubers.

Questions for Discussion

1. Create a life history timeline for a WOWBug. How does this WOWBug timeline compare to the life history of a human such as yourself?

2. What percentage of the cells in a mud dauber nest are attacked by WOWBugs? If a female mud dauber can only make about 12 nest cells in her lifetime, how many offspring would survive the WOWBugs to become part of next year's population? Why aren't mud daubers overrunning the world?

3. What is the purpose of a wasp's stinger? Can WOWBugs sting people? Why or why not?

4. How are predators, scavengers, parasites, and parasitoids alike? How are they different? Design a chart or table that shows this.

Applications

1. Many kinds of animals produce more of one sex than of the other. Usually the more abundant sex is the one that faces greater risks in its life. How do the lives of a male and female WOWBug fit into this picture?

2. When might you expect to find exponential growth in a mud dauber population? When might you expect to find it in a WOWBug population? In each case, what might happen to slow it down or stop it?

3. Scientists estimate that we have identified no more than 10 percent of the species of living organisms on earth. Do you think this lack of knowledge also applies to *Melittobia* species? If so, how many *Melittobia* species might exist in North America alone?

4. Design a food web that includes *Melittobia.* Then redraw the food web adding an exotic species. For example, suppose someone introduced into North America an Asian woodpecker that destroyed mud dauber nests. Refer to your food web, and name at least three ways that biodiversity would be affected by the introduction of this exotic species.

What's That Blob of Mud on the Wall?

6.2 Getting Acquainted with Spiders

Larry A. Weber, M.S.
The Marshall School, Duluth, Minnesota

Mr. Weber received his M.S. in biology from St. Mary's University in Winona, Minnesota, in 1971. He has taught for 30 years in all grades from seventh to graduate school. His phenology-based science teaching has earned several awards, including Minnesota Science Teacher of the Year for 1993. He is currently teaching at The Marshall School in Duluth, Minnesota. His writing and close-up photography have been part of his teaching, lecturing, and articles for years. He has spoken at science teacher conferences in much of the country. His studies include spiders and insects that he has observed extensively during the last 20 years. He is currently studying winter-active insects.

Overview

What has eight legs but may walk slowly, has eight eyes but usually poor sight, devours hundreds of insects but cannot chew, and flies without wings? Some can jump 20 times their body length, change color to fit surroundings, and construct homes and hunting nets from material within their body. Though nearly all are poisonous, less than 0.1 percent can hurt humans. What are these critters? Spiders! And most likely hundreds live in your yard.

What Are Spiders?

Though often thought of as insects, spiders differ in several ways. Insects have three body parts; spiders have two. Insects have six legs, usually four wings, and two antennae; spiders, eight legs with no wings or antennae. Insects and spiders are separate divisions within the phylum Arthropoda. Spiders are arachnids along with ticks, mites, scorpions, and harvestmen. A typical spider is pictured in Figure 1.

All eight legs are attached to the first body part, the cephalothorax. Here too are eyes, mouth, pedipalps, chelicerae, fangs, poison glands, and sucking stomach. The abdomen, usually larger than the cephalothorax, holds the heart, intestine, kidneys, book lungs (breathing parts), reproductive organs,

and silk glands. These glands produce five or six types of silk inside the body and lead to spinnerets outside. Most spiders have three pairs of spinnerets and use them in making webs, egg cases, shelters, and draglines; wrapping prey; ballooning; and mating rituals. Even the word *spider* is derived from spinder, referring to spinning.

How Spiders Eat

As predators of insects, you might think that not being able to chew would present some problems for spiders. However, they are well equipped to handle this situation. Once a spider gets its prey, either in a web or otherwise, it plunges fangs into the body. These fangs are on facial organs called chelicerae that act as jaws. Instantly venom from poison glands located internally below the eyes is injected into the struggling insect. The venom attacks nerves while enzymes convert body insides into liquid. To ingest its fluid food, the hungry spider uses powerful sucking stomach muscles. Large spiders crush the victim's body, while small ones leave it intact but hollow. Fangs, venom, and strong stomach muscles allow these hunters to cope well without chewing.

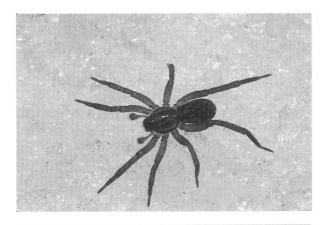

Figure 1 *Spiders have two body parts with eight legs. The boxing-glove shaped pedipalps in front of the head identify this as a male.*

Spider Families

Though worldwide spiders number about 40,000 species in nearly 100 families, we will look at only 10 common ones. All spiders are predators, but they can be put into two groups by how they hunt. Some families make webs to snare food, but most do not.

Webless

Perhaps best known of the webless spiders are wolf spiders (Lycosidae), such as the one pictured in Figure 2. Typically these spiders have hairy bodies of brown or gray, often striped. Their bodies (excluding legs) may be an inch long. We usually

Figure 2 *This wolf spider uses its large eyes to efficiently hunt prey at night.*

see them running on ground, sidewalks, streets, or maybe indoors. Wolf spiders get this name because they hunt at night using large posterior medial eyes to locate and run after prey. In late spring, females carry a ball-shaped egg sac attached to spinnerets. After hatching, spiderlings ride on the abdomen for about a week as mothers stay in hiding.

Often confused with wolf spiders are the nursery-web spiders (Pisauridae). They are also known as fishing or dock spiders because many live near water. Members of this group may be some of our largest spiders. When stretching out their legs, they could take up much of your palm. Often seen along water's edge, they are able to spread their legs and run over the surface. Mostly feeding on water insects, they can eat tadpoles and small fish as well.

Also hunting actively, jumping spiders (Salticidae) do their searching in the daytime. Unlike most spiders, they seek out bright sunlight and use large anterior medial eyes to find prey and leap on it. Small and colorful, these spiders are very adept at hunting flies, often jumping many times their body length. Deception is the hunting style adopted by the crab spiders (Thomisidae). Though many species are drab and look like the bark they live on, other bright ones are found on flowers. Some even change color when moving to another kind of flower. Here they wait with outstretched legs for a visiting bee, wasp, or fly that they quickly grasp. This pose gives the crab spider its name.

Web Makers

Web construction among spiders varies, and six families make four basic types of nets. Large circular orb webs may be best known but are not as common as cob, sheet, or funnel webs.

Cobwebs of cellar spiders (Pholcidae) and comb-footed spiders (Theridiidae) are similar and consist of an apparent haphazard network of threads. Spiders of both families hang upside down in webs. Cellar spiders get their name from often making webs indoors in basements. They have long, thin legs on gray bodies, and some have only six eyes. Comb-footed spiders have bristles (used to work silk) on the fourth pair of legs. The family includes well-known members such as the house spider and black widow.

Sheet-web spiders (Linyphiidae) construct a dome- or bowl-shaped web in trees and shrubs, often evergreens. Spiders hang under the dome and grasp struggling insects that fall into this trap. These spiders stay active far into fall and even winter.

Common in grass during late summer and fall are the funnel webs. Webs appear to be a sheet, but a closer look reveals a hole in the center. Here the owner sits ready to catch insects that blunder onto the snare. Funnel-web spiders (Agelenidae) are usually brown, often striped, with long spinnerets that look like tails. Found in lawns and woods, funnel-web spiders will also live in buildings. Barns, garages, and porches hold many webs.

Large and beautiful orb webs are the product of two families of spiders. Each makes the web of two kinds of silk. Nonsticky spokes lead to the center, while sticky threads make up the circling spirals. By walking on spokes, orb-web makers can avoid being caught in their own traps. Most orb-web spiders (Araneidae) are nearly blind and often have huge abdomens, so big that some can hardly walk. Webs hang in trees, shrubs, grasses, fences, and signs with the alert owner either in the middle or at the edge. Two well-known orb spiders are the spotted shamrock spider and the black-and-yellow garden spider. Other orb webs in meadows or swamps are the work of long-jawed spiders (Tetragnathidae). These thin, long-legged spiders with large chelicerae and fangs make webs usually more horizontal than the other orb makers.

Life History of Spiders

Though some spend winters as adults, most spiders appear to survive the cold as immatures or eggs. Growing during spring, most reach maturity in summer. Along with web making and hunting, spiders mate and lay eggs in warm months. Egg sacs, often left in or near webs, hatch out many tiny spiders known as spiderlings. Living on stored food at first, they stay nearby until the supply is gone. Still tiny, the babies disperse to other locations. Taking advantage of their small size, spiderlings climb on a branch or blade of grass and throw out thread from silk glands until breezes carry them off. This technique, known as ballooning, is highly effective; and young spiders have been known to travel hundreds of miles. For most, the trip is short; and discarded threads in lawns, trees, and fences tell of these travels. Ballooning happens often during the year but is most easily seen in fall among the bare trees. Once settled, spiders go through a series of molts until they are mature. Webs and hunting styles are developed during maturing time, and many meals of insects allow them to reach adulthood. Females are usually larger than males, and in some species, the female is 10 times the male's size. Males develop swellings in pedipalps where they carry sperm during mating, as seen in Figure 1.

Mating among webless spiders, such as wolf and jumping spiders, may involve elaborate and beautiful dances. With poor vision, web makers rely on other methods for attention. A male approaches the female in her web and despite the fact that he is trespassing close to a large, hungry owner, he is able to court her by plucking the threads in a series of vibrations that lets her know of his peaceful intent. A short time after insemination, she forms an egg sac and the cycle continues.

Construction of the Orb Web

In ingenuity and beauty, no web type equals that of the large circular orb, as pictured in Figure 3. Its construction follows a regular and routine fashion with little variation among the makers.

Orb webs are usually made at dusk and, depending on the size, can take about an hour to make. The vertical web is begun with a thread stretched across a space and anchored on each end. Once secured, the spider walks over this bridge and attaches another thread dropping down to make a Y-shaped pattern. The meeting site of this silk becomes the center, or hub, of the web. More threads are drawn out from this hub

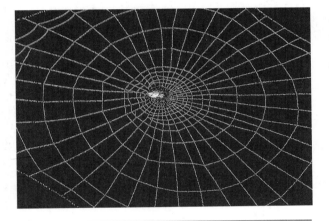

Figure 3 *This orb web shows characteristic sticky spirals and nonsticky spokes.*

to make a series of nonsticky radii, or spokes. Since the spider walks on these spokes to lay down the sticky spirals, spokes number more and are closer together in the small spiders with fewer spokes and further apart among larger spiders. A temporary spiral is fitted on the spokes before being finalized.

Most insects are caught during nocturnal hours. Their struggles tear the web; and this is often followed by a coating of morning dew, making most webs in need of repair by the next day. Owners will repair the snare if hunting is good but destroy it by ingesting it and moving on to another site if hunting is not good.

Spider Bites

Bites of spiders are often spoken about, and spiders are regularly blamed for the many itches and rashes that we may have. The spiders, however, are many times wrongly accused. These wounds may be the result of close contacts with some other critters. Some authorities say that up to 80 percent of "spider bites" are misdiagnosed. Few spiders are powerful enough to penetrate our skin; and among those that can, nearly all have a weak venom that leaves us with an itch or, at most, a small open sore.

Contrary to popular opinions, tarantulas are not true spiders and their bite is not poisonous; though their bite may be painful, it is no more dangerous than that of a bee sting. Spiders with venom powerful enough to hurt humans are rare but do exist, mostly in the warmer areas of the world, including the southern United States.

Two spiders that may be most venomous are the brown recluse (*Loxosceles reclusa*) and the black widow (*Lactrodectus mactans*). Both are more commonly found in the southern United States but may be transported north during the warmer months. Both spiders are shy and prefer to stay in hiding but have been known to bite when in close contact with humans.

Because of the fiddle-shaped pattern on its back, as shown in Figure 4, the brown recluse also has

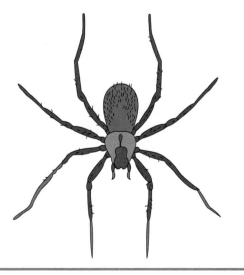

Figure 4   *The fiddle-shaped pattern on its back is the best identifying characteristic of the venomous brown recluse spider.*

been called the violin spider. Their painless bites may cause tissue death near the site and can create sores up to several inches in diameter. A dark blister results from the dead cells. Typically a victim will recover from this wound with no harm done; but in rare cases, depending on the physical condition of the victim, further complications can develop.

Black widows have a red "hour glass" pattern under the abdomen. Since they hang in a cob web upside down, this shape is easily seen on the black body. Affecting nerves, their venom can cause muscle cramps and pain in parts far from the bite site. Often pain is in the abdomen, chest, arms, or legs and may persist for a few days; but few people suffer lasting problems.

If you are concerned about being bitten, you don't need to touch spiders. Much can be observed of these fascinating critters by just watching.

Ten Activities You Can Do with Spiders (without Touching Any)

1. Photograph dew-covered spider webs in the early mornings of late summer.
2. Observe an orb-web spider making its web. Note when this happens and how long it takes. Observe the web later.
3. Watch how orb-web spiders catch and subdue their prey.
4. Count the number of webs on a dock or building on a summer evening.
5. Look for a spider that lives in the web of another spider and feeds on its food.
6. Locate funnel webs and try to see the spider sitting at the entrance of the hole.
7. Find a cob web with egg sacs present and watch what happens after the sacs open.
8. Search a sunny wall and try to locate jumping spiders.
9. Examine black-eyed susans and daisies and try to find crab spiders hunting there.
10. In a pond or swamp, watch a fishing spider run over the surface of the water. How does it do this?

Additional Resources

Crompton, J. 1950. *The Spider*. Nick Lyons Books. New York, NY.

    This book is pleasant and easy to read. The author describes life histories and habits of spiders. The interesting information reads like a novel.

Fabre, J. H. 1913. *The Life of the Spider*. Dodd, Mead. New York, NY.

    Though the book is dated, its reading style is enjoyable. Fabre, as an observer, is in a class by himself; and his stories are great additions to our knowledge of spiders.

Foelix, R. F. 1996. *Biology of Spiders*. Harvard Press. Cambridge, MA.

    Likely the most comprehensive book for the serious student of spiders. Nearly all aspects of spiders are covered, often with excellent pictures and diagrams.

Gertch, W. J. 1979. *American Spiders*. Van Nostrand Reinhold. New York, NY.

    An excellent overview of the spiders of this country. Different spider families are written about and the natural history of each explained. Much information about local spiders groups can be found here.

Hillyard, P. 1994. *The Book of the Spider*. Random House. New York, NY.

    The spider is examined historically and scientifically in this book. A great resource for the person interested in the spider in folklore as well as factual information.

Jones, D. 1983. *The Larousse Guide to Spiders*. Larousse Company. New York, NY.

    Even though the author deals with European spiders, the families are similar to American spiders; information, diagrams, and pictures are excellent.

Kaston, B. J. 1978. *How to Know the Spiders*. Wm. C. Brown Company. Dubuque, IA.

    Widely used (though dated and limited in the kinds of spiders identified), it still may be the easiest key to use.

Levi, H. W., L. R. Levi, and H. S. Zim. 1990. *Spiders and Their Kin*. Golden Press. New York, NY.

    Excellent and probably the best-known guide for American spiders. Can be used by both the beginner and experienced. Pictures, organization are excellent; limited species. Certainly this is the book to get if you are interested or can get only one book.

Questions for Discussion

1. List at least five ways in which spiders differ from insects.
2. What are five other arachnids besides spiders?
3. How do web and webless spiders subdue their prey?
4. Compare the advantages of spiders making webs to those that don't.

Applications

1. Find a web in your yard. What kind of spider is it? How can you tell if the web is still in use?
2. A strong insecticide is applied to a yard and kills 90 percent of all insects and spiders living there. What do you think the yard will be like in the next year and why?
3. Many spider webs show some rips from a night of hunting. On closer inspection, the threads may hold scales from moths' wings but no moths are seen. What does this tell you of the adaptations of moths?
4. It's an autumn day with clear, light winds. In the late afternoon, you look towards the sun and see hundreds of threads of spiders. What has been happening here? Why?
5. You capture a spider in your yard. It has a big abdomen. A day later it makes an egg sac in the jar it is in. What does this tell you about the spider? What will become of it and the egg sac?
6. Why is it not a good idea to put two live spiders in the same jar at the same time? What does this tell you about spiders' social lives?

6.3 ChimpanZoo

Virginia Landau, Ph.D.
ChimpanZoo, The Jane Goodall Institute
University of Arizona, Tucson, Arizona

Dr. Landau began her college education as an elementary education major. After many years as a military wife, she went back to school and earned a bachelor's degree in anthropology, followed by master's and doctoral degrees in comparative psychology and neuropsychology. Shortly thereafter, she began work as a primatologist with the Jane Goodall Institute. Her job was to revise and develop a new program called ChimpanZoo. Dr. Landau now directs the ChimpanZoo program and continues as a staff primatologist with the Jane Goodall Institute.

Overview

ChimpanZoo was established in 1984 as a collective effort between the Jane Goodall Institute, zoological facilities, and universities. The purpose of the program is to apply uniform research methods to learn more about chimpanzees *(Pan Troglodytes)* and their psychological and behavioral responses to a captive environment. ChimpanZoo now involves more than 150 chimps in 12 animal facilities throughout the world. Each member facility has a ChimpanZoo team consisting of volunteers, zoo administrators, and students.

ChimpanZoo research results serve to improve our understanding of higher apes in captive environments and help promote psychological well-being through enrichment activities. By 1997, the ChimpanZoo database, containing more than 49,000 individual observation samples, was the largest collection of accessible information on captive chimps in the world. A standardized research procedure is used to permit data collection and comparison from many different environments.

ChimpanZoo relies upon an intensive network of communications through newsletters, program reports, monthly reports, and site visits. Annual ChimpanZoo conferences make it possible for representatives from zoos and universities throughout the world to hear presentations of their data and to exchange research results.

Recognizing a Need

Dr. Jane Goodall is known worldwide for her pioneering research on the behavior of chimps in their native habitats. Perhaps less known to the general public are her efforts to improve the quality of life for chimps in captivity, zoos, and universities throughout the United States and the world.

Captive chimps, such as the one in Figure 1, face an existence much different from that experienced by their wild cousins. Wild chimps live in quiet forests among communities of family and friends.

Figure 1 *A chimp in a natural habitat in the ChimpanZoo program.*

In contrast, captive chimps are more likely to lead solitary existences or to communicate with only a limited number of other chimps. They may be raised by humans or by unrelated female chimps. They are often transported to distant institutions and new social groups, often for breeding purposes. Many older chimps spent their early years in circuses or as pets.

ChimpanZoo was created by Dr. Jane Goodall in 1986 as a program that would help to improve the physical and psychological well-being of chimps raised in captivity. Dr. Goodall had spent her life observing and recording the behavior of wild chimpanzees in Africa. She recognized that considerable research was needed to discover how chimps in captivity were affected by the unnatural world in which they lived.

ChimpanZoo researchers observe the social interactions among the chimps, how the type of enclosure influences aggressive or unnatural behavior, and how manipulated enrichments to their environment affect the chimps. The omnipresence of humans is a major factor in the lives of captive chimps. This is a major contrast to the lives led by wild chimps, who might only occasionally encounter humans. Consequently, captive chimps are often "street smart"—they are aware of and react to humans in ways much different than would their wild cousins.

Data Collection Is a Volunteer Effort

The Jane Goodall Institute ChimpanZoo office in Tucson, Arizona, serves as a central database for the observations collected by ChimpanZoo researchers from throughout the world. This database is remarkable for the fact that the observers who collect the data are a mix of both professionals and volunteers trained in animal research. Volunteers enroll in intensive training programs lasting up to 16 weeks, with classes twice a week, before they are allowed to collect research data. After successfully completing their training, volunteers are asked to commit to at least one year of data collection for at least two hours each week. It's not an easy task. They are tested every six months to ensure they maintain their observation skills. About half the volunteers quit after six months. But those who stay tend to remain in the program for many years.

Volunteers learn about general primate behavior and about chimps in particular. They study photos of each chimp at their zoo or university to learn to recognize individual chimps. They observe chimp behavior on videos and by watching chimps, with an instructor pointing out specific behaviors.

Making Observations

Data are recorded on a laptop computer using software developed especially for ChimpanZoo and the study of chimpanzee behavior at multiple sites. Data collection and database software are also applicable to research studies of other nonhuman primates as well as humans.

The ChimpanZoo data collection program (CZOO) is divided into two parts: (1) a header and (2) behavioral information. Header information identifies the researcher, subjects, institution, type of facility, date and time, length of time between point samples, duration of the observation session, and environmental factors (weather conditions, audience size, and noise levels).

When the observer completes entering the header information, a computer prompt reminds the observer to begin collecting behavioral data. The observer first chooses a contextual category, such as affinitive, mother-infant, agonistic, submissive, or solitary behavior. The observer selects the appropriate context and is then prompted by the computer to enter the observed behavior. Behavior can only be entered in appropriate contexts. If the observer attempts to enter a behavior that is inappropriate to the selected context, the computer responds with an error message. If a researcher misses a sample point, the program automatically restarts the clock for the next sample point.

Behavior is arranged in broad hierarchical categories. For example, aggressive behaviors can only be entered under the agonistic context. If an observer wished to record the observation of a charging display, the context *agonistic* would be entered followed by a four-letter code for a charging display. A submenu would then appear on the screen for the observer to indicate which stage of the several behaviors that make up a charging display was observed. An automatic prompt then appears on the computer screen to remind the observer to record the direction of the charge. (Who charged whom?) If the chimp

> *The omnipresence of humans is a major factor in the lives of captive chimps.*

<u>Beg</u> - A chimpanzee begs for food, a toy, or any desirable object from the possessor. There are four begging behaviors on the submenu:

> (C) <u>CLAPPING</u> - Some chimpanzees clap to produce attention-attracting noises. Score this behavior only when the clapping occurs on the beep.

> (H) <u>HAND</u> - A chimpanzee uses an extended hand or hands with palm facing up to beg. This response is directed towards a particular chimpanzee. This is not the same as a submissive hand response.

> (M) <u>MOUTH</u> - The chimpanzee begs for food or an object with its mouth. The begging chimp puts its lips to the object, which may be in the mouth, hand, or foot of another chimpanzee. This may result in mouth-to-mouth or hand-to-mouth transfer of food. It is a typical infant-to-mother behavior.

> (S) <u>STARE</u> - In some instances, chimpanzees stare (gaze intently) at another chimpanzee or human in an attempt to acquire food or objects. If the chimpanzee is staring intently at another chimpanzee while using its mouth or hands to beg, score the behavior mouth or hands. Stare is to be scored when the chimpanzee is using visual cues *only* to beg. This submenu behavior is scored when the chimp is staring at the beep.

Captive chimps beg from keepers and the public, as well as from each other. It is often accompanied by whimpering and if unsuccessful, the begger may throw a tantrum. (Code BEGG)

INSTRUCTION: Enter the context code; press ENTER, then the behavior code (BEGG). Enter the designated letter for a specific Begging behavior (CLAPPING, HAND, MOUTH, OR STARE). The code name of the interactive social partner; the direction of the behavior; and the use of the left, right, or both hands should be entered at the prompt.
Allowable Contexts: PUOR, AFFI, MAIF.

Figure 2   *This ethogram displays the types of data that ChimpanZoo observers enter into their laptop computer programs.*

uses a hand to hold, touch, grab, etc., a computer prompt reminds the observer to indicate the left or right hand or both hands. With this system, ChimpanZoo observers are able to record approximately 1,153 discrete behaviors using 58 behavioral codes. Zoos may alter the computer program to add new behaviors and to record narrative data in order to meet their specific research needs. Though a complete computer data collection sequence cannot easily be shown, Figure 2 describes some of the behaviors that observers might record.

Data are transferred from the laptop computer to diskette and are then sent to the ChimpanZoo headquarters to be placed in the combined database. This step will, in time, be replaced by electronic transfer of data via the Internet.

The ChimpanZoo data collections program for chimpanzees is fully documented with a training guide that includes an ethogram, instructional guide, and a guide to the recording of narrative data. ChimpanZoo data collections methods are taught in zoos and colleges and are currently being adapted for use in high school classes.

Enriching Chimps' Environments

One of the goals of ChimpanZoo is to discover ways to keep chimps busy within the bounds of their captive environments. In the wild, chimps spend much of their time foraging for food. To enhance that behavior in captivity, zookeepers and researchers devise novel "enrichment" activities that include food. For example, zookeepers might cover the floor with hay and then sprinkle sunflower seeds and raisins in it, forcing the chimps to pick through the hay to find the food. Other zoos have constructed artificial termite mounds in chimp enclosures. In nature, chimps poke sticks into termite mounds withdrawing them to lick off termites. Zookeepers inoculate honey into holes in the artificial termite mounds to encourage a similar behavior. Not all enrichment activities involve mimicking nature. Chimps also entertain themselves playing with rag dolls and old clothes and even brushing their teeth. Chimp behavior in captivity is most similar to that in the wild when other chimps are present. Large groups promote natural social behavior.

Chimps in captivity can live very long lives. In 1997, 42 chimps age 34 or older were recorded living in American Zoological Association zoos and the Taronga Zoo in Australia. The oldest is 54 years old. Thirty-four of the 42 known elderly chimps were born in the wild. This latter characteristic makes these elderly chimps particularly interesting to researchers because they are the last generation of captive chimps to have been born in the wild. Laws protecting wild chimpanzee populations now prohibit capture of chimps for transport to United States zoos.

These older chimps provide researchers with opportunities to observe the social roles of older chimps. Older female chimps often instruct new mothers and help with the care of infants. Older chimps may also serve as mediators of disputes among younger chimps. Creating long-term data-bases on individual chimps also provides researchers with the opportunity to document the changes in chimpanzee personality as they age. Male and female chimps exhibit specific, and very different, behavioral changes as they age. Female chimps become more agreeable, dependable, and emotionally stable as they mature. This pattern of change is similar to that observed for male and female humans in various western and nonwestern countries throughout the world. Male chimps, however, exhibit a different behavioral progression. Male chimps become less agreeable, less depend-able, and less emotionally stable as they age.

Towards Systemic Change

Jane Goodall wrote in her book *In the Shadow of Man* that captive chimps "should be given much improved living conditions. . . . we should make every effort to see that he is a well-treated and honored guest." The information gathered and the methods developed in the ChimpanZoo project are being used to accomplish just that—to ensure that these animals that contribute so much to humans have pleasant lives.

Additional Resources

ChimpanZoo: Research, Education, and Enrichment

The Geronimo Building 308, University Boulevard, Tuscon, AZ 85721, 520-621-4785.
Email: vlandau@ccit.arizona.edu

Established in 1984, ChimpanZoo is a collective effort between the Jane Goodall Institute, zoological facili-ties, and universities to apply uniform research methods to learn more about chimpanzees and their responses to a captive environment.

Goodall, J. 1988. *In the Shadow of Man*. San Diego State University Press, San Diego, CA.

A classic on primate research and one of the most enthralling portrayals of animal behavior ever written.

Goodall, J. 1996. *My Life with the Chimpanzees*. Pocket Books.

Her only autobiography written especially for younger readers, this book is illustrated with photos of the author's childhood and years in Africa.

Questions for Discussion

1. What is the function of ChimpanZoo?
2. Describe how ChimpanZoo research can affect the lives of captive chimps.
3. How are computers used in the study of chimp behavior at ChimpanZoo?
4. What are some differences between the aging process of male versus female chimps?
5. Describe how ChimpanZoo researchers study chimp behavior. How does this differ from studies of wild chimps?

Applications

1. What are some reasons why humans should treat chimps with compassion and respect?
2. Identify one other species of animal for which ChimpanZoo may serve as a model. Explain why you chose this particular species.

6.4 The Nature of Behavior

Jim Hutchins, Ph.D.
Department of Anatomy
University of Mississippi Medical Center, Jackson, Mississippi

Dr. Hutchins teaches histology and neuroanatomy to first-year medical students. His research interests include the development of the brain, especially the visual system. He also studies the factors that cause nerve cells to die and possible ways to save them. This knowledge may be able to help patients who have had a stroke. He has been involved in school outreach for almost a decade. In his spare time, he teaches dogs as well as humans, using the same basic principles.

Overview

We all study behavior whether we realize it or not. We must try to understand the behavior of others in order to communicate with them and to have an orderly society. Scientists have studied simple behaviors in animals such as the invertebrate sea slug, *Aplysia*. They have also studied both simple and complex behaviors in humans. A stimulus that evokes simple behaviors in simple organisms can result in complicated behaviors in complex systems. For example, the same light that causes a simple planaria to turn away can cause a human observer to perceive an entire scene and react to it. Bridging the gap between these simple, well-understood behaviors and the complex, poorly understood behaviors will occupy scientists and philosophers for many years to come.

Behavior Ranges from Simple to Complex

A typical textbook defines animal behavior as "all observable . . . responses to changes in an animal's internal or external environment." This definition refers to animals, but it can apply to plants and other types of organisms as well. You can say then that behavior is a characteristic of all living organisms. Behavior allows them to interact with their environment and with one another.

The complexity of animal behavior depends on the complexity of the animal's nervous system. This complexity, in turn, depends on the number of nerve cells present and the number of interconnections among them. Scientists judge behavioral complexity by the number of different behaviors an organism can perform and the number of possible reactions an organism can produce in response to one stimulus.

Simple Nervous Systems Produce Simple Behaviors

Organisms with relatively simple nervous systems usually have limited behavior compared to organisms with more complex nervous systems. Plants, bacteria, fungi, and protists have no nervous system; thus, they are capable of only simple behaviors. At the other extreme, scientists estimate that the number of neurons in the human brain range from 10 billion to 1 trillion. Each human neuron may have as many as 80,000 connections (synapses) with other neurons. Thus, humans have a vast range of behavior.

Because the human nervous system is complex, it is difficult to study the mechanisms by which human neurons produce specific behavior. Instead many scientists study organisms such as the sea slug, *Aplysia,* as shown in Figure 1, and the nematode *Caenorhabditis elegans*. These animals have

Figure 1 *The invertebrate sea slug,* Aplysia, *is widely used as a simple model of the nervous system.*

simple nervous systems. *Aplysia* has about 20,000 neurons and has been used to study how nerves function in reflexes and in simple types of learning. Because of its small size, researchers have been able to characterize the entire nervous system of *C. elegans* in detail. It contains only 302 neurons of 118 types. There are about 8,000 total synapses—about 200 to 300 per neuron.

You may think that it is a bad idea to study such simple nervous systems and apply the knowledge to humans. However, both *Aplysia* and *C. elegans* have quite complex behaviors associated with feeding and mating. Honeybees are another example. Their nervous systems are fairly simple, yet they build elaborate hives, have complex social structure within their colonies, and can communicate the locations of food to each other. On the other hand, organisms with complex nervous systems have some simple behaviors. An example is the knee jerk reflex in humans. This reflex requires the activity of no more than three neurons, as shown in Figure 2.

Complex Nervous Systems Produce a Wider Range of Behaviors

How do the behaviors differ between organisms with simple nervous systems and organisms with complex nervous systems? The greatest difference is in the ability to vary the behavioral response to a given stimulus. For example, compare a fly landing in a Venus flytrap with a fly landing on your arm. When the fly brushes against a trigger hair in the plant, the trap closes. The plant has no other possible behavior. When the fly on your arm touches a hair, you can choose to brush it away, try to swat it, or try to catch it in order to feed it to a pet lizard. You have a huge number of possible behavioral responses.

In this example, the plant has no nervous system, so its genetic makeup determines its behavioral response. In contrast, your response incorporates your past experience (memory) and your thought about the potential outcomes of your action (foresight). Thus, it is much harder to predict how a person will respond to the fly than to predict how the plant will respond.

In general, animals with simpler nervous systems depend more on genetically determined behaviors to adapt to their environment. These behaviors include instinct, reflexes, and taxes. A taxis is any movement toward or away from a stimulus such as light, an electric charge, or a chemical substance. Animals with more complex nervous systems are capable of learning, and they depend on it more as a way of adapting to the environment. A baby chick is able to walk, scratch, and peck at food within minutes of hatching. These behaviors are instinctive—they do not have to be learned. It's as if the chick's behaviors are hard wired in its nervous system, much like the wiring, switches, and outlets of a house's electrical system. However, a human baby must learn how to walk and feed itself. For humans, these are learned behaviors.

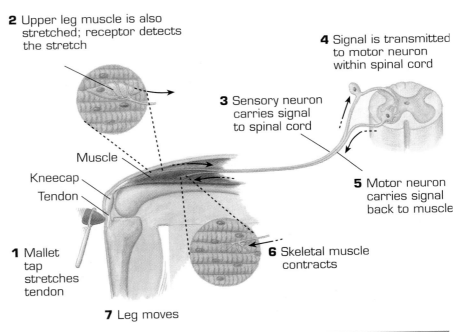

2 Upper leg muscle is also stretched; receptor detects the stretch

4 Signal is transmitted to motor neuron within spinal cord

3 Sensory neuron carries signal to spinal cord

Muscle

Kneecap

Tendon

5 Motor neuron carries signal back to muscle

1 Mallet tap stretches tendon

6 Skeletal muscle contracts

7 Leg moves

Figure 2   *The knee jerk reflex in humans is a simple behavior, requiring the action of three neurons at most.*

a

System without Memory or Foresight

Then

Now

External Influences

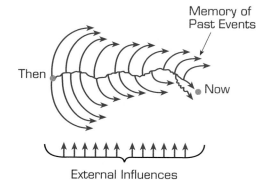

b

System with Memory but No Foresight

Memory of Past Events

Then

Now

External Influences

c

Systems with Memory and Foresight

Memory of Past Events

Then

Now

Envelope of Possible Futures

External Influences

Figure 3 *a. Organisms with very simple nervous systems usually respond in the same way to a repeated stimulus. b. An animal with a more complex nervous system is capable of memory of past events and can use that memory to vary behavior. c. Animals with the most complex nervous systems can choose behaviors based on predictions of possible outcomes.*

Another key difference exists between the behavior of humans and other organisms. Many human behaviors rely not only on experience and learning but also on cultural or societal factors. A human may learn not only to walk but to dance in complex patterns to the rhythm of music. He or she may learn not only how to eat like a baby but also how to dine at an elegant restaurant. Humans have the ability to evaluate their responses to a stimulus and to predict the outcome of each possible response. They base their decisions in part on the social or environmental context in which they find themselves. In a sense, this context acts as a filter that lets humans screen out improper responses. As you probably know, alcohol, drugs, and the urging of other people can often create large holes in the social filter. Use Figure 3 to compare the possible behavioral responses to a stimulus in three nervous systems of increasing complexity.

Examples of Behavioral Models

Genetics determines development of the basic structure of the nervous system. However, both the structure and its function can be modified throughout life by environmental factors. In simple organisms, the connection between input (stimulus) and output (behavior) is usually obvious. For example, most plants will turn or bend toward a source of light such as the sun. Plants do not turn toward a source of sound nor do they point away from the sun. An organism's behavior is limited by its ability to sense stimuli and by the mechanisms it has available to respond to stimuli. For example, when you turn a lamp toward a planaria, it can only turn away from the light. You, on the other hand, can choose to go toward or away from the light, ignore the light, shade your eyes from the light, and a whole variety of other responses.

In animals with simple nervous systems, there is also a fairly simple relationship between the input and output. For example, a harmful stimulus will always cause a withdrawal reaction. If the stimulus is repeated, the response will be the same each time. As nervous systems become more complex, they also become more capable of learning. Therefore, an organism can respond based on experience. At a very high level of complexity, the organism has a conscious awareness of memories and the ability to recall them at will. This awareness enables an organism to develop an ability to predict possible outcomes of various responses to stimuli.

Humans Adapt to a Wide Variety of Environments

Humans have adapted to a huge variety of environments on earth. They live almost from the

North Pole to the South Pole and at altitudes from below sea level to more than 15,000 feet. They survive in both wet and dry environments and at frigid temperatures and in deserts at 120°F. Humans can adapt to extreme conditions because they have a complex range of behaviors and can use learning, memory, and prediction to adjust their behaviors more readily than other species.

Humans are also the only animals able to increase the complexity of their environment beyond their capacity to adapt to it. The limitations of our sensory apparatus make it impossible to see nearby stationary objects when we pass them at the speed of sound. Using computers, we can access information faster than we can take it in. A unique feature of the human mind is the capacity to predict future events from the lessons of the past, to plot imaginary scenarios, and to grasp the consequences of decisions. How will we use these talents in the future to preserve and enrich our own species?

References

Grier, J. W. and T. Burke. 1993. *Biology of Animal Behavior*. New York. McGraw Hill.

Kandel, E. R., J. H. Schwartz, and T. M. Jessell (eds.). 1991. *Principles of Neural Sciences,* 3d ed. New York. Appleton and Lange.

Additional Resources

Cowan, W. M. 1979. The Development of the Brain. *Scientific American*. September.
    This article describes the basic development of the brain with an emphasis on human brain development. The drawings and photographs contained in the article are first-rate.

Kapit, W. and L. M. Elson. 1993. *Anatomy Coloring Book*. 2nd ed. New York. Harper-Collins.
    This book is an excellent resource for students whose learning styles are more visual than verbal.

Moore, K. M. 1993. *Before We Are Born*. 4th ed. Saunders. Philadelphia.
    While most college embryology texts contain a chapter on brain development, this book is for a more general audience and will help answer many questions about human development.

Shatz, C. J. 1992. The Developing Brain. *Scientific American*. September.
    This article contains descriptions of current research efforts aimed at understanding how neurons in the brain are able to form connections in a defined pattern. It focuses on the development of the visual system.

Shepherd, G. M. *Neurobiology*. 3rd ed. 1994. New York. Oxford.
    This college textbook contains an excellent discussion of invertebrate nervous systems.

Questions for Discussion

1. When does an organism with a complex nervous system have complex behavior? Give an example.

2. Invent a short scenario that illustrates how a human uses experience (memory) and the ability to evaluate outcomes (foresight) to determine a response to a stimulus.

3. In addition to experience and learning, list two other factors that influence human behavior.

Applications

1. Classically there are five senses that provide input to the nervous system (sight, sound, touch, taste, and smell). Neuroscientists would add more, including the vestibular sense (movement of the head in space) and proprioception (joint position sense). What forms of output are available to the nervous system?

2. Some people claim to have a "sixth sense," a form of intuition or feeling. What evidence do you have for this, and how might it function?

3. When we learn something, there are subtle changes in the structure and chemistry of the brain. In some forms of mental illness, these changes become severe and behavior is well outside of societal norms. Physical and mental abuse can change the structure and chemistry of the brain so severely that mental illness results. Do you think these findings should release the mentally ill who commit crimes from criminal punishment for their actions? Why or why not?

4. Give three or four examples of simple reflex behaviors that can be modified by effort or will. For example, if you want to, you can stop breathing. Give three examples of simple behaviors that cannot be modified by effort. For example, if you stop breathing long enough, you become unconscious, then begin breathing again.

6.5 The Neurochemistry of Attention Deficit Disorder

Ron C. Michaelis, Ph.D.
J. C. Self Research Institute
Greenwood Genetic Center, Greenwood, South Carolina

Although he now does genetic research, Dr. Michaelis received his Ph.D. in psychology. His first interest was in the neurochemistry of behavior. Some of his work involved the loss of memory and learning ability as people aged. However, the work he found most interesting involved the neurochemistry of drug abuse, especially stimulants. Today he combines his training in the field of drugs and behavior with his knowledge of genetics to search for genes that may be responsible for disorders such as mental retardation or autism.

Overview

You have probably heard of Attention Deficit Disorder (ADD). Many scientists who do research on the human nervous system think that the cause of ADD is in the brain system that controls the feeling we call pleasure. This essay describes one of the neurochemical systems in the brain and illustrates how certain drugs affect the activity of this system. This is a very simplified approach to this topic, in that it discusses only one of the many interacting brain systems that produce the feeling of pleasure. Although the essay discusses only one system, the link between the dopamine pathway and ADD illustrates some interesting principles about the neurochemical control of behavior.

ADD—A Chemical Imbalance

If you know someone who has Attention Deficit Disorder, ADD, you also know that the person finds it very difficult to concentrate for long periods of time on schoolwork, play, or hobbies. What do doctors look for when they diagnose ADD? Psychologists and psychiatrists use information from a book called the *Diagnostic and Statistical Manual* in order to diagnose ADD and other behavioral disorders. This manual says that a person with ADD has "difficulty sustaining attention in tasks or play activities" and "avoids, dislikes, or is reluctant to start tasks that require sustained mental effort." The person is easily distracted by things happening nearby, has trouble remaining seated, and seems always to be on the go.

People with ADD do not suffer from any sort of mental retardation. Instead they have the same range of intelligence as any group of people. But their short attention span makes it difficult for them to perform tasks that require prolonged attention. These types of tasks are important to successful performance at school or work.

Neuropsychologists and neuropsychiatrists are scientists who study the relationship between behavior and the operation of the nervous system. Some of these scientists think that one of the brain systems that malfunctions in some people with ADD is the system that controls feelings of pleasure or reward. They suggest that a person with ADD does not get the same feeling of reward from focusing on a task and carrying it to completion as do most people. Therefore, those with ADD have trouble performing tasks that require sustained attention. According to this idea, drugs that stimulate this pathway should help people with ADD focus their attention on a task for a longer time because they get more pleasure from performing the task.

The Medial Forebrain Bundle

In order to develop effective drugs, scientists needed to know, in part, how the brain controls feelings of pleasure or reward. One important part of this pathway is found in the brain structure known as the medial forebrain bundle, MFB, as shown in Figure 1. The MFB contains bundles of long nerve fibers, mainly from neurons whose cell bodies are in clusters located throughout the hindbrain and posterior midbrain.

Medial Forebrain
Bundle

Figure 1 *This diagram of the human brain shows the location of the medial forebrain bundle, MFB.*

Experiments with rats provide strong evidence that the MFB contains a pleasure pathway. Scientists place electrodes into the rats' brains and connect the electrodes to a source of electric current. These electrodes can deliver a small electrical current into the MFB. Rats are able to press a lever to give themselves the electrical stimulation. Amazingly rats press the lever repeatedly as fast as they can, even to the point of exhaustion. Rats also ignore food and water in favor of the electrical stimulus, even when they have been deprived of these vital materials. They will even walk across grids that give them an electric shock in order to reach the lever. Scientists conclude that the rats receive a sensation of pleasure from electric stimulation of the MFB. Otherwise, they would have no reason to keep pressing the lever.

A Neurotransmitter Called Dopamine

Neurotransmitters are the chemicals that pass a nerve impulse from one neuron to the next. When an impulse reaches the end of one neuron, the neuron secretes a neurotransmitter into the synapse, the small space between neurons. The neurotransmitter then binds to receptor proteins on the next neuron, starting an impulse in that neuron. Scientists often say that the neuron fires, as shown in Figure 2. One of the fiber bundles in the MFB contains neurons that secrete a neurotransmitter called dopamine, DA, whose chemical structure is shown in Figure 3, along with the chemical structures of five other drugs in the catecholamine family.

When it fires, one of these neurons releases dopamine into the synapse. The dopamine binds to receptor proteins on the surface of the next (postsynaptic) neuron. The dopamine causes the firing rate of the next neuron to increase, which, in turn, increases the firing rate of all of the following neurons in the chain. This stimulation of neurons in the MFB results in feelings of pleasure or reward. If the dopamine remains on the receptor proteins, the neuron fires again and again and may be damaged. To prevent this from happening, the dopamine is absorbed back into the first neuron. Research shows that drugs that block dopamine receptors greatly reduce the rewarding power caused by

The neuron fires, releasing dopamine (DA) into the synapse. The DA then binds to DA receptors on the postsynaptic neuron. This is enhanced by amphetamine and Ritalin.

Presynaptic neuron with dopamine (DA) storage vesicles

DA

DA   DA

DA

Postsynaptic neuron with DA receptors

DA transporter protein transports DA back to presynaptic DA neuron—inhibited by amphetamine and Ritalin.

Figure 2 *When a nerve impulse reaches the end of the presynaptic neuron on the left, the neuron secretes a chemical called a neurotransmitter into the synapse. When the chemical binds to the receptor proteins in the neuron on the right, an impulse begins in that neuron.*

Figure 3 *The chemical structure of dopamine compared to other catecholamine drugs. Notice the similarities in the chemical structures of dopamine and the drugs amphetamine and Ritalin. This similarity partly explains their similar activities.*

electric stimulation of the MFB. On the other hand, drugs that increase the activity of dopamine neurons increase the reward value. This suggests that these nuerons in the MFB are an important part of the "pleasure pathway." Therefore, scientists think that a person with ADD might benefit from drugs that increase the activity of dopamine-containing neurons. The drugs should increase the feelings of reward that the person receives from focusing on a task.

Amphetamine and Ritalin— The Lesser of Two Evils

Scientists know that the drugs amphetamine and Ritalin, shown in Figure 3, stimulate dopamine-containing neurons. They are also the most effec-tive drugs known for treating ADD in many patients. Both amphetamine and Ritalin act in two ways. First, they stimulate the release of dopamine into the synapse. Second, they inhibit the proteins that remove dopamine from the synapse and carry it back to the cell that released it. The result is that the cell releases more dopamine into the synapse and it remains there for a longer time.

People with ADD have taken amphetamine and Ritalin for many years now with a reasonable degree of success. However, physicians are always concerned about prescribing a drug that can be abused or that is addic-tive. They are especially cautious about prescribing such drugs for young chil-dren who will need to take the drug for several years. For these reasons, doctors usually prefer Ritalin over amphetamine. Ritalin is not addictive and does not have as many short-term side effects. These drugs do not help *every* patient with ADD. However, they have helped many patients with ADD increase their attention span and improve their performance at school, at work, and in their personal lives. Amphetamine and Ritalin appear to be, for some patients, the lesser of two evils.

The "Paradoxical" Effects of Stimulants on ADD Patients

Amphetamine and Ritalin usually cause people who do not have ADD to feel more energetic and animated. It seems strange that the same drugs let ADD patients calm down and be able to focus on an activity. However, the effects are not really as different as they seem. Both result from stimulation of the dopamine pathway in the brain. When amphetamine or Ritalin stimulates the dopamine pathway in people who do not have ADD, the people feel happy and more powerful. The same drugs also stimulate the dopamine pathway in people with ADD. However, this effect causes them to have the same feelings of pleasure and reward as other people experience when performing tasks that require prolonged attention.

ADD Management

Neuropsychologists and neuropsychiatrists believe that ADD results from a defect in the brain's dopamine pathway. The drugs amphetamine and Ritalin can increase activity in this pathway and enable some patients with ADD to focus their attention for longer periods of time. Drugs such as these carry risks for adverse effects, especially when taken for a long time. Doctors minimize the risks by keeping doses as low as possible. People should never take unneeded drugs; but for many ADD patients, these drugs can significantly improve the patient's life.

Additional Resources

Feldman, R. S. and L. F. Quenzer. 1984. *Fundamentals of Neuropsychopharmacology.* Sinauer Associates, Sunderland, MA. Chapter 7, pp. 151–204.
    A thorough and informative, yet highly readable, college level textbook. This chapter provides a detailed and well-illustrated discussion of systems in the brain that use the neurotransmitter DA or similar chemicals and how these systems influence behavior. It also discusses the effects of drugs on these systems.

Quillen, T. 1995. Myths & facts . . . about attention deficit disorder. *Nursing.* July; 25(7): p. 27.
    An overview about not only the facts, but some misperceptions about ADD.

Questions for Discussion

1. Explain how malfunction of the dopamine pathway affects people with ADD. What symptoms do such people exhibit?

2. What is the evidence that the MFB constitutes an important part of the pleasure, or dopamine, pathway in the brain?

3. How do amphetamine and Ritalin increase the activity of DA-containing neurons in the brain?

Applications

1. Your body's systems attempt to maintain a state of homeostasis, or physiological balance. For example, your body normally maintains a temperature at 37°C (98.6°F). If you enter a hot room, the cooling mechanisms in your body begin to try to keep your body temperature constant. You begin to sweat, and the evaporation of the sweat cools the skin as the sweat evaporates. Your skin becomes red as blood vessels near the surface of the skin enlarge and give off more heat to the skin's surface.

    The neurons in the brain function at an ideal level. Even when the balance of activities between systems is not correct, as in ADD, the neurons become accustomed to this unbalance as normal. Think about the effects that amphetamine and Ritalin have on neurons. Make a list of ways in which the nervous system might try to compensate for the fact that amphetamine or Ritalin upset what the ADD brain sees as its normal balance.

2. What types of therapy other than drugs might be useful for individuals with ADD?

7.1 A Genetic Legacy of Endangered Species

Stephen J. O'Brien, Ph.D.
Laboratory of Genomic Diversity, National Cancer Institute
Frederick Cancer Research and Development Center, Frederick, Maryland

Dr. O'Brien received his Ph.D. from Cornell University in 1966. He serves as Director, Section of Genetics and Laboratory of Viral Carcinogenesis, National Institutes of Health's National Cancer Institute in Frederick, Maryland. His research laboratory leads the fields in human and animal genetics, including studies of population genetics, epidemiology, and genetic action of RNA viruses (oncogenes, AIDS, and feline leukemia) in host populations. His critical work in human biology and his keen interest in the biology of wildlife species allow him to bring to wildlife biology the most critical advances from human biomedical research.

Overview

Extinctions have occurred since the beginnings of life on earth. The root causes of historical extinction events cannot always be determined. However, current human activities are clearly causing the most rapid extinction of mammals in the earth's history. To counter this trend, conservation biologists are using modern genetic methods. They are trying to prevent extinction of some endangered species. The first of these attempts focused on the African cheetah. Attention was drawn to the cheetah because it had experienced diminished wild populations and failure to breed in captivity.

Human Activity and Recent Extinctions

Since the first breath was drawn by a living thing, our planet has undergone several massive extinctions. The most famous is the disappearance of the dinosaurs that dominated the earth for more than 100 million years. No one is sure what caused dinosaurs to abruptly die around 63 million years ago; but the responsibility for a more recent extinction, one that is happening today, is not in doubt. It is the phenomenal ecological success of one species, ourselves—*Homo sapiens*. Some 10,000 years ago, our ancestors began farming. That new activity led to a huge population increase, global migration, and settlement of unoccupied areas. As populations grew and people moved into areas where other species lived, these people preyed on the other species, particularly on large mammals. The result has been the most accelerated rate of mammalian extinction in history.

Across the world, there is a nearly unanimous desire to slow or even reverse this process and to preserve these species for our children. Conservation of endangered species has become a clear call for ecologists, politicians, and ordinary people in every corner of the globe. In step with this resolve, the new biology with all its glitter and technology has brought to light some important secrets that can be of real value in managing our fragile endangered species. The discoveries were not so obvious with traditional field observation. Instead they required a sampling of blood and investigations into the underlying source code of living species, their genes.

Saving the African Cheetah

The species to first open scientists' eyes to the problem of recent extinctions was the magnificent African cheetah, the world's fastest land animal, shown in Figure 1. Sprinting across the African savannah at 60 to 70 mph, the cheetahs were having some problems. Numbers were dropping, primarily due to habitat loss, but there was another worrying situation. Zoos and wildlife management organizations were having a difficult time breeding cheetahs in captivity. Less than 15 percent of cheetah pairings succeeded in producing kittens. When they did, there were many birth defects that were frequently fatal. Further, when samples of semen from adult male cheetahs were examined, considerable physiological abnormalities were uncovered. Less than 30 percent of cheetah sperm in any individual were healthy; the rest were malformed and nonfunctional. The cause of these

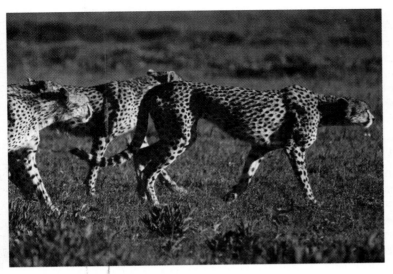

Figure 1 *The African cheetah is the fastest land animal.*

defects was a mystery. The defects looked like ones that were common among domestic animals that were bred with close relatives, a process termed "inbreeding." But every cheetah had congenital problems, including wild cheetahs sampled in their native African habitat. So what happened?

The answer came when scientists studied the genes of the cheetah and compared them to genes from reproductively healthy species like lions or even humans. New genetic technologies permit scientists to examine gene sequences and differences among individual cheetahs virtually by direct observation. These technologies were mostly invented for the Human Genome Project. The purpose of this international collaborative project is to determine the DNA sequence of human beings. The goal is to help understand the functioning or malfunctioning of the 80,000 different human genes that program a fertilized egg to develop into a person. The same technologies developed for the Human Genome Project are being used to learn more about cheetahs. The technology works by using chemical extractions to separate DNA (the written letters of the genetic code that comprise the

genes) from proteins, fats, and sugars in the circulating white blood cells. Most species examined for genetics variation have about one million DNA letter differences between unrelated individuals. But individual cheetahs were remarkably more similar, with about 1 percent as much variation between individuals as other species had shown.

Scientists knew that inbreeding among close relatives homogenizes genetic diversity because this is how inbred lab strains of mice and rats are made. Yet cheetahs were never inbred in any laboratory. Their genes must have become genetically uniform by a freak event in nature sometime in their past. Scientists now know that "freak" was a near extinction event. Some ten thousand years ago, the ancestors of all cheetahs escaped extinction by a whisker. Just before the last North American glaciation, cheetahs shared the planet with saber-toothed tigers, mastodons, and giant ground sloths. All of those other species are gone now. Probably what killed them was a devastating epidemic that affected the large mammals or their prey. Whatever killed them nearly got the cheetah as well. A few cheetah survivors probably migrated to Africa where they bred among close relatives. That resulted in a loss of their intrinsic genetic diversity. Today's cheetahs live with a genetic "hangover." Defects in reproduction, congenital abnormalities, and weakened immune defenses against deadly microbes are the result. The devastating hereditary defects arose due to the expression of pairs of rare mutations (gene defects) that appear frequently in two doses, one from each parent, when breeding between close relatives takes place.

Individual cheetahs were remarkably more similar, with about 1 percent as much variation between individuals as other species had shown.

The cheetah's legacy became a wake-up call for conservationists. There were clearly hidden perils afflicting endangered species. Those perils could spell disaster for small endangered populations. As a result, hundreds of species protection programs began to incorporate the most recent advances in genetics, reproduction, infectious disease, and clinical veterinary medicine. These enhanced programs served as critical monitors of threatened wildlife. This new monitoring was added to the monitoring ecologists had done for quite some time. Scientists were looking for footprints in the genes of threatened populations as evidence for narrow escapes from extinction.

Other Endangered Mammals

Unfortunately, the cheetah was neither the only nor the most severely affected species found with this problem. Other endangered species suffer with this curse of genetic homogenization after a near extinction event. Examining the genes of other species has shown evidence of inbreeding in species including Northern elephant seals, Asiatic lions, Florida panthers, and tigers, to name just a few.

Perhaps the most extreme example of hidden genetic problems involves the Florida panther, shown in Figure 2. This severely threatened subspecies of American puma is also called a mountain lion or a cougar. In the past century, the Florida panther had become displaced to the mosquito- and alligator-infested cypress swamps of southern Florida. This occurred due to habitat depletion, hunting, and other human activities. Thought to be extinct for 20 years, a tiny population of fewer than 30 adult panthers was discovered in the 1970s. This tiny population had rampant congenital heart defects and suffered with cryptochordism, which is the failure of baby male kittens' testicles to descend properly. The population had numerous microbial diseases and a 95 percent incidence of malformed sperm. The reason was again close inbreeding since DNA analysis of the Florida panther's genes revealed less diversity than in cheetahs.

Conservation managers

charged with protecting the panther had to act. They decided to supplement the panthers with neighboring Texas cougars. They analyzed population/genetic data in a predictive manner. The process is something like using computers to predict weather patterns. They concluded that if the Florida panther was left alone, the population would surely go extinct within 25 years. The idea was to get the number of pumas up and to introduce diverse genetic stock as a counterdefense to inbreeding. So far the strategy seems to be working as the population is gradually growing.

Biotechnology Tools for Conservation Management

Today biotechnology is a valuable tool for conservation management. The new data gathered from the endangered species have eliminated a lot of the guesswork. The data clearly show what the problems really are and sometimes suggest effective ways to reverse imminent extinction. In addition, DNA-based genetic testing has been used to identify marauding predators. One example is the puma attacks in recent years in California. The

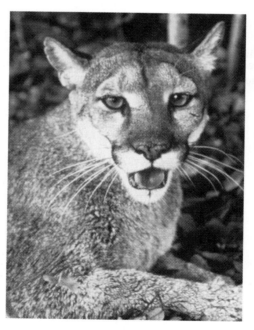

Figure 2 *Without genetic improvements, the Florida panther may be extinct in 25 years.*

testing has also made identifying endangered species and subspecies much more precise. That empowers law enforcement officials with evidence to prosecute violators who might have escaped before when no one could identify the animals with certainty. Finally, DNA sampling provides clues that help tell when infectious diseases are present. This use of the tests is especially important because an infectious disease can destroy a species as quickly as any climatic or environmental catastrophe.

Conservation biology is a young field. It has grown out of the powerful advances in biological research. Applications of these methods are revealing a great deal about our treasured but dwindling large mammals. Scientists are learning about the natural history, present makeup, and future prognosis of these animals. Ironically, human use of technology caused many species to become endangered. Now scientists hope to use technology to help stop the most dangerous extinction event in our planet's history.

Additional Resources

NOAHS Center
National Zoological Park
Smithsonian Institution
Washington, DC 20008

Much of the work using technology to help ensure the future of many endangered animals around the world takes place at the NOAHS Conservation and Research Center. NOAHS is an acronym for New Opportunities in Animal Health Sciences. Research at the Center focuses on the health, management, reproduction, and conservation of endangered species. The Center also focuses on maintenance of genetic diversity in captive and free-living populations.

O'Brien, S. J. 1994. A role for molecular genetics in biological conservation. *Proceedings of the National Academy of Science* 91: pp. 5748–5755.

The consequences of diminished population sizes are reviewed in terms of molecular genetic analyses of four endangered mammals: the African cheetah, lion, Florida panther, and humpback whale.

O'Brien, S. J. 1994. Genetic and phylogenetic analyses of endangered species. *Annual Review of Genetics* 28: pp. 467–489.

This article discusses the role of conservation genetics in managing populations of endangered species.

O'Brien, S.J. 1997. The family line: The human-cat connection. *National Geographic Magazine* 191: pp. 77–85.

This article describes research to map the cat genome using techniques and information from the Human Genome Project. The research goal is to identify the genetic basis of hereditary defects in cats.

O'Brien, S. J., D. E. Wildt, and M. Bush. 1986. The cheetah in genetic peril. *Scientific American* 254: pp. 84–92.

A description of the genetic history of the African cheetah and the molecular methods used to study it.

Questions for Discussion

1. How did scientists discover the cause of the cheetah's breeding problems?

2. When scientists compared the DNA of individual, unrelated cheetahs, about how many DNA bases were different? How does this compare to the genetic variation normally found in unrelated individuals of the same species?

3. What unusual natural event is thought to be the ultimate cause of the cheetah's current breeding problems?

4. How is DNA technology used by conservation biologists?

Applications

1. Describe a situation in which human activities might lead to a decrease in the genetic diversity of a species.

2. Predict and describe how on-going advances in gene therapy and reproductive biology might be applied to the quest to save endangered species.

7.2 Wetlands

Patricia Swain, Ph.D.
Massachusetts Division of Fisheries and Wildlife
Natural Heritage & Endangered Species Program, Westborough, Massachusetts

Dr. Swain is the plant community ecologist for the Massachusetts Division of Fisheries and Wildlife's Natural Heritage & Endangered Species Program. She started working with plant communities in graduate school at the University of Minnesota. There she analyzed fossil pollen grains from bogs around the state to study the history of the bogs. Then she could compare the past communities that were represented by the pollen with the plants that were present at the time of the study. Knowing how plant communities have changed since the glaciers receded from North America provides a good perspective on the diversity of plant communities in Massachusetts. This knowledge is useful for her job of classifying the plant communities of Massachusetts, identifying uncommon or exemplary ones, and providing advice on managing them.

Overview

Wetlands, lands that are wet, lands with water. In common American usage, water has been considered to be a public resource, to be protected and provided to all. But land is private, controlled by the owner. Wetlands exist between water and land, in ecological and legal transition areas. Wetlands issues can lead to clashes between landowner rights and public good. Sometimes the rights of one landowner conflict with rights of other landowners.

Are You Living on a Wetland?

Suppose you own some land along a river. The old-timers tell you that the yard floods in the spring but the house on a little hill stays dry. Many miles up the river another landowner has drained low places in his property, places he couldn't use because they were too wet to plant potatoes that he grows on the surrounding fields. One of his neighbors is filling part of a riverside marsh so she can build a house with a nice sand beach instead of a mucky shore. In a town along the river, people have built out onto the riverbank, straightening and narrowing the river. Some low, swampy areas away from the river were filled in for a shopping center. All of these activities were each fairly small, but they nibbled away the wetlands upriver from your property. In the United States, half of the wetlands that were here in the mid 1700s have been destroyed.

Consider what happens to this river when there is a big rainstorm. All the water from the rain flows across the land to the river, and the river rises. Before the farmer drained the fields, the low places held some of the rain water. Now the water goes through the field into the drains, then straight to the river. The lovely new house on the beach is where a marsh used to store some storm water. Now the water flows right through the new beach

> **All the water from the storm rushes down the river and arrives at your land in a flood.**

to the river. Water moves faster and faster through the straightened, narrowed river at the town. In the town and mall, the roads and rooftops keep the rain from entering the ground. Instead water is collected into pipes that go directly into the river. The fill under the mall doesn't hold much water. Instead of being stored in the swamp, now the water goes into drains that dump into the river. All the storm's water is going into the river at once. And the water is carrying mud and oil from the roads, manure from a hog farm, and chemicals and trash from a landfill.

All the water from the storm rushes down the river and arrives at your land in a flood. Your fields, front yard, and first floor flood. As you watch the water and trash from upriver rising in your yard, you remember the water never used to get into the house. Over the next few days, you wait for the river to return to normal. There's no electricity; your computer and TV don't work. There's nasty smelling mud in the kitchen. You and your neighbors wonder why this flood is so much worse than others in the past.

What has happened is the cumulative result of many separate actions that keep water from being absorbed by the land and slowed on its way to the river. Ditching, draining, and filling wetlands speed water out of the way. The farmer draining his field to improve his potato crop didn't mean to add to the flood in your living room. He wants to help feed the world and make more money. The mall was put into a marsh because it was cheap land and wasn't being used for other purposes the developer could see. The oil and other pollutants in the water weren't added to make your kitchen stink; they were just in the way of the water.

Because this scenario is repeated over and over throughout the country, many citizens want the government to do something. They worry about the effects of increasing floods, the quality of water in rivers and lakes, and the safety of drinking water. For many years, people concerned about loss of habitat for waterfowl have been worried about loss of wetlands. They have bought, protected, and even created wetlands. But the overall loss of wetlands has continued.

Even when people understand the abstract values of wetlands, many still object to being told that they can't make full use of their property. If there is a public benefit from leaving a wetland alone, they want to be reimbursed for providing that benefit, or they want to be able to use the land their own way. Many levels of government now regulate wetlands, controlling what people can do in them. Because there are many different kinds of wetlands, there are disagreements about legal definitions of them. Defining their boundaries is complicated by their being part of a transition from someplace all wet (like a lake) to somewhere higher that is relatively dry. Where boundary lines are placed can make a difference on what a person can do with his or her land. It can also make a difference in how

much storm protection a wetland can provide or how much habitat is left for wildlife. Scientists are closer to agreeing among themselves than are lawyers, but even in biology and geology, there are many different aspects of wetlands to consider.

Description and Functions of Wetlands

Wetlands are wet places. But some are not wet all year long or even for very long each year. Some are not even wet every year. Water runs downhill and collects in depressions. Sometimes the bottoms of the low areas have dense soil that keeps the water from draining into the ground. These wet areas are home to many plants that can also slow water movement. Because water stays in them awhile, wetlands serve to lower the peak of a flood—that is, they store water and let it slowly into a river. The areas that are only wet in extreme storms are particularly involved in storing storm water. The slow release also keeps the water level higher longer, which is nice for fish and boaters.

Figure 1 shows a vernal pool—a shallow, seasonally wet depression. *Vernal* means "spring": most of these temporary pools fill up with winter snow or rain and are full in the spring. Higher temperatures increase evaporation, and growing and transpiring plants increase water loss; so these pools dry as summer progresses. Some animal species such as wood frogs and mole salamanders depend on fish-free vernal pools for reproduction because fish eat amphibian eggs. These amphibians return to the vernal pools where they were hatched on the night of the first warm spring rain. Development of the eggs into tadpoles and then adults is a race against the drying of the pools. Insects and other invertebrates have a brief active life in the spring waters, then leave drought-resistant eggs or have some other protection from drying out. Vernal pools can be hard to identify when they are dry because they seldom have wetland plants in them.

Wetlands collect materials from uplands. When water slows down, it drops soil and other materials it is carrying. Wetlands keep mud and debris (natural and human derived) from going further. Plants use some of the nutrients that are brought

Many levels of government now regulate wetlands, controlling what people can do in them.

into wetlands for growing bigger or producing more flowers. Wetlands can also absorb or change toxic materials that come in from surrounding areas. Too much oil or pesticides (or even too many nutrients) can cause death of plants or changes in the plant communities. Animal habitat changes when the plants change. Wetlands are part of the habitats of many animals. Bear and deer often use wetlands for feeding in the summer before the upland fruits and acorns ripen. Secretive water birds like American bitterns nest and hunt frogs in wetlands. The wetlands that people protect for waterfowl provide breeding space and food for large flocks of migrating ducks and geese. Altering wetlands changes or destroys the habitats of many species. Wetlands work best for maintaining clean water and providing plant and animal habitat when they are not expected to remove many pollutants or handle excessive runoff.

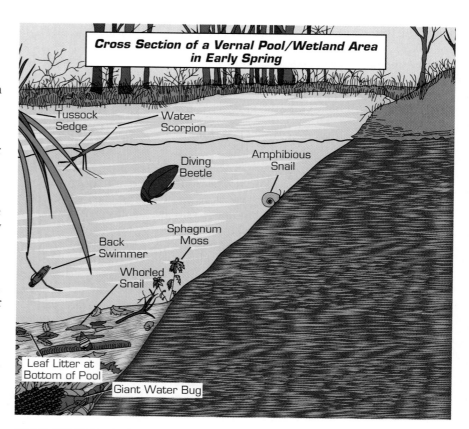

Figure 1 *This vernal pool is temporary but supports a diverse biological community when it is wet.*

Wetlands Conservation

How do we protect wetlands for their many values and beauty and still allow their use as land? As more people understand the important roles of wetlands, they want to protect those that remain. There are laws and regulations that restrict use of wetlands. The federal government, states, towns, and private conservation groups have bought many, many acres of wetlands and surrounding lands so they will be left as wetlands. Sometimes they purchase partial rights to a property to keep it from being developed, but the landowner retains some use of it, maybe for grazing or cutting hay. Some landowners decide on their own not to develop wet parts of their properties; lots of them like having special places on their land. Many people are working in many ways to protect the country's wetlands. The lucky ones get to work in them too.

References

Cowardin, L. M., V. Carter, F. C. Golet, and E. T. LaRoe. 1979. *Classification of wetlands and deepwater habitats of the United States.* U.S. Fish & Wildlife Service, Office of Biological Services. FWS/OBS-79/31. 131 pp.

Gosselink, J. G. and L. C. Lee. 1987. *Cumulative impact assessment in bottomland hardwood forests.* Center for Wetland Resources Louisiana State University, Baton Rouge, LA. Prepared for The U.S. Environmental Protection Agency, Office of Federal Activities, Washington, DC. 109 pp.

Jackson, S. 1995. *Delineating bordering vegetated wetlands under the Massachusetts Wetlands Protection Act.* Massachusetts Department of Environmental Protection, Division of Wetlands and Waterways. 89 pp.

Lewis, W. M., Jr., Chair. 1995. *Wetlands Characteristics and Boundaries.* Committee on Characterization of Wetlands.

National Research Council. National Academy Press, Washington, DC. 308 pp.

Mitsch, W. J. and J. G. Gosselink. 1997. *Wetlands.* Van Nostrand Reinhold Company, New York. 537 pp.

Pedevillano, C. 1995. *Habitat Values of New England Wetlands.* U.S. Army Corps of Engineers and U.S. Department of the Interior, Fish & Wildlife Service. 24 pp. plus appendices.

Rezendes, P. and P. Roy. 1996. *Wetlands: The Web of Life.* A Sierra Club book. San Francisco. 156 pp.

Vileisis, A. 1997. *Discovering the Unknown Landscape: A History of America's Wetlands.* Island Press, Washington, DC. 433 pp.

Additional Resources

Coburn, E A. 2004. *Vernal Pools.* The McDonald and Woodward Publishing Company, Blackburg, Virginia. 426 pages.
> Presents aspects of the organisms and ecology of these small, oftern temporary puddles.

Lewis, W. M., Jr., Chair. 1995. *Wetlands Characteristics and Boundaries.* Committee on Characterization of Wetlands. National Research Council. National Academy Press, Washington, DC.
> This is technical but has everything—biology, ecology, regulation, and controversy.

Mitchell, J. G. 1992. Our Disappearing Wetlands, in *National Geographic.* Vol. 182, no. 4: pp. 3–45.
> This article has wonderful photographs with a good discussion on the ecological roles of many types of wetlands and the areas lost.

Mitsch, W. J. and J. G. Gosselink. 1997. *Wetlands.* 3rd Edition. Van Nostrand Reinhold Company, New York.
> A textbook that covers the ecological aspects of all types of wetlands. The authors have worked on the floodplain forests of the Mississippi River and were among the early advocates of considering cumulative effects of wetland alterations.

Rezendes, P. and P. Roy. 1996. *Wetlands: The Web of Life.* A Sierra Club Book, San Francisco.
> The first author is a well-known natural history photographer, and the pictures of wetlands from all around North America are great. The text has a very good discussion of the different types of wetlands and their ecological functioning. The last chapter is about the techniques and patience required for taking good photographs of nature.

Vileisis, A. 1997. *Discovering the Unknown Landscape: A History of America's Wetlands.* Island Press, Washington, DC.
> This is a remarkably readable, fascinating, and infor- mative account of the history of changing attitudes and policies towards wetlands throughout the history of the United States.

Questions for Discussion

1. There are many different types of wetlands. (Bogs, swamps, marshes, and floodplains are a few.) What do all kinds of wetlands have in common?

2. What does the phrase *cumulative effects* mean? What are cumulative effects of wetland destruction, and why is the issue becoming increasingly important in national discussions of wetlands?

3. Wetland values are often cited as reasons to restrict development of wetlands. What are some of these values? What issues arise because some of the values come to society in general rather than directly to the landowner?

4. What happens to nutrients that are washed into a wetland from surrounding uplands?

5. Why are wetlands considered to be transi- tional areas?

Applications

1. What are some uses that wetlands have been put to? In your town or county, where are there areas that were probably wet in the past but are no longer as big as they once were or no longer exist at all as wetlands? What is the general condition of wetlands in your area?

2. What might be some human uses of wetlands that are compatible with wetlands' roles in maintaining values such as flood storage, wildlife habitat, or maintaining water quality in streams or lakes?

3. What might be the effect on the local wetlands if a development were put in that had town water but each house had its own septic system? What if each house had a private well but the town provided a sewer system to take waste water to a central location?

4. Some landowners respond to the increasing restrictions on uses of many natural resources by saying "my grandfather built there, didn't need a permit, drained, put in a dam, drove over the pond shore to fish, dumped his trash out there." What has changed in the world or society to change the way we expect people to treat the environment?

7.3 Biological Invasions

Robert D. Doyle, Ph.D.
University of North Texas and Lewisville Aquatic Ecosystem Research Facility
USAE, Lewisville, Texas

Dr. Doyle is a research ecologist for the Army Corps of Engineers, Waterways Experiment Station. Dr. Doyle's research focuses on the ecology of aquatic and wetland plants. Part of his duties include developing methods to promote the health of native aquatic plant communities and to minimize the negative impacts of exotic or nuisance plant species.

Overview

An invasion is now taking place in the waters of North America. Invasion? Perhaps that word conjures up images of some of the great invaders of the past. You know, Attila the Hun, Alexander the Great, or even the Allied forces landing on the beaches of Normandy during World War II. But the invasion forces we're talking about are not well-equipped armies; they are plants and animals that have been introduced to the lakes, rivers, and wetlands of North America from other parts of the world. These species, which are now living in areas where they did not originally exist, are called exotic, or nonindigenous, species.

Like military invasions, biological invasions can cause profound change and destruction. After an invasion, nothing is ever the same as before. Today there are many harmful exotic species that are rapidly spreading across the country. These species cause serious environmental and economic damage.

How Species Move Around

There are thousands of aquatic species now in North America that were not here when the pilgrims landed almost 300 years ago. How did these nonindigenous species get here? As you might expect, many species were accidentally introduced. Others were deliberately brought here from other parts of the world.

Accidental introductions most commonly occur when organisms are unintentionally transported along with other goods. When sailing ships departed Europe to explore the world, they often carried uninvited passengers such as rats and insects. Upon arrival in a new land, these stowaways simply jumped ship and found a new home. Today, with thousands of ships, planes, trains, and trucks transporting goods all around the globe, it is virtually impossible to stop the spread of species from one area to another. Although this form of hitch-hiking has been going on for thousands of years,

> *There are thousands of aquatic species now in North America that were not here when the Pilgrims landed almost 300 years ago.*

two recent examples show that it is still a major problem. The round goby, *Neogolious melanostomus,* is a fish that was introduced to the Great Lakes in the late 1980s. It came in ballast water of ocean-going ships. This aggressive fish, which grows to about 25 cm in length, has now spread to all the Great Lakes. The round goby appears to be displacing native fish from prime feeding and spawning areas. Similarly, the Asian tiger mosquito appears to have been recently imported along with shipments of used tires. This aggressive biting insect may be a vector for human diseases.

Many other problem species were deliberately introduced to North America. For example, the nutria, *Myocastor coypus,* is a semi-aquatic rodent from South America. Nutria were released into the wild in the United States about 1930. At that time, it was believed that nutria would enhance the fur industry. Unfortunately, North American hunters never valued nutria pelts. Thus, the population of the big rats has increased dramatically. Today nutria are causing serious damage as they eat away the coastal marshes across the United States. The aquarium industry has also imported thousands of species of plants, snails, and fish for sale. Unfortunately, many of these species have also escaped into the wild.

Problems Caused by Exotic Species

Survival of introduced organisms in a new environment is not easy. Most die because the conditions required for their survival and reproduction are not met in the new environment. Many other species survive but blend into the natural ecosystem and become "naturalized" without causing major disruptions. While no one knows for sure, there may be as many as 5,000 aquatic nonindigenous species in the United States. Only a few percent are actually considered a problem. Problematic invaders are usually those that seriously disrupt the natural balance of the ecosystem, threaten or destroy desirable native species, or interfere with the desired use of a natural resource.

Problems often occur when exotic species grow so much that they destroy the natural balance of a community. Then they may begin to dominate the community. What makes some species disruptive to the natural balance while others are not? In some cases, an introduced species may have a unique adaptation that allows it to grow into a nuisance. For example, water hyacinth, *Eichhornia crassipes,* is a floating plant from South America that grows more rapidly than just about any other plant in the world. The rapid growth rate of the plant is thought to be an adaptation that allows the species to survive the constant changes in water levels of the Amazon River. Each year the water levels of the Amazon River rise and fall by as much as 12 meters! Rapid growth of this plant along the Amazon River is rarely a problem since most plants get flushed on down the river by the flood waters. However, it presents a huge problem when the species is introduced to other places without similar floods. In subtropical regions like Florida and Louisiana, the plant quickly covers lakes and rivers. The thick, floating mats shade out desirable native underwater vegetation, interfere with navigation and recreation, and destroy the habitats needed by native animals, including the endangered Florida Everglades kite, *Rostrhamus sociabilis.*

Many problem nonindigenous species grow to nuisance levels simply because they are champion "World Class Weeds." To a gardener, a "weed" may be any plant growing in the wrong place. But to an ecologist, a weed is a species that is capable of rapid growth, reproduces profusely, and can survive in a wide variety of environments. Because of these adaptations, weeds usually get started first and expand quickly to dominate disturbed environments. It isn't surprising then that reservoirs, which are formed by building dams and flooding dry land, are often overgrown with weedy aquatic plants such as hydrilla, *Hydrilla verticillata,* or Eurasian watermilfoil, *Myriophyllum spicatum.* In many cases, the fast-growing weeds quickly colonize all available areas of a new reservoir and form a dense monoculture that prevents the establishment of a more desirable, diverse native community, as shown in Figure 1. In Texas, hydrilla is now expanding quickly in rivers containing several endangered aquatic species and may now be threatening the survival of these species, including Texas wildrice, *Zizania texana.*

Many wetlands around the country have been disturbed by the actions of humans and now suffer from the overgrowth of weedy exotic species. For example, much of the Florida Everglades is today dominated by nonindigenous plants such as the melaleuca tree, *Melaleuca quinquenervia.* The plant was originally imported as an ornamental tree from Australia. It has since invaded huge areas of the Everglades. The disturbed hydrology of the region, especially as large areas have been drained for crops and houses, has been linked to the rapid spread of this species.

Some introduced species are able to grow to problem levels because their natural enemies, which usually keep the population under control, are not present in the new habitat.

> *Problems often occur when exotic species grow so much that they destroy the natural balance of a community.*

A. Diverse community of native plants

B. Monospecific exotic population

Figure 1 *A) Aquatic plant communities composed of many different types of native plants offer diverse habitats that support many different types of animals. B) In contrast, some weedy, nonindigenous species grow as a monoculture (only one type of plant). This reduces the value of the habitat.*

Purple loosestrife, *Lythrum salicaria,* is a European wetland plant that is now overgrowing many wetlands of North America. In Europe, this species usually comprises less than 5 percent of a wetland plant community. In North America, it often displaces all other native species and grows as a dense monoculture. The stunning success of this plant here is due, at least in part, to the absence of the natural predators and diseases that control its rate of growth in Europe. Similarly, the zebra mussel, *Dreissena polymorpha,* which was only recently introduced to the Great Lakes, has spread quickly throughout the country. This rapid spread is in part because the rate of predation by native diving ducks and fish appears to be insignificant relative to the species' enormous growth rate. Zebra mussels are small, fingernail-sized clams that can grow on any surface in the water. They grow on docks, boat hulls, rocks, and even other zebra

mussels. Trouble often begins when their exuberant growth clogs water intake pipes. That prevents the operation of water control structures like dams and locks and causes billions of dollars of damage.

Control of Exotic Species

The serious problems posed by some nonindigenous species require us to try and prevent future expansions. The best defense, of course, it to prevent the organisms from reaching the United States in the first place or to eradicate them as soon as they are found. To that end, inspections of cargo from other countries have been increased. Import permits for foreign plants and animals have been tightened. Increased monitoring of our lakes, rivers, and wetlands will also help us find small colonies of exotic species. If these are found early enough, they can likely be eradicated before they spread. New pesticides and herbicides are now available that can effectively kill organisms in a target area while having little impact on adjacent desirable species. California, for example, has an aggressive hydrilla control program. If hydrilla is found in any water body in the state, that water body is quarantined and aggressively treated with appropriate herbicides to kill the hydrilla. This type of rapid response to biological invasions can contain and minimize damage by nonindigenous species.

Cases where problem exotic species have already become established and are widely distributed are more difficult to control. Careful use of pesticides and herbicides is needed to help curb the damage of many exotic species. For example, water hyacinth in Florida is now aggressively treated with herbicides early in the growing season when colonies are small. This strategy prevents the widespread expansion seen in years past and allows managers to use relatively little herbicide to control the plant effectively. In other cases, careful use of biological organisms to control problem species may be appropriate. Several beetle species that help control purple loosestrife in Europe are now being studied as "biological control" agents for the plant in this country. However, extensive testing is needed before any releases of nonindigenous organisms are allowed to ensure that the biological control agent won't itself become a nuisance.

Many, perhaps most, successful biological invasions occur in disturbed ecosystems. Thus, we can likely minimize the threat of nonindigenous species by more carefully managing our natural ecosystem. Ecosystems that are not stressed are less susceptible to problem levels of exotic species. Vigilance and careful management of earth's ecosystems are our best defenses.

Additional Resources

Elton, C. S. 1958. *The Ecology of Invasions by Animals and Plants*. (Reprinted in 1977 as a Science Paperback, Halsted Press, New York).
    An old but very readable discussion of problems caused by exotic species. Includes great black and white photos.

Sea Grant Nonindigenous Species Site
    http://www.ansc.purdue.edu/sgnis
    All information posted on this site has been reviewed by experts in the field (peer reviewed). The site focuses on major nonindigenous species of the Great Lakes Region.

The Great Lakes Information Network
    http://www.great-lakes.net/
    An outstanding and constantly updated site dedicated to providing accurate information about the Great Lakes. The "Environment" page has extensive information about many aspects of the Great Lakes, including problem exotic species.

U.S. Congress, Office of Technology Assessment. 1993. *Harmful Non-Indigenous Species of the United States*. U.S. Government Printing Office, 391 pp.
    A comprehensive review of problem exotic species.

Questions for Discussion

1. What is a nonindigenous species?

2. What makes some nonindigenous species a problem while others are not?

3. How are nonindigenous species spread around the world?

4. Why does water hyacinth cause problems in Florida but not in its natural Amazon River habitat?

5. The use of pesticides and herbicides as management tools in the environment often causes controversy. While no one wants to use these chemicals, many ecologists believe that the wise use of small amounts of these poisons is justified since they will minimize or prevent major problems later on. What do you think?

Applications

1. Describe some ways that you might accidentally transport a living organism to a new area. How might you avoid doing this?

2. Since disturbances to the natural environment appear to invite problem species to colonize, what do you think should be a top priority for managing our ecosystem?

7.4 The Loss and Restoration of Biodiversity

David Tonkyn, Ph.D.
Clemson University, Clemson, South Carolina

Dr. Tonkyn is an associate professor of biology at Clemson University in South Carolina. He teaches courses in ecology and conservation biology and has conducted research on organisms ranging from genetically engineered bacteria to endangered mammals.

Overview

Biodiversity is at risk not only in the tropics, as we hear in the news, but also in the United States. Some United States species have gone extinct and others are endangered, but a much larger number survive only in remote parts of their historic ranges. For example, Native Americans and early European settlers in the southeastern United States commonly encountered bison, elk, mountain lions, and wolves, all native to the region. Now a resident would have to travel all the way to Yellowstone National Park in Wyoming for a chance to see these four species together. Fortunately, there are many cases in which globally endangered or locally extinct species have been reintroduced and once again form visible and important parts of their ecosystems. These reintroductions are difficult and require the coordinated efforts of many kinds of biologists—from wildlife and behavior experts to geneticists and veterinarians.

Biodiversity on Earth

When people express concern about threats to biodiversity on earth, they often are thinking of threats in the tropics. After all, the tropics are famous for their extraordinary biodiversity. For example, a single large park in Peru, Manu National Park, which stretches from high in the Andes Mountains to lowland Amazonian rain forest, contains over 900 species of birds. This is about 10 percent of all bird species on earth, far more than

are found in the United States and Canada combined. Manu also contains over 1,200 species of plants, 200 species of mammals, 77 species of amphibians, and an estimated 500,000 species of insects and other arthropods! Obviously, the deforestation or loss of an area like Manu would place more species at risk than would a similar destruction of habitat in the temperate or arctic region. In addition, many tropical countries that are rich in biodiversity are poor in cash, and they are tempted to convert their forests to logs and then to farmland to meet the needs of their rapidly growing human populations. However, even in the temperate zone, in a rich country like the United States of America, there have been significant losses to biodiversity.

Some United States species have simply gone extinct. In 1809, a naturalist, Ramsay, described flocks of passenger pigeons so dense in South Carolina forests "as sometimes to break the limbs of trees on which they alight." These birds are now extinct, as are the Carolina parakeet and the ivory billed woodpecker, as shown in Figure 1, that also

Figure 1 *This ivory billed woodpecker is now extinct.*

lived in the state. Obviously, these species can never be brought back. An additional 31 species of plants and animals in South Carolina alone are currently listed by the federal government as being at risk of extinction. Nationally, there are 668 species of plants and 457 species of animal on this list, and their number only seems to increase with time.

But these figures are only part of the picture. There are many more species that are not extinct or even threatened with extinction that have disappeared from large parts of their historic range. They are no longer part of our environment, and we might only see them on television or on trips to zoos or on vacations to national parks hundreds of miles from home. Perhaps more importantly, these species are no longer parts of our functioning ecosystems. For example, early European settlers in South Carolina would often see native wolves and mountain lions sometimes chasing the native elk and bison that also were present. However, none of these species has occurred in the state in the last 100 years. For a long time, the only surviving wolves in the lower 48 states were along the Canadian border in Michigan, Minnesota, and Montana. The nearest mountain lions were the few dozen Florida panthers in south Florida or else in west Texas and beyond. The nearest elk were far west of the Mississippi River, and the closest wild bison were in parks in Nebraska and South Dakota.

This is a common condition in the United States. The extinction of local populations and even subspecies has occurred at a far faster pace than the extinction of entire species. Indeed, when wolves were reintroduced to Yellowstone National Park in Wyoming a few years ago, it became one of very few areas in the entire lower 48 states that could claim to contain all the native large animals that had been present at the time of European discovery.

Figure 2 *This peregrine falcon is preparing for a power dive to capture prey.*

It is possible to restore many species to areas from which they have been eliminated.

Reintroduction of Endangered Species

It is possible to restore many species to areas from which they have been eliminated. In South Carolina, as in many parts of the country, whitetail deer were once severely threatened by over-hunting. They are now back, perhaps even in record numbers, because the mix of young forests, farms, and suburbs provides better feeding than the historic, older closed forests. Bald eagles and turkeys, prominent symbols in American culture, had to be reintroduced to many areas of the United States, including South Carolina, as did the peregrine falcons, shown in Figure 2, which can reach awe-inspiring speeds of 180 miles-per-hour in their attacks on smaller birds. The American alligator, once endangered, now numbers an estimated 100,000 in South Carolina alone, mostly in rivers and coastal swamps. Further west, the California condor, once extinct in the wild, is now flying free over southern California and the Grand Canyon of Arizona; and black-footed ferrets once again hunt in prairie dog colonies in several states. This shows that the restoration of endangered species is possible, though not necessarily easy.

Many difficulties must be overcome for the successful reintroduction of an endangered species. First, there has to be suitable habitat for the species. For example, the red-cockaded woodpecker was once widely distributed throughout the southern and southeastern United States, but only among pine trees that were old enough to have rotten trunks that could be excavated for nesting cavities and where fires were frequent enough to eliminate other trees and woody shrubs. While there are still millions of acres of pine woodlands throughout the woodpeckers' historic range, much of it is logged at an early age or protected from fires, and the woodpecker is now endangered. Biologists seeking to restore red-cockaded woodpecker populations may have to create new habitat artificially by cutting nesting cavities into pine trees with chain saws and by deliberately cutting or burning understory shrubs and trees.

Sometimes suitable habitat must be present in vast areas for reintroductions to be successful. If a single wolf pack requires 100 square miles or more with few roads or humans, then there may only be a few areas in the East that could support a healthy population of many packs. The interior of Maine and the Adirondack Mountains of New York State are most often mentioned as possible reintroduction sites. The native wolf of the southeastern United States, known as the red wolf, as shown in Figure 3, has been reintroduced to relatively unpopulated parts of eastern North Carolina. As red wolves increased in number, they spread outward and quickly entered more populated areas. A second reintroduction site in the Great Smoky Mountain National Park on the Tennessee/North Carolina border has been plagued by the fact that the wolves occasionally run right out of the park and into neighboring towns. After all, these wolves can easily travel 50 miles in a single day. How many wildlands are left that are large enough for grizzlies, bison, or mountain lions and that would not also bring them into close contact with humans?

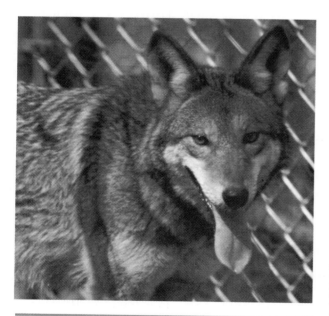

Figure 3 *This red wolf is native to the southeastern United States.*

A third requirement for the restoration of endangered species is that the original cause of endangerment must be removed. Peregrine falcons and bald eagles could not be returned to large areas of the United States until DDT and related pesticides that were poisoning their eggs were no longer used. Wolves could not return to some of their historic range until deer and other prey once again reached high densities and until ranchers found ways other than guns to protect their sheep and cattle or learned to accept some losses to the wolves.

A fourth factor is that suitable animals must be available for reintroduction. When biologists looked for mountain lions to add to the few individuals living in and around the Florida Everglades, they had no nearby source. All other mountain lions in the southeastern United States had been exterminated. The biologists finally decided to use mountain lions from west Texas, even though those animals were from a different subspecies and adapted to dry mountains and deserts totally unlike the wet, almost tropical climate of south Florida. We shall have to wait and see how well these animals and their descendants survive. Similar concerns will arise if we try to restore elk or bison to the East or grizzly bears, mountain goats, and bighorn sheep throughout the West since we will also be dependent on animals from other regions with other climates, prey, diseases, and so on. In at least one case, this has not been a problem. The peregrine falcons reintroduced throughout the United States came ultimately from wild birds collected from California, Alaska, Canada, Scotland, Spain, and Chile and, nevertheless, seem to have thrived everywhere they have been placed!

Many Questions Remain

Numerous other concerns must also be addressed before endangered species can be restored to their historic range. Are the individuals healthy so that they can survive the diseases they will encounter on release and not bring new diseases with them? If they have been held in captivity, will they know how to find prey and avoid predators? For example, young black-footed ferrets raised in captivity had no fear of natural enemies such as badgers and hawks. When they were shown a stuffed badger, they did not flee, as would be wise, but instead ran over to play with it! They had to be taught to show appropriate reactions. Are the animals to be released afraid of humans, or will they appear in backyards and highways looking for handouts? Should they be released one at a time or as close family groups? The reintroduction of a species can be enormously complex and may require the joint efforts of many specialists, including wildlife biologists, behavioral biologists, reproductive biologists, geneticists, zoo breeders, and veterinarians. Nevertheless, these efforts sometimes prove successful with the re-establishment of fully wild animals that not only fend for themselves, but once again can play their part in the health and function of their native ecosystem.

Additional Resources

Public Broadcasting System. Living Edens: Manu, Peru's Hidden Rain Forest.
ITEM CODE: A2882-WWV7
This 60-minute PBS video describes the Manu Biosphere Reserve, one of the richest Amazon preserves on earth. Ninety percent of the animals and plants in this reserve are still unidentified.

Reaka-Kudla, M. L., D. E. Wilson, and E. O. Wilson (eds.). 1992. *BioDiversity II*. Joseph Henry Press. Washington, DC.
This collection of articles provides an update on what is known—and how much remains to be learned about biodiversity on earth. The various articles discuss methods for studying and protecting biodiversity. These methods include technological, molecular, and museum contributions to the study.

Wilson, E. O. 1988. *BioDiversity*. National Academy Press. Washington, DC.
This book contains articles developed from the National Forum on Biodiversity, which was held in Washington, DC, in 1986. The articles discuss topics including challenges to maintaining biodiversity, human dependence on biodiversity, and what is being done to protect and restore biodiversity.

Wilson, E. O. 1992. *The Diversity of Life*. W. W. Norton & Company, New York.
In this book, the author describes the evolution of life and biodiversity on earth. He also documents the threats to biodiversity due to human activities and calls for a major effort to protect and restore biodiversity throughout the world.

Questions for Discussion

1. Why are biologists concerned about the loss of biodiversity in the tropics?

2. Why is biodiversity in northern countries such as the United States also at risk?

3. What are some species in the United States that have gone extinct in the last 200 years?

4. What animals in the United States have disappeared from large parts of their range?

5. What are some animals that have been restored to your region?

6. What are some factors that must be considered in reintroducing a species?

Applications

1. Read early explorers' accounts or early newspaper articles from your area to find out about historical wildlife. Even New York City was once covered with forests full of game, and the neighboring Hudson River was full of salmon and other fish. How did native Americans and early European settlers use or interact with these species? Have any of those species disappeared from your area or from the planet?

2. Check the U.S. Fish & Wildlife Service Web site at http://www.fws.gov for the current list of endangered plants and animals in your state. What kinds of species are on the list? How does your list compare with that from other states? Investigate and report on one of these species.

3. What roles did the various species identified above play in your local ecosystem? Is it important that they be reintroduced so they could once again serve this role? Is it practical to reintroduce them?

4. Use field guides or checklists to determine how many species of birds live in your state. Where do they occur? How many live on the coast, in the mountains, and on lakes and rivers. Which ones are summer residents? How does this compare with neighboring states? Which ones are endangered? Which ones are nonnative? Would you consider that group of organisms to be relatively safe or at risk?

7.5 Passenger Pigeon

John James Audubon
1785–1851

Adapted from: "Passenger Pigeon" in the Ornithological Biography *(1831–1839).*

John James Audubon traveled through the United States in the early 1800s drawing, painting, and writing about the birds he observed. He published his drawings and paintings in the four volumes of The Birds of America *in a series of manuscripts ending in 1938. A five-volume text describing the birds, the* Ornithological Biography, *accompanied Audubon's drawings and paintings. The bird illustrations and biographies were published together, in 1842, in the seven-volume* The Birds of America. *The Audubon Society, named for John James Audubon, was founded in 1886 initially to attempt to address the threatened extinction through uncontrolled hunting of birds such as the passenger pigeon.*

Overview

Visitors to the United States in its early years marveled at the profusion and diversity of the native wildlife. Passenger pigeons were especially abundant. They have been described as one of the most numerous species of bird on earth. They flew in enormous flocks, filling the sky for many miles, and occupied nesting sites so vast that they sometimes encompassed a hundred or more square miles of forest. This very abundance proved to be the cause of the passenger pigeon's rapid extinction. Millions of passenger pigeons were killed by wanton hunting. By the 1880s, the reduced numbers of passenger pigeons were obvious, but their threatened extinction was not evident until the 1890s. By 1900, passenger pigeons were absent in the wild; only a few birds persisted in captivity at zoos. The last passenger pigeon, pictured in Figure 1, died in the Cincinnati Zoo in 1914.

Audubon's essay, originally published in his *Ornithological Biography* (1831–1839) and later in his *The Birds of America* (1842), describes the passenger pigeon during the time when its flocks filled the sky and hunters slaughtered birds by the millions. This story serves as a reminder of how quickly human activities can cause the extinction of species.

The last surviving passenger pigeon died in 1914.

The passenger pigeon moves with extreme rapidity by repeated flapping of the wings, which it brings more or less close to its body, according to the degree of velocity required. Like the domestic Pigeon, it often flies in a circling manner during the love season, supporting itself with both wings elevated at an angle, and keeping them in that position until it is about to alight. Now and then during these circular flights, the tips of the primary quills of each wing are made to strike against each other, producing a smart rap which may be heard thirty or forty yards away. Before alighting, the Wild Pigeon, like the Carolina Parrot and a few other species of birds, breaks the force of its flight by repeated flapping, as if apprehensive of injury from too suddenly contacting the branch or spot of ground where it intends to settle.

I began my description of the Passenger Pigeon with an account of its flight, because the most important facts connected with its habits relate to its migrations. It migrates for food rather than with a view to escaping the severity of the northern weather, or to seek a southern climate for breeding. Consequently such flights do not take place at any fixed period or season of the year. Indeed it sometimes happens that a continuance of a supply of food in one district will keep these birds away from any other place for years. I know, at least, to a certainty, that in Kentucky they remained for several years constantly, and were nowhere else to be found. They all suddenly disappeared one season when the mast (nuts of forest trees) was exhausted, and they did not return for a long period. Similar facts have been observed in other States.

Their great power of flight enables them to survey and pass over an astonishing extent of country in a very short time. This is proved by well-known facts. Pigeons have been killed in the neighborhood of New York with their crops full of rice, which they must have collected in the fields of Georgia and Carolina. These districts are the nearest possible for a supply of such food. Their power of digestion is so remarkable that they will decompose food entirely in twelve hours; therefore, they must have traveled between three and four hundred miles in six hours, showing their speed to be at an average of about one mile a minute. A velocity such as this would enable one of these birds, were it so inclined, to visit the European continent in less than three days.

This great power of flight is seconded by as great a power of vision, which enables them, as they travel at that swift rate, to inspect the country below and to discover their food with facility. Thus they obtain the object of their journey. This I have also proved to be the case by having observed them flying high and in an extended front when passing over sterile or poor country. This enables them to survey hundreds of acres at once. On the other hand, when the land is richly covered with food, or the trees abundantly hung with mast, they fly low in order to discover the part most plentifully supplied.

Their body is of an elongated oval form, which they steer with a long, well-plumed tail and propel with well-set wings, the muscles of which are very large and powerful for the size of the bird. A bird seen gliding through the woods and close to the observer passes like a thought. The eye searches in vain to see it again; but the bird is gone.

The multitudes of Wild Pigeons in our [American] woods are astonishing. Indeed, after having viewed them so often and under so many circumstances, I now feel inclined to pause and reassure myself that what I am going to relate is fact. Yet I have seen it all, and in the company, too, of persons who, like myself, were struck with amazement.

In the autumn of 1813 I left my house at Henderson on the banks of the Ohio, on my way to Louisville. In passing over the barrens a few miles beyond Hardensburg, I observed the Passenger Pigeons flying from northeast to southwest in greater numbers than I had ever seen them before. Feeling an inclination to count the flocks that might pass within the reach of my eye in one hour, I dismounted, seated myself on an eminence, and began to mark a dot with my pencil for every flock that passed. In a short time, finding this task impracticable because the birds were pouring by in countless multitudes, I arose. I counted the dots that I had put down and found that one hundred and sixty-three had been recorded in twenty-one minutes. I travelled on, and met still more, farther on. The air was literally filled with Pigeons. The noon-day light was obscured as by an eclipse. The dung fell in spots not unlike melting flakes of snow; and the continuous buzz of wings tended to lull my senses.

While waiting for dinner at Young's Inn at the confluence of Salt River with the Ohio, I saw, at my leisure, immense legions still going by. Their front reached far beyond the Ohio on the west, and the beechwood forests directly east of me. Not a single bird alighted, for not a nut or acorn was that year to be seen in the neighborhood. Consequently, they flew so high that different attempts to reach them with a capital rifle proved ineffectual; nor did the reports disturb them in the least. I cannot describe to you the extreme beauty of their aerial evolutions when a Hawk chanced to press upon the rear of a flock. At once, like a torrent, and with a noise like thunder, they rushed

The multitudes of Wild Pigeons in our American woods are astonishing.

into a compact mass, pressing upon each other towards the center. In these almost solid masses they darted forward in undulating and angular lines, descended to the earth and swept close over it with inconceivable velocity, mounted perpendicularly so as to resemble a vast column, and, when high, they were seen wheeling and twisting within their continued lines, which resembled the coils of a gigantic serpent.

Before sunset I reached Louisville, fifty-five miles from Hardensburg. The Pigeons were still passing in undiminished numbers. They continued to do so for three days in succession. The people were all in arms. The banks of the Ohio were crowded with men and boys incessantly shooting at the pilgrims, which flew lower as they passed the river. Multitudes were thus destroyed. For a week or more, the population fed on no other flesh than that of Pigeons, and talked of nothing but Pigeons.

It is extremely interesting to see flock after flock performing exactly the same evolutions which a preceding flock had traced in the air. Thus should a Hawk charge on a group at a certain point, the angles, curves and undulations described by the birds, in their efforts to escape the dreaded talons of the plunderer, are undeviatingly followed by the next group that comes up. Should the bystander happen to witness one of these affrays and, struck with the rapidity and elegance of the motions, desire to see them repeated, his wishes will be gratified if he but remain in the same place until the next group of Pigeons comes along.

As soon as the Pigeons discover a sufficiency of food to entice them to alight, they fly around in circles, reviewing the countryside below. During these evolutions the dense mass which they form presents a beautiful appearance, as it changes its direction, turning a glistening sheet of azure, as the backs of the birds come simultaneously into view, to presenting a deep rich purple. They pass lower, over the woods, and for a moment are lost among the foliage, but they emerge and glide aloft. They may now alight, but the next moment, as if suddenly alarmed, take to wing, the flapping of their wings producing a noise like the roar of distant thunder, as they sweep through the forests to see if danger is near. However, hunger soon brings them to the ground. On alighting they industriously throw aside the withered leaves in quest of the fallen mast. The rear ranks continually rise, passing over the main body and alighting in front, in such rapid succession that the whole flock seems still on the wing. The quantity of ground swept in this way is astonishing. So completely has it been cleared that the gleaner who might follow in the rear of the flock would find his labor completely lost. While feeding, their avidity is at times so great that in attempting to swallow a large acorn or nut, they are seen gasping for a long while, as if in the agonies of suffocation.

When the woods are filled with these Pigeons, they are killed in immense numbers, although no apparent diminution comes of it. About the middle of the day, after their repast is finished, they settle on the trees to enjoy rest and digest their food. On the ground and on the branches they walk with ease, frequently jerking their beautiful tails and moving their necks backwards and forward in the most graceful manner. As the sun begins to sink beneath the horizon, they depart *en masse* for the roosting place, which not infrequently is hundreds of miles away, a fact ascertained by persons who have kept track of their arrivals and departures.

Let us now inspect their place of nightly rendezvous. One of these curious roosting places, on the banks of the Green River in Kentucky, I repeatedly visited. It was, as always, in a part of the forest where the trees were huge and where there was little underbrush. I rode through it for more than forty miles, and, on crossing it in different parts, found its average width to be rather more than three miles. My first view of it was at nearly two hours before sunset. Few of the Pigeons were then to be seen, but a great number of persons with horses and wagons, guns and ammunition had already camped on the edge of the forest.

Two farmers from the vicinity of Russellville, more than a hundred miles distant, had driven more than three hundred hogs to be fattened on the Pigeons which were to be slaughtered. Here and there, people employed in plucking and salting birds already killed sat amid large piles of dead birds. The dung lay several inches deep, covering the whole roosting place. Many trees two feet in diameter were broken off at no great distance from the ground; and the branches of many of the largest and tallest had given way, as if the forest had been swept by a tornado. Everything proved to me that the number of birds in this part of the forest must be immense beyond conception.

As the time of the arrival of the Passenger Pigeons approached, their foes anxiously prepared to receive them. Some persons were ready with iron pots containing sulfur, others with torches of pine knots; many with poles, and the rest with guns.

The sun went down, yet not a Pigeon had arrived. Everything was ready, and all eyes were gazing on the clear sky, which appeared in glimpses amid the tall trees.

Suddenly a general cry burst forth, "Here they come!" The noise they made, though still distant, reminded me of a hard gale at sea, passing through the rigging of a close-reefed vessel. As the birds arrived and passed over me, I felt a current of air that surprised me. Thousands of Pigeons were soon knocked down by the pole-men. More continued to pour in. The fires were lighted, and a magnificent, as well as wonderful, and almost terrifying sight presented itself. The Pigeons, arriving by the thousands, alighted everywhere, one above another, until solid masses were formed on the branches all around. Here and there the perches gave way under the weight with a crash, and fell to the ground, destroying hundreds of birds beneath, forcing down the dense groups of them with which every stick was loaded. It was a scene of uproar and confusion. I found it quite useless to speak, or even to shout to those persons nearest to me. Even the gun reports were seldom heard, and I was made aware of the firing only by seeing the shooters reloading.

No one dared venture near the devastation. The hogs had been penned up, leaving the picking up of the dead and wounded birds until the next morning. The Pigeons were constantly coming, and it was past midnight before I noticed any decrease in the number of those arriving. The uproar continued the whole night. I was anxious to know how far away the sound could be heard, so I sent off a man used to roaming the forest. He returned in two hours informing me that he had heard it distinctly three miles from the roosting place.

Towards the approach of day, the noise somewhat subsided. Long before I could distinguish them plainly, the Pigeons began to move off in a direction quite different from the one in which they arrived the evening before. By sunrise all that were able to fly had disappeared. The howling of the wolves now reached our ears, and the foxes, lynxes, cougars, bears, raccoons, opossums and polecats were seen sneaking off. Eagles and hawks, accompanied by a crowd of vultures, took their place and enjoyed their share of the spoils.

Then the authors of all this devastation began to move among the dead, the dying, and the mangled. They picked up the Pigeons and piled them in heaps, until each man had as many as he could possibly dispose of. Then, the hogs were let loose to feed on the remainder.

Persons unacquainted with these birds might naturally conclude that such dreadful havoc would soon put an end to the species. But I have satisfied myself, by long observation, that nothing but the gradual diminution of our forests can accomplish their decrease. They not infrequently quadruple their number yearly, and always at least double it. In 1805 I saw schooners loaded with Pigeons caught up the Hudson River, coming into the wharf at New York where the birds sold for a cent apiece. I knew a man in Pennsylvania who caught and killed more than five hundred dozen in a clap-net in one day. Sometimes the net took twenty dozens or more at a single haul. In March, 1830, the Passenger Pigeon was so abundant in the New York markets that piles of them met the eye in every direction. I have seen the Negroes grow weary of killing them as the birds alighted for weeks at a time to drink the water from the pipes at the saltworks of Shawnee Town, on the Tennessee-Kentucky border.

The breeding of the Wild Pigeon and places they choose for breeding are of interest. The time is not much influenced by season, and the place selected is where food is most plentiful and most attainable, and always at a convenient distance from water. The tallest trees of the forest are those in which the Pigeons nest. To these trees countless pairs resort and prepare to fulfill one of the great laws of nature. At this period the note of the Pigeon is a soft *coo—coo—coo—coo*, much shorter than that of the domestic species. The common

> **In March, 1830, the Passenger Pigeon was so abundant in the New York markets that piles of them met the eye in every direction.**

notes resemble *kee —kee—kee—kee,* the first of these being the loudest, and the others gradually diminishing in power. The male assumes a pompous demeanor, and follows the female whether on the ground or on the branches, with his tail spread and his wings drooping. His body is elevated, his throat swells, his eyes sparkle. He continues his cooing, and now and then rises on the wing and flies a few yards towards the fugitive and timorous female. Like the domestic Pigeon and others, they caress each other by billing, an action in which the bill of the one is placed transversely in that of the other. Both birds alternately disgorge the contents of their crops by repeated efforts. After these preliminaries, the Pigeons begin building their nest in peace and harmony. The nests are composed of a few dry twigs crossing each other in the fork of some branches.

Fifty to a hundred nests may be seen in the same tree. I might say a much greater number, were I not anxious that you should not feel disposed to refer my account of the Wild Pigeons to the marvelous.

The eggs are two in number, broadly elliptical and pure white. During incubation the male keeps the female supplied with food. Indeed the tenderness and affection shown by these birds towards their mates are striking in the highest degree. It is a remarkable fact that each brood hatched usually consists of a male and female.

Here again, the tyrant of creation, man, interferes, disturbing the harmony of this peaceful scene. As the young birds grow up, their enemies, armed with axes, reach the spot and seize and destroy all they can. The trees are felled, and are made to fall in such a way that the cutting of one causes the overthrow of another. Or the crash shakes the trees near by so much that the young Pigeons, or squabs, are violently tossed to the ground. In this way immense quantities are destroyed.

The young are fed by the parents as described above. In other words, the old bird puts its bill in the mouth of the young one crosswise, or with the back of the two parts of the bill opposite the young bird's open mouth and disgorges the contents of its crop. As soon as the young birds are able to shift for themselves, they leave their parents and continue apart until they reach maturity. By the end of six months they are capable of reproducing their species.

The flesh of the Wild Pigeon is of a dark color, but affords tolerable eating. That of young birds from the nest is much esteemed. The skin is covered with small white filmy scales. The feathers fall off at the least touch, like those of the Carolina Turtle Dove. Like other Pigeons, it immerses its head up to the eyes while drinking.

In March, 1830, I bought about three hundred and fifty of these birds in the New York market at four cents apiece. Most of these I carried alive to England and distributed them among several noblemen, giving some to the Zoological Society.

A curious change of habits has taken place in those which I presented to the Earl of Derby in 1830. That nobleman has assured me that ever since they began breeding in his aviaries near Liverpool they have laid only one egg. My noble friend has raised many and distributed them freely. It is therefore not surprising that some which have escaped confinement have been shot. But that the Passenger Pigeon should have a natural claim to be admitted into the British fauna appears to me very doubtful.

Epilogue

There have been no sightings anywhere in the United States of a live passenger pigeon since 1914. The species, *Ectopistes migratorius,* is assumed to have become extinct at about that time. As you know, once a species becomes extinct it can never return.

Additional Resources

Audubon, J. J. 1842. *The Birds of America.* J. J. Audubon, New York.

This seven-volume series combined Audubon's bird drawings and paintings (first published as *Birds of America* from 1840 to 1844) and his descriptive essays (originally published in the five volumes of *Ornithological Biography* from 1831 to 1839).

Balouet, J.-C. 1990. *Extinct Species of the World.* Barron's, New York, NY.

A study of our planet's extinct animal life—from prehistoric times to those animals that have disappeared during our own century. One hundred and eighty illustrations.

Morrison, S. 1990. *The Passenger Pigeon: Gone Forever.* Silver Burdett Press, New York, NY.

Discusses the history of the passenger pigeon, which at one time made up one-quarter of the birds of America but is now extinct.

Roop, P. 1987. *Capturing Nature: The Writings & Art of John James Audubon*. Abbeville Press, Inc., New York, NY. A first-person adventure story through nature. Readers learn of a world gone by and develop a greater respect for the earth upon which they live. Audubon's writing is engaging and easily accepted as authentic.

Questions for Discussion

1. Describe some of the apparent differences in appearance between the pigeon with which you are familiar and the passenger pigeon.

2. Describe one very unique characteristic of passenger pigeon behavior.

3. Discuss the abundance of the passenger pigeon in the early 1800s and how this abundance contributed to its extinction.

4. Why was it so easy for humans to capture and/or kill passenger pigeons?

Applications

1. Describe the series of events that made it possible for the passenger pigeon to become extinct. Discuss your attitudes about this particular extinction.

2. Identify an organism in your community that is an endangered species. Predict what you think will happen to local populations of this species. What factors might cause it to become extinct or to increase its present population size?

3. What do you propose could be done to reduce the present greatly accelerated rate of extinctions due to human activities?

7.6 The Origin of Water on Earth: Frozen Comets from Space

Louis A. Frank, Ph.D.
Space Physics
University of Iowa, Iowa City, Iowa

Dr. Frank, a world-class physicist and native Iowan, holds the Carver-Van Allen Chair in Physics at the University of Iowa. He has been an experimentor and a coinvestigator for instruments on 22 spacecraft and principal investigator on 14 other space missions. He also helped calibrate the first U.S. lunar probes. While working with the Dynamics Explorer mission, he collected data that led to the discovery of small comets.

Overview

Dr. Frank's recent assertion that the water on Earth comes from comets from space has sparked heated debate in the scientific community. Dr. Frank's respected scientific reputation and generally conservative outlook on life make his championing of this issue all the more surprising. This very personal essay details Dr. Frank's observations and musings as he developed the hypothesis that water on Earth comes from comets.

The Beginnings

I live on the plains of Iowa, drive a pick-up truck, and build instruments for satellites that study the Earth. I am conservative in the way I dress, in the way I lead my life, in the people I vote for, and in the way I do science. Science is my life. I have had experiments on about forty spacecraft. People tell me I have had more instruments on more spacecraft than anyone else on this planet. Building and using technology has put me in the forefront of many space physics discoveries. I made the first measurements of the plasma ring around Saturn. I was the first to measure solar wind plasmas funneling directly into the Earth's polar atmosphere. I was the first to observe with a satellite instrument the belt of ions around the Earth that is now known as the "ring current." But I was always cautious, looking for evidence to support my ideas. Often I looked for the very data that would disprove my own ideas.

An Adventure in Science

In 1986, pictures relayed from an orbiting satellite led me to a radical departure from the scientific mainstream. I proposed that the Earth was being showered by a vast number of previously unde-tected small comets (Figure 1). I calculated about twenty of these comets (each about the size of a small house and made essentially of water and ice) plunge through our atmosphere each and every minute of every day. If I was correct, then the water that we fish in, bathe in, drink, and are made of is of extraterrestrial origin. The proposi-tion that a rain of cosmic ice is presently bombarding the Earth held staggering implications for us and our planet.

"That's as crazy as they come," said one astronomer. "I'm amazed," said an oceanographer. "I've never heard anything like it." I was accused of making a mountain out of a molehill. But what else could people say to someone who claimed to

> *If I was correct, then the water that we fish in, bathe in, drink, and are made of is of extraterrestrial origin.*

have discovered the existence of celestial objects never before seen by astronomers that may be responsible for the origin of the oceans, the origin of life, the death of the dinosaurs, the unexplained falls of ice from the sky, the fireballs seen in our nighttime atmosphere, the mysterious bright flashes sometimes seen on the Moon, the channel-marked surface of Mars, the ice moons of the outer planets, and a host of other phenomena throughout the solar system?

An incoming snowball, perhaps 40 feet in diameter, is hard to observe.

The comet breaks up into fragments when it is 600 miles to 15,000 miles above Earth.

Exposure to sunlight rapidly vaporizes the snow; the vapor cloud expands to 30 miles across.

Vapor cloud flattens into pancake; winds disperse it; water condenses.

Figure 1 *Thousands of comets hit the Earth's atmosphere every day. The water and dust in these comets are dispersed into the Earth's atmosphere.*

The evidence that led colleagues and I to propose such a massive infall of objects into the Earth's atmosphere came from a high-altitude, polar-orbiting satellite called *Dynamics Explorer.* The satellite carries an ultraviolet camera that takes pictures of the Earth in the light that lies just beyond the violet end of the visible light range. These otherwise normal ultraviolet images were speckled with some very puzzling dark spots. We found more than 30,000 such spots in the images during some 2,000 hours of observing time.

John Sigwarth, one of my graduate students, and my colleague John Craven, a research scientist at the University of Iowa, scrutinized the data for possible computer glitches, random flaws, radio transmission noise, failing sensors, even the possibility of paint flecks on the camera. It became clear that the spots on the images represented something that lay between the satellite itself and the region of the upper atmosphere we were observing. Analysis of these spots indicated the presence of water. But these dark spots were enormous, measuring about thirty miles in diameter. No amount of evaporation from the surface of the Earth could produce such large clouds of water vapor at that altitude. The water had to come from out there. The source clearly had to be extraterrestrial.

Whatever had caused this large cloud in our images had to be in a form other than water vapor when it was well away from the Earth. When far away, I calculated, it had to be a relatively loosely packed ball of water-snow the size of a small house. At one to two thousand miles above the Earth, either the action of tidal forces, which are produced by the planet's gravity, or perhaps static electricity would then have broken up the object and the sun would have vaporized its contents into a ball of gas. By the time it had plunged to within about 300 miles of the Earth, this hundred-ton spray of water and snow, traveling at about twenty times the speed of sound, would have expanded to a thin ball of gas some thirty miles across. That is not much water. It is thinner than a London fog. But it would have been enough to produce the black spots in our images.

At about fifty miles above us in the atmosphere, the vapor cloud would have slowed to subsonic speeds but continued to plummet until it reached a height of about thirty-five miles where it would get mixed up with the air in the upper atmosphere. Circulating into the stratosphere would then turn the water vapor into ice crystals. These ice crystals would fall and become part of the water vapor present at low altitudes, eventually turning into precipitation and falling on land and sea.

This, of course, is the scenario for just one cometlike object. At the observed rate of twenty per minute, over a year's time, you would get about one ten-thousandths of an inch of water if spread uniformly on the Earth's surface. That is but a tiny fraction of the annual rainfall and quite indistinguishable from it. It is a mere drop in the bucket. But the icing on the cometary cake, so to speak, is that if you add up all the drops accumulated over the age of the Earth, you would have enough water to fill the oceans and more.

That is how we came to the startling conclusion that the dark spots in the images were being formed by small cometike objects entering the Earth's atmosphere. The mind rebels. It is disturbing. But it is really quite reasonable. I can explain why the black spots in the satellite images cannot be anything else. I can explain why we are not seeing these comets all the time. I can explain just how the water from these comets manages to survive through the atmosphere.

The Traditional View

Current wisdom has longed favored the view that most of the Earth's water has been here since the birth of our planet, which is estimated to have occurred some 4.5 billion years ago. It is widely believed that the Earth was formed through the accumulation of cosmic debris left over from the giant nebula, essentially a dust and gas cloud, that formed the sun itself. The debris particles, which are thought to have contained water, eventually collected together through the force of gravity to produce our planet. The water then remained trapped in the Earth until the initial crust solidified and the gases from the interior were released in volcanic events. As the Earth's temperature fell, water condensed out of the atmosphere. When the rains came, the original crustal minerals were eroded and weathered, forming sediments and an initial ocean.

But not until the late stages of formation was the Earth either large enough or cool enough to support water. In the early stages of formation, the Earth was nothing but a large, hot cinder that had grown from collisions with many smaller cinders. Though it was eventually large enough for gravity to prevent the easy escape of hydrogen, helium, and water from its atmosphere, the Earth still could not support liquid water on its surface until it had cooled considerably. So it seems that any water present during the Earth's formation from the cinders would very likely have escaped back into space.

Another popular view is that water was brought to the still primitive Earth in a massive bombardment of large comets, which are conjectured to have been quite common in those first hundred million years or so of the Earth's history. Then the comets stopped arriving. Though appealing to some scientists, this scenario for water delivery through an early comet swarm is still not well defined.

But in either case, it has generally been agreed that the Earth probably had most of its water quite early in its history. I, too, had always assumed that the oceans were here in the beginning. I thought it had long been accepted as proven fact. I had never given it a second thought. Then one day a colleague suggested that the small comets, if they were real, could have brought in enough water over time to supply the world's oceans.

The Process of Discovery

Sigwarth and I analyzed over 10,000 images. Our interpretation of the events continued to involve meteor impacts into the Earth's upper atmosphere. By counting the dark spots in our images, we were able to estimate the rate at which these objects appeared. We saw 10 holes per minute on the daylight side of the Earth. So we doubled that figure to obtain the rate of these objects over the entire face of the Earth.

But what looked like little dark spots on the images turned out, in reality, to be about thirty miles across. They could not be rocks because such large rocks would just smash the surface of the earth to pieces. These were clouds of water vapor.

It was the only reasonable explanation we could find. Some engineers suggested that the black spots might be due to satellite parts falling into the atmosphere. But that is not possible. First of all, there are not 10 million satellite parts falling down on us each year. And secondly, they are not thirty miles across. Many people said there had to be other explanations for the dark spots. But no one has ever come out with one.

We interpreted these events in terms of 10 million objects falling into the Earth's atmosphere every year. That is an infall of material that is about ten thousand times more than anyone had ever imagined. So psychologically, emotionally, the interpretation was difficult to accept. But intellectually, it was trivial. There was no other reasonable explanation.

In the planetary sciences, the relative amounts of the isotopes of hydrogen, oxygen, and sulfur present in a sample can serve as a fingerprint of its origins. Isotopes are the members in the family of a given element, such as hydrogen, for instance, which has an isotope called deuterium. Recently it was found that the deuterium content of large comets, such as Halley's Comet, is too large to account for the Earth's oceans. Thus, scientists are trying to devise ways to measure this fingerprint of deuterium in the small comets to see if this water source is the culprit. The bottom line is that the oceans could well have come from the small comets.

With a little vaporization and a little cooking from the sun, the mantle on the comets should resemble nature's version of plastic wrap. If you start out with simple carbon compounds and expose them to millions of years of energetic charged particles and ultraviolet radiation from the sun and distant places in the cosmos, it is quite possible to produce a black crust about half an inch thick on a comet. This carbon coating would bind the comet together. Such a carbon mantle would give the small comets, coming no closer than the Earth's distance from the sun, just the lifespan they need— a hundred thousand years to one million years.

I proposed this black crust well before we learned that Halley's Comet itself had a very dark surface. It annoys people when I mention this, but it was just a natural extension of our work. Everyone had expected Halley's to look like a dirty white snowball. But the probes found that large areas of its surface were extremely black. In fact, it was described as one of the blackest things ever seen in the solar system.

Large comets traveling into the inner solar system are known to split and flare. No one knows why. They just break apart. I thought if the small comets are really there, then no large comet could exist very long without being hit by them. So I did some calculations. It turns out that the number of small comets is just about what you would expect to account for the random splitting and flaring of large comets. Not only that, but it is also the right number required to put the several visible holes in the black surface of Halley's Comet.

The amount of carbon brought in through the influx of small comets each year can also account for the total amount of carbon on the Earth. If the comets have been coming in steadily over the age of the Earth, they would not only have brought us the oceans, but most of the carbon on this planet as well. If it is true, then the carbon in the trees around us and the carbon in our own bodies would have come from comets as well. You might say we are all extraterrestrials in origin.

Life and its origin are delicate subjects. Conventional wisdom holds that the key molecular building blocks of life were formed on the Earth itself. Modern laboratory experiments suggest that gases in the Earth's primitive atmosphere—such as water vapor, methane, and ammonia—were broken up, either by exposure to the sun's ultraviolet light or to lightning discharges. They then recombined to form other molecules, such as hydrogen cyanide and formaldehyde, which are thought by many scientists to be chemical building blocks of carbon-based life.

We interpreted these events in terms of 10 million objects falling into the Earth's atmosphere every year.

Scientists during the past three decades have considered an entirely different scenario for the origin of life. The idea is that comets may have supplied the Earth with the organic materials needed to create life. Many critics have objected to the idea on the grounds that a single object large enough to contain all necessary ingredients for life and large enough not to burn up in the Earth's atmosphere would hit the Earth with such force as to destroy the organic material. Several studies, though, indicate the Earth's atmosphere used to be more dense. A dense atmosphere would slow a comet down, reducing its impact. And our small comets would have lower speeds and less impact force. These small comets could have deposited significant amounts of organic matter. In fact, they may have been responsible for the atmosphere itself!

Aeronomers, scientists who study the upper atmosphere, do not like the notion of a wet upper atmosphere. They generally assume that the amount of water vapor up there falls sharply above 40 miles because air carried from lower altitudes has been dried by frigid temperatures. There are a number of measurements in the literature that do not show this expected dryness. These higher water content measurements cannot be explained by simple upward movement of water vapor. Aeronomers are quite correct. The water is not rising from below. It is falling down from above.

It is also fairly obvious that an increase in the number of small comets could cause clouds to form about fifty miles up, reflecting sunlight and cooling the Earth. Comet storms could create a global ice cloud and may have been responsible for the Ice Ages.

The implications were piling up. We were not just talking about bringing water (and lots of it) down to the Earth, but the very ingredients for life itself and more—like a good portion of the atmosphere. It seems that the small comet theory also addresses the problem of how early life, which needed oxygen

to protect itself from the sun's ultraviolet rays, could have flourished on a primitive Earth thought to have been devoid of oxygen. Some of the water molecules in these comets would have broken apart from the heat of impact and formed oxygen and hydrogen gases. This would automatically have produced a shield of oxygen to protect life from damaging ultraviolet rays.

So it may be that these small comets provided not only the chemical seeds for life on Earth, but the oxygen to protect it from the sun, as well as the marine incubator—the ocean—in which it could grow and thrive.

> *It seems that the small comet theory also addresses the problem of how early life, which needed oxygen to protect itself from the sun's ultraviolet rays, could have flourished on a primitive earth thought to have been devoid of oxygen.*

Two weeks after publication of the small comet papers, John Sigwarth and I presented our findings at the spring meeting of the American Geophysical Union in Baltimore. This was the first time we had gone public. The meeting room was packed. A television monitor was provided so that the dozens outside the room could also witness the proceedings. It was hot in the room, and rivers of sweat rolled down my face and soaked my white shirt. I removed my jacket and loosened my red tie. One of my colleagues told a reporter: "There's nothing like a good bloody brawl in science."

Since that time, collected data continue to support our explanations. After the 1997 American Geophysical Meeting, various scientists were quoted by the *New York Times* (May 29, 1997). Frank can "definitely demonstrate that there are objects entering the Earth's upper atmosphere that contain a lot of water," said Dr. Thomas Donahue. Dr. Robert Hoffman called it ". . . a remarkable . . . and important phenomenon." Dr. Donahue went on to say, "These results certainly vindicate Lou Frank's earlier observations."

Now when many others are agreeing with us about the origin of water on Earth, it sure feels good to have studied, analyzed, and fought for an explanation that covered all the facts. Science is a marvelous process.

Additional Resources

Frank, L. A. and P. Huyghe. 1990. *The Big Splash*. Carol Publishing Group, New York, NY.

A scientific discovery that revolutionizes the way we view the origin of life, the water we drink, the death of the dinosaurs, the creation of the oceans, the nature of the cosmos, and the very future of the Earth itself.

Sagan, C. and A. Druyan. 1985. *Comet*. Random House, New York, NY.

Carl Sagan, an astronomer noted for his broad interests in the heavens and the search for extraterrestrial intelligence, provides a broad look at comets. He provides a look at comets as seen by ancient observers and the myths associated with them and continues on to present times. Along the way, he offers information about comets, their impacts on the Earth, suggestions about how to spot one, and the roles of amateurs in spotting them; he even looks at the probabilities that earth will be struck by yet another. This general book about comets is a nice place to begin further study of these interplanetary wanderers.

Questions for Discussion

1. What made Dr. Frank and his colleagues think the black spots were water?

2. What evidence did they have that the water was coming in the form of comets?

3. What was the reaction of other scientists to their ideas?

4. How does Dr. Frank's theory on the origin of water on Earth differ from the ideas of other scientists?

Applications

1. If the water on Earth really came from comets, how might that have affected the history of life on Earth?

2. How can you explain the fact that scientists said that Dr. Frank was wrong in suggesting that water came from comets?

3. Why should we spend our tax money to study the origin of black spots on satellite images? Formulate a rationale for funding Dr. Frank's research.

8.1 Bringing Back the Water: The Mono Lake Story

Bartshe Miller
Mono Lake Committee
Lee Vining, California

The Mono Lake Committee is a nonprofit citizens' group dedicated to the protection and restoration of the Mono Basin ecosystem, educating the public about Mono Lake and the impacts of excessive water use on the environment, and promoting cooperative solutions that protect Mono Lake without transferring environmental problems to other areas. As education director, Mr. Miller oversees the committee's education programs in Los Angeles and at Mono Lake.

Overview

Mono Lake lies at the foot of the Sierra Nevada mountains just east of Yosemite National Park. This ancient inland sea sits within a high desert basin surrounded by mountains and volcanoes. Despite an extreme chemical environment, its waters are home to one of the most productive aquatic ecosystems in North America. In 1941, water diversion from Mono Lake's tributary streams caused the lake level to decline gradually, threatening the health of its thriving ecosystem. As the lake's condition deteriorated, it became the focus of a long and controversial environmental struggle over water.

A Lake Like No Other

Within five miles, the Sierra Nevada mountains rise nearly 6,000 feet above Mono Lake. From every vantage point, mountains or volcanoes line the horizon, as shown in Figure 1. No water flows out of the lake. Thousands of years of evaporation have concentrated salts and other minerals in the lake. Freshwater runoff from mountain snow feeds the streams that empty into the lake, replacing evaporated water.

Mono Lake is a "triple-water" lake. Salt, carbonates, and sulfates dominate its chemistry. You can make a close approximation of Mono Lake water by using household chemicals, combining 2.5 tablespoons of table salt, 4.5 tablespoons of baking soda, 2 teaspoons of Epsom salt, a pinch of borax, and a pinch of laundry detergent in 1 quart of water. There is no other lake quite like it on earth. To find a similar lake, you would have to travel around the world to East Africa's Rift Valley.

Figure 1 *Mono Lake is surrounded by the rugged Sierra Nevada mountains.*

Simple Abundance

Because the lake is both saline (twice as salty as the Pacific Ocean) and extremely alkaline (pH 10), few aquatic organisms can tolerate its waters. No fish live in the lake, yet its waters brim with life in the summer months. Trillions of brine shrimp and alkali flies feed on an abundant supply of microscopic algae. The lake's harsh chemistry limits aquatic predators (like fish) and competition from other species, allowing for a simple but productive ecosystem. In terms of biomass, or the weight of living organisms per square meter of water, Mono Lake is among the most productive waters in North America.

Brine shrimp fill the lake by midsummer. The species found at Mono Lake, no larger than a thumbnail, is found nowhere else in the world. The life cycle of the Mono Lake brine shrimp is shown in Figure 2. Grazing on microscopic algae, the shrimp become so numerous by midsummer that the shade of the lake changes from green to blue as the amount of algae in the lake decreases. Colder weather brings about the shrimp's demise; but before this happens, the females release dormant eggs, called cysts, that survive the winter. As the lake warms in the spring, the cysts hatch and the cycle continues. The effects of seasonal stratification of the lake on the brine shrimp population is shown in Figure 3.

Most visitors to Mono Lake notice the alkali flies before the brine shrimp. Massed at the shoreline in thick, black carpets, the flies intimidate people who are unaware of their habits. More interested in eating algae than humans, the alkali fly is completely harmless. Most of its life cycle occurs

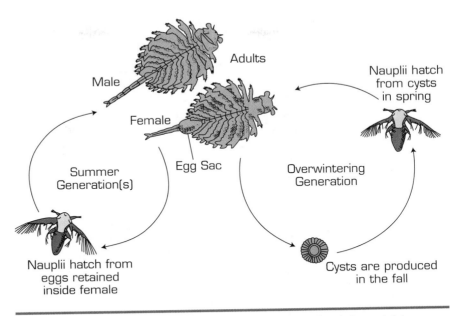

Figure 2 *Life cycle of Mono Lake's brine shrimp. Eggs hatch into miniatures, called* naupli, *which reach adulthood in 8–12 weeks. Most adults die in autumn, but not before producing egglike* cysts *that hatch into naupli the following spring. (Adapted from illustration by Joyce Jonte, the Mono Lake Committee.*

The species found at Mono Lake, no larger than a thumbnail, is found nowhere else in the world.

beneath the surface of the lake. With tiny hairs that trap air, adult flies will "scuba dive" beneath the water to deposit eggs in shallow water. These eggs hatch into tiny worms. The worms develop into pupae that anchor themselves to hard surfaces beneath the lake. This cocoonlike pupal stage protects the fly as it develops into an adult. When the adult is ready to emerge, its head separates as a small air sac inflates to pop the top off of the pupa case. The air sac deflates, the head reassembles, and the fly floats to the surface to begin its adult life. This life cycle is illustrated in Figure 4.

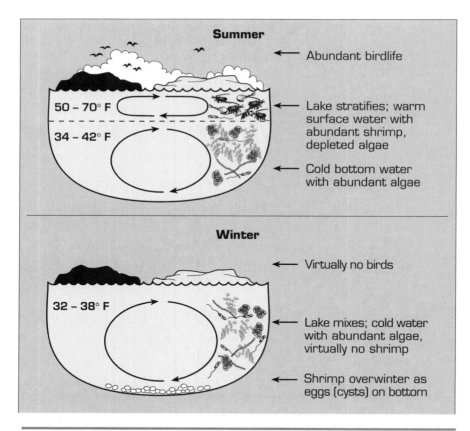

Figure 3 *In summer, Mono Lake stratifies into two layers that don't mix: an upper well-oxygenated layer of warm temperatures, abundant shrimp, and depleted algae and a deep region of cold temperatures, little oxygen, very few shrimp, and numerous algae. In winter, the surface water chills and sinks, causing the lake to mix from top to bottom. Shrimp vanish and algae thrive.*

Nursery, Gas Station, and International Airport

Millions of migratory birds stop at Mono Lake to take advantage of the abundant alkali flies and brine shrimp. Nearly one hundred different species of birds use the lake for nesting or migratory stops—some on their way to Central and South America. For a few species, the lake is a critical habitat for large numbers of their populations.

The California gull, as seen in Figure 5, comes to Mono Lake to breed on its islands. Safe from predators, these islands offer a place to nest and raise their young. Eighty-two percent of the state's population of California gulls are born at the lake. After Great Salt Lake, Mono Lake is home to the second largest California gull nesting colony in North America.

The eared grebe, a diving ducklike bird that spends its whole life on water, arrives at Mono Lake in the greatest numbers. Upwards of 2 million birds swim about the lake's surface in October devouring brine shrimp. Mono Lake provides a huge staging area for nearly half of the eared grebe population. The birds put on weight and grow new feathers before departing for winter destinations.

Of all the birds that come to Mono Lake, the Wilson's phalarope is the greatest traveler. These small shorebirds, not much larger than a fist, arrive at Mono Lake in midsummer after breeding in the northern United States and southern Canada. At Mono Lake, they molt their feathers and double their weight after several weeks. By mid-August they are gone, having departed for a nonstop journey to South America. The fact that these birds fly over 3,000 nonstop miles to South America is amazing enough, but what is truly astonishing is the time it takes for these little birds to reach their destination—three days.

Island Volcanoes and Strange Towers

The region surrounding Mono Lake is the setting for dramatic geology. The Mono Craters rise south of the lake, forming a nine-mile-long chain of volcanoes. Because they resemble plug-dome volcanoes more than actual craters, geologists consider the Mono Craters an active range. Panum Crater, the

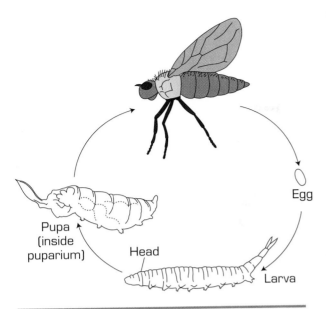

Figure 4 *Life cycle of the alkali fly. Females crawl underwater to lay eggs, which hatch into wriggly aquatic larvae. After fattening on algae for several weeks, the larvae secure themselves to tufa, pupate, and emerge weeks later as winged adults. (Adapted from illustration by Joyce Jonte, the Mono Lake Committee.*

youngest volcano in the chain, erupted less than 700 years ago. The most recent eruption at Mono Lake formed Paoha Island, the large gray island in the middle of the lake, which emerged from beneath the lake around 300 years ago. Rising magma pushed the bottom of the lake above its surface, giving Paoha its gray color. A few explosion pits, lava flows, and active steam vents add variety to the island's gray lake sediments. The other volcanic island is Negit Island, a small black cinder cone that looks more like a volcano than Paoha.

Tufa (pronounced too-fah, and not to be confused with tofu) grows around springs beneath the surface of the lake. Freshwater springs bearing dissolved calcium react with lake water carbonates creating calcium carbonate, or limestone. Resembling stalagmites, these limestone towers grow rapidly, reaching a height of 20 feet or more. Tufa towers line the shoreline, as shown in Figure 6. When water diversions began, only a few tufa stood above the level of the lake. You can see how much Mono Lake has dropped by how high the tufa towers stand above its surface.

The Water Flows South

In 1941, the Los Angeles Department of Water and Power (DWP) extended its aqueduct system into the Mono Basin to satisfy the water needs of a growing city. DWP diverted three of the lake's four major tributary streams and brought the water 335 miles south to the city of Los Angeles. When the water diversions began, few people ever visited Mono Lake, and only a handful of people lived near its shores. After DWP bought land and water rights, they began to build an aqueduct extension. A few people opposed the idea, but most accepted it and no one could legally stop it. Water rights were water rights in the eyes of the courts, and in 1941, nobody thought much about the environmental consequences.

As the lake water level declined, interest in the lake grew. In 1976, a group of undergraduate students launched a comprehensive ecological study of the lake. Little scientific information was available on the lake's ecology, and no one could say for certain what effects continued water diversions would have upon the lake's ecosystem. The researchers gathered specific data on the lake's hydrology and chemistry and every aspect of the lake's biology–algae, brine shrimp, alkali flies, birds, and plants. The ecological study answered specific questions about the state of the lake's ecology and unveiled a rich and unique ecosystem. There was far more to Mono Lake than anyone realized, and diversions threatened to change it forever.

Soon after the study, a landbridge emerged between Negit Island and the mainland. Nearly all

Figure 5 *California Gulls nest on the islands in Mono Lake.*

Figure 6 *These tufa towers were formed under water and thus stand as testaments to the magnitude of water level change.*

Geographic. Visitation at the lake increased. "Save Mono Lake" bumper stickers began to appear throughout California.

But diversions continued to lower the lake level. Coyotes soon crossed the landbridge and forced the gulls to abandon Negit Island for its neighboring islets. Toxic alkali dust storms rose from the exposed lake bed, violating federal air quality standards. By the end of 1981, the lake had dropped to its historic low level, 45 vertical feet below where it stood in 1941 when water diversions began. With one-half its volume depleted, the lake's salinity doubled, threatening the productivity of the lake's ecosystem and the habitat for millions of migrating birds.

With momentum and increasing awareness, Mono Lake Committee joined a lawsuit with California Audubon against the Los Angeles Department of Water and Power. The lawsuit grew from the idea of the Public Trust, a little-known doctrine going back to ancient Roman Law that certain lands and resources belong to the people and that the government has a responsibility to maintain them. The Public Trust Lawsuit seemed like a long shot. Nobody had tested the Public Trust in such a way—challenging the water rights of the second largest city in the United States on behalf of a salty desert lake.

the California gulls nested on Negit Island. If steps weren't taken, coyotes would soon invade the gull rookery and prey on helpless chicks. The California National Guard attempted to blow up the landbridge and widen the channel between the mainland and the island. Though the attempts failed, the explosions made great publicity for the newly formed Mono Lake Committee.

A City's Water in Question

On hand for the ecological study was David Gaines. A devoted birder, David grew up in Southern California and often visited the eastern Sierra Nevada. Appalled by the situation at Mono Lake, David and friends went on to form the Mono Lake Committee. They began spreading the word about the ecological significance and unparalleled beauty of this ancient high desert lake, giving slide shows to clubs, schools, service organizations, legislators—anyone who would listen. David did not envision "saving" Mono Lake, but he believed that if people could just see Mono Lake and understand its importance, they would join the fight to protect it. The response was overwhelming. People joined the Mono Lake Committee in support of its cause. Articles appeared in *Life, Audubon,* and *National*

> *In 1976, a group of undergraduate students launched a comprehensive ecological study of the lake.*

The lawsuit lasted four long years, eventually coming before the California State Supreme Court. On February 17, 1983, the court made a decision that shook the foundations of water and environmental law. The court ruled that the public trust applied to Mono Lake. Los Angeles' water rights could be revised. The ruling established a revolutionary precedent. The environment had value in the eyes of the public, and that value had to be considered with the city's right to divert water. Mono Lake made legal history. Water rights were no longer absolute.

Finding Solutions

Ironically the Public Trust ruling did not put water back into Mono Lake; it only opened up the possibility. The issue of nonnative trout provoked the lawsuit that finally put some water back into Mono Basin streams. Even though trout were not native to the Mono Basin, a trout fishery existed in the streams before diversions began, and DWP evaded a California law requiring minimum stream flows below dams to maintain fisheries.

In 1986, for the first time in decades, water began to flow year-round in Rush and Lee Vining Creeks. But even this did not guarantee a long-term solution for Mono Lake. The tide had clearly turned in favor of Mono Lake by 1988. But a severe drought had struck California with no relief on the horizon, and one question had yet to be answered—how much water did the lake need to protect its vital ecosystem?

Drought persuaded people throughout California to conserve water. Conservation was particularly successful in Los Angeles when the city conserved up to 30 percent of its past water use in 1991—more than the amount needed to replace Mono Lake water. Water reclamation, or water recycling, also looked promising. By promoting water conservation and securing funds for new water recycling plants, the Mono Lake Committee was able to strike a deal with DWP, permanently replacing a portion of water diverted from Mono Lake's streams.

When Compromise Is Victory

In 1994, the California State Water Resources Control Board made a final decision on the fate of Mono Lake. A year of public testimony and scientific hearings followed the release of a weighty environmental impact report. The Water Board considered seven different lake levels. They chose one of the highest: 6,392 feet above sea level—25 feet below the lake's 1941 prediversion level and 20 feet above its historic low, a compromise

that served the Public Trust, balancing environmental value with water diversions. Los Angeles would continue to divert water, but more water would flow into the lake. For the Mono Lake Committee, National Audubon Society, and several public agencies involved in the Water Board hearings, the decision was a victory.

The Water Board decision hinged on two important factors—the health of the lake's ecosystem and air quality. Biologists demonstrated that a higher lake would increase the overall productivity of the ecosystem as the lake became less saline. Experts also established that a higher lake level was the only practical way to diminish the severe dust storms that plagued the Mono Basin on windy days—a potential threat to human health.

The Story Is Just Beginning

Mono Lake is on the rise, and restoration of its damaged streams is under way. Stream diversions to Los Angles continue but at a reduced rate. Unless the Water Board someday decides otherwise, the lake will eventually reach its management level. The future of the lake seems bright, but it also poses new questions and challenges.

Controversy lingers in California over water use and the environment. Pollution, dams, and inefficient water use threaten the health of the Colorado River, the San Francisco Bay Delta, and the Salton Sea. Dramatic population growth in California through the year 2025 will add 18 million people on top of the state's 33 million people. Where will water for 18 million new people come from? What will the environmental consequences be for Mono Lake and other valued water resources?

Additional Resources

Gaines, D. 1988. *Mono Lake Guidebook*. Kutsavi Books, Lee Vining, CA.
   This easy-to-read book is a good beginner's guide to Mono Lake with new information on the lake's natural history and political status. This book includes maps and photographs.

Hart, J. 1996. *Storm Over Mono*. University of California Press, Berkeley, CA.
   This book is an excellent resource for a complete background on the Mono Lake water issue. The book covers the story of the struggle to protect the lake from the beginning. It includes many maps and photographs.

Mono Lake and the Evolution of a New Water Future, Mono Lake Committee, Mono Lake Committee Slideshow/Video, 1998.

The updated Mono Lake story with new images, natural history information, and information on the lake's future. An excellent resource for studying both the natural history and the water issue. Approximately 20 minutes.

Mono Lake Committee
www.monolake.org

The site for Mono Lake natural history, information on the Mono Lake Committee, and the current level and status of the lake. A photo gallery, Mono Lake activities, interactive map, current weather conditions, and live video of the lake are just a few of the features of this web site.

Of Ice and Fire: A Portrait of the Mono Basin, Mono Basin National Forest Scenic Area, Inyo National Forest, 1992.

This film investigates the Mono Basin's cultural and natural history. An excellent film produced by the Mono Basin National Forest Scenic Area. Approximately 20 minutes.

Questions for Discussion

1. Why is the Mono Basin ecosystem so productive?

2. Why did Los Angeles water use directly affect Mono Lake?

3. What new "water supply" helped put more water back into Mono Lake?

4. Why did the California Water Board choose the lake level they did?

Applications

1. How might the Dead Sea in Israel be compared to Mono Lake?

2. If Mono Lake continued to decline, what do you think would happen to the brine shrimp and alkali flies? How would the birds respond?

3. How can the Public Trust decision be applied to other threatened water resources?

4. Mono Lake represents an unusual environmental success story. Do you think Mono Lake is saved? Why or why not?

8.2 How to Keep a Society Going and Going and Going and . . .

Laura R. White, Ph. D.
West Stockholm, New York

Dr. White has a Ph.D. in ecology with a conservation biology emphasis. Her research focuses on the conservation of North America's native freshwater mussels, many of which are threatened or endangered. She recently developed a molecular genetic key to the freshwater mussels in a Pennsylvania creek.

Overview

With its incessant marching and steadily beating drum, the pink bunny seems as if it can keep going and going and going forever. We know that at its core, however, there is a battery that will someday die and bring the bunny grinding to a halt. So too with modern society: We are lulled into believing that life as we know it can continue unchanged forever; but our society is, in fact, unsustainable in many respects.

We face countless environmental crises—air and water pollution; depletion of fossil fuels, minerals, and groundwater; hazardous and solid waste accumulation; pesticide contamination; rangeland and farmland destruction; food shortages and starvation; species extinctions. All are symptoms of unsustainable living. The unsustainability, in turn, can be traced back to a handful of underlying problems afflicting modern society. These include overpopulation, overconsumption of resources, inefficient use of resources, fossil fuel dependence, and a frontier mentality that considers resource supplies to be unlimited and stewardship to be unnecessary.

These root causes of unsustainability must surely be tackled if the environmental crises are to be battled successfully and efficiently. But how, exactly, can humanity be steered onto a sustainable path?

The Biological Principles of Sustainability

To begin answering this question, Daniel Chiras sought insight from natural ecosystems—those relatively unaffected by human activities. He recognized that (in the absence of huge catastrophes) natural ecosystems are reasonably self-sustaining. By investigating how such ecosystems are able to keep going and going and going, Chiras hoped to learn some lessons that would be useful for establishing a sustainable human society. Chiras examined a variety of natural ecosystems and identified five biological principles of sustainability. These are 1) conservation, 2) recycling, 3) renewable resource use, 4) population control, and 5) regeneration, or self-healing.

The principle of conservation refers to the fact that organisms tend not to waste resources; instead, they are efficient in their use of resources, taking only what they need. Amassing resources takes energy. Individuals who waste resources are, therefore, squandering energy. Such individuals are likely to have fewer descendants than individuals who put all of their energy into surviving and reproducing. Thus, the principle of conservation is a consequence of evolution by means of natural selection.

The principle of recycling refers to the fact that organisms in natural ecosystems use the same atoms over and over again endlessly. Water, carbon, nitrogen, and other essential substances cycle through organisms, the earth, and the atmosphere. One species' metabolic wastes are another species' nutrients. A dead carcass is a set of blocks for building new organisms.

The principle of renewable resource use refers to the tendencies of organisms in natural ecosystems to rely on resources that can be replenished. The four major renewable resources sustaining natural ecosystems are air, soil, water, and plants. In stable ecosystems, these resources are used no faster than they are able to be replenished. Only the energy source—the sun—is nonrenewable (thanks to the laws of thermodynamics). The timescale over which the sun's energy is depleted is so long, however, that its nonrenewability can be ignored.

The principle of population control refers to the fact that natural ecosystems that persist are made up of populations of organisms whose numbers are somehow kept in check. Often population sizes are controlled by environmental factors (for example, weather, shortages of essential nutrients, space limitations, predators, and disease). Sometimes population sizes are controlled from within the populations themselves. In highly territorial species such as the tawny owl, a pair breeds only if it has a territory and rears only as many young as the territory's prey supply can support.

The mechanism through which ecosystems repair themselves (recover) is known as succession.

The principle of regeneration, or self-healing, refers to the tendency of natural ecosystems to recover from disturbances (both natural and human). The mechanism through which ecosystems repair themselves (recover) is known as succession.

Applying the Principles

The biological prescriptions for building a sustainable human society are clear:

◆ We must use resources more sparingly and more efficiently.

◆ We must recycle more of our wastes and avoid producing wastes that are toxic.

◆ We must use renewable resources instead of nonrenewable ones as much as possible.

◆ We must curb our population growth.

◆ We must work to protect and restore ecosystems and natural resources—e.g., forests, wetlands, prairies, rivers, topsoil, and fresh water—that we have damaged or neglected.

Increasingly, individuals and organizations all over the world are attempting to put these principles of sustainability into practice. One such organization is The Florida House Foundation, Inc., a nonprofit group that conceived, funded, and coordinated the construction of Florida House in Sarasota. The house's design emphasizes efficiency, recycling, and renewable resource use. It was constructed from recycled and nontoxic materials as much as possible. Locally manufactured products were favored, both to reduce the need for transportation and to support local businesses.

Numerous energy- and water-conserving features were incorporated into the house. To minimize the need for air-conditioning, the house has a well-insulated attic, energy-saving lighting fixtures (which give off less heat than regular fixtures), and large enclosed porches and wide roof overhangs that keep direct sunlight out of the house (except in the winter). To minimize the need for well water or municipally treated water, the house has two large cisterns for collecting rain. A metal roof aids in rainwater collection. Although it is not drinkable, the rainwater is used for most other indoor purposes and for watering the lawn and shrubbery. "Gray water" (i.e., water that's been used for bathing, dishwashing, and laundry) is also automatically used to water the lawn. The yard is landscaped with plants that can tolerate dry conditions. Many of the plants are edible. Compost is used for mulch. For the tens of thousands of visitors who have toured it, Florida House is visible proof that sustainable living really is possible—not just sometime in the future, but now.

References and Additional Resources

Chiras, D. D. 1993. Eco-Logic: Teaching the biological principles of sustainability. *The American Biology Teacher* 55(2): pp. 71–76.

This article provides in-depth descriptions of the principles of biological sustainability and the ways in which the principles must be applied to build a sustainable society.

Gould, J. L. 1982. *Ethology: The Mechanisms and Evolution of Behavior.* W. W. Norton & Co., New York.

This textbook gives numerous examples of ways in which population sizes of certain species are controlled from within the populations themselves.

Logsdon, G. 1994. *At Nature's Pace: Farming and the American Dream.* Pantheon Books, New York.

This book is a thought-provoking collection of essays on the unsustainability of America's megafarms and the cities that rely on them. Amish farms are discussed as models of sustainable agricultural ecosystems.

Roch, P. 1996. Philippe Roch on sustainability. Sustainability: Ecology comes of age. theearthtime@cdp.UUCP, 23-Feb-96.

This piece outlines 12 principles of sustainable development—four ecological, four economic, two social, one scientific, and one cultural. The principles complement those identified by Chiras.

Questions for Discussion

1. Briefly discuss three root causes of unsustainability in our society.

2. In your own words, summarize the biological principles of sustainability identified by Daniel Chiras.

Applications

1. Imagine that the price of gasoline (a nonrenewable resource) suddenly tripled. How would this affect your life-style directly and indirectly? What changes would you need to make in your life-style?

2. Imagine that a catastrophic storm hit your area. For two weeks, all the homes in your county were without electricity and running water, and travel by nonemergency vehicles was banned. What challenges would this present? How would you meet the challenges?

3. What are three respects in which your current life-style is unsustainable? How might you change your life-style to live more sustainably?

8.3 Desertification: 130 Million Hectares of Land Lost Forever

William H. Leonard, Ph. D.
Clemson University, Clemson, South Carolina

Dr. Leonard is one of the authors of Biology: A Community Context. *He grew up in California and was a biology teacher in San Jose for 12 years. He has bachelor's and master's degrees from San Jose State University and a Ph.D. from the University of California at Berkeley. He is an active biology curriculum developer and science education researcher and is particularly interested in inquiry learning. Dr. Leonard has earned university awards for both teaching and research.*

Overview

According to the new *World Atlas of Desertification*, worldwide nearly 130 million hectares of land are lost forever for food production due to desertification. Combined, this unusable land amounts to the total land area of France, Italy, and Spain.

Desertification is the process of changing productive drylands to desert. Currently drylands make up about 40 percent of the earth's land surface. Drylands are ecologically fragile, and human activity in particular appears to be accelerating the process of the desertification of these lands.

What Are Drylands?

Drylands are areas with less than 60 cm (25 inches) of annual rainfall. This definition includes all deserts on the earth. It also includes those areas of short-grass prairies and treeless plains called savannas. With the exceptions of the Pacific Coast and mountainous regions, most of the western United States is drylands. A United States dryland is shown in Figure 1. If you live near Los Angeles, San Jose, Phoenix, Salt Lake City, Spokane, Cheyenne, El Paso, or Albuquerque, you are in a dryland area. Worldwide much of the

Figure 1 *Chaparral drylands are found throughout California.*

Mediterranean coast, northern and eastern Africa, central Asia, western Australia, and western South America are mostly drylands. The three types of drylands are short-grass prairie, American savanna dryland, and chaparral dryland. Soil degradation in these areas is one of the earth's most pressing problems. This is a global issue, and it is getting worse.

Drylands contain rich and diverse life-forms not found in other climatic regions. They provide critical habitats for wildlife, including reptiles, large mammals, and migratory birds. Many important food crops, such as barley and sorghum, began in the dryland areas of the earth. Drylands provide genetic material for plant breeders, drugs, resins, waxes, oils, and other commercial products. One-third of the plant-based drugs in the United States come from dryland areas. Many drylands in the United States are also used for large-scale grazing by cattle or sheep.

Why Is Desertification a Problem?

Drylands are particularly vulnerable to changes in the amount and quality of the soil. Dryland soils have a thin layer of humus in their topsoil, which provides the needed microorganisms to support growth of plants and animals. That drylands, by definition, receive little rainfall makes them very susceptible to erosion by wind, water, and human travel. This process is known as soil degradation. Once eroded to the point of being a desert, drylands can almost never recover to the point of being biologically productive.

Scientists estimate that about 20 percent of the topsoil in the midwestern United States has already washed down the Mississippi River. Almost all of this loss has happened since this land was changed from small farms to large-scale farming uses over the last 100 years. For example, during the 1920s and 1930s, areas of Oklahoma that were once productive farmland were turned into a desert, as shown in Figure 2. The area was called the Dust Bowl.

These changes are not limited to the United States. There are other worldwide examples of desertification. Poor irrigation and farming practices dried up the rivers that fed large lakes, such as the Aral Sea in Kazakhstan and Lake Chad in central Africa. What is now left are much smaller bodies of water surrounded by desert. In the case of the Aral Sea, 75 percent of its water volume was lost, and once plentiful fish have almost completely disappeared. Not only have the fish suffered, but 60,000 people lost their jobs as a result of this climatic change. When such water bodies are also borders between countries, political and economic tensions often result.

According to the United Nations, about 70 percent of the productive drylands of the world are now affected by desertification. Of this, 30 percent are lightly degraded, 50 percent are moderately degraded, and 16 percent are severely degraded.

The United Nations further estimates that 25 percent of the productive farmland in North America and Europe, 38 percent of Asia, and 45 percent of Africa are affected by soil degradation. The world areas considered to be in crisis include Mexico, China, the Amazon basin, Central America, eastern Iran, large portions of Iraq, and southern Africa.

Once a dryland area is changed into desert, it cannot be changed back. Some 15 percent of the earth's land surface may have already changed to new desert areas. New deserts are found in northwest China, central Asia, and subsahara Africa. Sadly there is evidence of early stages of desertification in Spain, Portugal, Greece, and Italy.

> *Once eroded to the point of being a desert, drylands can almost never recover to the point of being biologically productive.*

Figure 2 *During the 1920s and 1930s, huge dust storms rolled across a vast region of dry, eroded soil in the midwestern United States. This region was, therefore, called the Dust Bowl.*

What Are Some of the Causes of Desertification?

Irrigation, using water from deep in the ground for agriculture, is one cause. Taking water from the underground aquifer system lowers the water table. If you want to use this water, you have to drill deeper than before to reach it. Once you take more out, you again have to drill deeper to reach water. It becomes a vicious cycle. Near coastal areas, pulling the water from the ground creates a void that tends to be replaced by nearby saltwater. This process, called salinization, disrupts native and agricultural growth just as if you poured salt water into your garden. It kills the natural vegetation and makes the coastal area vulnerable to becoming a coastal desert. Although diverting the natural source of water may be the largest cause of creating new deserts, other causes of desertification include overgrazing, overcultivation, and firewood cutting.

Overuse of farmland or grazing land is another cause. If the soil nutrients are depleted, the soil will no longer be productive in growing plants. Fewer plants will hold less moisture. Soils with few plants become subject to both wind and water erosion. Over time, rich topsoil is lost and the land becomes desertified.

Tilling of farmland may also cause desertification. Tilling breaks the topsoil and makes it much more susceptible to erosion. Erosion can take away the rich humus needed to grow plants. Erosion can cause farmland to become barren, unsuited for growing crops. This barren land can almost never recover.

Finally, slash-and-burn agriculture also causes desertification. This is particularly true in the tropics where the topsoil is so thin. This soil is quickly depleted of nutrients by crops as they are harvested. When the soil is no longer deemed productive, farmers move on to new land, leaving this fragile land to easy erosion. When the topsoil is gone, few plants grow and the area becomes essentially a desert.

People and the way they live contribute to the creation of new deserts. Many societies living in drylands today still depend on fires to cook food. For these people, an easy source of fuel for fire is wood from trees and shrubs. As the trees and shrubs are removed for firewood, the land changes. No longer do the trees and shrubs help hold the soil in place. The soil becomes vulnerable to wind erosion. When it does rain, the lack of vegetation makes it easier for topsoil to wash away. This cycle speeds up the desertification process. When changes like this occur, famine often results because the soil in which to plant crops is no longer there. When a famine happens in a large area such as a country, people often leave the area to find a place where they can grow food. Many times they move to a nearby country, creating a refugee problem. This often causes trouble between the neighboring countries.

Desertification can also affect the weather. Changing from a dryland to a desert reduces the surface moisture even more. Water in the soil is important because it tends to hold solar energy. When soil water does evaporate, it uses solar energy. The less water there is in the soil, the more solar energy will tend to reflect into the atmosphere. This process further heats the atmosphere in the new desert area, and heat tends to create unstable weather patterns.

What Can You Do to Prevent Desertification?

◆ Most attempts by humans to modify their natural environment tend to have effects that were not intended. As a citizen, you can encourage your government to require careful studies before large-scale projects that could affect the environment are started. The building of dams, strip mining, building of major transportation systems, urban development, and even the way fields are plowed by farmers all need to be carried out with attention to potential hazards.

◆ Encourage and practice activities that do not hurt the environment. Some examples are using renewable energy sources such as solar and wind power. New methods of plowing land in dry areas can help. There are also newer methods of watering crops that use less water than older irrigation methods. This includes percolation and soil-level watering. Always use recycling as a practice to reuse the resources we have.

◆ Conserve energy, water, and other natural resources so that our resources are not wasted. The simple act of fixing a leaking faucet can prevent gallons of water from being wasted every day.

◆ Protect topsoil from erosion at all costs. Once topsoil is lost, it takes many human life spans to replace. In many cases, once topsoil is lost, it cannot be recovered. Planting trees, shrubs, and grasses can help prevent wind erosion and create new topsoil. Using modern plowing techniques will also prevent the unnecessary loss of topsoil without eliminating productive use of the soil.

Additional Resources

Brown, L. R., C. Flavin, and H. French. 1997. *State of the World*. W. W. Norton & Co., New York.
   An immense accumulation of important environmental data.

Commoner, B. 1971. *The Closing Circle: Nature, Man and Technology*. Knopf, New York, NY.
   One of the most classic environmental books. Contains Commoner's famous "4 rules of ecology," which have served as guideposts for future understanding of our environmental challenges.

Desertification Web site
http://www.oneworld.org/ips2/oct/desertification.html
   Up-to-date information on desertification and related global concerns. Links to additional information at other Web sites.

Questions for Discussion

1. Define desertification using the term *drylands*.

2. What are the major causes of desertification?

3. Why is desertification a global problem?

4. What can you do as an individual to help prevent desertification? What are some ways other than those given in this essay?

Applications

1. Find the Aral Sea and Lake Chad on a world map. Explain why a loss of these bodies of water could affect life in other areas.

2. Convert 130 million hectares to square miles. Describe an area this large in the United States. What would be some consequences in this country if this area became desertified?

3. What is the relationship between topsoil and desertification?

4. Why is it that most desertification would be essentially irreversible?

8.4 Global Warming: How Real Is It?

William H. Leonard, Ph. D.
Clemson University, Clemson, South Carolina

Dr. Leonard is one of the authors of Biology: A Community Context. *He grew up in California and was a biology teacher in San Jose for 12 years. He has bachelor's and master's degrees from San Jose State University and a Ph.D. from the University of California at Berkeley. He is an active biology curriculum developer and science education researcher and is particularly interested in inquiry learning. Dr. Leonard has earned university awards for both teaching and research.*

Overview

Do you like warm weather? Just wait; the earth's atmosphere is getting warmer by the year. Average air temperature in the United States has increased 2 to 4°F during this century. And in the past 100 years, the global surface temperature has risen about 1°F. Global warming refers to the gradual increase in the temperature of the atmosphere and surface of the earth. The climate cycle of the earth during its 3.5 billion years of supporting life has had warmer and cooler periods. However, scientists have measured a disturbing increase in temperature since the industrial revolution. Increases in gaseous pollutants in the air due to human activities may be responsible.

The Greenhouse Effect

The sun is the source of energy for the earth. Sunlight shining on the earth is a mix of both visible and nonvisible light. Before it reaches the earth, it must pass through our atmosphere. As it reaches the surface of the earth, much of the nonvisible, or high-frequency, light is converted to low-frequency infrared radiation. Infrared radiation is basically heat, like what you feel from the walls of a fireplace. When the infrared radiation bounces back into the atmosphere from the surface of the earth, much of it is trapped within the atmosphere. This, in turn, warms the atmosphere and the environment in which organisms live. The gases in the earth's atmosphere act like a blanket and help to keep the earth warm enough to be habitable. Some atmospheric gases react more to this warming than others. These gases are called greenhouse gases. The primary greenhouse gas is carbon dioxide. But there are others, such as carbon monoxide, methane, ozone, and oxides of nitrogen and sulfur. Greenhouse gases surround the earth, as shown in Figure 1.

Carbon dioxide levels in the earth's atmosphere are rising, as shown in Figure 2. Some scientists predict that, at the current rate of increase, the amount of carbon dioxide will double from preindustrial levels by the year 2030. Evidence suggests that there is a relationship between the concentration of carbon dioxide in our atmosphere and the temperature of the surface of our planet. Some scientists also believe human activity is responsible for the increase. They point out that our factories, cars, and cities have caused much of this change in carbon dioxide levels. Another measure of this change is atmospheric methane, which has risen by 145 percent, mostly due to large-scale agricultural practices and raising cattle.

Is Global Warming Fact or Fiction?

The 10 warmest years on record have occurred in the last 15 years. The 1990s have been the warmest decade on record. Those are disturbing facts for scientists. In the fall of 1995, scientists with the Intergovernmental Panel on Climate Change reached two conclusions: 1) the increase in the average global temperature that has been observed over the last century is probably not entirely natural and 2) global warming is due to human activity. The Panel estimated that the earth could warm another 2° to 6°F by the year 2050.

Global warming is a very slow process. Increases of temperature by tenths of a degree over a 10-year period are barely noticeable to humans. When compared to the changes you feel during the seasons from winter to summer and back again,

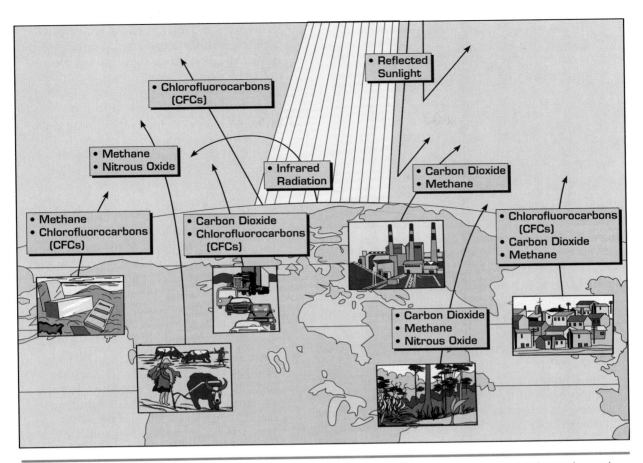

Figure 1 *Greenhouse gases, such as carbon dioxide, surround the earth, reflecting solar radiation and warming the atmosphere.*

these slight changes seem like nothing. Just because you can't feel the change of global warming doesn't mean that very small increases are not happening. Surface temperatures at specific locations on earth are measured using standard thermometers housed in observation enclosures. Satellites are used to measure global or upper atmospheric temperatures. The technology humans develop and use has contributed to global warming, but now technology is also being used to detect global warming. Scientists can use technology to look at the trends in earth temperature over centuries instead of decades.

Two major factors in global warming are world population growth and energy waste by humans. For every billion people on the earth, 4 billion tons of carbon dioxide are released into the atmosphere each year. The earth's population is now six billion. That means about 24 billion tons of carbon dioxide are released each year. The per person rate of carbon

dioxide emissions in the United States is five times higher than the world figure. Americans make up just 5 percent of the world population, but they use 22 percent of the world's oil.

What Are the Predicted Consequences of Global Warming?

Global warming is predicted to have both direct and indirect consequences. Some of these you can feel and see easily. Other effects will show up only after observing the world over longer periods of time. They are all likely to be real, however. Here are a few:

◆ Oceans are getting warmer. Ocean areas where the surface reaches 80°F have increased by one-sixth during the past 20 years. That

745

Figure 2 *The level of carbon dioxide in the earth's atmosphere is rising.*

increases the chances of severe weather in coastal areas. (About 50 percent of the United States population lives within 50 miles of the ocean.)

- ◆ Polar ice caps are melting, which is causing sea levels to rise worldwide. For example, the sea level on the Atlantic coast has risen an entire foot during the past 100 years. That has caused beaches and other shorelines to move inward from 200 to 300 feet. During the next 20 years, seas could rise by 5 to 8 inches. At this rate, the ocean will rise over a foot just during your adult life. One extreme example is the Republic of Maldives in the Indian Ocean. The country is made up of over 1,000 islands that are only 6 feet above sea level. The 200,000 people who live there will probably need to find a new home by the end of the 21st century if the oceans keep rising.

- ◆ Weather is more severe. Weather systems, especially storms like hurricanes and tornadoes, are driven by energy in the atmosphere. A warmer climate will bring more severe weather. This will be dramatically stronger during El Niño years. In fact, there is evidence that global warming is causing progressively stronger El Niño effects. Insurance companies are already facing a 30 percent rise in damage loss claims from weather and storms.

- ◆ Ocean communities may be destroyed. Organisms, especially aquatic microorganisms such as plankton, are very sensitive to temperature change. Plankton are the key to the food

chain of the oceans. Even a 2°F increase in their environment can upset the entire ocean food chain. This would have indirect consequences for terrestrial organisms, including humans, because of the relationship between ocean-based and land-based life-forms.

- ◆ Farmlands may be turned into unproductive areas. The total amount of water on the earth is finite. Moisture in the atmosphere can move due to climate change from global warming, causing areas of higher rainfall to shift also. This shift is causing slow changes in distribution of vegetated areas. We are also seeing movement of the world's agricultural belts. There are frequent stories in the media where drought in Central Africa has resulted in the creation of deserts and famine. The agricultural belts of North America, Asia, and Europe may move northward, leaving virtual dust bowls in much of what is now arable and productive land.

- ◆ Acid rain may increase. A hazy umbrella of sulfur particles is being added to our atmosphere due to burning of fossil fuels (oil and gas). This is something that environmental chemist Robert Charlson calls the Parasol Effect. The haze created greatly limits visibility and is unhealthy to the respiratory system. When sulfur combines with oxygen, sulfur dioxide, a destructive greenhouse gas, is created. When sulfur dioxide combines with water vapor, the result is acid rain. The greatest Parasol concentrations are the Great Lakes and Central Europe, which are also the largest geographic sources of acid rain.

What Are Some Important Factors Related to Global Warming?

Ecology is the study of the relationships between organisms and their environment. There is a delicate balance between the populations of organisms and the world food chain. That balance can be drastically upset by changes in the environment. When one group of organisms is affected, eventually most others are as well. Sometimes even small changes in the physical environment, such as temperature, have a tremendous effect on the earth's energy cycles. These changes also directly affect organisms.

Although we are concerned about the earth's greenhouse gases, they also have a beneficial effect. They protect us and other organisms from dangerous ultraviolet (UV) radiation from the sun. UV radiation can be a major contributor to cancer. It also disrupts the way genes function in living organisms. Unfortunately, ozone, the primary greenhouse gas responsible for shielding UV radiation, is being slowly destroyed by the release of chloroflorocarbons, the gases that are used in older air conditioners and were once used in aerosol cans.

What Can Be Done to Curb Global Warming?

Most of the things you can do to help curb or stop global warming are also good practices for preserving our environment. Here are a few:

◆ Conserve energy by insulating your homes and using more energy-saving home construction methods and materials.

◆ Reduce, reuse, and recycle. One scientist stated that if you discard rather than recycle an aluminum can, you waste as much energy as if you half-filled the can with gasoline and poured it on the ground.

◆ Stop polluting the atmosphere. Reduce emissions of heat-trapping gases by using less polluting and more fuel-efficient forms of transportation. (A typical commuter car in the United States now releases five times its weight in carbon dioxide each year.)

◆ Encourage the development of renewable forms of energy such as solar, wind, tidal, and geothermal.

References and Additional Resources

Berreby, D. Parasol Effect. *Discover,* July 1991.
Discusses how materials other than carbon dioxide, especially sulfur, are enhancing global warming.

Brown, L. R., C. Flavin, and H. French. 1997. *State of the World.* W. W. Norton & Co., New York.
A wonderful resource of detailed data about our environment. Request this at your library if it is not available.

Interactive Earth: A Global Learning Tool, Worldlink Media.
A CD-based curriculum and data resource on a variety of earth topics, including global warming. Lots of information here and very interestingly presented.

Linden, E. 1994. Burned by Warming. *Time Magazine,* 14 March.
Discusses briefly some of the real effects of global warming.

Revkin, A. 1992. *Global Warming.* Abbeville Press, New York.
One of the most authoritative books on the subject with some remarkably vivid photographs.

The Global Resources Program
http://www.ucsusa.org/resources/index.html
This Web site was developed to express scientists' concerns about ecosystem damage and to provide information to the public. Four major topic areas are addressed: biodiversity, global warming, ozone depletion, and population growth. Relevant links are provided.

Questions for Discussion

1. What is global warming? What are some data that support its existence?

2. What causes global warming?

3. How is the greenhouse effect related to global warming?

4. What are thought to be some of the effects of global warming?

Applications

1. What evidence is there of warming trends in your city?

2. What could global warming do in your community during your lifetime?

3. What has global warming done to the weather patterns in your community? For example, 1998 is considered an El Niño year. What El Niño effects do you recall where you live?

4. What can you do in your community to help halt global warming? Why would individual contributions to the global warming problem make a difference?

8.5 Sustainable Manufacturing

Ray C. Anderson
Interface, Inc., Atlanta, Georgia

Mr. Anderson currently serves as co-chair of the President's Council on Sustainable Development and is the Chairman and CEO of Interface, Inc., located in Atlanta, Georgia. Interface, Inc., manufactures and sells free-lay carpet tiles, broadloom carpet, interior fabrics, chemicals, and architectural products for commercial interiors. With 28 factories around the world, Interface, Inc., produces 40 percent of the world's carpet tiles. Mr. Anderson holds a B.S. in industrial engineering from the Georgia Institute of Technology.

Overview

My company, Interface, Inc., operates factories that process raw materials into finished manufactured products that many routinely use and specify for others to use. Our raw material suppliers also operate factories. As shown in Figure 1, last year our factories and suppliers together extracted from the earth and processed more than 1.2 billion pounds of material so we could produce those products—1.2 billion pounds of materials from earth's stored natural capital.

Using Natural Resources

Of the 1.2 billion pounds, I know that about 400 million pounds are relatively abundant inorganic materials, mostly mined from the earth's crust, and 800 million pounds are petro-based, coming from either oil, coal, or natural gas. Sadly, about two-thirds of that 800 million pounds of irreplaceable, nonrenewable, exhaustible, precious natural resource was *burned up*—two-thirds burned to produce the energy to convert the other one-third, along with 400 million pounds of inorganic material, into products. That fossil fuel, with its complex, precious, organic molecular structure, is gone forever—changed into the carbon dioxide and other substances, many toxic, that were produced in the burning of it. This cannot go on indefinitely, can it?

I stand convicted by me, myself alone (and not by anyone else) as a plunderer of the earth. But by our civilization's definition, I am a captain of industry, a kind of modern-day hero, an entrepreneur who founded a company that provides over 7,000 people with jobs. Anyway, hasn't Interface paid fair market prices for every pound of material we have bought and processed? We don't violate any laws.

Yes, but does the market's *price* cover the *cost*? Who pays for the military power projected into the Middle East to protect the oil at its source? Why, you have, in your taxes. Thank you very much. And who is paying for the damage done by storms, tornadoes, and hurricanes that result from global warming? Why, you are, of course, with your insurance premiums. Who will pay for the future losses in Florida and the coastal areas as the oceans continue rising? Future generations, your children,

	Interface, Inc. Production		
Year	Raw Materials (billions of pounds)	Sales (million)	Pounds/Dollar of Sales
1994	1.123	$725	1.55
1995	1.227	$802	1.53
1996	1.242	$1,002	1.24
1997	1.362	$1,135	1.20

Figure 1 *Raw materials use and Interface sales, 1994–1997.*

that's who. We are stealing from our own children. When earth runs out of finite, exhaustible resources and ecosystems collapse, our descendants will be left holding the empty bag. Someday people like me may be put in jail.

A Sustainable Vision

I can't solve all the world's problems, but I have challenged the people of my company to make us the first industrial company in the whole world to achieve environmental sustainability and then to go beyond, becoming restorative. To me, being restorative means to put back more than we take and to do good to earth; it means more than just not harming the earth. I have a strategy (you know this one, at least in part): Reduce, reuse, reclaim, recycle, redesign, adopt best practices, advance, and share these strategies.

The technologies of the future will enable us to feed our factories with recycled raw materials. We will close the materials and energy loop, recycling raw materials that come from harvesting the billions of square yards of existing carpets and textiles. I envision nylon face pile recycled into new nylon yarn to be made into new carpet and backing material recycled into new backing materials for new carpet. In our textile business, polyester fabrics can be recycled into polyester fiber, then made into new fabrics. This is closing the loop, using those precious organic molecules over and over in cyclical fashion rather than sending them to land-fills or incinerating them or downcycling them into lower value forms by the linear processes of the first industrial revolution.

Linear must go; cyclical must replace it. That's nature's way. In nature, there is no long-term waste; one organism's waste is another's food. Of course, the recycling operations will have to be driven by renewable energy, too. Otherwise, we may consume more petro-material for the energy to recycle than we will save in virgin raw materials by recycling in the first place.

The technologies of the future will enable us to send zero waste and scrap to the landfill. We're already well down this track at Interface. In the

> *The technologies of the future will enable us to feed our factories with recycled raw materials.*

first three years of our effort, we have reduced total waste in our worldwide business by 32 percent, saving nearly $50 million. This is now paying the bills for all the rest of this revolution in our company.

We're redesigning our products for greater resource efficiency, producing carpets with lighter face weights (less pile) and *better* durability. The embodied energy *not* used in the nylon *not* consumed is already enough to power the entire factory making the redesigned products!

The technologies of the future will enable us to operate without emitting anything into the air or water that hurts the ecosystem. Imagine factories with no outlet pipes for effluent and no smoke-stacks because they don't need them! And, of course, not having to build pipes and stacks saves even more money.

In reinventing our current system to achieve zero waste, carpet will not be bought or sold at all. Leasing carpet rather than selling it and being responsible for it cradle-to-cradle is the future and the better way. Toward this end, last year we created and offered to the world market the first ever perpetual lease for carpet. We will eventually sell only the *services* of the carpet: color, design, texture, warmth, acoustics, comfort under foot, cleanliness, and improved indoor air quality, but not the carpet itself. In this way we can make carpet into a "product of service."

We take responsibility for installing the carpet and maintaining it. Not only do we clean the carpet regularly, but because they are free-lay carpet tiles, we selectively replace worn and damaged areas one 18-inch square at a time. We implement a rolling, progressive, continuous face-lift by periodically, over the years, replacing modules and, most importantly, recycling the carpet tiles that come up. We continue to own the carpet. Title for the carpet tiles never passes to the user; it stays with us, the manufacturer, along with the ultimate liability for the used up, exhausted carpet tiles.

Teams all through our company in manufac-turing locations on four continents are working together on hundreds of projects and technologies that are taking us toward sustainability. We started this whole effort in our company by a focus on waste reduction. We define waste as *any* cost that goes into our product that does not produce value for our customers. Since any waste is bad, we're measuring progress against a zero-based waste goal. Waste means off-quality and scrap, and it means anything else we don't do right the first time—a misdirected shipment, a mispriced invoice, a bad debt, and so forth. Even the minimum of energy needed to drive our processes is waste by our definition as long as it comes from nonrenewable sources. One quick result: Landfill waste from our factories is down over 60 percent since the beginning of 1995.

The Next Industrial Revolution

In the 21st century, I believe the winners will be the resource-efficient. At whose expense will they win? At the expense of the resource-*in*efficient. Technology at its best, emulating nature, will eliminate the inefficient adapters. The well-known environmental impact equation, first described by Paul and Anne Ehrlich, declares that:

$$I = P \times A \times T$$

In the equation, I is environmental impact (bigger is worse), P is population, A is affluence, and T is technology. An increase in P, A, or T results in a greater (worse) environmental impact. In this equation, Technology *is* part of the problem. What a dilemma! T is not the answer. T will not lead us out of the environmental mess, no matter how vigorously the technophiles assert it will. The more technology we have, the greater (worse) the impact. But that is the technology of the first industrial revolution.

The technologies of the first industrial revolution are, for the most part, extractive and linear (take-make-waste), fossil fuel-driven, focused on labor productivity, abusive to the biosphere, and wasteful. And they are unsustainable.

What if the characteristics of T were changed with technologies of the next industrial revolution? Let's say they were *renewable,* rather than extractive; *cyclical* (cradle-to-cradle), rather than linear; *solar-* or *hydrogen-driven,* rather than fossil fuel-driven; focused on *resource productivity,* rather than labor productivity; *benign* in their effects on the biosphere, rather than abusive; and *emulated nature* (where there is no waste), rather than wasteful.

It might then be possible to restate the environmental impact equation as:

$$I = \frac{P \times A}{T}$$

Move T from the numerator to the denominator and we change the world as we have known it. Now the more technology, the better (less impact). Technology becomes part of the solution rather than part of the problem. T must move to the denominator.

Changing Our Points of View and Our Actions

Deep into his book *Ishmael,* author Daniel Quinn uses a metaphor to describe our civilization. He likens our civilization to one of those early attempts to build the first airplane—the one with the flapping wings and the guy pedaling away to make the wings go. In the metaphor, the man and the plane go off of a very, very high cliff; the guy is pedaling away, the wings are flapping, the wind is in his face, and the man thinks he's flying. But, in fact, he is in free fall and just doesn't realize it because the ground is so far away. Why is his plane not flying? Because it isn't built according to the laws of aerodynamics, and it is subject, like everything else, to the law of gravity.

Quinn says that our civilization is in free fall, too, for the same reason: It wasn't built according to the laws of "aerodynamics," but we will surely crash instead unless we redesign our craft—our civilization—according to natural laws. If we followed natural laws, substances from earth's crust would not systematically increase in the ecosphere, as shown in Figure 2. We can no longer extract fossil fuels, metals, and other minerals faster than they can be reintegrated into earth's crust. Following natural laws further, substances we produce must not systematically increase in the ecosphere. Synthetic materials must not be produced at a faster pace than they can be broken down and integrated back into the cycles of nature. If we follow natural laws, productivity and diversity of nature will not be systematically diminished. If we prevent overharvest or reductions in our ecosystem, their productive capacities and diversity will systematically flourish—species will be preserved.

Our organizations must *systematically decrease* their economic dependence on underground

Prototypical Company of the 21st Century
The Interface Model

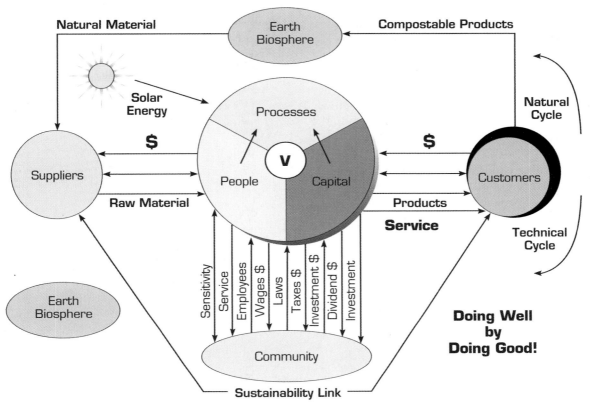

Figure 2 *Organizational chart for a prototypical company of the 21st century.*

metals and fuels and other minerals. Our organizations must *systematically decrease* their economic dependence on the production of persistent, unnatural, synthetic substances. Our organizations must *systematically decrease* their economic dependence on activities that encroach on the productive parts of nature. And our organizations must *systematically decrease* their economic dependence on the use of unnecessary amounts of resources in relation to added human value.

Reinventing civilization is a tall order. Either we do it and find harmony with nature, or nature will whittle us down to size and do it for us, or to us. Earth's resources *are* finite; earth's capacity to endure abuse, limited. We all have a choice—let's make the right one for our children and their children. I and Interface, Inc., are doing our parts by reducing our use of the earth's resources by using less raw material, recycling and reusing materials, and eliminating waste at every turn. And a significant part of our process is that we take full responsibility for our actions and our products, never passing on our liabilities to our customers or children. I hope you can see ways to do the same with your efforts and your lives.

Additional Resources

Gore, A. 1993. *Earth in the Balance*. Plume Books, New York.
  A critical and insightful look at current environmental practice with suggestions for a sustainable future.

Hawken, P. 1993. *The Ecology of Commerce*. Harper Business, New York.
  A look at how raw materials do not reflect their value, only the cost of extracting them.

Quinn, D. 1992. *Ishmael*. Bantam Books, New York. A philosophical look at our civilization and our roles within it. Told as a most interesting story through a conversation between a gorilla and a man.

The Interface, Inc., home page: http://www.IFSIA.com/

Questions for Discussion

1. Mr. Anderson proposes to lease the services of carpet rather than selling it. Discuss how this might work in both businesses and residences. What might be some positive and negative outcomes?

2. If we were in the habit of leasing services rather than owning products, how might businesses change? What new businesses might develop?

Applications

1. Using Mr. Anderson's definition of "waste," what could you do in your school to reduce such waste?

2. What are some "services" you could lease in your school or home rather than purchasing the products outright?

Glossary

Glossary

A

aerobic   Any oxygen-requiring biological process.

agonistic   Combative in nature.

AIDS   Acquired immune deficiency syndrome, caused by the human immunodeficiency virus (HIV), which attacks the immune system; transmitted from one person to another by the exchange of body fluids.

algae   Aquatic, plantlike protists that are photosynthetic and play an important role in oxygen production.

allele   One of two or more contrasting genes at the same locus of a chromosome that help to determine the expression of a trait.

alveoli   The very thin-walled tiny air sacs in the lungs.

amniotic fluid   Fluid that fills the cavity that surrounds the fetus during a pregnancy.

amphetamine   A drug that exhibits a marked stimulant action on the central nervous system.

anencephaly   A neural tube defect characterized by partial or complete absence of the skull, which is not compatible with life for more than a few hours.

antibodies   Molecules in the blood that recognize and bind to specific antigens.

antigen   A protein that causes a specific immune response.

aquaculture   The growing of fish or aquatic plants in controlled fresh, brackish, or salt water environments.

Attention Deficit Disorder (ADD)   A psychiatric term used to describe individuals who exhibit poor attention due to impulsivity and distractibility.

ATP: Adenosine triphosphate, an energy-carrying compound in the cell.

autosomes: All the chromosomes in the nucleus except the sex chromosomes.

autotroph: An organism that uses energy from the environment to produce organic molecules.

axon   The usually single, long process of a nerve cell that conducts a nerve impulse away from the cell body.

B

behavior   An organism's response to stimulation or its environment.

behavioral disorder   A condition in which an individual's actions are constantly in conflict and at odds with the environment in which they occur.

biodegradable   Capable of being broken down by microorganisms by natural decomposition processes.

biodegradable biopolymers   Chemically engineered plastics substitutes that degrade similarly to organic matter.

biodegradation   Breaking something down chemically by biological processes.

biodiversity   The wide variation that is present, phenotypically and genotypically, in all the different organisms on the earth.

biology   The study of living systems.

biomass   The total mass of a defined group of organisms in an ecosystem.

biopolymers   Very large organic molecules consisting of many simple molecules linked together.

biosolids   Solid organic material remaining after processing of raw sewage.

biosphere   The surface, water, and atmosphere of the earth.

biotechnology   Techniques for the application of biological processes to make a defined product for use in medicine or industry.

C

Calorie   A kiloCalorie when spelled with capital "C". The amount of heat energy needed to raise the temperature of one kilogram of water by 1 degree Celsius.

capillary   Small blood vessel that connects arteries and veins.

capillary rise   The movement of liquid or dissolved solutes up a very small diameter tube due to the pull of the liquid up the wall of the tube being greater than the downward pull of gravity.

carbohydrate   Molecules containing carbon, oxygen, and hydrogen that serve as energy sources.

carrying capacity   A theoretical maximum number of individuals of a species that a given environment can sustain.

cell The fundamental organizational unit making up all living things.

cell cycle The complete life history of a cell through nuclear and cell division.

cell membrane A liquid bilayer covering all cells that regulates substances moving into and out of the cell.

cell wall A rigid covering around the cell membrane of plant, fungi, and some protistan and moneran cells.

cellular respiration The cellular transfer of energy from chemical bonds in organic molecules to ATP.

cellulose Polysaccharide that forms plant cell walls and provides structural support for plants.

cephalothorax A fused head and chest area in arachnids to which legs are attached.

chelicerae A pair of clawlike appendages in arachnids used to inject poison into prey.

chlorophyll The primary pigment in phytosynthesizers that is responsible for the capture and conversion of sunlight energy to chemical energy.

chloroplast A chlorophyll-containing organelle inside algal and plant cells that carries out photosynthesis.

chromatid One of a pair of DNA strands in a duplicated chromosome.

chromosomes DNA molecules in the cell nucleus that carry genetic information.

codon The RNA segment that codes for a specific amino acid in protein production.

cohesion Adhesion of two molecules or substances to each other.

cold-blooded Describes an organism with no internal mechanism to regulate its body temperature, which fluctuates, approximating that of the surrounding environment (e.g., fish and reptiles); exothermic.

CAT-scan A diagnostic test involving recording "slices" of soft tissues of the body with an x-ray scanner and then integrating these slices by computer to generate cross-sectional images.

community Closely interacting populations of different species in an ecosystem.

consumers Organisms that depend on photosynthesizers for a source of food, e.g., animals, fungi.

controls The parts of an experiment that are kept the same so that whatever results occur can be explained by one cause variable.

cyanobacteria Photosynthetic blue-green bacteria that contain chlorophyll; also referred to as blue-green algae.

cytokinesis The part of a cell cycle in which there is a division of the cytoplasm into two new cells.

D

data Results, often numerical, from scientific inquiry.

decomposers Organisms such as bacteria and fungi that feed on dead organic material.

degradability Capacity to be broken down by microorganisms.

demographers Scientists who study the distribution, density, and vital statistics of human populations.

dependent variables The results or effects in an experiment.

desertification The process of converting a semiarid environment into desert as a consequence of human activity.

diastolic pressure The pressure in the arteries of the body between heartbeats.

diatoms Microscopic phytoplankton organisms with silica shells.

differentiation The time during early embryo development when cell division results in specialized cells, which thereafter can reproduce only the same type of tissue.

diffusion Movement of molecules from a more concentrated to a less concentrated state due to random thermal energy of molecules.

digestion The chemical breakdown of foods to produce molecules that are small enough to enter a cell.

dinoflagellates Unicellular, photosynthetic or heterotrophic organisms with two flagella that possess characteristics of both plants (chlorophyll and cellulose) and animals (ingestion of food).

dinosaurs Land-dwelling and aquatic reptiles of the Mesozoic Era that are now extinct.

diploid Having a complete set of both homologous chromosomes.

disaccharide A sugar composed of two monosaccharide units.

disease An abnormal and harmful condition affecting an organism, often caused by another organism.

DNA Deoxyribonucleic acid, the molecule that provides genetic information that is passed from parent to child.

DNA fingerprint A sample of the unique DNA makeup of an individual; used for positive identification.

dominant An allele that expresses a trait whether it is paired with an identical or alternative allele.

dopamine A neurotransmitter that is essential for normal nervous system activity.

dyzygotic twins A pair of twins who arise from the fertilization of two separate egg cells; each is no more alike than ordinary siblings; commonly referred to as fraternal twins.

E

ecological niche A population's role in an ecosystem, including everything that a population removes from and returns to the biosphere.

ecosystem Interacting populations of organisms and their non-living environment.

ectoderm The outermost primary tissue layer of a developing embryo that gives rise to tissues of the nervous system and skin.

effluent An outflow or discharge of liquid waste.

element A substance that cannot be broken down into simpler substances by chemical means.

embryo An immature individual formed from a zygote.

embryology The study of the early development of an organism immediately after fertilization.

emigration The process of individuals leaving a population.

encephalocele A type of neural tube defect characterized by protrusion of brain tissue through a skull defect, usually resulting in severe mental and physical disorders.

endangered Describing a species with numbers of individuals so low that it is in danger of becoming extinct.

endoderm The innermost primary tissue layer of a developing embryo that gives rise to the gastrointestinal tract and respiratory tract.

endogenous Developing from within an area.

endoplasmic reticulum A network of canals inside the cell that aids in intracellular transport and molecular synthesis.

endorphins Neurotransmitters in the central nervous system that function as painkillers.

endothermic An organism able to internally regulate its body temperature regardless of environmental temperature; commonly referred to as warm-blooded.

energy The capacity to do work; comes in forms such as solar, chemical, and electrical.

energy pyramid A diagram that shows the decreasing amounts of energy that are available to organisms at successively higher trophic levels as energy flows through the ecosystem.

enzymes Proteins that increase the rate of chemical reactions.

essential plant nutrients Elements such as nitrogen, phosphorous, potassium, magnesium, calcium, zinc, copper, and iron that a plant must obtain in order to sustain life and grow.

ethogram A physical representation of the characteristic behavior patterns of an animal.

eukaryote An organism that contains membrane-bound organelles and a nucleus.

eutrophication Nutrient enrichment of a body of water that typically results in excess growth of plants and algae.

evolution Changes in life forms over time; changes in allele frequencies in populations over time.

evolutionary theory A well-developed explanation for how life forms have changed.

excrete To eliminate wastes from the body.

exothermic An organism lacking any internal mechanisms to raise or lower its body temperature; commonly referred to as cold-blooded.

exotics Organisms living in areas where they did not originally exist; nonindigenous species; introduced species.

exponential growth Growth, as in the size of a population, that is simply dependent on the original size. The larger the original size, the faster it will grow.

extinction The complete disappearance of a species caused by the death of its last surviving member.

F

fermentation   A process whereby some organisms use the energy from carbohydrates in the absence of oxygen; typically produces ethyl alcohol and carbon dioxide.

First Law of Thermodynamics Energy is not created; nor is it destroyed during conversion to another form.

first trimester   The first three months of pregnancy in humans.

food web   A network showing the interconnections between one organism and all other organisms to which it relates.

forebrain   The furthest forward region of the brain consisting of the cerebrum and cerebral cortex, the olfactory lobes, and the hypothalamus.

Fragile X syndrome (FXS)   An inherited disorder characterized by learning difficulties, mental retardation, and physical abnormalities due to a defective gene on the female (X) chromosome.

fry   A very young, or infant, fish.

G

gamete   A haploid sex cell such as a sperm or egg.

gene   One specific section of DNA on a chromosome; a unit of information about an inherited trait.

genetic disorder   An inherited abnormality that may result in a range of outcomes, from no noticeable effect to severe mental and physical problems.

genetic engineering   Cutting segments of DNA from one organism and inserting them into the DNA of another organism or rearranging the DNA of a single organism.

genetics   The study of inheritable traits and the factors that cause them.

genome   The sum of all the DNA making up the genes of an individual.

genotype   The genetic makeup of an individual.

gestation   The period of development of offspring from fertilization to birth.

global warming   A rise in the average temperature of the earth due to an increase in greenhouse gases in the atmosphere, resulting in changes in climate patterns.

Golgi apparatus   An organelle in the eukaryotic cell that functions in synthesis and export of materials from cells.

greenhouse gases Atmospheric gases such as carbon dioxide, ozone, methane, nitrous oxide, and chlorofluorocarbons that trap heat.

H

haversian canal   One of many small canals that branch out through compact bone containing blood and lymphatic vessels and nerves.

heat   A form of energy; temperature is a measure of heat energy.

hemoglobin   A complex protein molecule in vertebrate blood cells that carries oxygen molecules.

heredity   The genetic makeup and inheritance patterns of an organism.

heterodisomy   A form of uniparental disomy in which the offspring inherits one copy of each of the two chromosomes in a pair.

histology   The branch of anatomy dealing with the microscopic study of the structure of tissues.

home range   The area required by an organism to secure food and shelter and to raise offspring.

homeostasis   Attempts by an organism to maintain an internal physiological balance that allows for ideal metabolic conditions.

homolog   One of a pair of complementary chromosomes that contains genes for the same traits.

homologous chromosome   A pair of chromosomes that are identical in size and shape and in the genes they carry.

hormones   Powerful chemicals that regulate metabolic functions.

hypothesis   A prediction about the relationship between a cause and an effect variable.

I

immigration   The process of individuals entering a population.

immunity   A cascade of defenses against a foreign particle that is introduced into an organism, such as an infection.

imprinted genes   Genes for which only the maternally derived or the paternally derived copy is expressed, but not both.

inbreeding Matings within a gene pool between closely related individuals.

impulse An electrochemical message that is sent through a neuron or string of neurons.

independent assortment of alleles During meiosis when homologous chromosomes segregate to one or the other pole of the new cell without regard to the segregation and direction of other homologous chromosomes.

independent variables Variables that can be manipulated or changed by the investigator; cause variables.

inheritance The transmission of genetic qualities from parent to offspring, dictating the biological characteristics of an individual.

inquiry The process of investigating a question.

insect A group of small arthropod animals characterized by the division of the body into head, thorax, and abdomen; three pairs of legs on the thorax;

with or without two pairs of membranous wings and two antennae.

Internet A communication and information system of interlocking computers throughout the world.

isodisomy A form of uniparental disomy in which the offspring inherits two identical copies of one chromosome from a parent.

K

karyotype A photograph of chromosomes from a single cell, arranged according to size and banding patterns.

keystone species Important species in a community that help to maintain the ecological balance of other organisms.

kingdom One of the five most inclusive groupings of living things (Monera, Protista, Fungi, Plantae, and Animalia).

L

lignin A substance that strengthens and waterproofs cell walls in tissues of vascular plants.

limiting factors Independent variables that regulate the size of a population.

linkage group Genes that occur in close proximity to each other on the same chromosome; they generally do not segregate or assort independently during gamete formation.

lipids Molecules containing carbon, oxygen, and hydrogen that serve as energy reserves and part of the structure of organs.

M

mass The measurable amount of matter in an object.

matter That which has mass and occupies space.

meiosis The division of a cell before it becomes a gamete, reducing the number of chromosomes by half.

menstruation Monthly sloughing of the internal lining of the uterus of a human female of childbearing years.

mesoderm The middle primary tissue layer of a developing embryo that gives rise to muscles, reproductive organs, and circulatory vessels.

metabolic rate The rate of all chemical processes in an organism.

metabolism The sum of all the chemical processes in cells and tissues.

metric ton A unit of mass equaling 1,000 kilograms.

microenvironment A very small area in which organisms live and reproduce.

micropaleontologist A paleontologist who specializes in the study of microfossils.

microscope An instrument consisting of a lens or series of lenses used to magnify very small objects or specimens.

mitochondrion Bean-shaped organelles in the cell that carry out cellular respiration.

mitosis The division of a cell nucleus before the cell divides; produces two identical cells.

model A simple representation of a real object; may be used to study complex phenomena.

molecule A naturally occurring combination of atoms, such as H_2O or CO_2.

monosaccharide A simple sugar often containing six carbon atoms, such as glucose ($C_6H_{12}O_6$), or fructose.

monozygotic twins A pair of twins who arise from the fertilization of a single egg cell that subsequently divides to give two separate, genetically identical fetuses; commonly referred to as identical twins.

mutation A chemical change in a gene that can result in a different expression of a trait.

myotonic dystrophy Hereditary disorder of the muscle fibers, caused by trinucleotide repeat amplifications, that results in abnormally prolonged muscle contractions.

N

natural selection Darwin's explanation for speciation; organisms with beneficial genetic composition will have a survival advantage and produce more offspring over time.

Neandertals (Neanderthals) A now-extinct species of primate that inhabited Europe and western Asia 300,000 to 33,000 years ago.

neural tube defect (NTD) A group of congenital abnormalities of the brain or spinal cord caused by the failure of the neural tube to close.

neuroanatomy The branch of anatomy dealing with the study of the structure of the nervous system.

neuron A nerve cell of an animal.

neuropsychology The study of behavioral patterns and their causation within the central nervous system.

neurotransmitters Signaling molecules that diffuse across the synapse between neurons to transmit the impulse to an adjacent neuron.

niche An organism's role or function in a community with respect to the source of its food energy and the energy that it supplies to other organisms.

nitrogen-fixing organisms Certain bacteria and blue-green algae that change atmospheric nitrogen into nitrates and nitrites.

nondisjunction When chromosomes fail to segregate during the first division in meiosis.

nucleotide Building block of nucleic acids; formed from a simple sugar, a nitrogen base, and a phosphate group.

nucleus A major organelle in all eukaryotic cells that contains genetic material.

O

organelle Small bodies in a cell that have a specific function; examples are mitochondria and chloroplasts.

organic A molecule that contains the element carbon; characteristic of living organisms.

organism A living thing.

osmosis The diffusion of water through a selectively permeable membrane.

osmotic gradient Difference in solute concentrations in two regions that drives the process of osmosis.

osmotic potential The concentration gradient produced by the tendency of water to move from an area of less solute concentration to an area of more concentrated solutes.

P

paleontologist A scientist who studies the fossil record to trace the evolution of organisms.

parasites Organisms that obtain nutrients directly from

tissue of a living host, which they may or may not kill.

pathogen An infectious, disease-causing agent such as bacteria, fungi, or viruses.

pedipalps A pair of appendages in arachnids that aid in chewing and sensory perception.

pH A value on a scale of 0 to 14 that is used to describe the acidity of a sample; a pH of 7 is neutral, a pH >7 is basic, a pH <7 is acidic.

phenotype The observed expression of a gene for a specific trait.

photosynthesis The process by which plants and some other organisms use energy from sunlight to synthesize carbohydrates from carbon dioxide and water.

phytoplankton Plants and protists floating in the upper layers of a body of water that carry out photosynthesis and are the main producers in aquatic biomes.

pigments Molecules that absorb light energy.

placenta A temporary organ composed of maternal tissues and embryonic membranes that delivers nutrients to and accepts wastes from the fetus throughout a pregnancy.

plasma The liquid portion of blood.

plasmid A tiny ring of DNA in a bacterium that carries genetic information in addition to what is carried in the chromosomes and can be transferred readily from one bacterial cell to another.

polymerase chain reaction (PCR)   A biotechnology technique to amplify small samples of DNA to produce numerous copies for further testing.

population   A group of individuals of the same species that live in the same geographic area.

population density   The number of individuals in a given area or volume.

population distribution   How individuals are spread through a designated area.

postsynaptic neurons   Neurons that receive stimuli from adjacent neurons by transmission of neurotransmitters across a synapse.

prediction   A statement about what is expected to happen.

premutation   A condition in which a gene is altered, but the mutation is not expressed.

probability   The chance of an event occurring out of the total possible outcomes.

producer   Plants and some microorganisms that capture energy from the sun.

prokaryotic   Primitive organisms that lack a membrane-bounded nucleus, such as bacteria.

protein   Molecules containing nitrogen, carbon, hydrogen, and oxygen that make up much of the structure of muscles, skin, and other organs.

R

recessive   The trait that is not fully expressed unless present in the homozygous condition.

recycling   Collecting traditional waste materials, such as plastics, paper, metals, and organic matter, and processing them for a new use or function.

respirometer   An instrument used for the measurement of oxygen consumption.

response   An action that an organism takes due to an external stimulus.

restriction fragment length polymorphism (RFLP)   The use of restriction enzymes to cut DNA samples into their unique banding patterns for comparison and analysis against other samples.

ribosome   Site of protein synthesis inside cells; located along the endoplasmic reticulum and in the cytoplasm.

Ritalin   A strong stimulant drug used to control behavior in treatment of disorders such as ADD and narcolepsy.

RNA   A nucleic acid constructed from a DNA template that directs the production of specific proteins in the cell.

root pressure   The force that builds up within the cortex of a plant due to excess water and nutrients, causing water to move into the xylem; a major driving force behind the movement of water from roots to leaves.

S

sample   A part or an item taken as a representative example of a whole thing, group, or species, often used for further study and analysis.

science   A process of inquiry and the knowledge that is gained through inquiry.

scientist   A person who is highly trained in one or more of the sciences and does research to gain new knowledge.

Second Law of Thermodynamics   The energy available to do work decreases during successive energy conversions, resulting in an increase in the randomness (entropy) of energy.

sediment   Small particles that settle to the bottom of a liquid or body or water.

segregation of alleles   The separation of homologous chromosomes during cell division and movement to opposite poles of the cell.

sex chromosomes   In a human, the two chromosomes that determine sex and sexual development; a normal female has two "X" chromosomes; a normal male has one "X" chromosome and on "Y" chromosome.

sludge   The organic by-product of raw sewage after water has been removed.

spawn   The process of breeding fish and other animals that results in the release of a large number of eggs into the environment.

speciation   The formation of a new species that is different enough not to be able to produce offspring with another species.

species   A type of organism with similar anatomical features and that can interbreed to produce fertile offspring.

sphygmomanometer An instrument that is used to measure blood pressure.

spiders A group of small arachnids having a body composed of a cephalothorax bearing legs and an abdomen bearing two or more pair of spinnerets used to spin silk thread for webs.

spina bifida A neural tube defect characterized by the absence of vertebral arches, resulting in pouching of spinal membranes or tissues along the back.

stimulus An event to which an organism can respond.

stomates Tiny pores in the surface of a leaf through which gases and water vapor are exchanged to or from the atmosphere.

sustainability Use of environmental resources that preserves them so that they are available for the future.

sustainable Capable of continuing indefinitely in present form and state.

synapse The space between nerve cells through which an impulse must travel.

syndrome A host of symptoms that collectively indicate a complex physiological condition.

synthetic Products not of natural origin; humanmade products.

systolic pressure The pressure of the blood in arteries as the left ventricle of the heart pumps.

T

taxonomy The grouping and naming of organisms on the basis of structural, genetic, and ecological similarities.

tracheid One of two types of xylem cells in flowering plants that serves to conduct water and dissolved minerals.

trait One genetically determined characteristic of an organism, such as shape in peas.

transgenic A genetically engineered organism containing recombinant DNA that gives the organism the ability to produce products not natural to itself.

transpiration The loss of water by evaporation from the pores (stoma) of leaves of a plant.

trinucleotide repeat Three joined nucleotides that repeat abnormally in a DNA chain, resulting in a mutation.

trisomy An abnormal genetic condition in which individual cells have three chromosomes of the same type instead of the usual pair of chromosomes.

trophic level The level on the energy pyramid that represents the source of an organism's food.

U

uniparental disomy (UPD) The abnormal inheritance of both members of a chromosome pair from one parent rather than inheriting one from each parent as usually occurs.

V

variable A factor that is subject to change.

variation Genetic differences in individuals that are produced by chemical changes in the DNA.

virus A tiny particle containing nucleic acid covered by protein that lives and replicates only inside cells; many viruses cause health problems such as colds, AIDS, and influenza.

volume The space that matter occupies.

W

warm-blooded Describing an organism having a body temperature that remains relatively constant, independent of the surrounding environment (e.g., mammals and birds); endothermic.

waste by-product Substances produced by everyday activities, including biological processes, that are no longer useful.

wetlands Environments in which the roots of plants are under water for at least a portion of the year.

X

X-linked A genetic trait located on the female (X) chromosome.

xylem The tissue that transports water and solutes through the plant body in vascular plants.

Z

zygote A fertilized egg.

Credits

Credits

Photo Credits

Cover, PhotoDisk/Panoramic Views; Wikipedia; Flickr/Rob Pongsajapan; Flickr/Nature Freak 07.
Page 1, NASA.
Page 2, PhotoDisc/Environmental Concerns; Flickr/cottergarage.
Page 5, PhotoDisc/Environmental Concerns.
Page 6, Riley N. Kinman/Dept. of Civil & Environmental Engineering – University of Cincinnati.
Page 9, William Rathje – The Garbage Project, Stanford University.
Page 10, John Trapiano.
Page 12, Joseph R. Higgins.
Page 14, Jeffrey Greenberg.
Page 16, Brian Koldyke, Clemson World, Clemson University.
Page 17, Flickr/Nick Ritak/Kirsten Bradley.
Page 18, Jeffrey Greenberg.
Page 19, Aluminum Company of America.
Page 23, William P. McEligot.
Page 24, Jeffrey Greenberg.
Page 25, University of Wisconsin Department of Bacteriology.
Page 27, Jeanne White.
Page 29, Wikipedia.
Page 32, Joseph R. Higgins.
Page 35, Joseph R. Higgins.
Page 38, PhotoDisc/Nature, Wildlife and the Environment.
Page 40, Flickr; Joshua Wickerham.
Page 45, Jeffrey Greenberg.
Page 49, University of Wisconsin – Stevens Point/Cooperative Extension.
Page 51, Ellie Broom.
Page 52, Joseph R. Higgins.
Page 57, Aluminum Corporation of America.
Page 58, PhotoDisc/Nature, Wildlife and the Environment.
Page 60, PhotoDisc/Environmental Concerns.
Page 65, Wikipedia.

Page 66, Larry White.
Page 70, Rick White.
Page 72, Ducktown Basin Museum.
Page 74, Ducktown Basin Museum.
Page 75, Ducktown Basin Museum.
Page 76, Ducktown Basin Museum (all).
Page 77, Ducktown Basin Museum (all).
Page 79, Jeffrey Greenberg.
Page 81, Barbara Speziale.
Page 82, Wikipedia/Marek Szczepanek; PhotoDisc/Nature, Wildlife and the Environment; Flickr.
Page 87, J. William Shopf, University of California.
Page 88, USDA.
Page 90, Kathy Stecker.
Page 93, Wikipedia (all).
Page 96, NASA.
Page 98, Nature Scene, Pennsylvania State Archives.
Page 99, Flickr/Sparkyd.
Page 104, Pennsylvania State Archives; Wikipedia.
Page 105, Michigan Sea Grant (University of Michigan).
Page 106, Flickr.
Page 114 Leslie Saul Gershenz (all).
Page 120, Wikipedia/Peter Halasz.
Page 121, Jeffrey Greenberg.
Page 122, Rick White.
Page 126, Colt Bowles, South Carolina Department of Health and Environmental Control.
Page 129, USDA.
Page 130, USDA.
Page 138, PhotoDisc/ Nature, Wildlife and the Environment.
Page 140, NASA.
Page 141, Mike Beedell (all).
Page 142, US Fish & Wildlife Service/ Milton Friend.
Page 143, USDA.

Page 145, PhotoDisc. PhotoDisc/ Nature, Wildlife and the Environment 2.
Page 146, Leslie Saul.
Page 150, Jeffrey Greenberg.
Page 151, US Department of Commerce/ Bureau of the Census.
Page 152, Flickr.
Page 155, Jeffrey Greenberg.
Page 158, Wikipedia.
Page 159, USCIS.
Page 161, Bill Leonard.
Page 162, PhotoDisc. PhotoDisc/ Nature, Wildlife and the Environment
Page 163, Jeffrey Greenberg.
Page 164, Jeffrey Greenberg.
Page 165, Wikipedia.
Page 170, Kings Tourist Office.
Page 174, PhotoDisc/Moments in Life.
Page 175, PhotoDisc/Mature Lifestyles.
Page 178, PhotoDisc/Everyday Animals.
Page 183, Manning Selvage & Lee.
Page 184, Flickr/Maartyn.
Page 185, Flickr.
Page 188, Wikipedia.
Page 189, US Fish & Wildlife Service.
Page 196, PhotoDisc/Business and Industry.
Page 198, Flickr/Sparked.
Page 199, PhotoDisc/ Nature, Wildlife and the Environment.
Page 201, Flickr.
Page 203, Jeffrey Greenberg.
Page 205, Bill Leonard.
Page 206, Flickr/NatureFreak07.
Page 208, Wikipedia.
Page 210, Wikipedia.
Page 214, Wikipedia.
Page 216, Wikipedia; PhotoDisc/Digital Stock.
Page 217, Wikipedia.
Page 219, PhotoDisc/Health and Medicine.
Page 221, Bond Shymanthy.
Page 222, Wikipedia.
Page 227, PhotoDisc/Science, Technology and Medicine.
Page 228, Wikipedia, PhotoDisc/Moments in Life.
Page 233, Jeffrey Greenberg (all).

Page 234, Jeffrey Greenberg.
Page 239, PhotoDisc/Nature, Wildlife and the Environment.
Page 241, Digital Stock/Sports & Fitness.
Page 242, Carmen Fignole.
Page 243, Center for Disease Control/ Dept. of Health and Human Services.
Page 246, Center for Disease Control.
Page 247, Flickr/Adnan.
Page 248, Center for Disease Control.
Page 253, Bill Leonard.
Page 254, Jeffrey Greenberg.
Page 256, PhotoDisc/Action Sports.
Page 257, PhotoDisc/Everyday Animals.
Page 258, Wikipedia.
Page 280, PhotoDisc/Family and Lifestyles.
Page 284, PhotoDisc/People and Lifestyles.
Page 286, PhotoDisc/Health and Medicine.
Page 291, Richard Kelley & Mitzi Kuroda/ AAAS & Science Magazine; www.PDImages.com.
Page 293, Patrick D. Wright/Clemson University.
Page 298, Bill Leonard.
Page 300, Patrick D. Wright/Clemson University.
Page 314, Wikipedia (all).
Page 315, Wikipedia.
Page 316, Wikipedia.
Page 321, Peter Ginter/Hereditary Disease Foundation.
Page 322, Flickr.
Page 324, Felix "Rick" Farrar.
Page 326, Wikipedia (all).
Page 333, Patrick D. Wright/Clemson University.
Page 348, Center for Disease Control/ Dept. of Health and Human Services.
Page 349, Center for Disease Control/Dept. of Health and Human Services/James Gathany.
Page 354, National Library of Medicine.
Page 356, PhotoDisc/Health and Medicine.
Page 364, PhotoDisc/Science, Technology and Medicine.
Page 368, American Association for the Advancement of Science.
Page 369, Jeffrey Greenberg.
Page 372, Sidney Gauthreaux, Clemson University.

Page 373, Sidney Gauthreaux,
  Clemson University.
Page 376, Digital Stock/Medicine and Healthcare.
Page 379, Jeffrey Greenberg.
Page 381, Wikipedia.
Page 382, Joseph Higgins.
Page 385, Jeff Potter.
Page 387, Jeffrey Greenberg (all).
Page 390, Jeffrey Greenberg.
Page 401, Joe Baxter.
Page 405, PhotoDisc/Business and Occupation.
Page 407, Leslie Saul Gershenz & John Hafernik.
Page 409, Patrick D. Wright, Clemson University.
Page 410, Patrick D. Wright, Clemson University.
Page 411, Patrick D. Wright, Clemson University.
Page 412, Jeffrey Greenberg.
Page 424, PhotoDisc/Nature, Wildlife
  and the Environment.
Page 426, US Fish & Wildlife Service/
  Gary Muehlenhardt.
Page 435, PhotoDisc/Everyday Animals;
  PhotoDisc/Homes and Gardens;
  PhotoDisc/Nature, Wildlife and the
  Environment; Jeffrey Greenberg.
Page 439, Flickr/Lisa Hendrickson;
  Digital Stock/Animals in Action.
Page 440, Flickr/gwarcita; PhotoDisc/
  Nature, Wildlife and the Environment;
  Digital Stock/Animals in Action.
Page 441, Wikipedia.
Page 443, Wikipedia.
Page 446, PhotoDisc/Environmental Concerns;
  Wikipedia (all).
Page 447, Wikipedia (all).
Page 448, Wikipedia (all).
Page 449, Wikipedia (all).
Page 450, PhotoDisc/Science, Technology
  and Medicine.
Page 451, David Dilcher.
Page 452, Wikipedia.
Page 453, Barbara Speziale; Bill Leonard.
Page 454, Bill Leonard.
Page 456, Wikipedia.
Page 457, PhotoDisc/US Landmarks and Travel.

Page 458, Rachel Canto.
Page 460, Wikipedia.
Page 463, Bill Leonard.
Page 465, Kathleen Futrell.
Page 467, Wikipedia (all).
Page 468, PhotoDisc/Agriculture.
Page 471, John J. Haines.
Page 472, John Fairey/Clemson University.
Page 474, Bill Leonard.
Page 475, P. Mac Horton/Clemson University.
Page 478, Wikipedia.
Page 479, PhotoDisc/Nature, Wildlife and
  the Environment.
Page 480, Wikipedia.
Page 488, PhotoDisc/Business and Industry. Page
490, Digital Stock/New York City.
Page 492, Bill Leonard (all).
Page 494, PhotoDisc/Agriculture.
Page 496, Reuters/Corbis-Bettmann;
  United Nations.
Page 498, Mel Goodwin.
Page 501, Tom Klare.
Page 506, Bill Leonard.
Page 513 PhotoDisc/Nature, Wildlife and
  the Environment.
Page 515, Flickr/Irri Rice; Natural Resources
  Conservation Service/Jeff Vanuga;
  PhotoDisc/Environmental Concerns.
Page 517, Bill Leonard.
Page 518, PhotoDisc/US Landmarks and Travel.
Page 525, Jeffrey Greenberg.
Page 547, Flickr/TerryMcT; US National Oceanic
  and Atmospheric Administration.
Page 548, John J. Haines (two); Rick Berken.
Page 549, Al Greening.
Page 573, E. David Dickens, Clemson University,
  Biosystem Engineering.
Page 577, Edwin Edmondson and
  Ocean Arts International.
Page 581, US Fish and Wildlife Service National
  Image Library.
Page 588, Agricultural & Biological
  Engineering/Clemson University.
Page 602, Mickie Swisher.

Index

Index

A

Abstract, 45
Accessory pigments, 87
Acidity, 52
Acid rain, 72
Acquired Immune Deficiency Syndrome (AIDS), 243, 246–47, 316, 521
Actin, 391–92
Active energy, 88
Active transport, 201
Adenine (A), 331, 338
Adenosine triphosphate (ATP), 38–39, 201, 209, 437
Adrenal glands, 241
Aerobic, 571, 578, 590, 650
Aerobic respiration, 31, 39, 583
Agar, 202–04
Agonistic, 691
Agriculture, family sustainable, 501
AIDS. See Acquired Immune Deficiency Syndrome
Alanine, 336
Albinism, 324
Albumen, 211–12, 267
Algae
   blue-green, 432, 446
   green, 445
   in pond water, 447–48
Alleles, 310–11
   dominant vs. recessive, 315
   for Huntington's disease, 318
   law of segregation of, 320
   multiple, 322–23
Allergies, 247
Aluminum
   chemical symbol for, 33
   oxide, 33
   recycling, 18
Alveoli, 237–38
Amazon River, 460
American Transfer Co., 10
Amino acids, 335–37
Ammonia, 93
Amniocentesis, 288–89
Amniotic fluid, 670
Amoeba, 447
Amoeba dubia, 329
Amphibians, 463, 466
Amylase, 262–66
Amylose molecule, 35
Anaerobic respiration, 37
   input and outputs from, 31
   in photosynthesis, 39
Androgens, 304–05
Anemia, sickle–cell, 312–13, 315, 325–26, 337, 339
Anencephaly, 640–41
Animalia, 442, 448. *See also* Animals

Animals
   behavior of, 399–400
   cells of, 210–14, 295
   as consumers, 81
   early plants and, 433
   evolutionary origins of, 438
   See also Animalia
Antibiotics, 249
Antibodies, 246
   allergies and, 247
   in phenotype, 323
Antigen-antibody reaction, 267–68
Antigens, 244–45
   antibodies binding to, 246
   in phenotype, 323
Antihistamines, 247, 378
Ants, fire, 475–76
Anus, 225
Anvil, 375
Aorta, 235
Aquaculture, 515
Aquatic ecosystem, plants in, 450
Archaebacteria, 442
Archeologist, 6, 497
Arginine, 336
Arteries, 231–32, 235
Arterioles, 229–31
Arthropods, 392–96
Artifacts, 9
Artificial insemination, 477
Asexual reproduction, 297
Asiatic wild horse, 478
Asparagine, 336
Aspartate, 336
Asthma, 247
Atom, 33
ATP. *See* Adenosine triphosphate
Attention Deficit Disorder (ADD), 698–701
Auditory canal, 375
Auditory stimulus variable, 387
Australia, population data for, 185
Austria, population data for, 173
Automobile insurance rates, 360–61
Autosomes, 291
Autotrophs, 106
Aves, 466
Axon, 373

B

Baboons, 239
Baby boom, 174–75
Bacteria
   antibiotic-resistant, 249
   discovery of new, 443
   nitrogen-fixing, 91–92
   plasmid, 351–52
   in pond water, 446
   Rhizobium, 93
   in septic tanks, 42

   washing hands of, 253–55
Balance
   enzymes and, 265–67
   sense of, 375
   of water and salts, 218–20
   what is? 198–205
Balanced chemical equation, 34
Barbados, population of, 182–85
Baxter, Joe, 401
B-cells, 245–46
Beans, 130
Beetle, 435, 461
Behavior
   brain coordination and, 369–71
   chemicals and, 366–67
   genotypes and, 380–81
   in shopping mall, 405–07
   physiology and, 373–75
   magnetic fields' effect on, 372
   natural selection and, 380–81
   nervous system and, 365–423
   observing animal, 399–400
   what is? 367
Behavioral disorder, 699
Behavioral scientist, 367
Bicarbonate, 265
Bicarbonate ion, 240
Biodegradable, 5, 13, 16, 20, 580
Biodegradable biopolymers, 580
Biodegradable material
   waste stream for, 13
   as packaging, 16
   in landfills, 20
Biodegradation, 5, 21
Biodiversity, 425–87
   calculating, 443–45. *See also* Simpson Diversity Index
   expeditions to explore, 460
   informing public about, 482–83
   origin of present, 430–33
   protection and restoration of, 480
   unity in, 437
   what is, 430–34
   world, 434
BioIssue
   biodiversity, 460
   brain injury and personality, 368
   environmentally safe products, 356
   explosion of Lake Nyos, 89
   Fresh Kills landfill, 4
   Nile perch in Lake Victoria, 452
   population control, 156
   ranch-raised minks, 508
   sacrificing baboons for humans, 239
   sick children at school, 250
   sickle-cell anemia, 339
   sustainability vs. population growth, 516
Biological carbon cycle, 39–40
Biological evolution, 457–58

endocrine system and hormones, 240–41
expression of six traits by, 454
eye, 85, 374
heart, 236
immune system, 244–47
internal transport mechanisms in, 228
kidney, 218–20
muscle system, 391–92
nervous system of, 373
physiological balance of, 198–201
respiratory system, 237–38
skeletal system, 391–92
tongue, taste receptor areas on, 409
urinary system, 220
Human development, 347
Human Genome Project, 352–53
Human immunodeficiency virus (HIV), 243, 246–47, 316, 521
Human male, sperm formation in, 304
Human neuron, 374. *See also* Neuron
Human physiology, behavior and, 373–75
Human population
carrying capacity of, 169
skin color distribution in, 323
Humans
calorie consumption of, 112
body of. *See* Human body
as *Homo sapiens*, 142. *See also Homo sapiens*
impact on biodiversity, 462
impact on earth, 490–96
interaction with biotic environment, 430
number of chromosomes in, 290, 292
sacrificing baboons to save, 239
taxonomic classifications of, 437
today's niche for, 497, 499–500
in web of life, 436
Humus, 79
Huntington's disease, 309–11, 317–21
Hybridization, 441
Hydra, 448
Hydration, 28
Hydrogen, 33, 35
Hypertension, 235
Hypothalamus, 241

I

Ice age, 466, 473–74
IKI. *See* Iodine-potassium iodide
Immigration, 157
Immune response, 246, 267–68
Immune system, 244–47, 430
reactions of, 247
response to foreign antigens, 245
Immunization, 246
Imprinted genes, 672–75
Inbreeding, 321, 703–04
Inbreeding depression, 478
Incineration, 56
garbage, 17
waste stream and, 13
Independent research, 413–14

Independent variables, 27, 50
India
food consumption in, 505
population data, 185
rice crop virus in, 468
Infrared wave, 87
Ingestion, 222–24
Inheritance, 280–363
patterns of, 316–17
polygenic, 323
Inherited traits, 315–16
Inner ear, 375
Insect, 101, 571, 599, 605, 630, 680–81, 683, 685
evolution of, 433
See also Insecta
Insecta, 461, 466. *See also* Insect
Insecticides, 366–67, 569
Inspiratory reserve volume, 255–57
Insulin, 352
Internal transport mechanisms, 228
Internet, 584–86
Interrelationships, web of, 433
invertebrates, in pond water, 448–50
Iodine-potassium iodide (IKI), 262–65
Iris, 374
Iron, 32
Irrigation, sustainable, 514
Isodisomy, 673, 675
Isoleucine, 336

J

Japan, age-sex distribution in, 173
Japanese honeysuckle, 472
Jurassic period, 432
Juvenile justice system, 418–20

K

Karyotypes, 285–88
Kenya
age-sex distribution in, 173
age-sex pyramid for, 171
fertility rate in, 169–70
population growth in, 174
Kidney, 218–20
disease and dialysis, 219–20
in female reproductive system, 306
in male reproductive system, 305
role in homeostasis, 219
in urinary system, 220
Kilocalories, 107
Kinetic energy, 88
Kingdom, 437, 441–42
Knee-jerk reflex, 390
Komodo dragon, 460
Krebs cycle, 39
Kudzu, 472

L

Labia, 306
Lactase, 267
Lactose intolerant, 267
Lake, Wisconsin, 103
Lake Nyos, 89
Lake Victoria, 452
Lamarck, Jean Baptiste, 457

Land
grazing, 504
quantity needed, 106–11
Landfills, 5–6, 20–22
cross-section of, 11
decomposition in, 19
Extended Inquiry 1.3, 56
modern sanitary, 22
reducing space needed for, 42
sealed, 21
waste stream and, 13
Languages, 520
Large intestine, 225
Larvae, mosquito, 449–50
Larynx, 237
Lavies, Bianca, 53, 114
Law of the minimum, 167
Leaf, stomates in epidermis of, 120–21
Learning
ability, 381
limits of, 378–80
Least abundant essential factor, 167
Lenses, eye, 410–12
Lespedeza plants, 93
Leucine, 336
LH. *See* Luteinizing hormone
Liebig, Justus, 167
Life
beginnings of, 430
in Cambrian period oceans, 433
cell as basic unit of, 206
characteristics of, 27
diversity of, 425–87
DNA as chemical basis of, 329–31
evolution of, 432–33
shared characteristics of, 437
Lifespan, average, 175
Light
energy, 84–87
role in photosynthesis, 38, 82–84
ultraviolet, 431
visible, 85–86
Lignin, 702
Limiting factors, 165–68
Linked genes, 322
Linnaeus, Carolus, 439, 441
Lipid bilayer, 207
Liver, 225
Livingston, Patsy, 298
Lorax, 119–20
Lumber, by-products of, 516–17
Lungs
in human respiratory system, 237–38
smoker's vs. nonsmoker's, 28
volume of, 255–57
Luteinizing hormone (LH), 304, 306–08
Lymphocytes, 244–46
Lysine, 336

M

Macromolecules, 430
Macrophages, 246
Magnetic fields, 372
Malaria, 315
Male reproductive system, 304–05
Malpighi, Marcello, 230

recent discoveries of new, 461
    scientists studying, 471–72
    trophic levels of, 102
Ornithologist, 471
Osmosis, 211
Osmotic gradient, 594
Osmotic potential, 594
Ostrich egg, 205
OTC drugs. See Over-the-counter drugs
Our Common Future, 513
Outer ear, 375
Ovaries, 241, 305
    in human female reproductive
        system, 306
    as location for meiosis, 306
Over-the-counter (OTC) drugs, 376–78
Oviduct, 305–06
Ovulation, 305–06, 308
Oxygen
    atom, possible bonds with, 35
    chemical symbol for, 33
    gas, chemical formula for, 37
    in lungs, 238
    molecular, 36–37
    photosynthesis and, 431
    as photosynthesis waste product, 38
    production of, 87

P

Pacific Ocean, 104
Packaging, biodegradable, 16
Paleocene epoch, 432
Paleontologist, 608, 646–47
Paleozoic era, 432–33
Pancreas
    in endocrine system, 241
    role in digestion, 225
Pangaea, breakup of, 463
Papain, 267
Paper, in landfills, 20
Paper chromatography, 83–84
Paramecium, 222–24, 447
Paramedic, 242
Parasites, 430
Parathyroid glands, 241
Parietal lobe, 398
Pasteur, Louis, 218
Pasteurization, 218
Paternity testing, 348
Pathogen, 578
Pea plant, inheritance patterns of, 316–17
Pea seeds, germinating, 260–61
Pedigree analysis, 310
Pedipalps, 685
Penfield, Dr. Wilder, 397
Penicillin, 249
Penis, 304–05
Perch, Nile, 452
Peripheral nervous system, 373
Permian period, 432
Personality, effect of brain injury
    on, 368
Personal pledge, 524

Pest control, 401
Petroleum, recycling goods made
    from, 19
pH, 567, 571, 582, 599
pH scale, 52
Pharynx, 237
Phenolphthalein, 202
Phenotype, 318, 323
    for blood type, 322–23
    of sickle-cell anemia, 326
    species, 439
Phenotypic trait, 380
Phenylalanine, 336
Phosphorus, 126–27
Photosynthesis, 38–40
    in algae, 447
    biomass and, 81
    in carbon cycle, 40
    on early earth, 431
    energy transformations and, 88
    flow of energy and matter during, 88
    process of, 88
    role of light and pigments in, 82–84
Photosynthetic pigments, 86–87
Phycobilins, 87
Phycologist, 471
Phylum, 437
Phytoplankton, 610
Pigments, photosynthetic, 82–87
Pike, Zebulon, 474
Pill bug experiment, 394–96
Pineal gland, 241
Pisaster, 104
Pituitary gland, 241, 304
Placebo, 378
Placenta, 289, 307
Plantae, 442. *See also* Plants
Plant cells, 210
    balance of water in, 214–16
    mitosis in, 296
    turgor pressure in, 216
Plants
    early animals and, 433
    evolutionary origins of, 438
    flowering, first, 463
    nitrogen sources for, 91–93
    pigments of, 83–84
    in pond water, 450
    as producers, 81
    See also Plantae
Plasmid, 208–09, 351
Plastic
    recycled, 19
    waste stream for normal, 13
Platelets, 228
Pleistocene epoch, 432
Pliocene epoch, 432
Points of origin, 12
Pollen grains, 450
Pollination, 459

Pollution
    non-point source, 126–27
    See also Environmental problems
Polygenic inheritance, 323
Polysaccharide, 262–63
Pond water, organisms in, 446–50
Population, 139–95
    age structure of, 174–75
    census, 147–51
    control of, 156
    demographics of, 169–74
    density of, 145, 147–49
    describing, 145–46
    development of differences in, 440
    distribution of, 146, 149–50
    growing your own, 143–45, 177–78,
        511
    growth of. *See* Population growth
    sampling of, 151–53
    size of, 145, 148–49, 167
    studying, 147–50
    sustaining world's, 468
    what is? 141–42
    world, 140–41
Population growth, 157–61
    in Barbados, 182–85
    carrying capacity and, 166
    economics and human, 458
    with limiting resources, 192
    models of, 159–60
    stable, 192
    sustainability vs. 516
    unchecked, 165
    without limits, 191
    in your town, 185
Population Reference Bureau (PRB), 161
Postsynaptic neurons, 705
Potential energy, 88
Pou, Belfondia, 221
Prairie
    biomass in, 474
    disappearance of, 473–75
Precambrian era, 432
Predator-prey relationships, 459–60
Predator-prey simulation, 162–65
Pregnancy, 288–89, 307
Premutation, 664
Prenatal genetic tests, 284
Prescription drugs, 377–78
Preston, Richard, 248
Primary consumers, 502
Primates, first, 463
Prism, 82–83
Producers
    autotrophs as, 106
    in energy pyramid, 502
    in food web, 102
    as kingdom grouping criterion, 441
    plants and microorganisms as, 81
Progesterone, 241, 306–08

Sperm, 304, 307
Sphygmomanometer, 234, 237
Spiders, 681, 685–89
Spina bifida, 640
Spinal cord
    human brain and, 398
    in human nervous system, 373
Spiroplasma, 460
Spores, water mold, 448
Spotted knapweed, 473
Spruce budworms, 104
Starch, 262–63
Starling, 473
Starvation, mass, 468
Stecker, Kathy, 90
Stellar's Sea Cow, 467
Stentor, 447
Steroid hormones, 241
Stimuli, response to, 27
Stirrup, 375
Stockholm Conference, 496–97
Stomach, 225
Stomates, 120–21
Stored energy, 88
Strata, 457
Subsistence, 165–66
Substrates, 266
Sucrose, 55, 225–26
Sugar
    disappearing act, 54–55
    human metabolism of, 225
    in photosynthesis process, 38–39
    See also Glucose
Sulfur dioxide, 72–75
Sunlight energy, 82, 84–87
Sustainability, 501, 511–14, 516, 519,
    526, 737–39, 748–751
Sustainable, 496–97, 501, 504, 511–15,
    519, 526, 566–67, 570, 601–02,
    605–07, 625, 737–39, 748–49, 751
Sustainable development, 513–14
Sustainable rice farming, 501
Synapse, 694–95, 699
Syndrome, 286
Synthetic, 39, 307, 652,
    659, 750–01
Systema Natura, 439
Systolic pressure, 236

T

Tactile stimulus variable, 388
Tall grass prairie 473–74
Taste, awareness of, 408–10
Taxonomic model, 436
Taxonomic system, 441–42
Taxonomy
    defined, 436–42
    early efforts at, 439
    quandaries in, 442
T-cells, 245–46
Temperature
    awareness of, 408
    body, 200
    effects on earthworms' heart
        rate, 257–59
    enzyme activity and body, 265
    measuring compost, 49

Temporal lobe, 398
Tennessee Copper Basin. *See*
    Copper Basin
Tennessee Valley Authority (TVA), 76
Tertiary consumers, 502
Tertiary period, 432
Testes, 241, 304–05
Testosterone, 304
Thalamus, 398
Thermodynamics, laws of, 88
Threonine, 336
Thymine (T), 330, 338
Thymus gland, 241
Thyroid gland, 241
Tidal volume, 255–57
Tiglion, 441
Time, effect on natural processes, 507
Timeline
    5-billion-year, 428–30
    biodiversity, 462
    earth's, 428–30
    personal, 428–29
    since last ice age, 466–67
Tobacco mosaic virus, 210
Topsoil, in compost pile, 16
Touch receptors, 396–97
Toxic chemicals, 366–67
Toxic waste, 58
Trachea, 237
Tracheid, 593–96
Trait
    chances of inheriting single, 318–20
    common species, 439
    dominant, 316–17
    expression of six human, 454
    inherited, 315–16
    marker, 352
    phenotypic, 380
    probabilities of multiple, 343–44
    recessive, 316–17
    sex-linked, 316
Transgenic, 676–78
Translation, 337
Transpiration, 592, 594–96
Transplantation, primate-to-human, 239
Transport processes, 201, 228
Trash
    audit, 7–9
    biology of, 2–5
    lessons from, 6
    local issues about, 57
    sorting stations for, 10
    See also Garbage
Trees
    first, 463
    lumber vs., 516
Triassic period, 432
Trinucleotide repeat amplification, 663–66
Trisomy 21, 301
tRNA, 337
Tropic levels, 99–102, 502
Trophic pyramids, 103–05
Trophic scavenger hunt, 99–102
Tropiano, John, 10, 18
Tropical hot spots, 476–77
Tryptophan, 336

Turgor pressure, 216
Tyrosine, 336

U

Ultraviolet light, 431
Ultraviolet rays, 87
Uniform distribution, 146
Uniparental disomy (UPD), 672, 675
Unique Tire Recycling, 19
United Nations
    Conference on Environment and
        Development (UNCED), 496
    Environment Program, 496
United States
    net migration in, 158
    population of, 170, 172–74, 185
Uracil (U), 331
Urban ecologist, 498
Ureter, 220, 305–06
Urethra, 220, 304–06
Urinary bladder, 305
Urinary system, 220
U.S. Census Bureau, 151
U.S. Department of Agriculture
    Forest Service, 77
Uterus, 289, 305–07

V

Vaccination, 246
Vacuole, 209, 215
Vagina, 289, 306–07
Valine, 336, 338
Variables, 27–28
Variation
    diversity and, 426
    evolutionary change and, 453–55
    within species, 440, 453
Vas deferens, 304–05
Vegetation
    natural U.S., 97
    restoring Copper Basin's, 75–77
Veins, human, 231–32
Velocci, Rocco, 10
Venous system, 231–32
Venules, 231
Vertebrates
    evolution of, 433
    known extinctions of, 466
Vibrations, 375
Victoria (Queen), 314
Virus, 210–11
    human immunodeficiency, 243.
        See also HIV
    Indian rice field, 468
Visible light, 85–86
Vision
    20/20, 411
    acuity of, 410–12
    sense of, 374–75
Visual stimulus variable, 387
Vital capacity, 255–57
Volcanoes, 431, 440, 462
Volume
    lung, 255–57
    surface area to, 204